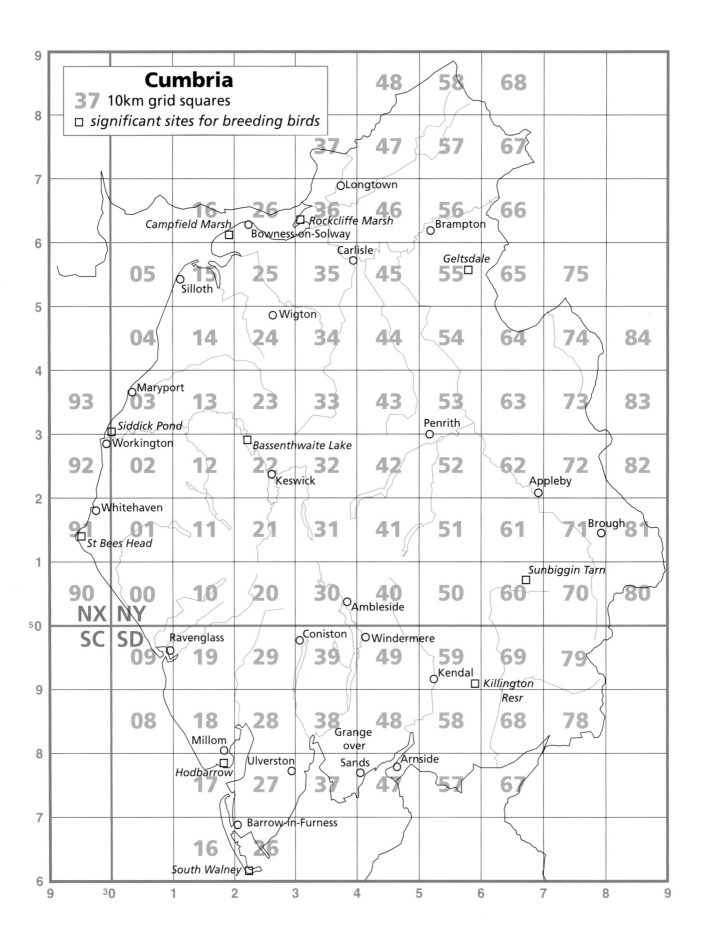

**Cumbria**
**37** 10km grid squares
□ *significant sites for breeding birds*

9

8

7 ○Longtown

6 Campfield Marsh □ ○ □ Rockcliffe Marsh ○Brampton
Bowness-on-Solway
Carlisle ○ Geltsdale □

5 Silloth ○

○Wigton

4 Maryport ○

3 ○ Siddick Pond Penrith ○
Workington ○ □Bassenthwaite Lake

2 Keswick ○ Appleby ○
Whitehaven ○ Brough

1 □ St Bees Head

Sunbiggin Tarn □

0 Ambleside ○
NX NY
SC SD
Ravenglass ○ Coniston ○ ○Windermere
Kendal ○ □Killington
Resr

Grange over
Millom
Ulverston ○ Sands Arnside ○
□ Hodbarrow

Barrow-in-Furness ○

South Walney □

48 58 68
37 47 57 67
16 26 36 46 56 66
05 15 25 35 45 55 65 75
04 14 24 34 44 54 64 74 84
93 03 13 23 33 43 53 63 73 83
92 02 12 22 32 42 52 62 72 82
91 01 11 21 31 41 51 61 71 81
90 00 10 20 30 40 50 60 70 80
09 19 29 39 49 59 69 79
08 18 28 38 48 58 68 78
17 27 37 47 57 67
16 26

9 30 1 2 3 4 5 6 7 8 9

# THE BREEDING BIRDS OF CUMBRIA
## A tetrad atlas 1997–2001

Dedicated to the memory of Bob Spencer whose spirit and visionary inspiration sowed the seed for this atlas of the breeding birds of Cumbria

*What would the world be, once bereft of wet and wildness?*
*Let them be left, O let them be left, wildness and wet;*
*Long live the weeds and the wilderness yet.*

From *'Inversnaid'*
Gerard Manley Hopkins

# The Breeding Birds of Cumbria

## A tetrad atlas 1997–2001

Editors

Malcolm Stott

John Callion

Ian Kinley

Colin Raven

Jeremy Roberts

Foreword

Dr Derek Ratcliffe

Published by

Cumbria Bird Club

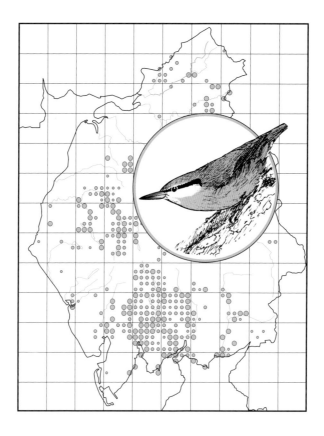

Cumbria Bird Club
Breeding Bird Atlas Project

Copyright: © 2002 Cumbria Bird Club

First published 2002 by Cumbria Bird Club

ISBN  0-9543249-0-0

Design by Jeremy Roberts

Artwork and production by Jonathan Rimmer, Essential Design, Dunham-on-the-Hill, WA6 0JL

Printed by Wood Mitchell Printers Limited, Festival Way, Festival Park, Stoke-on-Trent ST1 5TH

Cover painting, *Black Grouse at lek, Geltsdale,* by Ashley Boon

# Cumbria Bird Club: Breeding Bird Atlas Project

**Atlas Working Groups**

**Steering Committee**
Roy Atkins, Phil Byle (1998-2002), John Callion (Chair), Mike Carrier, Alistair Crowle (1997-2000), Pete Davies, Stuart Halder (1997), Ian Kinley, Bill Makin (1997-1999), Jake Manson, Malcolm Priestley, Colin Raven (1999-2002), Jeremy Roberts, Malcolm Stott & Dave Walker

**Methodology Group**
Roy Atkins, Phil Byle, Malcolm Stott (Chair) & Dave Walker

**Editorial Group**
John Callion, Ian Kinley, Colin Raven, Jeremy Roberts & Malcolm Stott (Chair)

**Publicity & Fund Raising Group**
John Callion & Pete Davies

**Regional Organizers**
John Callion (Northwest), Ian Kinley (South), Jake Manson (Southwest), Malcolm Priestley (Southeast), Malcolm Stott (Northeast), Dave Walker (Centre)

**Data management and Analysis**
Phil Byle & Malcolm Stott

**Data input**
Geoff Naylor

**Mapping**
Stephen Hewitt (Tullie House Museum, Carlisle) & Jeremy Roberts

**Species Account Authors**
Ian Armstrong, Roy Atkins, Peter Barron, Phil Byle, John Callion, Mike Carrier, Alistair Crowle, Pete Davies, Tim Dean, Steve Garnett, Clive Hartley, Derek Hayward, Norman Healy, Norman Holton, Bill Kenmir, Ian Kinley, Nick Littlewood, Allan Mackenzie, Jake Manson, Nick Mason, Derek McAlone, Malcolm Priestley, Colin Raven, Sean Reed, Jeremy Roberts, Dave Shackleton, Malcolm Stott, Arnold Strand, Dave Walker

**Illustrators**
Roy Atkins (pages 224, 344, 348), Trevor Charlton (page 154), Sian Davies (pages 58, 126, 128, 130, 134, 136, 138, 140, 142, 148, 156, 166, 170, 172, 220, 222, 230, 232, 304, 308, 310, 312, 314, 316), Jane Dunstan (pages 4, 60, 66, 84, 168, 174, 238), Peter Finn (pages 78, 100, 124, 196, 208, 212, 218, 226, 242, 244, 248, 250, 258, 264, 274, 282, 306, 318, 322, 324, 326, 328, 330, 340, 346), Alan Hart (pages 114, 118, 122, 158, 164, 186, 256), Ray Hawley (pages 76, 88, 90, 116, 204, 210, 252, 280, 292, 342), Sarah Holton (pages 52, 176, 178, 180, 182), John Hooson (pages 46, 48, 56, 64, 80, 82, 86, 152, 160, 184, 190, 246, 270, 286, 288, 332, 336), Christine Isherwood (pages 50, 68, 70, 72, 92, 104, 110, 112, 132, 144, 146, 150, 188, 192, 206, 214, 216, 228, 234, 236, 240, 254, 260, 262, 266, 268, 272, 276, 278, 284, 290, 294, 296, 298, 300, 302, 320, 334, 338), Ann Robinson (pages 62, 74, 94, 96, 98, 102, 106, 108, 120, 162, 194, 198, 200, 202)

| Cover painting | Title page illustration |
| --- | --- |
| Ashley Boon | Christine Isherwood (Principal Illustrator) |

**Photographs**
English Nature (Plate 17), John Graham (Plates 19, 21, 26, 32), Bill Kenmir (Plate 33), Ronny Mitchell (Plates 3, 4, 6, 12, 18, 20), Jeremy Roberts (Plates 1, 5, 27, 29), Dave Shackleton (Plates 10, 11, 14, 22) & Malcolm Stott (Plates 2, 7, 8, 9, 15, 16, 23, 24, 25, 28, 30, 31)

## Cumbria Bird Club

Cumbria, a county dominated by its dramatic landscapes, has always been a difficult county to move around in; its centres of population have developed in relative isolation. Cumbria Bird Club was formed in 1989, with its main aim of bringing together enthusiasts, from all over the county and beyond, who enjoyed watching birds in our beautiful county. These individuals were united in the desire to improve our understanding of Cumbrian birds and therefore assist in their conservation.

Fieldwork is the fundamental tool at our disposal. We have instigated several ornithological surveys since our formation, adding greatly to our knowledge of Cumbrian birds. *The Breeding Birds of Cumbria: a tetrad atlas* is the culmination of the committed efforts of our members and is our greatest achievement so far.

We are responsible for the birds section of the county annual wildlife report *Birds and Wildlife in Cumbria*, and welcome the submission of any records. Membership benefits include a quarterly newsletter, a full winter programme of indoor lectures, and field trips with expert guidance.

CBC is for anyone who is passionate about Cumbria and its birds. For further information visit our website at http://www.cumbriabirdclub.freeserve.co.uk, or contact the secretary: David Piercy, Derwentwater Youth Hostel, Borrowdale, Keswick, CA12 5UR.

Peter Ullrich
CBC Chairman
May 2002

# Contents

★    ★    ★

# Foreword

The birds of the old counties of Cumberland, Westmorland and Lancashire North of the Sands received their first full treatment in the Revd H. A. Macpherson's scholarly *A Vertebrate Fauna of Lakeland* in 1892. Macpherson named the region as the faunal area of Lakeland, and the same definition was adopted by the authors of *The Birds of Lakeland* in 1943. Periodic supplements updated this work and a further review of bird status and distribution in the region was Ralph Stokoe's *Birds of the Lake Counties* in 1962. In the boundary changes of 1974, the new county of Cumbria happily coincided with the wider Lakeland, plus the addition of a sizeable piece of former northwest Yorkshire – doubtless to the chagrin of Yorkshire naturalists. In more recent years the annual county bird reports have increasingly given a picture of birdlife throughout the year, and now introduce each species with a brief statement of status.

While there is, accordingly, a good deal of both historical and recent information, some of us have longed to see a new work on the birds of Cumbria, or at least one in the modern vogue of mapping the distribution of the county's breeding species. Now our wish has come true with the Cumbria Bird Club's compilation of this *The Breeding Birds of Cumbria,* the labour of love of 230 dedicated recorders led by six regional organisers in John Callion, Ian Kinley, Jake Manson, Malcolm Priestley, Malcolm Stott and Dave Walker. With mapping at a tetrad scale this gives an accurate visual statement of both distribution and abundance of the 152 species recorded as breeding in Cumbria during 1997–2001. The accompanying texts for each species are highly informative and valuable in providing a fuller understanding of history as well as present occurrence and status. Every effort has been made to refine the methodology of recording, so that it gives a repeatable baseline, which will be scientifically rigorous. While the atlas is largely the work of spare-time birders, in the best traditions of amateur natural history, it also has an admirable professionalism.

Cumbria has a greater variety of bird habitats than any other English county, and this ecological diversity goes far to explain its richness in breeding birds. A well-illustrated chapter on The Natural Diversity of Cumbria suitably brings out this varied tapestry of landscape and its bird inhabitants, extending from the seashore to the highest fell tops. The dot records are printed on a coloured base relief map showing the Ordnance Survey grid of 10km squares, and in the three categories of possible, probable and confirmed breeding. Additional panels compare the maps from the *Atlas of Breeding Birds in Britain & Ireland* with the current status during this atlas, graphically illustrating a 30-year change. The survey data, population and conservation status in Europe, Britain and Cumbria are summarized for each species, which is also attractively illustrated by a line drawing.

This is a magnificent work to pore over or dip into with much pleasure and gain in knowledge, and all those involved in its production deserve congratulation. It is a fine contribution to British ornithology, and one which every serious birder should have, whether resident or visitor to Cumbria, or simply interested from afar. There are many intriguing insights to be had or theories advanced to explain the patterns of distribution, and this atlas is something to return to repeatedly for fresh stimulus.

The enjoyment from its perusal must nevertheless be tempered by the messages that some species convey. The birds of prey are mostly in the ascendant, but when it comes to the Hen Harrier we might as well be living a century ago, from the relentless destruction handed out to the bird on the North Pennine grouse moors. Nor have the eggers given up their obsessive looting of Peregrine and Raven eyries in particular. And, though it is an incidental effect of modern agriculture, many farmland birds in the region show the alarming declines that recent surveys of the British Trust for Ornithology and the Royal Society for the Protection of Birds have highlighted as national trends. Some birds are prone to ups and downs in the normal course of events, but rather too many are showing a long-term downward trend. The northwards spread of southerners such as the Nuthatch could be a gain from global warming, but perhaps the Dotterel has already begun to fade out and show us the down-side.

So this *The Breeding Birds of Cumbria* should give much food for thought over the conservation of the regional avifauna. Its hard data will strengthen the arguments that have to be made and illuminate the problems needing to be resolved, if a more favourable balance between losses and gains is to be achieved. A virtue of the atlas treatment, especially at the tetrad scale, is that it provides a monitoring base-line, against which future surveys can be matched to give accurate measures of change in species' populations. In the meantime, let us hope that this work will stimulate enthusiasts not only to further recording effort and bird study, but also to engagement in the campaign to restore or enhance the numbers of those birds which have declined steeply, or are held far below their natural level by deliberate human actions.

Derek Ratcliffe, Cambridge, 10th April 2002

# Introduction

*At once a voice arose among*
*The bleak twigs overhead*
*In a full-hearted evensong*
*Of joy illimited;*
*An aged thrush, frail, gaunt, and small,*
*In blast-beruffled plume,*
*Had chosen thus to fling his soul*
*Upon the growing gloom.*

*So little cause for carolings*
*Of such ecstatic sound*
*Was written on terrestial things*
*Afar or nigh around,*
*That I could think there trembled through*
*His happy good-night air*
*Some blessed Hope, whereof he knew*
*And I was unaware.*

*Thomas Hardy, 31st December 1900*

Even though written almost exactly 100 years ago at the beginning of the 20th century, many of the sentiments expressed in Hardy's 'Darkling Thrush' still ring true today: though Hardy would scarcely have pictured the transformation of the English rural landscape, it seems his words had some prophecy in them. At a time when man has the frightening ability to destroy so much 'at a stroke' it is vital that conservation bodies have unsentimental, accurate, reliable information available. The data from *The Breeding Birds of Cumbria* will provide this quality of information.

Historically, there has been little detailed knowledge available on the populations of many of Cumbria's breeding birds. A few popular or geographically isolated species such as Peregrine and Raven in the uplands, Eiders around Walney Island or the colonial seabirds at St Bees Head have been regularly monitored, as have other species, albeit in a temporal or limited manner, through long-running surveys by the British Trust for Ornithology. However, for expanding or declining populations of species such as Buzzard and Corn Bunting we had only the vaguest notion on distribution and abundance. Although the *Atlas of Breeding Birds in Britain & Ireland* and the *New Atlas of Breeding Birds,* both carried out on a 10km square basis, gave us some idea, even those are too general to map accurately many species, and they fail to match the aspirations set out as the objective for the present work: to map the distribution of all breeding birds, to quantify their abundance, and to estimate, wherever possible, the size of their populations. This atlas, because of its methodology, will be definitive and repeatable: two strengths that will give future generations a base-line resolution for continuing the task of bird conservation and habitat protection.

Although the fieldwork began in 1997, the idea of a county atlas was conceived with the formation of the Cumbria Bird Club; indeed, for some, that was the *raison d'être* of the newly-formed club in 1989. Many members had previous fieldwork experience with various BTO surveys and the Bird Club tested its members and methods with earlier breeding enquiries into the county distribution of the woodpeckers, Rook, Nuthatch and Sand Martin.

Highlights of these atlas years include the first breeding of Mediterranean Gull and Common Rosefinch, the discovery of breeding Honey Buzzard, and – perhaps most spectacular of all – the return of the Osprey, after an absence of 170 years, to rear its young in Cumbrian woods. Conversely, the near-extinction of the Corncrake and Corn Bunting as breeding birds is a sad indictment of living in a changing world.

While there is no doubt that these atlas years have been enjoyable and memorable, giving a sense of satisfaction to all those involved in completing such a momentous enterprise, we should not lose sight of the fact that it was conceived and fostered by those who have a love and attachment for Cumbria and its birds, and who are concerned for their future. Its greatest testament would be that as a consequence of this work, the county became a better and more secure place for many of its birds.

The present government is committed to using bird populations as one indicator to the 'Quality of Life'; in fact the current indications are that common birds are declining, woodland ones modestly and farmland ones steeply, causing considerable concern. The United Kingdom's Biodiversity Action Plan will test the success of its actions. Whereas nationally, populations can be affected by many factors such as migration, wintering quarters and climate, detailed local breeding population studies can give a more accurate indication of trends. This atlas will provide a county barometer with which to assess the effectiveness of some key Biodiversity Action Plans in Cumbria.

Cumbria is a county of aesthetic and atmospheric landscapes renowned for its spectacular and inspiring scenery, which create a lasting impression of wonder and astonishment. There is little doubt that Wordsworth, one of Cumbria's earliest naturalists and most famous sons, would be irate if he saw the unnatural impoverishment of his beloved inspirational vales. A landscape devoid of birds would be a joyless spectacle, beyond contemplation; they most singularly through sight and sound enliven any panorama with a feeling of contentment and enrichment.

# Acknowledgements

This has been an eclectic work, planned, actioned and compiled by Cumbria Bird Club members. The financial support given over the five years by all our sponsors has allowed the atlas committees to concentrate on the fieldwork and mapping rather than worry about funding. We are very grateful for that assurance.

Together with atlas committees and club members, many other organizations and individuals have willingly and freely given their time or premises. At an inaugural meeting at Scotby School, John Day and Mike Hodgson of the Northumberland and Tyneside Bird Club presented their recently-published *Atlas of Breeding Birds in Northumbria,* and gave us many valuable insights into how we might initiate a similar project for Cumbria. For the many regular meetings thereafter, we are grateful for the use of Cumbria Wildlife Trust offices at Brockhole and later Westmorland Services at Tebay. To Bob Bunce and David Howard at the Centre for Ecology and Hydrology we are grateful for their patience and assistance with the National Land Classification and Steve Buckland at St Andrews University for his guidance with the statistical analyses. David Gibbons is no stranger to atlas work and we are indebted to him for his enthusiasm and sound advice. Above all we are deeply indebted to Stephen Hewitt and his staff at Tullie House Museum for their unwavering support from the outset and the use of their facilities without hesitation or conditions. The great burden of inputting of some 73,000 records fell largely upon the shoulders of Geoff Naylor, working on behalf of Cumbria Bird Club. We also extend our gratitude to Derek Ratcliffe for his fitting and timely foreword.

No work of this magnitude can be accomplished without the unstinting effort and commitment of many contributors. Although the editors diligently spent much time revising species accounts to ensure accuracy and consistency, the text originated from twenty-nine authors whose names appear with their contributions. The talents of eleven artists who contributed their work freely have enhanced the text immeasurably. Ashley Boon's superb cover captures the essence of one of Cumbria's most exciting bird spectacles, in an atmospheric and realistic landscape. The colour photographs that illustrate the character of Cumbria are inspirational and the photographers' contributions are enormously appreciated. Phil Byle assiduously conducted the line transect analysis, Jackie Stott meticulously compiled the gazetteer and reference section, and at the near-final stage, Jeremy and Margaret Roberts undertook the task of proof-reading and checking scripts, avoiding numerous errors at the print stage. We are grateful to Jonathan Rimmer for his generous and friendly advice throughout and for lifting the burden of publishing from our shoulders, and also to the printers who handled the project with great efficiency.

Such a time-consuming project could not have been contemplated without the support and forbearance of our families over the last five years. Lastly, although not least, the substance within these covers will provide everlasting testament to the efforts of over 230 fieldworkers who recorded birds in some of the most difficult terrain and hostile weather Cumbria can offer. The list on the next page acknowledges all those whose contributions amounted to in excess of 10,000 hours of fieldwork. Should we have inadvertently omitted anyone's name please accept our unreserved apologies.

# Fieldworkers

(Names in bold are those who undertook timed counts and/or line transect work)

| | | | |
|---|---|---|---|
| **Mike Abbs** | **J&C Adams** | Gary Agar | **Mike Ainscough** |
| Tony Allaker | Colin Armistead | **A&B Armstrong** | **Ian Armstrong** |
| Roy Armstrong | **GI Ashworth** | **Roy Atkins** | **Kathleen Atkinson** |
| Nick Attwood | **Colin Auld** | Judith Aveyard | **Ron Baines** |
| Sheila Bamforth | Stuart Bamforth | Sam Barker | Charles Barraclough |
| **Pete Barron** | **Ian Bedford** | **Peter Blinco** | **Brian Bottomley** |
| **Roy Bottomley** | **Peter Brady** | **Susan Brandes** | David Brass |
| **Robbie Bridson** | **Cliff Brockbank** | **Richard Brown** | **David Bruin** |
| **R Brundall** | **Peter Buchanan** | Harry Butcher | **Phil Byle** |
| **John Callion** | Ian Campbell | Marjorie Campion | **Mike Carrier** |
| **Paul Carver** | **George Casson** | Trish Chadwick | **Keith Clark** |
| **Gordon Clarke** | **Ingram Cleasby** | Sheila Cooper | Mark Cornish |
| **David Cousins** | Alan Cremin | **Mike Critchley** | **Alistair Crowle** |
| John Curtis | Tom Curwen | **Jill Damment** | **Peter Davies** |
| **Sian Davies** | Harold Dean | Geoffery Dent | **Richard Dixon** |
| **Aidan Doherty** | **Eric Donnelly** | **Ken Dorman** | Tony Doy |
| Stephen Dunstan | Stephen Dutton | **Paul Eale** | **Mike Easton** |
| R Eddleston | **RJ Eland** | **Stan Elliott** | Colin Fearnley |
| **Peter Finn** | **Toby Fisher** | **Clive Flindall** | **Nathan Fox** |
| **Brian Furness** | **Steve Garnett** | **Colin Gay** | **Rosalyn Gay** |
| **Rex George** | **Paul Glading** | **Fred Gould** | **Lindsay Gould** |
| **David Greenway** | **Derek Griffiths** | **Les Grisedale** | **Jim Hadfield** |
| C Haigh | **Stuart Halder** | Diana Hall | **John Hamer** |
| **Michael Harrison** | **Patrick Harrison** | **Clive Hartley** | **Ken Hay** |
| **Bob Hayward** | Norman Healy | **Neil Henderson** | Stephen Hewitt |
| **Mark Hill** | **Chris Hind** | **Dudley Hind** | Ken Hindmarch |
| **Richard Hockin** | Thomas Holden | **Norman Holton** | Mike Houston |
| **Allan Hubbold** | **Ian Hufton** | **Malcolm Hutcheson** | **Marjorie Hutchin** |
| **Neil Hutchin** | **Ronnie Irving** | **Mark Jacques** | **Patricia Jacques** |
| **Sam Jacques** | **Derek Jewell** | **JG Jones** | **Bob Jones** |
| **Bill Kenmir** | **Bill Kennedy** | **Ian Kinley** | **Sandra Kruger** |
| **Steve Kruger** | **Steve Lewer** | **Jonathan Lishman** | **Nick Littlewood** |
| C Lodge | **Geoff Longrigg** | Alan Mackay | **Allan Mackenzie** |
| **Bill Makin** | **Jake Manson** | **Dave Mark** | Barry Marrs |
| **Tony Marshall** | **Heather Marshall** | **Nick Mason** | **Frank Mawby** |
| **Derek McAlone** | **Alan Meakin** | **Ian Meredith** | **Kerry Milligan** |
| **Nicholas Mitchell** | **Ken Moss** | **John Mounsey** | Geoff Naylor |
| **Barbara Nelson** | **Val Nixon** | Colin Norman | Mike O'Brien |
| **Matthew Parsons** | **John Peatfield** | **Steve Peter** | S Petty |
| **Dave Piercy** | **Caroline Poyntz-Wright** | **Richard Poyntz-Wright** | **Graeme Prest** |
| **David Preston** | Elizabeth Priestley | **Laura Priestley** | **Malcolm Priestley** |
| **Colin Raven** | Mike Ryan | Susan Ryan | **Sean Reed** |
| **Jeremy Roberts** | Jean Roberts | **Andy Robinson** | **Ann Robinson** |
| **Craig Robinson** | **Derek Robinson** | **Terry Robinson** | **Andrew Robson** |
| **Lew Sanderson** | Peter Sandford | Dave Satterthwaite | Jean Scott |
| **M Scott** | **Sedgwick Society** | **Dave Shackleton** | **Bob Shaw** |
| R Shepherd | Sue Shiels | **Sheila Shuttleworth** | Colin Simpson |
| **Pete Singleton** | Trevor Smith | **Brian Spencer** | Geoff Stansfield |
| Allan Stewart | **Malcolm Stott** | **Arnold Strand** | **Keith Temple** |
| **Dave Thexton** | **George Tinkler** | **Bob Treen** | **Audrey Tuer** |
| **Mike Tulloch** | **Peter Ullrich** | **Peter Unwin** | H Venables |
| DT Vigar | **David Walker** | Walney BO | P Warren |
| **Jonathan Webb** | **Maynall Weir** | **Terry Wells** | **Derek West** |
| **Stephen Westerberg** | **Denis White** | Norman White | **Rachel Whiteley** |
| Ray Whittam | **Ted Williams** | **Michael Williams** | Alan Wills |
| Kathleen Wilson | **MW Wilson** | **Rob Wilson** | **Richard Wimpress** |
| **Nigel Winn** | | | |

# Cumbria: the Natural Areas

Geology is the basis of all landscapes and such features are most striking in Cumbria. The solid central knot of old rocks and mountains is surrounded by gentler hills and green dales, and beyond these lie fertile plains; a high world of tranquillity and wilderness overshadows a lower one which in spring seems to hide behind the fresh foliage of hedges. Linking the two extremes are habitats diversely rich: fast-flowing becks and rivulets, roaring through hanging woodlands and thundering over rocks in a cascade of sparkling water, eventually to replenish broader valley rivers that drain the county.

To help appreciate the geographical influences that relate to the bird communities and their distributions, the county has been divided into eight units, broadly based on 'Natural Areas' **(Figure 1: Natural Areas, overleaf)**. Although these divisions are not intended to be exact or precisely defined they do offer the layperson an interpretation of the geological complexity that is Cumbria. Due to the general similarities of the Eden Valley and Solway Basin Areas, and of the North Pennines and Border Uplands Areas, respectively, these are jointly discussed in this chapter.

Plate 1: Eden valley from Cross Fell, Lakeland Fells beyond

## Eden Valley and Solway Basin (Areas C; B)

The broad funnel-shaped Eden valley **(Plate 1)** separates the Pennine escarpment in the east from the Lakeland fells in the west before merging into the Solway Basin, to the east of Carlisle. Permian and Triassic rocks, which collectively form the New Red Sandstone, underlie the whole area with a band of Carboniferous limestone outcrops occupying the transitional zone with neighbouring fells. Great spreads of glacial drift, comprising fluvio-glacial sands, gravel and boulder clay overlie much of the area and give rise to the gently undulating topography of the Solway Basin. These drift deposits tend to yield fairly acidic, sandy and permeable soils that are of modest fertility.

This area is the driest and sunniest part of Cumbria, with the annual level of rainfall ranging from 750mm around the inner Solway to 1000mm in foothill locations such as Caldbeck and Kirkby Stephen. This factor, along with the combination of low altitude and reasonably fertile soils, has given rise to a predominantly agricultural landscape of intensively farmed arable, mainly barley, and highly productive grassland **(Plate 2)**. Hedgerows and trees feature strongly as field boundaries in contrast to the walled fields and predominant pastures of the upper Eden Valley. Although agricultural intensification has resulted in a reduction in farmland bird populations in recent years, this area still provides an important habitat for nesting birds, such as **Lapwing** and **Yellowhammer**. It is also one of the English strongholds of the **Barn Owl**.

Plate 2: Ploughing, Eden valley

**Figure 1: The Natural Areas of Cumbria**

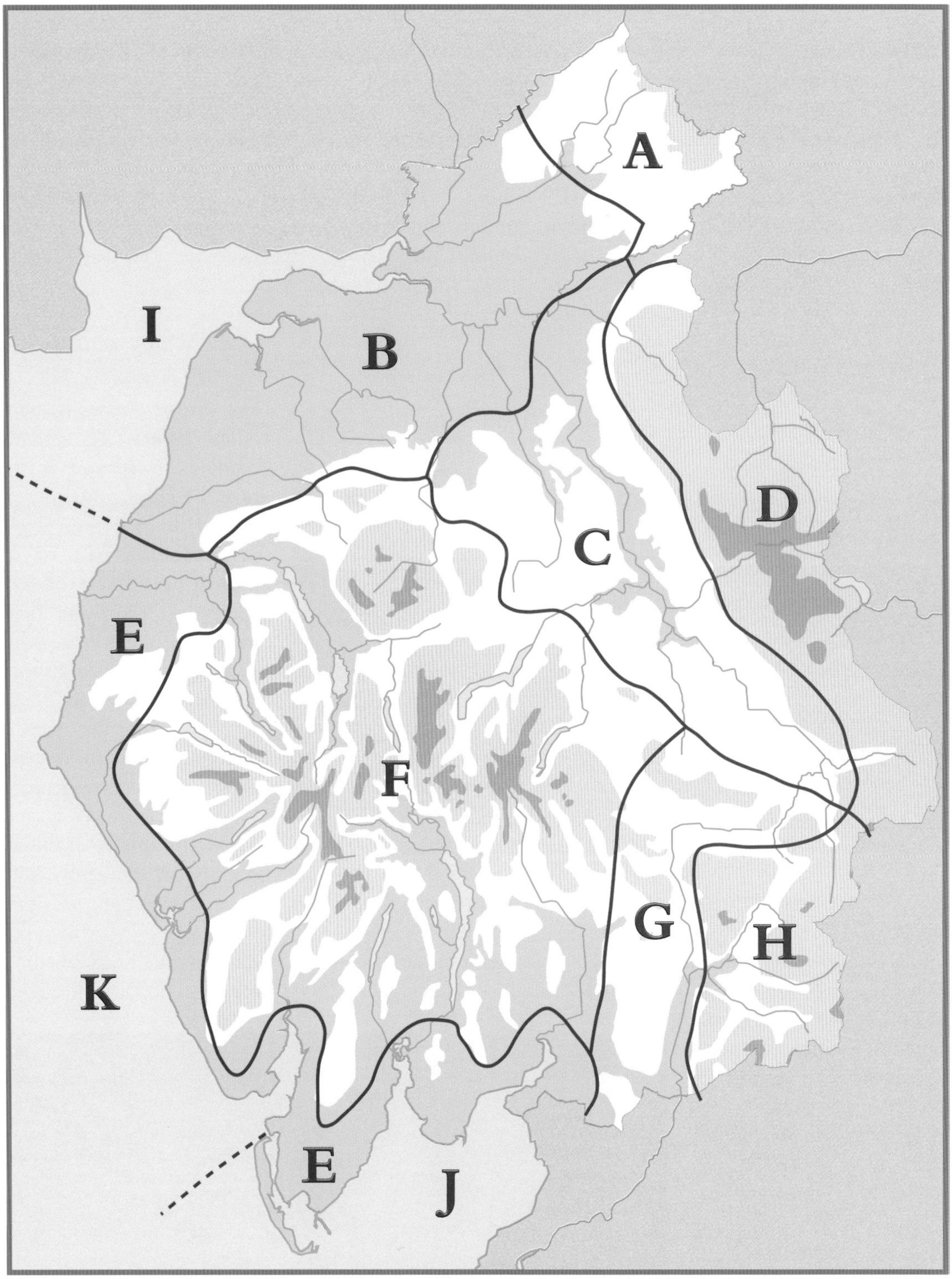

| A: Border Uplands | B: Solway Basin | C: Eden Valley |
| D: North Pennines | E: Coastal Plain | F: Lakeland |
| G: Lune Valley | H: Cumbria Dales | I: Solway Firth |
| J: Morecambe Bay | K: Cumbria Coast | |

Many rivers and streams, deriving their headwaters from the surrounding Pennines and Lakeland fells, drain the area. These include the Rivers Esk and Eden along with their tributaries, the Liddle, Lyne, Irthing, Gelt, Petteril and Caldew, and also the Rivers Wampool and Waver in the west. These river systems support a range of breeding birds, including **Oystercatcher, Common Sandpiper, Sand Martin, Dipper, Grey Wagtail, Kingfisher** and **Goosander.**

The Esk and Eden and their tributaries have, in places, cut ravines through the rocks that outcrop along their lengths.

**Plate 3: Commercial peat-stripping, Solway Moss**

Woodlands of oak and alder are to be found fringing these sandstone ravines at locations such as Penton Linns, Kirklinton, Lanercost, Brampton, Armathwaite and Wreay on the aforementioned rivers. Limestone exposures on the Caldew above Sebergham and at The Howk ravine near Caldbeck have a base-rich woodland flora, with a good deal of ash, wych elm, hazel and elder, although the effect of Dutch Elm disease from the 1960s has modified the composition. 'Amenity' woodlands planted on the large estates of Netherby, near Longtown and Naworth, near Brampton, add further diversity to the woodland habitat available within this area. Many of these woodlands provide nesting habitats for birds such as **Redstart, Pied Flycatcher, Wood Warbler** and **Tree Pipit,** with both **Nuthatch** and **Marsh Tit** extending their range into these areas in recent years.

Some significant 'islands' of raised bog, together with a few fragments of more nutrient-rich fen, occur within the lower reaches of the river systems within the Solway Basin. These remnant habitats once occupied extensive parts of this area prior to its reclamation for agriculture. Two of the largest remaining raised bogs, Solway Moss and Wedholme Flow, have been extensively worked by the removal of moss litter as horticultural peat, but still contain areas of ecological importance **(Plate 3)**. Wedholme Flow, Oulton Moss, Glasson Moss, Drumburgh Moss and Bowness Common form an important group of raised bogs in close proximity to each other to the west of Carlisle. Further inland, the undulating drift country to the north and east of Carlisle contains many more small pockets of bog, including Moorthwaite Moss, Cumwhitton Moss, Faugh Moss, Black Dub, Unity Bog, Walton Moss and Broom Hill Moss. The latter two, along with the severely worked Bolton Fell Moss, are intermediate between raised mire and blanket bog. In their most natural form, these lowland peat mosses have a gently undulating surface dominated by Sphagnum mosses. During the 20th century peat cutting and reclamation to agriculture has significantly reduced the area of these mosses and created artificial edges with the surrounding farmland, resulting in a lowering of the water table, the drying of their surfaces and a reduction in Sphagnum cover. Initially this drying out process is characterized by extensive areas of cotton grass and heather, but this, in turn, can be subject to extensive colonization by silver birch and Scots pine and, ultimately, by oak. These different phases in this natural progression often support

**Plate 4: Rockcliffe Marsh & Solway Firth**

**Plate 5: Upper Irthing valley at Wiley Sike**

different species of birds; **Reed Bunting** in open, wet areas dominated by Sphagnum mosses and cotton grass; **Curlew** and **Whinchat** on drier areas characterized by a mix of heather and invasive saplings; **Willow Tit** in the mature mossland woods. This typical mosaic of habitats in southern counties would support **Hobby**, a species whose breeding range is extending north and which now nests within a 10km square of the county boundary. **Black Grouse** were once common here, while **Red Grouse** are still present in small numbers.

Newton Reigny Moss, Biglands Bog and Salta Moss represent the few remaining fragments of nutrient-rich fen within this area of sedge swamp and willow carr. These well-vegetated wetlands provide nest sites for a wide-range of species such as **Reed Bunting, Sedge Warbler** and **Moorhen.** More open waterbodies such as those found at Talkin Tarn, Thurstonfield Lough, Martin Tarn, Colmire, Tarns Dub and the flooded gravel pits around Longtown cater for **Great Crested Grebe, Little Grebe, Coot, Tufted Duck, Canada Goose** and **Mute Swan.**

The coast of the innermost part of the Solway Firth is characterized by the great saltmarshes of Skinburness, Newton Arlosh, Burgh and Rockcliffe **(Plate 4)**, areas heavily grazed by sheep and cattle for much of the year and predominantly short-cropped swards dominated by common saltmarsh grass, alongside the bare mud of creeks and tidal pools. Red fescue is common at higher levels within the saltmarsh. **Lapwing, Oystercatcher, Redshank** and **Skylark** are typical breeding birds of these open saltmarsh communities. A large colony of breeding **Lesser Black-backed** and **Herring Gulls** is found on Rockcliffe Marsh, along with a lesser number of **Common Terns.** From Grune Point southwards, coastal processes have led to the building of sand dunes and shingle beaches. These deposits are mainly of a non-calcareous nature, with slacks poorly represented and, consequently the dune flora is rather limited. Gorse and other scrub vegetation provide cover for nesting birds such as **Linnet, Whitethroat** and **Stonechat** and the now rare **Corn Bunting.** Areas of shingle provide open nesting sites for **Oystercatcher** and **Ringed Plover.**

## North Pennines and the Border Uplands (Areas D; A)

The escarpment of the high Pennines, which runs from Whernside north to the Tyne Gap and includes the adjoining moorland district above Bewcastle and Gilsland, dominates the eastern edge of Cumbria **(Plate 5)**. These areas are all formed of Carboniferous rocks, with a preponderance of acidic gritstones and shales, and with limestone exposed at various localities. The summit of Cross Fell, at an altitude of 893m, represents the highest point of this last great 'wilderness' area **(Plate 6)**. Thick layers of glacial drift overlie most of the lower slopes of the North Pennines and Border Uplands, often obscuring the underlying Carboniferous limestone and thereby complicating the relationship between solid geology, plant and animal communities. These areas of drift are quite often strongly calcareous giving rise to some extensive areas of relatively fertile soils. This, together with the slightly lower rainfall in this area, has resulted in a much higher farmland limit than in central Lakeland. Hay meadows and enclosed pastures occur up to an altitude of 560m at Moor House, for example, where rainfall is 1773mm a year. These upland meadows, with their dry stone walls, hold nationally important numbers of breeding waders, including **Snipe, Curlew, Oystercatcher, Redshank** and **Lapwing,** along with **Wheatear, Skylark** and now scarce **Yellow Wagtail.** Conversion of traditional hay meadows to high production grass leys and the introduction of silage in place of haymaking, with its

**Plate 6: Cross Fell (893m); Great Dun Fell beyond**

much earlier harvesting date, has contributed to a decline in the numbers of some of these birds in recent years, although perhaps not on such a dramatic scale as in other parts of Britain.

Above the upper limits of enclosed farmland, many scarp slopes are given over to open sheep walks where extensive areas of acidic grassland have become dominant, with fescues and bent grass on drier slopes and mat grass with heath rush on less well-drained ground and on areas subjected to heavy grazing pressure. These areas of acidic grassland are the most extensive of the semi-natural vegetation types in Cumbria and provide breeding grounds for birds such as **Snipe, Curlew** and **Meadow Pipit** and hunting areas for **Short-eared Owls.** On more base-rich soils associated with the Carboniferous limestone, the unenclosed grazed swards are composed of a species-rich mixture of grasses, sedges and herbs. Elsewhere, on moderate to steep slopes below 600m asl, heather moorland dominates the landscape. Where management for **Red Grouse** is practised, this habitat is extensive and usually represents a heath community degraded by over-burning. In many areas the characteristic dwarf shrubs have been replaced by grasslands due to intolerable grazing pressure or through 'land improvement' **(Plate 7)**, with effects detrimental to birds that have a strong affinity towards this habitat such as **Hen Harrier** and **Merlin**. In some instances, however, **Skylark** and **Meadow Pipit** populations appear to show a positive correlation with the higher ratio of grass to heather. At a number of locations, the headwaters of the Eden and its tributaries have cut deep gills at right angles into the Pennine escarpment, exposing areas of high-level crag and scree. The quartz dolerite cliffs and screes of High Cup Nick are the most impressive example. There are also cliffs at locations such as Mallerstang Edge and Christianbury Crags that are composed of Millstone Grit. Traditionally these sites have provided haunts for birds like **Raven, Peregrine** and **Ring Ouzel.**

Woodland is no longer extensive in these areas, but where it does appear it has a great influence on upland bird communities. The relic woodland pastures at Geltsdale provide a unique insight into bird assemblages of this lost element of wildwoods **(Plate 8)**. The veteran trees provide natural nest-holes and crevices for **Pied Flycatcher** and **Redstart,** with **Wood Warblers** and **Tree Pipits** taking advantage of the open canopy. **Black Grouse** exploit the woodland edge as they have done for centuries. Shelter belts and clumps of trees, of both native and exotic species, have been widely planted on the lower slopes high above the Eden Valley, both as 'amenity' woodland and to give protection to livestock from inclement weather; they provide a similar function for birds. Large-scale commercial afforestation is mainly confined to the Border Uplands of Bewcastle and Gilsland. This took place around the middle of the 20th century, with a high proportion of the ground below 450m asl being planted with Sitka spruce and some lodgepole pine and larch. These woodlands have provided new habitats for birds such as **Crossbill, Goldcrest, Redpoll,**

**Plate 7: Ling, with over-grazed moor beyond fence, Geltsdale**

**Plate 8: Relic woodland pasture, Geltsdale**

**Siskin** and probably assisted the **Goshawk** to spread more rapidly. Within the Pennines, the presence of common land and sporting interests has restricted large-scale commercial forestry.

Beyond the scarp slopes, gently undulating moorlands occupy the watersheds of the Pennines and Border Uplands. Here drainage impediment has led to the formation of extensive areas of blanket bog over deep peats, which are often interspersed with bog pools and stretches of dry, stony grassland with gritstone blocks, particularly in heavily eroded areas **(Plate 9)**. The trilling of **Dunlin** and the plaintive calls of **Golden Plover** characterize these high windswept moors, and provide perhaps the only regular breeding grounds of **Short-eared Owl** in Cumbria.

## Lakeland (Area F)

The Lake District is a very distinct geographical entity that occupies the area between the Eden Valley and the narrow Coastal Plain. It takes the form of a great central dome that has been subjected to successive and complex folding and uplifting and to the removal, through erosion, of all the younger rocks that once formed its cap. The result is a central mass of silty slates and volcanic rocks of Ordovician and Silurian age appearing from beneath the newer, softer rocks of Carboniferous age which encircle Lakeland proper. This central dome is drained by a number of steep-sided valleys which radiate out, like the spokes in a wheel, from a hub that is located near the Langdale range. Some of these valleys contain lakes but others have none. Each valley and each lake has its own striking individual character and each makes an important contribution to the scenic beauty and ecology of the National Park.

The oldest rocks in Lakeland are the Skiddaw Slates, a group of metamorphosed sedimentary rocks that are mostly of a silty nature. They form much of the northern part of the area, extending from the foot of Ennerdale, through Grasmere, to beyond Skiddaw. The geology has produced an upland landscape that is characterized by long, smooth sided, scree-covered slopes, deeply cleft gills and broken cliffs, with extensive areas of heather moor and acidic grassland existing on the base-deficient soils of their watersheds **(Plate 10)**. Bird communities here are more akin to the Pennines than to the rest of the Lake District.

The relative softness of the rocks around Skiddaw has led to the main valleys being wider and their lakes shallower than those to the south, with a larger proportion of enclosed farmland and amenity woodland within their catchments. Run-off from this farmland, in combination with the relative shallowness and sheltered nature of the bays within these lakes, has contributed towards the development of areas of emergent vegetation, including fen and willow carr, around parts of Derwent Water and Bassenthwaite Lake and some of the surrounding tarns **(Plate 11)**. These provide

**Plate 9: Pool in blanket bog, showing exposure of deep peat**

nest sites for a variety of water birds, including **Great Crested Grebe, Little Grebe, Water Rail, Sedge Warbler, Grasshopper Warbler, Reed Warbler** and **Willow Tit.** Less typical of this area are the twin lakes of Buttermere and Crummock Water, which have clear, nutrient-deficient waters that are incapable of supporting such rich plant and vertebrate communities. This is because the rocks within this part of the Skiddaw Slate belt have been further metamorphosed by heat and are therefore, much harder and more resistant to weathering than the norm.

**Plate 10: Skiddaw & Blencathra from Grizedale Pike**

To the south of a line between Ennerdale and the head of Derwent Water and eastwards to the foot of Ullswater, the mountainous heart of the Lake District presents a sharply contrasting type of scenery to that found in most of the Skiddaw belt. This area is composed of a diverse group of volcanic rocks, varying from hard flinty tuffs and lavas to friable breccias, know as the Borrowdale Volcanic Series. These are interspersed with outcrops of granite, which are mostly similar to the Borrowdale Volcanics in terms of their influence on the topography and scenery, in that they all provide areas of base-deficient rock, with predominantly acidic and infertile soils. The variable hardness of these rocks in response to the processes of weathering and sculpting by ice has given rise to the rugged character of the central fells with their crag-girt valley sides, boulder fields and scree slopes. It has also contributed to the development of the numerous hanging valleys, with lower waterfall ravines, which drain into the main dales, the latter being of typically U-shaped form and containing the large, ice-gouged lakes that are such an important feature of the Lake District. The **Raven**'s harsh calls echo in these valleys, where **Wood Warblers** sing from the cover of craggy trees and a bright flash of sulphur along a beck tells of the presence of **Grey Wagtails.**

The central heart of the Lake District contains by far the largest and steepest inland cliffs in England. Corrie formation is most pronounced on the eastern ranges of Helvellyn **(Plate 12)**, Fairfield and High Street, while the Scafell range is notable for the deep chasms carved out along fault lines and volcanic dykes. Amongst these cliffs and ravines, usually in locations away from the main attentions of climbers and hill walkers, **Wheatears, Ring Ouzels, Ravens, Peregrines** and England's only regular nesting pair of **Golden Eagle** are to be found. Some of the highest peaks have a sub-alpine vegetation community unique in England and attract specialist birds such as the **Dotterel**.

**Plate 11: Bassenthwaite Lake, southern bays.**

Much of the Borrowdale Volcanic Series is non-calcareous and yields acidic substrates that are extremely limited in terms of their botanical variety. Extensive areas of fescue and bent grasses form the dominant plant community within the central fells, with mat grass and heath rush in damper areas and indicative of ecological impoverishment through over-grazing. Some of these grassland areas contain breeding birds such as **Golden Plover**.

The Lakeland fells have narrower watersheds than their Pennine equivalent and blanket bog is, therefore, of more limited

**Plate 12: The eastern corries and summit of Helvellyn (950m)**

occurrence. Where the abundant rainfall of these fells emerges on lower slopes and collects in hollows, there are frequent and sometimes extensive flush and valley mires with species-rich plant communities. The damp pastures around Brothers Water, Wet Sleddale and Swindale are good examples of this, providing nest sites for birds such as **Snipe, Redshank, Curlew** and in the past **Yellow Wagtail.**

Heath communities within the Borrowdale Volcanics belt are confined to areas on Armboth Fells and elsewhere limited to steeper 'edges' and areas of semi-stable scree. In such locations they are least likely to be subject to the combination of heavy grazing and repeated burning, that has rapidly replaced dwarf shrubs with acidic grasslands and bracken, both of which have competitive advantages in the high rainfall area of the central fells. Where heather moor still survives, **Red Grouse** are present, albeit less numerous in comparison to the managed moors on the Pennines.

The narrowness of the valleys within central Lakeland and their steep-sided nature, together with the combination of hard acidic rocks, poor soils, heavy rainfall and exposure to wind, has resulted in only a relatively small area of land being available for cultivation **(Plate 13)**. The upper limit of enclosed farmland within the central fells is only 150–250m asl in the west and 250–350m asl in the east, compared to 560m asl in parts of the Pennines. Even within the valley floors, the climate can be quite inhospitable for much of the year, with sunshine hardly penetrating some of the valleys in winter and night temperature inversions producing especially severe frosts.

**Plate 13: Upper Newlands Valley**

The patchwork of walled fields, farm clusters and villages within the valley floors are the result of a long history of human occupation, which has seen some important changes in the way in which the land is managed. Formerly the traditionally late hay crop and the need to use valley meadows for the late lambing of hill sheep was associated with a relatively species-rich meadow community, which once supported **Yellow Wagtails** and **Corncrakes.** Changes in grassland management over the last 50 years, involving drainage, reseeding, increased fertilization and the replacement of haymaking with silage operations, have seen the disappearance of many of the old floristically-rich meadows, along with the bird communities they once supported. By way of contrast, the existence of extensive areas of bracken towards the upper limits of enclosure is often indicative of areas that were once more intensively cultivated than at present. These bracken-covered slopes often provide a suitable habitat for birds such as **Whinchat** in the absence of scrub.

The lakes and tarns of this area tend to have rocky shorelines and waters that are deficient in nutrients and, therefore, only capable of supporting limited plant and animal communities. Exceptions include the small, relatively nutrient rich lakes of Rydal Water and Brothers

Water, together with the northern end of Ullswater, where areas of emergent vegetation support breeding waterbirds such as **Little Grebe, Coot** and **Tufted Duck. Common Sandpipers** nest around the edges of some of the lakes and tarns in the central fells, but human disturbance tends to limit their occurrence.

A number of woodlands exist within the valleys of central Lakeland. Some, such as those in the Rydal–Grasmere and lower Borrowdale valleys, are 'primary' woods which were re-planted in the late 18th and early 19th centuries with native species, mainly oak, on the site of original

**Plate 14: Glencoyne Wood, Ullswater**

forests. Despite the presence of non-native trees such as larch and beech, they now have a natural feel **(Plate 14)**. Others, such as the commercial afforestation that took place at Ennerdale and Thirlmere during the 1920s and 1930s, using mainly larch and Norway spruce, have a less 'natural' feel, but provide breeding sites for **Crossbill, Siskin, Lesser Redpoll** and **Sparrowhawk,** thereby adding to the diversity of species in the area. Alder trees that border the lower courses of some of the becks in the area help provide habitat for the **Grey Wagtail.**

Remnants of mixed deciduous woodland, which contain a predominance of oak, along with ash, silver birch and hazel, still hang on to some of the steeper, well-drained slopes up to an altitude of about 500m within the central Lakeland fells. These include the woods at Keskadale and Rigg Beck in the Newlands valley, the Borrowdale woods around Seatoller, Scales Wood by Buttermere, Glencoyne and Hallin Fell woods by Ullswater, Low Wood by Brothers Water, Naddle Forest above Haweswater, the woods of Longsleddale and the Baysbrown woods in Great Langdale. Many of these relic woodlands are the haunt for breeding **Buzzards, Sparrowhawks, Redstarts, Wood Warblers** and **Pied Flycatchers.**

## Cumbria Dales and Lune Valley (Areas G; H)

To the southeast of Lakeland and west of the Pennines lies a tract of countryside, known as the Cumbria Dales, that link the Lake District and the Yorkshire Dales National Parks. The outlying Howgills and the Middleton and Barbon Fells south of Sedbergh dominate the area **(Plate 15)**. The bird communities, influenced by the dominance of mat grass, include **Curlew, Meadow Pipit,** and **Wheatear,** with **Whinchat** on some lower, bracken-covered slopes.

Immediately north of the Howgills, between Orton and Kirkby Stephen, Carboniferous limestone occupies the watershed between the Lune and Eden Valleys at 300m asl. Where it is drift covered, this provides areas of acidic grassland and heather moor, which contrast with the extensive limestone pavements at Great Asby, Sunbiggin and Orton and the important calcareous wetland of Sunbiggin Tarn **(Plate 16)**. This latter site, with its fringing fen, holds a **Black-headed Gull**

**Plate 15: Howgills, beyond Killington Reservoir**

colony, breeding **Gadwall** and **Tufted Duck**. The adjoining Tarn Moor, with its wet pastures and acidic bog, provides nest sites for a richness of wetland and moorland birds such as **Redshank** and **Snipe**, along with the odd pair of **Dunlin**.

The River Lune drains the whole of this southeastern corner of Cumbria. The upper reaches of the river are swift-flowing and support breeding **Dipper, Grey Wagtail** and **Common Sandpiper**. Lower down, to the south of Sedbergh, the river slows and widens into an alluvial valley, with some areas of damp meadow which still hold small numbers of **Redshank** and **Yellow Wagtail**.

Plate 16: Sunbiggin Tarn

## Furness and Morecambe Bay (Areas E; J)

The southward-draining valleys of the Lake District, extending from the Duddon Estuary in the west to beyond the Kent Estuary in the east are situated on a group of sedimentary flags, grits and shales of Silurian age that have produced a landscape that is scenically much tamer than that of the Borrowdale Volcanics to the north. The area is generally of lower altitude than central Lakeland, with soils that are more fertile and a milder, drier climate. It has a long history of human occupation centred on cottage industries associated with woodland management, the legacy which remains pertinent to birds today.

Woodlands of oak, ash, wych elm and silver birch run up the valley sides between the dale meadows and the rough broken ground of the high ridges, to produce one of the largest continuous areas of semi-natural woodland in the north of England. These include a number of neglected coppices in the lower parts of the Duddon Valley, Furness Fells and the area around Skelwith that are now particularly valuable to cavity-nesting birds such as **Redstart, Nuthatch, Marsh Tit** and **Little Owl**. Prior to the 1930s, many of these woodlands were systematically coppiced, on a rotation of between 14 and 17 years, for the production of charcoal and as raw material for the bobbin mills. Although the status of some birds, such as the **Nightjar**, has probably suffered as a result of the cessation of coppicing activity and the loss of transitional habitats which this provided, the habitats that have succeeded them are equally valuable in their own right and provide some of the richest bird areas in the county **(Plate 17)**.

Management plans have been adopted at Grizedale Forest, where similar coppiced management is aimed to maintain woodland diversity as part of the process to high forest. These areas of managed hardwood are of benefit to breeding birds such as **Woodcock, Pied Flycatcher, Tree Pipit** and **Wood Warbler,** alongside new softwoods that provide breeding sites for **Lesser Redpoll, Siskin** and **Crossbill.**

The area contains the large lakes of Windermere and Coniston Water, along with Esthwaite Water and a large number of predominantly lowland tarns.

Plate 17: Hazel coppice, Howe Ridding Wood

Because these waterbodies lie in areas of gentler relief and more fertile soils, their waters are more nutrient-rich and, therefore, capable of supporting far more plant and animal life. Esthwaite Water and many of the smaller tarns contain areas of reed fen and willow/alder carr, which provide breeding sites for **Great Crested Grebe, Coot, Tufted Duck, Sedge Warbler** and **Reed Bunting.** The larger lakes hold breeding **Red-breasted Merganser** and **Goosander,** whilst Killington Reservoir, to the east of Kendal, supports large breeding colonies of **Black-headed Gulls** and **Canada Geese (Plate 15).**

Between the Silurian zone and the coast, there is a broad but discontinuous belt of Carboniferous limestone, which extends from Millom eastwards around the Duddon Estuary and Morecambe Bay. It outcrops as small coastal cliffs in places, notably at Humphrey Head, and then is increasingly exposed as low, rocky hills in a wedge of country stretching from the west of Kendal southwards to Hutton Roof and Arnside. At Middlebarrow, Hutton Roof Crags and Farleton Fell the limestone reaches the surface as limestone pavements, whilst at Whitbarrow Scar, Scout Scar, Cunswick Scar and Arnside Knott it outcrops in some notable crags and associated scree. Areas of mixed woodland and scrub, dominated by ash and hazel, are of frequent occurrence in this limestone district. They support a wide variety of breeding birds, including **Hawfinch, Green Woodpecker, Little Owl** and **Woodcock.**

Extensive saltmarsh systems are to be found around the main estuaries of Morecambe Bay and to a lesser extent on the Duddon Estuary, to the north of the Furness peninsula. These saltmarshes have developed on mainly sandy substrate, which are quick draining following inundation by the tide. Their plant communities exhibit a successional sequence from colonization of bare tidal sand flats by common saltmarsh grass and common cord grass, to red fescue at higher levels within the saltmarsh. The swards of many of these marshes are heavily grazed by sheep and cattle and are subject to rotational turf removal. Consequently their breeding birds are similar to, but fewer than, those of the Solway Firth and include **Oystercatcher, Curlew, Redshank** and **Shelduck.**

Raised bogs occur within the hinterland of both the Duddon Estuary and Morecambe Bay, with the Rusland, Roudsea, Witherslack, Meathop and Duddon mosses all occupying quite extensive areas. These have a similar flora to the raised bogs of the Solway Basin, with a successional sequence from Sphagnum mosses through to mixed mossland woods of silver birch, Scots pine and oak, that is associated with the drying out of their surfaces following drainage activity on surrounding farmland. The large area of Foulshaw Moss has been largely replaced by commercial afforestation, which is currently in the process of being clear felled by the Cumbria Wildlife Trust to restore its value as raised mire. A few churring **Nightjars** continue to inhabit these lowland peat mosses, while other breeding birds include **Reed Bunting, Grasshopper Warbler** and **Sedge Warbler.**

**Plate 18: Walney Island: South End Haws, gravel extraction lagoons**

**Plate 19: Hodbarrow**

At the western extremity of the Furness peninsula lies Walney Island, with its complex of saltmarsh, shingle, dunes, flooded gravel pits and heath **(Plate 18)**. It possesses one of the largest gull colonies in Europe, with both **Herring Gulls** and **Lesser Black-backed Gulls** present in plentiful numbers and one of the largest **Great Black-backed Gull** colonies in England. Its relatively unimproved farmland still supports good numbers of **Lapwings**. On the opposite side of the Walney Channel, and jutting out into Morecambe Bay, is the small shingle island of Foulney. **Arctic Terns** occupy the nesting area on the tip of the island, whilst **Ringed Plover** nest amongst the shingle. Along with neighbouring Walney Island, Foulney provides the southernmost breeding **Eider** colony on the west coast of Britain. On the mainland, at Barrow-in-Furness, reedbeds border the industrial complex at Cavendish Dock and hold breeding **Sedge** and **Reed Warblers.**

## Coastal Plain and Cumbria Coast (Areas E; K)

To the north of the Duddon Estuary a group of Permian and Triassic rocks, collectively known as the New Red Sandstone, occupy the narrow coastal plain from Millom up to St Bees Head; most of which is covered by glacial drift giving rise to a tract of gently undulating country.

The whole of this southern part of the coastal belt is very windswept, with the prevailing westerly winds. This has contributed to the development of sand-dunes on both sides of the Duddon Estuary, at Sandscale Haws and Haverigg, and on both sides of the Irt Estuary, at Eskmeals and Drigg. The dunes at Drigg once contained the largest **Black-headed Gull** colony in Europe, but this disappeared in 1982, along with nesting terns. The dunes at Sandscale Haws are lime-rich and contain areas of wet slack. These provide breeding sites for wetland birds, such as **Reed Buntings.**

**Plate 20: St Bees Head**

**Plate 21: Siddick Pond, Workington**

Relics of an iron and steel industry exist on the north side of the Duddon Estuary, at Millom. At coastal sites like Hodbarrow huge ore-mine excavations have been flooded to form an artificial lake, which provides new facilities for an increasing leisure industry **(Plate 19)**. It seems incongruous to watch **Sandwich Terns,** and lesser numbers of **Common** and **Little Terns** nesting and feeding successfully alongside high-powered boats and water-skiing activities. It also provides a breeding site for species such as **Great Crested Grebe, Little Grebe, Coot, Tufted Duck, Sedge Warbler, Grasshopper Warbler** and **Lesser Whitethroat.**

St Bees Head itself provides the only significant sea cliffs in Cumbria, rising to a height of 100m and fronting some six kilometres of shore **(Plate 20)**. It holds the largest seabird colony on the west coast of England, the bulk of which is made up of **Guillemot, Razorbill** and **Kittiwake,** but with small numbers of **Fulmar** and **Cormorant** and a few pairs of **Puffin** and **Black Guillemot** – the only site in England for this last species.

From St Bees Head northwards to Maryport, the New Red Sandstone gives way to younger sedimentary rocks of Carboniferous age, which has produced a low-lying, undulating landscape. Coal seams within these sedimentary rocks have been worked along the coastal strip from Whitehaven to Aspatria since the 17th century. This coal, together with haematite ore deposits to the east and south of Whitehaven, provided the raw material for an iron and steel industry which flourished in West Cumbria, particularly during the late 19th and early 20th centuries. The depletion of these raw materials in more recent years and the consolidation of productive capacity on the steelworks at Workington has left the area with a legacy of abandoned mines, quarries and spoil heaps, some of which provide an important habitat for birds. One such area is Siddick Pond **(Plate 21)**, where open water and reedbeds occupy the site of a former colliery working and provide a breeding haunt for birds such as **Little Grebe, Tufted Duck, Pochard, Shoveler** and **Reed Warbler.** The slag banks of the Workington steelworks, together with the harbours at Workington and Maryport, provide nesting sites for **Rock Pipits,** while the handsome **Stonechat** has long been associated with this narrow coastal fringe.

# Cumbria: the changing landscape

"When the first settlers entered this region (says an animated writer) they found it overspread with wood; forest trees, the fir, the oak, the ash and birch had skirted the fells, tufted the hills, and shaded the valleys, through centuries of silent solitude; the birds and beasts of prey reigned over the meeker species; and the *bellum inter omnia* maintained the balance of Nature in the empire of beasts."

William Wordsworth: *Guide to the Lakes (various vols 1835–1853)*

Daniel Defoe, describing Westmorland in 1726, said, "nor were these hills high and formidable only, but they had a kind of inhospitable terror in them". The fells "lacked profitable pits" and were "all barren and wild, of no use or advantage either to man or beast". Urban symmetry and pastoral scenes better pleased the Georgians: although the wild mountains were 'horrid' they had some virtue as picturesque sepia images.

The Victorians perceived metaphors of grandeur in the rock-girt fells and deep glacial valleys of Lakeland, where hanging woodlands were mirrored in lakeside reflections, and 'wilderness' a stark contrast to grimy cities. People travelled from afar to experience tranquillity, to seek spiritual solace, and enjoy natural aspect. Such a view persisted through the next century, the 'English Lake District' becoming the second area to receive designation as a National Park in June 1951, the Peak District being the first.

Today Cumbria is often romanticized as 'Wordsworth country', but he might find little familiar in its intensively managed landscapes and manicured hedges. In Wordsworth's youth, the county would be much enriched with wildlife through a diverse rural economy – wide-scale coppiced woodlands managed for charcoal production and raw materials for the bobbin industry, family-owned slate quarries, mining in the rich ore fields, and many supportive cottage industries. Farming practices were similarly diverse, with small-scale arable fodder crops and oats grown within a pastoral system that

**Plate 22: Ullswater**

maintained flower-rich meadows and damp pastures, which would resonate with the vibrant spring sound of songsters and wading birds. The higher ground was not then so denuded. Wood-pastures and tree-filled ghylls allowed tree cover to penetrate the high fells; gorse and juniper formed a discontinuous shrub layer and the now-ubiquitous bracken was managed as a humble component of a complex woodland community before its rampant dominance of today's bare fells.

A century and a half later at the

**Plate 23: Herbicide spraying of bracken, North Pennines**

beginning of the 21st century – hardly a millisecond on an ecological timescale – present-day accounts readily mask the real state of the county's landscapes. Few indeed are prepared to catalogue the unrelenting ecological change wrought by man upon its 'naturalness'.

As early as 1892 the Revd H.A. Macpherson, in his classic work *A Vertebrate Fauna of Lakeland,* was lamenting the gradual loss of the wild, scrubby countryside he knew as a young man.

The pace of change in the countryside increased throughout the 20th century. After mid-century, land 'improvement' grants

**Plate 24: 'Improved land', retreating heather beyond, Howgills**

stemming from government obsession with national self-sufficiency forced abandonment of more traditional farming practices, and rapid adoption of the drive to 'intensification'. Recent decades have seen that intensification become yet more intense, with an ever-greater reliance on mechanization and chemicals.

Yet, in a progressively global market for its products, the attempts to keep agriculture 'competitive' and 'profitable' have proved chimeric, with consequences harmful to the fabric of the countryside, and disastrous for its wildlife and its birds. No corner of Cumbria has escaped, and to catalogue, even in the brief outline to follow, the declining natural diversity and environmental health of so large an area makes for uncomfortable reading.

Ploughing and reseeding, and applications of fertilizer and herbicide cause the ancient, diverse, and colourful tapestries of meadow and pasture herbs at once to give way to a few lush grass species: a catastrophic decline in

**Plate 25: Veteran alder, Geltsdale**

natural diversity, and in visual interest. As the herbs vanish, so too must the invertebrates dependent upon them, and then the birds. The lurid deep blue-green of 'enrichment' is visible far across the valleys and, where it climbs the fell-sides, contrasts ever more incongruously against the brown-green shades of the unimproved grasslands above. The lushness of silage growth is too dense, tall, and cloying for most meadow birds; the ever-earlier cutting dates ensure the destruction of chicks before fledging.

During the last fifty years sheep numbers in Cumbria built up to 15% of the English national flock, half that of the entire Welsh flock: in conservation terms, six million mouths eating into the fabric of the countryside; this before the wide-scale pre-emptive culling to stem the virulence of foot-and-mouth disease. As a direct result of sheep over-grazing, heather cover on Cumbria's moors declined by a third between 1940 and 1980. On the fell-sides, the visually appealing wood-pastures so characteristic of both Lakeland and the North Pennines have retreated: no replacements for the veteran pollards can succeed against relentless grazing pressure.

Land reclamation and drainage, to increase the land's stock-carrying capacity, destroyed two-thirds of the county's heritage of species-rich grassland between 1930 and 1970, with much more lost since. As pasture dries through drainage, the increased density of grazing stock compacts topsoil, denying soil invertebrates to the probing Curlews and other waders. There is no protection from trampling stock for nests

**Plate 26: Flourishing hedges, north Cumbria**

and chicks in the lawn-smooth swards; the rushy tussocks which once provided concealment have gone. Pasture-nesting birds rarely raise their young; the old birds faithfully return, but, with no recruitment, in steadily declining numbers, and they have vanished from many areas.

In the past, manure provided an essential improver for cropped and grazed land. Now the great quantities of dung generated by the sheer numbers of stock animals create major problems of disposal and pollution. The nutrient, whether directly from inorganic fertilizers, indirectly as manure, or spread as slurry, over-enriches soils, to further diminish natural diversity, and finally burdens ground-waters, streams, rivers and lakes, eutrophicating aquatic habitats, harming wildlife, fisheries and drinking supplies, and diverting resources in costly attempts to minimise its impact. The UK government has so far failed to implement fully the 1991 Nitrates Directive, which seeks to redress some of the damage to water supplies and aquatic environments.

The aerial pollutants of dust and ammonia generated from animal activity and slurry spread insidiously and widely disperse enrichment and toxins. Trees lose their ancient garb of multicoloured lichen festoons; roadside banks – the last retreat of meadow flowers since the destruction of meadows themselves – become swamped with coarse grasses, or are sprayed with herbicide as they develop beds of 'weeds'. The aerial transfer of nutrient shifts even the delicate ecology of neighbouring mineral-poor heathlands and moors, and the vibrant colours and textures diminish as heath plants decline.

Hedges are long-established artefacts in the countryside. Maintained for strictly utilitarian reasons, their conservation potential in the open habitats of agricultural land cannot be over-emphasized. Yet 5,000 miles of hedge were lost in England and Wales every year between 1946 and 1963; loss still continues, although today as much by neglect as by deliberate destruction. Too often, the hedge is 'thrashed' low and often, to maintain at low cost the appearance of neatness and order. As a consequence, no buds remain to blossom, and so no fruits develop to feed the birds and mammals through the winter. The hedge-bottom is eaten out by stock, even to the bark, and so cannot provide for those birds, such as Yellowhammer and Grey Partridge, which would feed in the fields, but nest in the shelter of the hedge-base. If not regularly laid, the hedge becomes ever more open and gapped at the base. Eventually

it no longer retains stock, a wire fence is put up, and the hedge is defunct; it becomes derelict and vanishes.

'Clean' seed stocks, herbicide and pesticide applications, efficient harvesting, and early ploughing of stubbles to allow autumn sowing of cereals, all reduce the availability of seeds to farmland birds. Three million Skylarks have been lost from the British countryside since the onset of intensification.

Deciduous woodland of native species has been widely ousted by underplanting with alien conifers, the old trees often left standing, but ring-barked. Many copses,

**Plate 27: 'Trimmed' hedge, north Cumbria**

**Plate 28: Melancholy Thistles on an unsprayed verge, Alston**

outwardly picturesque, mask ugly secrets within: pheasant-release pens, with long wire-netting walls, black threads strung about between the trees to discourage birds of prey, snares and gin-traps sunk in pipes.

Very many plants and animals require 'edge habitats', where woodland grades into scrub and scrub into pasture; pasture into marsh, marsh into swamp, and swamp into open water; often-tilled ground into seldom-tilled ground into grassland. Such a mosaic of transition-zones was once a part of extensive agriculture, giving variety, diversity, and visual appeal to the countryside. Now all have given way to abrupt breaks at barbed-wire fence-lines: one side trampled, sprayed or ploughed, the other rank with an overgrowth of tall herbs.

In open countryside, and even along the roadsides, the patches of bramble and blackthorn, gorse and broom thickets, nettle and willowherb beds – essential cover for nesting birds – are perceived as unsightly and unproductive; they are grubbed out, fired, or sprayed.

In the past, grants were available for 'gripping' the upland moors: driving deep ditches through the peat, even down to the bedrock: a now-notorious example of dubious zeal – to make one's mark on virgin land! Exposed peat surfaces are very vulnerable to erosion by wind and water. The results are obvious everywhere on the moors: deepening gulleys, eroding peat hags, streams choked with the wash-off, and the loss of the bog-moss surface, and of its special plants and animals. We now understand, rather too late, that the wet bog-moss surface of the moors is a precious resource to be valued and conserved: acting as a vast sponge, it would absorb the heaviest rains, and thus even out the flow into the rivers. Given the huge former extent of blanket bog, its conservation would have had correspondingly large beneficial consequences. Whether the effects of gripping can be reversed is uncertain.

The persistent pattern of moor-burning characterises much Pennine moorland. Reduced manpower and unfavourable weather have caused a change from the more traditional burning practice – a quick singe burning with the wind – to today's reliance on back-burning – a hotter, slower burn against the wind – as a means of stimulating the growth of young ling heather, food for the Red Grouse. This has an adverse affect on the friable peat, to the exclusion of many plant species. The resultant monoculture supports only a very limited selection of moorland birds. Where there has also been heavy grazing pressure from large numbers of sheep, as on many moors, heather itself has declined, as have grouse bags, with an increase of unpalatable grasses and rushes.

Peat extraction over the centuries has affected all lowland raised bogs, but it was the arrival of commercial peat stripping which sealed the fate of some of our most extensive peatlands. Although stripping has been stopped at some sites – by huge compensation payments from the public purse – it continues at others. Some extensively damaged areas have been given over to conservation, although what sort of habitat will develop is uncertain. The restoration of an actively growing bog-moss surface might

**Plate 29: Butterburn Flow**

**Plate 30: Traditional heather burning, North Pennines**

be a long-term aim, but the accumulation of depths of peat is a process requiring millennia.

'Streams' are now a rarity in the lowlands. Routinely canalized, often under misdirected grants, to allow quicker removal of water, and lowering of water-tables, today they are no more than ditches draining nutrient-enriched water, incapable of supporting the diverse plant, bird, and animal life which once flourished. Frequently, indeed, the ditches have vanished into culverts, the past existence of streams hardly discernible in the folds of the modern agricultural prairieland.

Farmers have at last won their generations-long battle to dry their lands, but with what cost to the community? Water now drains with great rapidity off the fellsides lacerated by drains, and it cannot be absorbed by the compacted soils of inbye and valley fields. Time was when rainwater would be held back within the upland bogs, in marshes and swamps, in damp soils and wet hollows, in carrs and undrained fellside woods, to drain gradually into the rivers. Thus was the flow maintained during drought. Now, rivers are subject to sudden short and damaging spates, and yet all too readily shrivel to mere trickles, a cycle causing great harm to river life and to a vital community asset. In any heavy rain, the flood plains cannot contain the onrush of water from the landscape, with the consequences we see ever more often in communities all down the courses of the overloaded rivers. Yet how rarely we see acknowledged the links between over-zealous upland drainage and lowland flooding! While it may profit the individual, is it really in the wider interests of the community to allow land to be drained until every last damp field-corner is dry? In the same processes, the muddy waters carry away the silt – the irreplaceable soil of Cumbria – to the sea, or smother it over the gravel shoals where game-fish would spawn.

In such circumstances it is easy to claim that those words which still have such agreeable resonance for us all – streambank, beckside, lane, hedgerow, copse, woodland, coppice, pollard, meadow, pasture, park, pond, barn, farmyard, fell, moor, heath – have within the space of a few decades become redundant, or – where the terms are still used – they refer to something utterly different, utterly debased, from what our parents and grandparents knew.

As for 'countryside' itself – where, today, should one seek it? The modern agricultural landscape is surely not that? Endless swathes of deep green ryegrass, barbed wire, black plastic, and the pervasive racket of ever-larger machines,

**Plate 31: 'Canalized' beck, Tindale**

are an industrial, not a rural, landscape. If 'nature' does still survive in that landscape, then it is in spite of, rather than because of, modern agricultural policy and practice.

There was a starkly telling irony in the springtime of 2001: having lost their stock to foot-and-mouth culling, farmers reported how 'silent' their farms had become. True: when the stock had gone, there was indeed silence – no exuberant medley of Skylarks, Lapwings and Curlews in the fields, no lively chorus of songbirds from the hedges.

On the reins of huge public

subsidy, modern farming has been a bonanza for some, and a living for many. But the darker side of the same coin, too often overshadowed or rubbished in the gloss put on the fervent quest for 'jobs' and a 'vibrant farming sector', is that of reduced opportunity, spiralling cost and disadvantage for the wider community; degrading habitats and declining diversity; increasing ugliness and despoiled visual amenity; and public alienation and suspicion. Many of the negative impacts mentioned here have tended to worsen, a legacy of the application to our landscape of the Common Agricultural Policy.

It is a fact that, over the same period, if a building possessed structural features of architectural interest, or any significant events had been enacted within its walls, it would be considered worthy of preservation, funds would be raised, and every effort made to prevent its destruction. Yet the landscape, which we as a people have treasured over generations, chronicles a history at least as prolonged, at least as illuminating, informing and enriching, and as equally irreplaceable, as any artefact. Have we allowed a precious part of our heritage to be frittered away, for profit?

There is a growing acceptance by government that habitat loss and degradation, especially that caused through agricultural intensification, is the reason for many bird declines, and that this is a matter for general concern. In May 1999, the Department of the Environment, Transport and the Regions (DETR) published the White Paper *A Better Quality of Life*, which contains 150 indicators of the sustainability of lifestyles in the UK. Within these is a set of 14 annually updated 'headline' indicators, including a wildlife indicator based on population trends of breeding birds. The wild bird indicator summarises information on the status of nearly 140 breeding species over the last 30 years, based on Common Bird Census trends between 1970 and 1999. During this period the common bird index has fallen by around 7%; woodland birds show a slow but steady drop in numbers of 20%, and farmland birds have been in steep decline, down by 40%, over the same period.

Given the large proportion of Cumbria which is upland, hill farming is a crucial part of the rural economy, now increasingly under threat. Refocussed upland agriculture is vital to the future of a vibrant countryside, to tackle ecological impoverishment, enhance visual appearance, and help sustain the cultural heritage at the heart of upland communities. Rewards for sustainable and wildlife-compatible farming will be central to reversing current declining trends, and these will inevitably mean changes in vegetation structures, and more reliance on traditional practices. Agri-environmental schemes such as the Countryside Stewardship Scheme will play a vital role in moving the emphasis from headage to environment support. The Curry Report (a government enquiry into farming in the wake of foot-and-mouth disease) focuses on English agriculture, although its recommendations have far-reaching implications across the whole UK.

'We are a nation of farmers' – the sentiment perhaps refers to our yeoman ancestry. Certainly farmers, having charge over environmental outcomes over such large portions of the county, must be involved at the forefront of evolving a less-intensively used landscape, but it will take a fundamental change of philosophy and vision in our – and in their – leaders. Future rewards for farming must be not simply a commensurate income for creating quality-assured products for local markets, but also for maintaining and enhancing the fabric of a vibrant countryside, where rural communities and natural diversity may both thrive. To take the analogy of a traditional three-legged milking stool: environmental conservation is perhaps best placed to balance and support the needs both of farming and of the wider community which supports it. A stool is a stable structure; remove any one leg, and at once one embarks upon a balancing trick without end, and with an uncertain outcome.

In parallel with changes in the farmed landscape, change in other landscapes has effects just as severe, even if with a more restricted reach. To take a single example: scrub habitats support diverse and prolific wildlife populations. But 'scrub' is in ecological terms a transitional feature, part-way to colonization by taller trees. So scrub must be allowed to renew itself constantly by colonization of ground newly-bared by human or natural processes. Too often the remaining pockets of scrub in a

**Plate 32: Pebble beach, Allonby**

region occupy land earmarked for change: development for industry, housing or leisure pursuits, landscaping, regrading of land profiles, opencast mining, quarrying, gravel extraction, and many other uses. Since 'scrub' has in many minds a connotation of neglect and waste, there is little incentive for its conservation and renewal. It must be seen as an integral and significant aspect of a diverse and living landscape.

Precisely the same case must be made for many other impermanent habitats, each making its contribution to the survival of particular suites of plants with their associated animals

**Plate 33: Dodd Wood Osprey watchpoint**

and birds: reedbeds, river banks and lake and reservoir shores, shingle beaches and gravel shoals, dunes, wasteland, roadsides and motorway verges, unused and underused areas of public parks and industrial estates. Whilst a different strategy might be required in each case – even if that is merely non-intervention – the wildlife potential and significance must be considered along with the other conflicting objectives.

Much biodiverse habitat is damaged or lost through neglect and carelessness. Flytipping of rubbish, toxic residues, waste and debris, so prevalent today, ironically triggered by moves to rationalize such materials, is symptomatic of a general lack of concern about our environment. How much of this carelessness is a result of a sense of alienation from the wider landscape – as if it is 'not for us'? The 'culture' engendered in our urban sprawls where so many have to live does not encourage participation in the landscape beyond. Yet the success of the many and varied schemes to interest young people in 'the environment', at school and beyond, shows that it must be the milieu which is the souring influence. The spectacle of wild birds can provide a link between urban communities and the wider environment.

In the wake of foot-and-mouth disease, 2001 was a disastrous year for many in rural Cumbria, facing a less certain future. From those funeral pyres that blackened and choked the spring skies arises a challenging phoenix: an opportunity, perhaps, to begin to build a vision for the future of the countryside, and an expectation, certainly, to see a change in focus of agricultural policy and funding.

To achieve these ideals requires politicians and planners at every level to be environmentally conversant, acknowledge changing horizons, and recognize public awareness of, and rising concern over, rural issues. Whilst land managers may still claim to be 'custodians of the countryside', as taxpayers we are the bursars of their subsidies. Thus we have every right to seek value for our money, and a duty to influence decision-makers accordingly.

The attempt to preserve particular endangered habitats in the landscape as nature reserves has been standard practice over the last century, attempting to 'freeze in time' such areas. We now know that the isolated small populations of animals and plants in such 'islands' are prone to extinction. Large populations of organisms are required to maintain diversity in the long run, and large populations require large areas. As conservationists our job therefore is not to isolate and hope to preserve elements within a dynamic landscape, but to manage wider change so that diversity is retained and enhanced throughout. In a landscape such as we anticipate, wildlife would exist as an integral part, as it did in past times, thus removing any need to manage it as a separate entity.

The aim of this work has been firstly to provide quantitative information on bird populations and distributions within the county. As much, however, we hope that it may have other outcomes: clearly, to promote appreciation of birds, both for themselves – joyous and spirited participants in our shared planet – and as symbols of a prospering environment; to strengthen the case for bird conservation; and to alert residents and visitors to the enjoyment for the individual, and welfare and economic benefits for the community, to be realised from exploring, understanding, and nurturing our natural inheritance.

As an indication of how, in these days of rapid information dispersal, public perception and appreciation can be so readily harnessed, events in 2001 propelled one pair of Ospreys from a curiosity for birdwatchers into a linchpin of local economic survival for a beleaguered tourist industry during a difficult year. The first Osprey watch at Dodd

Wood, Bassenthwaite attracted 25,000 visitors in the brief five weeks it was open. Imaginatively marketed, other species could have similar impact for the tourist industry: Black Grouse and Hen Harrier in the North Pennines, wildfowl on the lakes, and the spectacle of large concentrations of geese and waders on our estuaries.

The immense growth of interest in and appreciation of the value of environmental conservation was a remarkable phenomenon of the late 20th century. Yet, although it is hardly less valued today than the bricks and mortar of our ancient buildings, it still needs friends and advocates, those like the 'plain russet-coated captain' of Cromwell's call, who 'knows what he fights for and loves what he knows'.

## Aim

To produce an accurate account of Cumbria's breeding avifauna as a benchmark for the start of the 21st century.

## Objectives

To undertake a systematic collection of field data within the county, for a tetrad distribution map of each breeding species recorded during the survey period 1997–2001.

To carry out timed counts within all county tetrads to assess species abundance by frequency indices for all breeding birds, for an abundance map of each species.

To carry out line transects and produce quantifiable data, in addition to timed counts, to establish population estimates for as many breeding species as possible recorded during the survey period.

To analyse the survey data and present its results in a manner which promotes the widest appreciation of Cumbria's rich and diverse breeding bird communities, and to further the cause of bird conservation at a county, regional and national level.

The survey area is extensive: Cumbria is the second largest county in England, covering 6820km$^2$, with a further 300km$^2$ between high and low tide marks. Its landscapes represent some of the largest, wildest and most mountainous tracts of semi-natural habitat anywhere in England (Figure 2: Relief map). It has a total human population of 492,900, the majority of whom live in a few large urban areas; most of the county is sparsely populated at 0.7 people/km$^2$, much lower than the 3.4 km$^2$ average population density for England and Wales (National Population statistics 1999).

Internationally renowned for its inspirational scenery and its rich cultural heritage, Cumbria is also of national importance for some bird species; it hosts the only regularly nesting pairs of Golden Eagles and Dotterels in England, as well as the only English breeding colony of Black Guillemots. Its mountains, lakes, rivers, moorlands, coastlands, peatlands, woodlands, grasslands and cultivation make a collective contribution to a unique natural tapestry with a rich and diverse bird community.

The natural character of Cumbria is complex; montane habitats are present on the summits of the central massif, while the numerous steep-sided valleys, which radiate outwards dissecting the majestic fells, offer sheltered woodlands, pastures and a variety of wetlands. The long whaleback ridge of the Pennines forms the county's eastern boundary, reaching its height at Cross Fell (890m), and is dominated by blanket bogs, acid grassland and heather moorland. The Border Uplands have been extensively afforested, in contrast to the denuded hills of the Howgills in the southeast which connect the Pennines to the eastern fells of Lakeland, otherwise separated by the Mallerstang and Lune gorges. To the north, the Vale of Eden intrudes through the upland blocks, broadening its fertile floor as it reaches the Solway Basin. North of Carlisle, a narrow coastal belt extends west then south, where lowland agriculture blends with an industrial past and links up with similar farmland south of Lakeland. Two important intertidal areas flank the county, Morecambe Bay in the south and the Border estuary of the Solway Firth.

The significance and extent of this diverse natural heritage is recognized through both National and European designations. Cumbria contributes to the North Pennines Special Protection Area, which is also a candidate Special Area for Conservation, as is the Lake District. The Duddon Estuary, Morecambe Bay and the Solway Firth are renowned for their international importance. The Lake District National Park represents 34% of Cumbria, and a further 3% of the Cumbria Dales are embodied within another, the Yorkshire Dales National Park. The county has two large Environmentally Sensitive Areas designated, and a major part of the North Pennines is recognized as an Area of Outstanding Natural Beauty. Many more Sites of Special Scientific Interest, national, regional and local nature reserves combine to reflect the county's importance for nature conservation.

The mountainous nature, limited roads and low population density of Cumbria posed a potential problem in finding sufficient fieldworkers prepared to undertake the task, most of whom were recruited from within the Cumbria Bird Club, through local meetings and mailings. To complete a tetrad survey of this magnitude, covering 7,120km$^2$, in a five-year period was a huge undertaking. Its achievement is a remarkable testament to the dedication and enthusiasm of club members.

## Data collection

Data collection followed the now customary format for atlas work, with one major exception: the amount of time actually spent collecting field data was increased from the typical 2 × 1 hour visits to 2 × 2 hour visits in each tetrad. The rationale for increasing the time spent gathering field data was two fold: a) to reflect the amount of difficult terrain in Cumbria; and b) to gain optimal coverage of each tetrad.

Wherever practical standard atlas fieldwork methodology was adhered to, to facilitate comparison of data between the present work and *The Atlas of Breeding Birds in Britain and Ireland* to show change in species distribution over a 30-year period.

The survey unit, in which all observations and data were recorded, is the **tetrad** or two-kilometre square of the Ordnance Survey National Grid; one ten-

**Figure 2. Relief map of Cumbria**

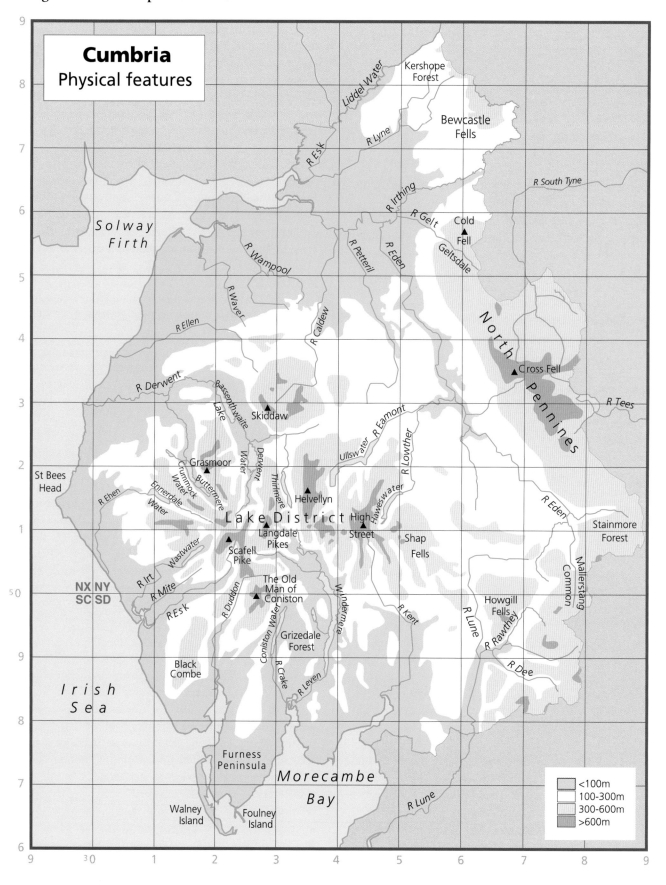

kilometre square may be divided into 25 tetrads. Each tetrad is referenced by a five-character code in a standard form, as used by the British Trust for Ornithology (BTO) in national surveys and adopted by other county atlas works. First, the two letters identify each 100km block on the Ordnance Survey national grid and prefix two digits that represent the 'easting' and 'northing'. Using a standardized grid of letters A–Z (omitting O), individual tetrads can be identified, eg. NY35T (Figure 3).

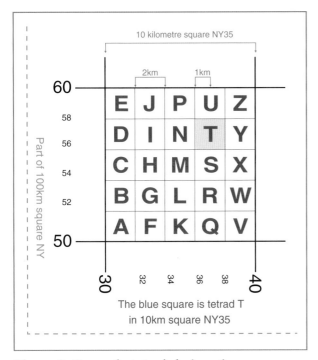

**Figure 3. Example tetrad designation**

All **full** tetrads (ie. those not cut by the county boundary or high water mark) received a minimum of four hours of fieldwork. For the majority of tetrads this was split into two two-hour visits on separate occasions (see below).

All **part-tetrads** were split into two categories according to predetermined criteria. Some of these had 'timed count' visits, on a pro-rata basis; others were deselected and received a supplementary visit for completeness. The criterion for timed count selection was based on the amount of available land falling above high water mark (including freshwater) or within the county boundary. For example, in a tetrad where the centre of only one 1km square fell within the prescribed area it invoked a 'timed count' of 2 × 30 minutes and so on, depending on whether one, two or three centres fell within the county. For other 1km squares where land, but not the centre of any 1km square, fell above high water or within the county boundary they received a visit (but not a timed count), the findings recorded separately onto a 'Supplementary Sheet'.

In all, 1,542 tetrads received full four-hour timed count visits, a further 250 part-tetrads received a timed count pro-rata and another 52 had a supplementary visit for completeness.

The **breeding season** was defined, for most species, as being 1st April to 31st July inclusive and all counts were conducted during this period, with early mornings, between 06.00 and 10.00 hours, being preferable, but not always possible given the long walk-in required by the remoteness of some tetrads. Fieldworkers were discouraged from attempting counts on days with heavy rain, poor visibility or strong wind. It was important to cover the entire breeding season of all species, so the date of the visit was more critical for some birds than others, eg. early-nesting Crossbills and late-arriving Spotted Flycatchers. To compensate for this the count period was split into 'early season' and 'late season', with a first two-hour visit taking place during 1st April to 31st May, and the second two-hour visit, ideally not less than two weeks after the first, from 1st June to 31st July. A dispensation was given to a few tetrads in remote locations, where a single four-hour visit was allowed, with a caveat that the visit be made after the 15th May when late migrants would be present.

The four hours spent in each full tetrad represent minimum visits, since many tetrads also received supplementary visits to record the more elusive species. Dawn and dusk visits were encouraged to record the presence of nocturnal or crepuscular species, such as Tawny Owl and Woodcock, with pre-season visits to some habitats to detect earlier breeding species such as Raven and Crossbill. This type of visit was recorded on a Supplementary Sheet.

**Breeding record categories** conformed to those used in the *The Atlas of Breeding Birds in Britain and Ireland;* the lowest category did not take account of any over-flying birds, which may have clouded and confused the data. The breeding status categories for all species were: possible breeding, probable breeding and confirmed breeding, using the following criteria.

**Possible breeding** – presence in tetrad:
[i]   species present during the survey period in possible nesting habitat, but with no other indication of breeding. Presumed passage migrants were not recorded.

**Probable breeding** – observations of one or more of the following activities during the survey period:
[i]   singing male heard, or breeding calls heard;
[ii]  pair observed in suitable nesting habitat during the survey period;

[iii] display or courtship;

[iv] birds visiting a probable nest site;

[v] birds seen to be carrying nesting material.

**Confirmed breeding** – observations of any one or more of the following activities during the survey period:

[i] agitated behaviour or anxiety calls from adults suggesting a nest or young close by;

[ii] distraction display or injury feigning from adults;

[iii] a nest that has obviously been used or egg shells found;

[iv] adults seen carrying food for young;

[v] adults seen carrying faecal sac away from nest site;

[vi] nest with eggs;

[vii] nest with young or downy young in the case of waders, gamebirds and other nidifugous species;

[viii] recently fledged young;

[ix] soliciting calls from young birds.

The county was sub-divided into six geographical areas and Regional Organizers were assigned to each cluster of 10km squares (Figure 4). The Regional Organizers then allocated a number of 10km squares or individual tetrads to competent fieldworkers, who during the period 1997–2001 visited all 1,844 tetrads and recorded all bird species according to the criteria above.

Confidentiality was recognized as being an important consideration, which could limit information flow on some local rarities, such as Honey Buzzard and Osprey. This was countered by allowing observers to submit sensitive records separately, through the county recorder system, if deemed necessary. A prior agreement, not to map vulnerable species down to a tetrad level, provided some form of reassurance. In all instances, species were not mapped without the consent of the individual concerned.

Within each tetrad, the fieldworker selected a route visiting all major habitat types within the tetrad, and walked at a methodical pace recording in notebook or to cassette recorder all adult birds seen or heard, including feral and introduced species. For each species, the strongest proof of breeding, according to the categories above, was noted. In circumstances where a colonial species was found nesting during the timed visit, such as Grey Heron, Rook or Sand Martin, the time was noted and an

estimate made of all apparently occupied nests, before the time was checked again allowing the surveyor to compensate for any lost time before resuming the count.

Fieldworkers completed a 'Record Sheet' for each tetrad, recording the highest breeding status of each species and the number of individual birds counted for all species noted (Figure 5). All Schedule One species names were shaded grey and all colonial species were highlighted in bold, as an *aide memoire,* to assist fieldworkers.

**Supplementary records** were used to enhance distribution data collected from the timed visits. By utilizing the same breeding criteria and combining the two sets of data a more realistic picture of species distribution patterns has emerged. Supplementary records were collected by casual observations and recorded on a separate 'Supplementary Sheet' for each 10km square (Figure 6). The forms were made widely available and Cumbria Bird Club members were encouraged to participate to maximize observer effort and gain as many records as possible.

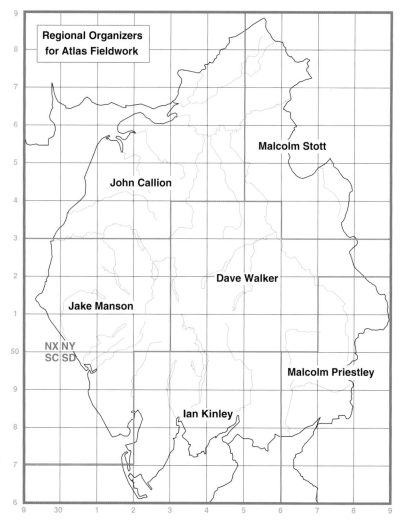

**Figure 4. Regional Organizers**

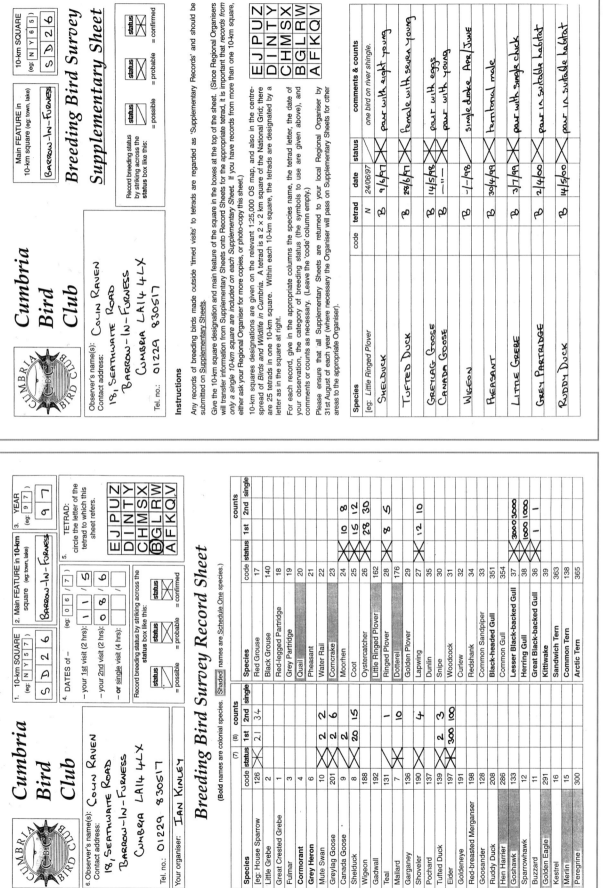

**Figure 6. Sample Supplementary Sheet, side 1 (reduced scale)**

**Figure 5. Sample Record Sheet, side 1 (reduced scale)**

Because supplementary information was not collected during timed periods, any counts made could not be directly compared with counts gathered during the timed visits; hence supplementary counts could not be amalgamated into the abundance data. **Thus the distribution map for a species may show a symbol for breeding status in a particular tetrad, but there is no symbol for that tetrad on the equivalent abundance map.**

A number of long-term surveys ran concurrently with the period of recording for the present work, namely the BTO-led Breeding Bird Survey, Common Bird Census and Wetland Bird Survey, and several coordinated national species surveys such as the Heronries Survey, 1998 Lapwing and Hen Harrier Surveys, 1999 Ring Ouzel Survey, Seabird 2000 and the Naturalized Goose Survey 2000. All these provided useful sources of information to enhance the species distribution maps; such records were transcribed onto Supplementary Record Sheets.

County bird record cards, submitted to the Cumbria Bird Club at the end of each year, were scrutinized and any relevant records extracted and passed to Regional Organizers for validation and possible inclusion in a similar way. While proving tedious and time-consuming, the exercise made available valuable extra information on species distributions.

Coverage of all tetrads in the county was anticipated to take four breeding seasons, given the high level of support from Cumbria Bird Club members; in the event it took five years. This was partially due to poor spring weather in 1997 and 1998 that hampered fieldwork, especially in upland areas. By the start of the 1999 field-season only 125 full and 35 part-tetrads remained uncompleted from the 1,844 total. By the end of the dedicated survey period only two full tetrads and eight part-tetrads remained uncompleted. Whilst work was proceeding on species texts editing and data analysis during the summer of 2001, the remaining tetrads were completed, despite severe access restrictions in the countryside due to foot-and-mouth disease.

**Data management** started after each field visit with the fieldworker transcribing data from the timed tetrad visit onto the Breeding Bird Survey Sheets, and taking great care to avoid transcription errors, before the completed sheets were returned to the Regional Organizer. This procedure, if strictly adhered to, reduced the risk of irreplaceable data being lost if original notes were lost. On receiving the completed forms each Regional Organizer photocopied and retained a duplicate set to resolve any potential queries and for security reasons, before forwarding the originals onto Tullie House Museum for data inputting at the end of each season. Regional Organizers also received all supplementary records relevant to their geographical area and composed a summary 'Mastersheet' of all tetrads, by their respective 10km square, using data from the timed visits to form the basic information, with supplementary records added to upgrade breeding status or include any species new to individual tetrads (Figure 7).

Accuracy and potential errors were highlighted on checking data from the Mastersheet copy of each 10km square against computer printouts from the database. At this stage any ambiguities could be identified and filtered out of the database. The additional records from 'Supplementary' sources were colour-coded to identify the year of all upgrades and new additions and thus provided an extra reference point if cross-referencing was necessary in order to validate the authenticity and accuracy of any record. This procedure was repeated after each season's fieldwork before the final definitive distribution map for each species recorded as breeding in the county was generated. All the original data sheets are archived at Tullie House Museum, Carlisle along with the database, for future reference.

## Population Estimates

Population estimates for individual species are an important aspect of the species accounts, adding an extra dimension to the distribution and abundance displayed on the species maps. An estimate of population level was derived for all species breeding in Cumbria at the time of this atlas. This was further refined into numbers of breeding pairs and densities for some species, depending on the quality and availability of information.

The most scientifically robust data was gained from line transect counts; however this was not the most suitable technique for a range of species, for reasons outlined in the Discussion section, and other sources proved an invaluable backup.

The methods used to assess populations for all species are given in the accounts and listed in Appendix (Table D, page 371).

## Line Transect Survey

The methodology for data collection was effectively an enhanced version of the BTO's Breeding Bird Survey, the key differences being:
- An additional band, giving 0–10m; 10–25m compared to the BBS band of 0–25m;
- Separate recording of the number of males seen/heard;
- Recording breeding status.

The Centre for Ecology and Hydrology (CEH) provided a stratified random sample of 120 1km

**Figure 7. Sample Mastersheet – part of side 1 (nb: colour coding marks here shown in black)**

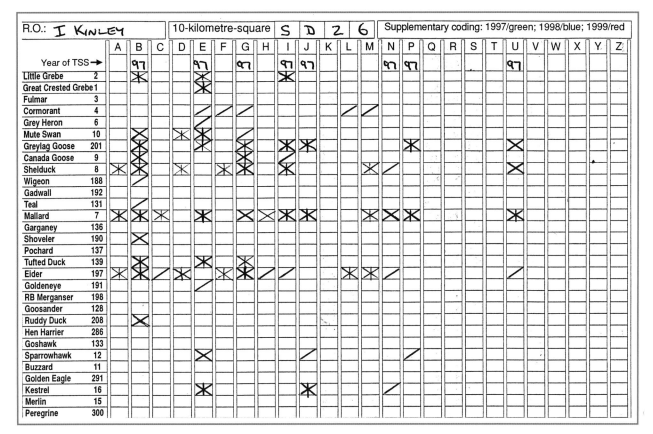

squares to survey (Figure 8). These were taken to be a representative sample of the county and allocated to the appropriate Regional Organizers who organized the fieldworkers. With the exception of some remote upland squares, fieldworkers were asked to visit the square three times:

- A reconnaissance to record habitat, plan the transect routes, and obtain the necessary permission;
- The first survey visit between 22nd April and 7th May 2000 inclusive;
- The second survey visit between 19th May and 11th June 2000 inclusive.

Fieldworkers were asked to leave 3–4 weeks between visits. Remote high fells were visited just once, between 19th May and 11th June inclusive.

Where access could not be gained or the square was physically inaccessible to survey, a replacement square of the same Land Class was allocated. This was also done if less than four of the 10 ideal transect sections were located on dry land, above mean high water, or fell within the county boundary.

Fieldworkers were asked to stick as closely as possible to the 'ideal' counting route through the square (the transect route). This consisted of two parallel lines (north–south or east–west), 500m apart and 250m in from the edge of the square. Each transect was divided into five equal sections 200m in length. Minor

intrusions into adjacent squares, where unavoidable, were permitted and fieldworkers were asked to ensure that they recorded the exact route on the habitat form. If the transect route deviated from the 'ideal', fieldworkers were asked to record the average distance from the ideal, as well as recording habitat. At no point were the lines to be closer than 200m.

Fieldworkers recorded the most appropriate habitat codes for each of the 10 sections on a Habitat Transect Recording Form (Figure 9). The relevant area for each section was defined as a linear habitat 200m long and 25m, each side of the line transect. The coding allowed choice for a primary and secondary habitat to be recorded. Weather details for the visit as a whole were recorded and scored. Fieldworkers were asked to avoid conditions of heavy rain, poor visibility or strong wind.

With the exception of remote and less accessible areas, counts were made between 06.00–10.00 hours.

All fieldworkers were encouraged to familiarize themselves with the standard BTO species codes and where possible record the sex of each bird. At the start of the transect line (section 1–5) the time was noted and the route walked at a slow, methodical pace with regular brief pauses to listen for bird song.

Birds seen or heard in each 200m section were noted on a 'Field Recording Form' (Figure 10) in the relevant band category in which they were first located (0–10m, 10–25m, 25–100m, more than 100m or birds over-

**Figure 8. Locations of line transect 1km squares**

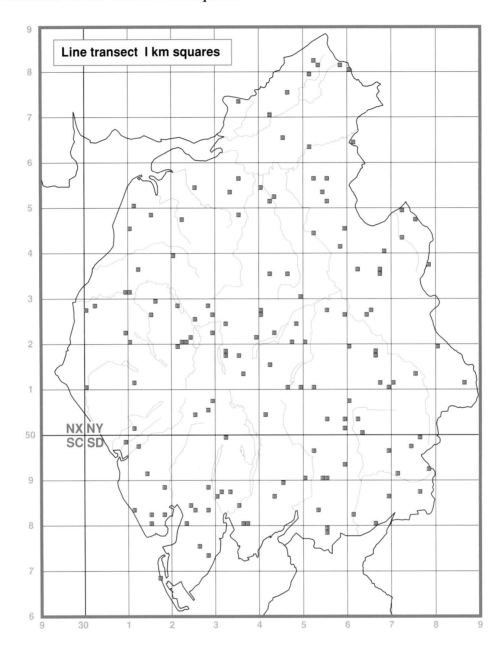

flying). Distances were measured at right angles to the transect route and all birds, even those located outside the square boundary, were recorded. However, juveniles and colonial nesting species (eg. Grey Heron, Rook or Sand Martin) were ignored along with birds immediately behind or beyond the transect line being monitored. Species with a display flight (eg. Skylark) were recorded at the relevant distance band, while striking an arrow through the relevant species code highlighted birds merely over-flying. However a bird seen to take off or land was recorded in the appropriate distance band at that position. After completing the fifth transect, the time was again noted and fieldworkers moved to the second half of the transect route (section 6–10) where the procedure was repeated.

During the second visit, it was imperative that the exact same route was followed and the same methodology applied, noting major changes in habitat between the two timed visits (eg. fields cut for silage). For each species recorded, the species code, name and number of the species seen within each band were noted along with the weather. Habitat data were recorded on a separate Habitat Recoding Form.

After completion of the second series of transects, all data were transferred onto a Count Summary Sheet (Figure 11), which also incorporated a box allowing fieldworkers to record the highest breeding category noted (ie confirmed, probable or possible) for each species during the course of the visit.

**Figure 9. Sample Habitat Recording Form**

**Cumbria Breeding Birds Survey - Habitat Transect Recording Form**

Observer Name & address  Colin Raven, 18 Seathwaite Road, Barrow

1 Km Square Reference  SD1768

| Transect Section | First Habitat — Levels | | | | | Second Habitat — Levels | | | | | Average Distance From Ideal Position (m) | Ideal — First Habitat — Levels | | | | | Ideal — Second Habitat — Levels | | | | |
|---|---|---|---|---|---|---|---|---|---|---|---|---|---|---|---|---|---|---|---|---|---|
| | type | 1 | 2 | 3 | 4 | type | 1 | 2 | 3 | 4 | | type | 1 | 2 | 3 | 4 | type | 1 | 2 | 3 | 4 |
| 1 | F | 1 | 1 | 2 2 | 9 | F | 2 | 3 | - - | - | 100 | F | 2 | 3 | - 9 | - | | | | | |
| 2 | F | 1 | 1 | 2 2 | 9 | | | | | | 150 | F | 2 | 3 | - 9 | - | | | | | |
| 3 | F | 1 | 1 | 2 2 | 9 | | | | | | 50 | F | 2 | 3 | - 9 | - | | | | | |
| 4 | F | 2 | 3 | - 9 | - | F | 1 | 1 | 2 2 | 9 | 75 | F | 1 | 1 | 2 2 | 9 | F | 2 | 3 | - 9 | - |
| 5 | F | 2 | 3 | - 9 | - | F | 1 | 1 | 2 2 | 9 | 100 | F | 1 | 1 | 2 2 | 9 | F | 2 | 3 | - 9 | - |
| 6 | H | 1 | 3 | 6 3 | 9 | F | 2 | 3 | - 9 | - | 60 | H | 1 | 3 | 6 3 | 9 | F | 2 | 3 | - 9 | - |
| 7 | H | 1 | 3 | 6 3 | 9 | F | 2 | 3 | - 9 | - | 0 | H | 1 | 3 | 6 3 | 9 | F | 2 | 3 | - 9 | - |
| 8 | H | 1 | 3 | 6 3 | 9 | F | 2 | 3 | - 9 | - | 125 | H | 1 | 1 | 7 3 | - | | | | | |
| 9 | H | 1 | 3 | 6 3 | 9 | F | 2 | 3 | - 9 | - | 150 | H | 1 | 3 | 7 3 | - | | | | | |
| 10 | H | 1 | 3 | 6 3 | 9 | F | 2 | 3 | 5 9 | - | 250 | H | 1 | 3 | 7 3 | - | | | | | |

**Analysis of the Line Transect data** was completed using 'Distance 3.5', a computer programme developed by the Research Unit for Wildlife Population Assessment at the University of St Andrews. Counts were split into early (20th May 2000 and before) and late (after 20th May 2000). Data were divided into five bands (0–10m; 10–25m; 25–100m; >100m; and flying). The default model parameters used a half-normal detection function with a cosine series expansion.

Several analyses were carried out, based on only early counts, only late counts, and for all counts combined. For all counts combined, doubling the section distance from 0.2km to 0.4km standardized effort. For all three analyses, the data were analysed both with and without stratification by National Land Class. For species where sufficient numbers of males were counted, this sub-sector of data was also analysed both within and without stratification by habitat for early, late and all counts.

On advice from CEH, Land Classes 5 and 7, and Land Classes 8, 17, and 18, were grouped together for some species, since individually they had relatively small areas that made statistical analysis difficult for some species.

Table A, page 363 in the appendices shows the results of the line transect work (253 visits to 141 one-kilometre squares). For each species, the table provides the following data:

- Data used to calculate the population (E = early count only; L = late count only; A = all data). For some species, particularly passerines, only counts of male birds were used (shown by 'M').
- 'Sample size' is the number of birds seen on the count used.
- Mean, plus 95% confidence limits: whilst a calculated mean is provided, the 95% confidence limits provide a better indication of the population size. In all cases, the calculated mean population figure was rounded down to the nearest 100; 1000; 10,000 and 100,000 to reflect a percentage of non-breeding birds in each species.
- For comparative purposes, we have provided the number of occupied tetrads from the main atlas tetrad visits.
- Breakdown, where this could be calculated, of the population between the different National Land Classes. Below the estimate is the calculated density. The area of each National Land Class in Cumbria is given at the top of the table.

We calculated population estimates both for data stratified by National Land Class and the unstratified results. If these were statistically not significant (using 't-test') we used the stratified estimate in the Appendix. This provides useful information about which areas are more important for species. Where differences did occur, we used the unstratified estimate, eg. for Dipper.

It was also necessary to group together some smaller land classes for some species. These amalgamated land classes are shown 'boxed in' in Table A. It was felt that this would provide more useful information than simply using the unstratified Cumbrian data, eg. Pied Wagtail.

We accept that no individual census techniques can provide an adequate estimate of every bird population. For example, birds such as Dipper, which favour more linear habitats, might well have been better censused by walking transects up/along streams and rivers. In such circumstance other data have proved to be invaluable as a source of gaining a population estimate. (See also the discussion in the next chapter.)

The estimates should be used as a benchmark, with which later census data can be compared.

## Data Presentation

Taxonomy and names are according to the systematic order and scientific names are as the BOURC's 26th Report (*Ibis* **142:** 173–176) and revised according to the 27th Report (*Ibis*: **143:** 171–175). The **Distribution map** shows the Cumbrian geographical range, using three categories of breeding based on the criteria established by the BTO and

**Figure 10. Sample Line Transect Field Recording Form (part)**

| | 100 | 25 | 10 | 0 | 10 | 25 | 100 / 0 |
|---|---|---|---|---|---|---|---|
| 3 | | | | | 2HG | | 20 |
| | | ——— | ——— 2LI ——— | ——— | ——→ | | 40 |
| | 10SG | | | | 2HS | | 60 |
| | | ——— | ——— 2SG ——— | ——— | ——→ | | 80 |
| | | ——— | ——— HG ——— | ——— | ——→ | SG | 100 |
| | | | HS | (B) | HG | 2HG | 120 |
| | | | 2B(1) | | 2SG | | 140 |
| | | | (HS) | | HG | | 160 |
| | 12SG | | (LI) | | | | 180 |
| | | | (WH) | | | | 200 |

**Figure 11. Sample Count Summary Sheet (part)**

| | | | |
|---|---|---|---|
| Observer Name: Colin Raven | ~~First~~/Second Visit - delete as applicable | 1 Km Grid Reference | SD1768 |
| | **Date of Visit** 27/05/00 | | |
| Observer Address: 18, Seathwaite Road, Barrow-In-Furness, Cumbria, LA14 4LX | Start Time (HH:MM) 06:25 | | |
| | Finish Time (HH:MM) 07:30 | | |

| Weather | Cloud | Rain | Wind | Visibility |
|---|---|---|---|---|
| | 1 | 1 | 1 | 1 |

| Two Letter Species Code and Species name | Distance Category | 1 M | 1 Un | 2 M | 2 Un | 3 M | 3 Un | 4 M | 4 Un | 5 M | 5 Un | 6 M | 6 Un | 7 M | 7 Un | 8 M | 8 Un | 9 M | 9 Un | 10 M | 10 Un | Breeding Status |
|---|---|---|---|---|---|---|---|---|---|---|---|---|---|---|---|---|---|---|---|---|---|---|
| HS House Sparrow | 0-10m | | | 2 | 1 | 1 | 1 | | | | 1 | | | | | | | | | | | ~~Present~~ |
| | 11-25m | | | 1 | 4 | | 2 | | 1 | | | | | | | | | | 2 | | | ~~Probable~~ |
| | 26-100m | 1 | | | | | | | | | | | | | | | | | | | | Confirmed |
| | >100m | | | | | | | | | | 1 | | | | | | | | | | | |
| | Flying | | | | 2 | | | | | | 2 | | | | | | | | | | | |
| LI Linnet | 0-10m | | | | | 1 | | | | | | | | | | | | 1 | 2 | 1 | 1 | ~~Present~~ |
| | 11-25m | | | | | | | | | | | | | | | | | | 1 | | | Probable |
| | 26-100m | | | | | | | | | | | | | | 3 | | 2 | 1 | 2 | | | ~~Confirmed~~ |
| | >100m | | | | | | | | | | | | | | | | | | | | | |
| | Flying | | | | | | 2 | | 1 | | | | | | 1 | | | | 2 | | | |

(Columns 1–10: Number and Sex of Birds (male or female/unidentified) recorded on each transect section)

European Ornithological Atlas Committee. The incremental-sized circles represent possible, probable and confirmed breeding in ascending order of size. The absence of a symbol indicates that no records of the species were received for the survey period, either from timed visits, supplementary visits, or casual sightings.

The **Abundance map** again uses different-sized circles for each of three abundance bands. The band limits vary between species. The smallest symbol is used for the lowest 50% of all timed tetrad counts for that species; the middle symbol is used for the middle 30% of counts, and the largest symbol shows the top 20% of counts. (The 50:30:20 ratio was chosen from a range of sample maps with different ratios, and for a variety of species from common to local, as providing the best visual display of abundance.) To calculate the limits of the bands, individual species files were prepared, consisting of all timed visit counts, ranked by count-size. The median count number in the rank was determined, and all counts of this median number, and below, were taken to represent the lower 50% of the counts, and form the lowest band. These lower 50% (including all counts of the median number itself) were then discarded from the file. Of the remaining counts in the file, the lower 60% were again selected by a similar process (i.e. equivalent to 30% of the total count) and taken for the middle band, and the upper 40% (i.e. equivalent to 20% of the total count) represent the top band.

With hindsight the quality of data gained from the tetrad survey could have been enhanced greatly by further sub-dividing each tetrad into 1km squares and apportioning time and data collection accordingly. There would have been associated considerable extra burdens of data collection, inputting and management, but the data would have been more amenable to a wider range of analyses.

The **Small maps** allow comparisons to be made of a species' Cumbrian distribution over a 30-year time scale. They show at a 10km square level the county distribution based on i) data presented in *The Atlas of Breeding Birds in Britain and Ireland* (1968–1972) and ii) the results of this atlas. The highest category of breeding (ie. 'possible', 'probable', or 'confirmed') recorded within each 10km square is plotted using three circle sizes.

Writing **Species accounts** was assigned to county birdwatchers considered to have some local knowledge of the species and therefore some detailed experience as a basis to assimilate and interpret data from this survey. In all, 29 authors wrote texts for 152 species given a full treatment, with a further 22 occasional or past breeders and 12 feral species. Each

author was given specific guidelines and a list of conventions, which would ensure that all accounts followed a consistent and complementary format. An example text was also provided. After the first round of editorial intervention, species texts were then returned to the originators accompanied by information on data analysis, abundance and distribution maps. Authors were then asked to amend the text according to further instructions.

**Artwork,** to a very high standard, enhances each of the 152 full-species texts. Eleven illustrators produced the line drawings to standard specifications and often-tight deadlines. Both species account authors and illustrators gave freely of their time and readily agreed a copyright assignment in consideration of this publication, *The Breeding Birds of Cumbria: a tetrad atlas 1997–2001*, in favour of the Cumbria Bird Club.

The **Conservation box** provides an accessible source of summary information on the species, with European and UK conservation status and breeding populations, to place Cumbria into the wider context. The conservation status has been derived from the current revised (2002–07) list in *Birds of Conservation Concern in the United Kingdom, Channel Islands and Isle of Man*. The current revised Red-list of species includes those globally threatened or in rapid decline in the UK currently or historically. Amber-list species are in moderate decline, rare, localized, internationally important or of an unfavourable conservation status in Europe. The Red, Amber or Green status is given, with abbreviations indicating the criteria for inclusion in that list. The abbreviations are explained on page 45. See also Tables 9 & 10 on pages 41/42.

European population figures are derived from Hagemeijer *et al* (1997). It is unclear from this source whether the quoted figures refer to pairs or individuals. Following Mead (2000) the figures have been given appropriate rounding.

British population estimates are derived from Stone *et al* (1997), again quoted by Mead (2000).

Cumbria population estimates are summarized from the species account population paragraph. These are quoted as a single figure, or as a range in those instances where either a population fluctuated markedly during the survey years, or where it has been difficult to estimate figures more precisely. (Explanation of the interpretation and implementation of Line Transect Survey data, or alternative sources of population estimates, is given in the discussion on page 35. Table D on page 371 lists the source of the population estimate for each species.)

Key database statistics from the results of this atlas survey are also presented.

## Summary of weather during the atlas period

### 1997

April was largely dry with the wettest days towards the end of the month; May was wet with temperatures and sunshine about normal, however, frost occurred on the 9th and 23rd causing damage to plants. The last few days became sunny and hot with temperatures around 25°C. Overall, spring was warm with near average sunshine and rainfall below normal. June was generally unsettled with cyclonic weather; July was sunny with the highest sunshine totals and temperatures reaching 27°C. Heavy downpours occurred over the Solway Basin on the 13th causing flooding.

### 1998

The winter months of 1997/98 were exceptionally mild with 16°C recorded at Aspatria in January. The spring of this year was the warmest since 1959 with nine consecutive May days exceeding 20°C, some 5°C above normal values. June was cool and very wet with many places receiving more than twice their normal rainfall, and consequently there were only six sunny days; Ambleside recorded its wettest June since 1948. July was also dull and wet. A vigorous westerly jet-stream moving south of its usual summer position caused prolonged wet conditions.

### 1999

The winter of 1998/99 was again mild with Keswick recording 12°C during January and February; the absence of easterly winds helped maintain ambient temperatures. April temperatures were mild, and consequently rainfall was above normal; the beginning of the month saw a southeast airflow of Mediterranean origin resulting in temperatures as high as 19°C. May was warm and generally wet; a thunderstorm at Drumburgh brought 36mm of rain in 2 hours. June again was cool and very wet with sunshine totals below normal; towards the end of the month thundery rain brought 32mm of rain to Eskmeals. July was warm and dry with above normal sunshine; it was the driest for a decade and the warmest since 1995, with four days exceeding 25°C. December was a very wet month of contrasting weather types with spells of very cold wintry conditions, including snow showers on Christmas Day.

### 2000

January and February were mild with little frost or snow; again another favourable winter survival for most passerines. April was a cold dull month. Over England as a whole this was the wettest April since 1818. May was warm and dry with some Cumbrian temperatures the best in Britain. June began cool and wet but by the second week it became drier and warmer; by the 15th temperatures rose rapidly, approaching 30°C in many areas. July was disappointing, with mean temperatures around 1°C below normal; the 6th was an exceptionally poor day, with a temperature 6°C below the norm.

### 2001

The poor early spring weather continued throughout April, which was wet and cold, with an Atlantic depression bringing heavy rain during the last few days of the month. May was a good deal warmer with only brief unsettled spells; on the 12th, Keswick recorded a temperature of 27°C. The total amount of sunshine recorded was well above normal, due to the exceptionally sunny first half of the month. June was different, with a run of cool, dull days dominated by a series of depressions that swept southwards over Scandinavia, pulling cold northerly winds of polar origins; on the 3rd temperature fell close to freezing to give the coldest June night for over 10 years. The warmer weather during the last week did nothing to balance the cold start. Despite some cool mid-month days July had a good deal of warm sunny weather, though Cumbria largely missed the heat wave that affected much of central and southern England where temperatures of 32°C were recorded.

# Discussion

## Population change

The only constant factor in population dynamics is that of change – and birds are no exception. Ignoring for the moment human influences, changes in population numbers are in general in response to natural phenomena such as extreme weather patterns or more prolonged climatic influences. Shorter troughs and peaks of weather create short-term aberrations in population, quickly restored to equilibrium without serious long-term effects. In recent times such abnormal manifestations have been very striking, especially in many of our migrant birds where populations have 'crashed' dramatically between years, as was evident in warblers such as the Whitethroat during the Sahel droughts of 1968/69 and 1983/84. At home, severe winters and prolonged periods of freezing weather take their toll on some resident birds like the Kingfisher, reducing populations down to a fraction of that previously. Some other species, 'partial migrants' like the Stonechat, adopt a clever survival strategy: part of the population migrates to escape the unpredictability of a British winter, the rest stay locally, thus avoiding the uncertainties of long migrations. In the long term, a variety of behavioural traits may be required within a population to maintain a species in a particular part of its range.

Whatever strategy birds may adopt, they do respond quickly to change, and that is why they are a good indicator as to the 'health' of their – and our – environment. While the change in local status of some species may currently be inexplicable, in others cases the reasons seem obvious. For instance, as extensive tracts of maturing post-war conifer plantations came into seed production during the last 30 years, the Siskin's Cumbrian population dramatically increased by 725%. Changes in landscape management can also have powerful negative influences; during the latter half of the 20th century catastrophic declines were observed in populations of, for example, Corncrake, Black Grouse, and Corn Bunting. The Tree Sparrow looks likely to join these birds in a state of decline. These birds responded negatively to agricultural policies that ranked short-term productivity above long-term environmental health. Regrettably, it took a series of somewhat disastrous events in the agriculture sector before government began to make the necessary changes to rectify this imbalance – changes which as environmentalists and conservationists we welcome as a tentative first step in restoring a more harmonious countryside.

Between these two extremes, less obvious population changes may be occurring in our commoner countryside birds, movements which until now remained obscure and difficult to monitor without the fundamental knowledge to act as a basis from which to work.

With climate change predicted on a global scale, and regional amelioration in weather patterns a symptom, there will be profound future impacts on our wildlife, making the task of the amateur to chronicle change as it affects bird populations even more important.

## Estimating population size

Acquiring population statistics for all breeding birds in the county was a challenge that proved more problematic for some species than others. The first real test was to find a rational backcloth against which to measure meaningful densities. Although national Phase-one habitat data of the county was an obvious choice – since Cumbria is fortunate in having complete survey coverage – the absence of this data in digital format severely limited its usefulness. We were fortunate to stumble across the Institute for Terrestrial Ecology's National Land Classification system, and we are very grateful for the constructive advice from ITE staff. This proved ideal in bridging the shortfall, by offering countywide uniformity and a stable base for future re-surveys. Although the continuum of national land classes worked very well for widespread species, it highlighted serious limitations for more specialist birds like Reed Warbler and Lesser Whitethroat. The main difficulty was perhaps that the national Land Class resolution was simply too broad and did not accommodate individual habitat components, especially those very small and fragmented elements, such as reedbeds and scrub. This tended to overly emphasise their occurrence, hence causing inflated population estimates for particular niche species.

The line transect data methodology and analysis are explained in the previous chapter. The use of the line transect bands and mean estimates for a particular species was dependent on the sample size for that species – in other words, the number of occasions on which the species was contacted. The numbers of contacts for every species were ranked in descending order of sample size, and banded into three categories: above 48; 47–15; and below 15. For those species with more than 48 contacts, the mean population figure has been used without reservation. For species with between 47 and 15 contacts the findings become progressively statistically less robust, and as a consequence it was thought appropriate to add a qualifying phrase to the calculated mean population figure in these instances. The findings for species from the lowest band (ie. below 15 contacts) were considered potentially misleading, and other methods of estimating those populations used. A number of species which were not located in line transect work are also included in this category.

The width of the 95% confidence limits band, quoted in the accounts for the first two categories above, also gives a good sense of the robustness or otherwise of the analyses. In layman's terms, there is a 95% chance – in other words, a very strong chance indeed – that the actual population of that species within the county falls within the limits of the band given. As would be predicted, the width of the band widens dramatically with decreasing sample size. In rather general terms, therefore, the width of the 95% confidence limits band reflects inversely the number of contacts.

Line transect methodology does not work well for various categories of birds: those, such as many wildfowl, which tend to have 'clumped' or very localized distributions; those with specific habitat preferences, such as reedbeds, where that habitat is rare and local; and those with linear distribution patterns, such as waterside and river species. Population estimates under these circumstances were derived from various types of count data, enhanced by supplementary records and local knowledge of the species, rather than the line transect results. (All line transect results are summarised in Table A page 363.) With few exceptions, it was considered prudent to quote actual figures taken from recent countywide species surveys, where these were available. Included were seabird counts by the RSPB; Cumbria Raptor Study Group figures for scarcer raptors such as Hen Harrier, Merlin, Peregrine, Honey Buzzard, Osprey and Goshawk; and recent Cumbria Bird Club survey results for Sand Martin and Rook. Population estimates for scarcer species or colonial breeders that are regularly counted by county birdwatchers, such as Grey Heron, and some waterfowl, gulls and terns, allowed greater confidence.

Given that bird populations are dynamic, both in terms of range and number, the findings of this atlas provide a baseline against which future populations trends can be measured and quantified. The methods of data collection were designed to be readily repeatable, whether used in future for single species monitoring or multi-species surveys such as the farmland bird example given below, allowing the evaluation of landscape quality through a representative suite of species.

## Diversity maps

These maps can be readily generated from the database. They are particularly useful in giving a visual 'feel' for the important bird areas in Cumbria. Band intervals on individual maps were chosen more for visual impact than with any statistical justification.

The **Species Richness** map (Figure 12) gives a readily appreciable image of the county's avian diversity, depicting clearly the richest bird areas. Conversely the

paucity of bird species over large areas of the uplands is also striking. Two tetrads, NY21U and NY22I, in adjacent 10km squares, are particularly noteworthy within a pocket of high diversity. South of Lakeland, the greater variety of species reflects the habitat diversity in this area, including the extensive former coppiced woodland, combined with the continuance of a mixed small-scale arable and pastoral landscape. A milder climate and locally sheltered aspect will also encourage diversity. Another major area of diversity is east of Carlisle on the north-western flanks of the Pennines. Although the climate is considerably harsher, there is again a more diverse topography here, giving a varied landscape upon which the excesses of agricultural and silvicultural intensification have not as yet been visited.

Mapping of BoCC-listed species reveals two distinctive patterns (see under Tables 9 & 10 below for further explanation of BoCC lists). The **Red-listed species** map (Figure 13) shows much more of a peripheral distribution with 'hotspots' cropping up along the coastal lowlands, and locally in the northeast, while the **Amber-listed species** map (Figure 14) has perhaps a more even pattern, and concentrations of these birds are in those areas already mentioned as having a generally high species diversity.

Finally, such thematic maps allow, at a glance, a comparison of tetrad quality, and by selective means a degree of habitat assessment is also possible. Taking **Farmland species** as an example (Figure 15): by selecting a suite of species representative of the cross-section of agriculture in Cumbria (in this case, Grey Partridge, Lapwing, Redshank, Stock Dove, Barn Owl, Little Owl, Swallow, Tree Sparrow & Yellowhammer), we can gauge and compare habitat quality based on bird diversity. This can provide an effective tool for those administering government-initiated agri-environmental schemes, for instance to assess priorities, and act as a blueprint for local planners. The results of this atlas suggest how public money targeted towards enhancing farmland bird populations might be effectively deployed in the agricultural basins of Abbeytown and the central and upper Eden Valley where many such species still occur, rather than say in Lakeland, where a paucity of those birds possibly reflects the steep-sided valleys and limited scope of agricultural land.

## Population trends

The fieldwork for the present atlas was conducted ten years after that for *The New Atlas of Breeding Birds in Britain and Ireland: 1988–1991*. It was felt that this time interval was too brief for any but short-term population fluctuations to be revealed by a comparison of data between the two works. Populations of a number of species will undoubtedly have altered considerably in that short time, but the differences in

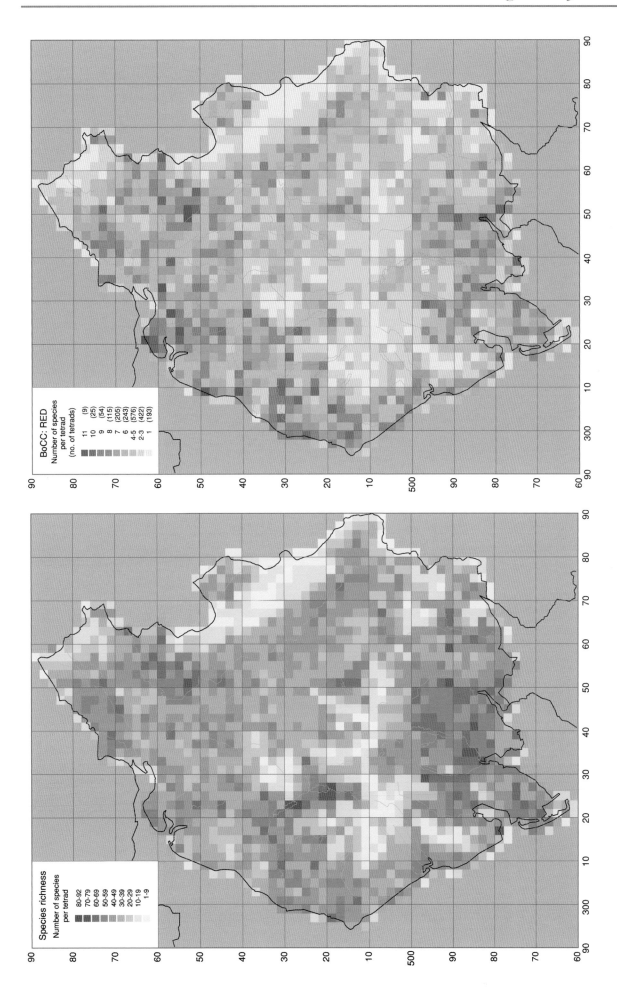

**Figure 13: BoCC Red-listed species**

**Figure 12: Species richness**

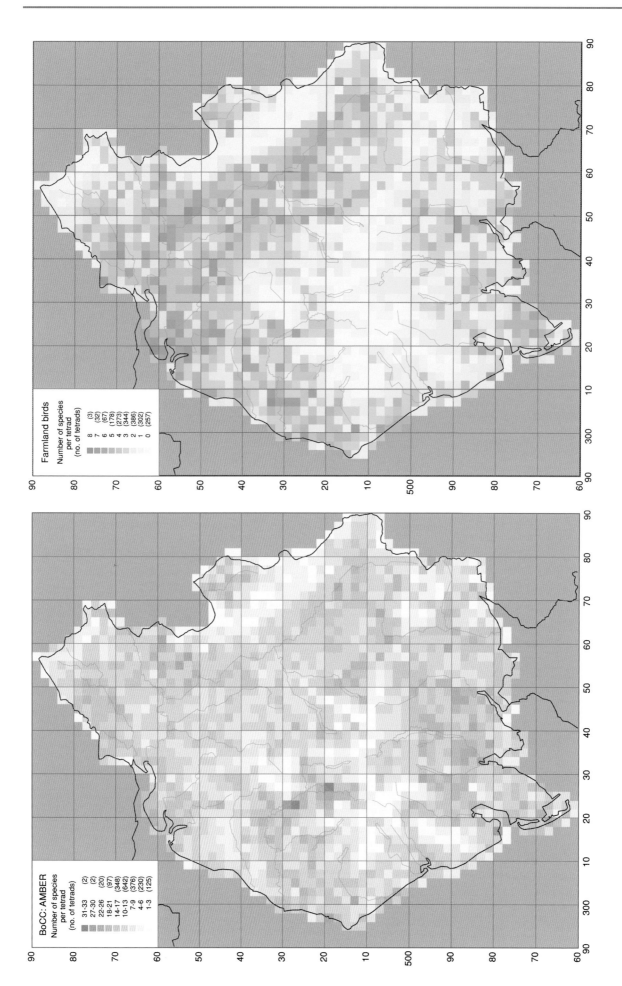

Farmland birds
Number of species
per tetrad
(no. of tetrads)

| 8 | (3) |
| 7 | (32) |
| 6 | (67) |
| 5 | (178) |
| 4 | (273) |
| 3 | (344) |
| 2 | (386) |
| 1 | (302) |
| 0 | (257) |

Figure 15: Nine farmland species

BoCC: AMBER
Number of species
per tetrad
(no. of tetrads)

| 31-33 | (2) |
| 27-30 | (2) |
| 22-26 | (20) |
| 18-21 | (97) |
| 14-17 | (348) |
| 10-13 | (642) |
| 7-9 | (376) |
| 4-6 | (230) |
| 1-3 | (125) |

Figure 14: BoCC Amber-listed species

scope between the two surveys meant that figures for the population change for those species, derived from comparisons of numbers of occupied tetrads, could not be relied upon to give any other than broad trends. For a few species, dedicated surveys have revealed short-term changes with greater reliability, and these are mentioned in the species accounts.

For Tables 2 to 10 we use Cumbrian data derived from *The Atlas of Breeding Birds in Britain and Ireland* (referred to in the tables as the *'Old Atlas'*), the fieldwork for which was conducted in 1968–72, to give a figure of change over a 30-year interval. The 10km square unit gives a much coarser resolution than does the tetrad, and the fieldwork effort per square was not standardised in the earlier atlas, but it is felt that overall the change figures give a reasonable sense of change in range, if not in numbers, over that interval.

## Tables 1 & 2

The top two most widespread birds, Carrion Crow and Wren, achieve their position by occurring not only universally in the lowlands, but also throughout the extensive uplands, albeit often at low densities. Conversely, species with predominantly upland preferences such as Meadow Pipit are of only irregular occurrence in the lowlands – the more so since agricultural intensification has altered or destroyed many pockets of lowland heath where such species would have found a home in times past. Yet Carrion Crow does not find a place in the top 21 most abundant birds (occupying position 22, with 33,000 pairs).

Whilst both Chaffinch and Willow Warbler achieve their pre-eminent position in abundance by occupying a wide range of wooded habitats, even the smallest patch of trees and scrub in the uplands, the position of Meadow Pipit in third place is a testament to the high density that this bird can achieve on blanket bogs and moorland plateaux: although it occupies only a small range of habitats, the combined areas of those habitats in Cumbria is large. It is encouraging to find Swallow and Starling, two species that have recently been moved to a level of greater concern in the revised BoCC listing, are amongst our top ten species in terms both of numbers and range.

## Table 3 & 4

New colonists since the first national atlas in 1968-72 number 12 species. Remarkably, and encouragingly, a quarter of these are raptors, the most celebrated being the re-appearance after 170 years of the Osprey. Others such as Fieldfare and Common Rosefinch may never in the foreseeable future be more than exceptional and irregular breeders, whilst we can hope that birds such as Mediterranean Gull, Reed Warbler and Crossbill continue to advance in their different circumstances.

On the flipside of the coin, we have lost just four species, two wildfowl which were never consistent breeding birds in the county, a tern in widespread decline, and the Black-tailed Godwit. Recent instances of displaying pairs of this last species in the north of the county give some hope that the situation for this species may be only temporary.

Table 1: Top 21 most widespread species in Cumbria

|  | | No. of tetrads | % tetrads |
|---|---|---|---|
| 1. | Carrion Crow | 1624 | 92.3 |
| 2. | Wren | 1618 | 91.9 |
| 3. | Chaffinch | 1568 | 89.0 |
| 4. | Willow Warbler | 1494 | 84.9 |
| 5. | Robin | 1455 | 82.7 |
| 6. | Swallow | 1434 | 81.5 |
| 7. | Blackbird | 1425 | 81.0 |
| 8. | Woodpigeon | 1409 | 80.0 |
| 9. | Blue Tit | 1383 | 78.6 |
| 10. | Pied Wagtail | 1359 | 77.2 |
| 11. | Meadow Pipit | 1296 | 73.6 |
| 12. | Song Thrush | 1241 | 70.5 |
| 13. | Great Tit | 1233 | 70.0 |
| 14. | Jackdaw | 1186 | 67.4 |
| 15. | Curlew | 1180 | 67.0 |
| 16. | Skylark | 1178 | 66.9 |
| 17. | Starling | 1137 | 64.6 |
| 18. | Dunnock | 1116 | 63.4 |
| 19. | Pheasant | 1035 | 58.8 |
| 20. | House Sparrow | 1034 | 58.7 |
| 21. | Buzzard | 1026 | 58.3 |

Table 2: Top 21 most abundant species in Cumbria

|  | | Estimated no. of pairs | % of total no. of pairs |
|---|---|---|---|
| 1. | Chaffinch | 360,000 | 13.3 |
| 2. | Willow Warbler | 240,000 | 8.9 |
| 3. | Meadow Pipit | 205,000 | 7.6 |
| 4. | Blackbird | 170,000 | 6.3 |
| 5. | House Sparrow | 165,000 | 6.1 |
| 6. | Wren | 130,000 | 4.8 |
| 7. | Blue Tit | 120,000 | 4.4 |
| 8. | Robin | 115,000 | 4.3 |
| 9. | Starling | 100,000 | 3.7 |
| 10. | Swallow | 85,000 | 3.1 |
| 11. | Jackdaw | 75,000 | 2.8 |
| 12. | Great Tit | 53,000 | 2.0 |
| 13. | Woodpigeon | 50,000 | 1.9 |
| 14. | Pied Wagtail | 48,000 | 1.8 |
| 15. | Linnet | 46,500 | 1.7 |
| 16. | Rook | 45,000 | 1.7 |
| 17. | Goldfinch | 43,500 | 1.6 |
| 18. | Dunnock | 41,500 | 1.5 |
| 19. | House Martin | 41,500 | 1.5 |
| 20. | Greenfinch | 34,000 | 1.3 |
| 21. | Lesser Black-backed Gull | 33,500 | 1.2 |

**Table 3: Species recorded breeding in Cumbria during *this Atlas* but not in the *Old Atlas***

**Table 3: Species recorded breeding in Cumbria during *this Atlas* but not in the *Old Atlas***

| | Occupied 10km squares |
|---|---|
| | |
| Mandarin | 3 |
| Ruddy Duck | 10 |
| Honey Buzzard | 2 |
| Hen Harrier | 16 |
| Goshawk | 20 |
| Osprey | 8 |
| Red-legged Partridge | 33 |
| Mediterranean Gull | 2 |
| Fieldfare | 5 |
| Reed Warbler | 16 |
| Crossbill | 28 |
| Common Rosefinch | 1 |

**Table 4: Species recorded breeding in Cumbria during the *Old Atlas* but not in *this Atlas***

| | Occupied 10km squares |
|---|---|
| | |
| Pintail | 1 |
| Wood Duck | 1 |
| Black-tailed Godwit | 3 |
| Roseate Tern | 1 |

## Tables 5 & 6

Given the county's general altitude, high precipitation and absence of widespread tillage, it is surprising to find Red-legged Partridge heading the non-passerine list of range expansion, and with such a huge increase. However, just how many of these records refer merely to new releases from game-farms remains unknown; in the absence of releases, this species, and perhaps also the apparently well-established Pheasant, might rapidly disappear.

Although the top three passerine species are possibly more predictable, and therefore less of a surprise, the extent of the increase of Siskin, Crossbill and Nuthatch has been emphatic. In the case of the first two, the maturing of vast areas of coniferous forest has been crucial. It is not clear why the Nuthatch was previously absent from large areas of apparently suitable woodland in the north of the county, which it is now actively colonizing. Perhaps a climatic factor has been at work, as might also be the case with Reed Warbler and Lesser Whitethroat.

## Tables 7 & 8

It is an alarming fact that 11 out of 20 species exhibit a contraction in range of 50% or more; this is especially poignant given that the top three non-passerine and top two passerine species were once regarded as widespread and frequent birds in the Cumbria of 50 years ago. We can perhaps take solace, without complacency, that unlike the national trend only four species in the top half of both tables can be regarded as farmland birds. Besides that obvious trend, the probable reasons for the declines in other cases are various, and will likely include climatic deterioration whether here or on wintering grounds, habitat destruction and alteration, deliberate or accidental disturbance, increased competition or predation – all factors which may be crucial or contributory in any particular case.

## Tables 9 & 10

*Red Data Birds in Britain* (Batten *et al* 1990) lists 117 species, 109 of which qualified on one or more quantitative criteria referring to rarity, localized

**Table 5: Species showing largest expansion in 10km square distribution since the *Old Atlas* (top ten non-passerines)**

| | | *Old Atlas* | *this Atlas* | % change |
|---|---|---|---|---|
| | | | | |
| 1. | Red-legged Partridge | 1 | 33 | +3,200.0 |
| 2. | Eider (1) | 1 | 6 | +500.0 |
| 3. | Hen Harrier | 3 | 16 | +433.3 |
| 4. | Black-necked Grebe (1) | 1 | 5 | +400.0 |
| 5. | Cormorant (1) | 2 | 8 | +300.0 |
| 6. | Little Ringed Plover (1) | 2 | 7 | +250.0 |
| 7. | Herring Gull | 9 | 31 | +244.4 |
| 8. | Quail | 3 | 10 | +233.3 |
| 9. | Lesser Black-backed Gull | 13 | 42 | +223.0 |
| 10. | Great Black-backed Gull | 5 | 15 | +200.0 |

(1) based on small sample size

**Table 6: Species showing largest expansion in 10km square distribution since the *Old Atlas* (top ten passerines)**

| | | *Old Atlas* | *this Atlas* | % change |
|---|---|---|---|---|
| | | | | |
| 1. | Siskin | 8 | 66 | +725.0 |
| 2. | Nuthatch | 8 | 63 | +687.5 |
| 3. | Crossbill | 4 | 28 | +600.0 |
| 4. | Reed Warbler | 3 | 16 | +433.3 |
| 5. | Lesser Whitethroat | 15 | 37 | +146.6 |
| 6. | Rock Pipit (1) | 2 | 4 | +100.0 |
| 7. | Stonechat | 40 | 56 | +40.0 |
| 8. | Pied Flycatcher | 41 | 57 | +39.0 |
| 9. | Raven | 47 | 55 | +17.0 |
| 10. | Chiffchaff | 69 | 80 | +15.9 |

(1) based on small sample size

**Table 7: Species showing largest contraction in 10km square distribution since the *Old Atlas* (top ten non-passerines)**

| | | *Old Atlas* | *this Atlas* | % change |
|---|---|---|---|---|
| 1. | Corncrake | 40 | 3 | −92.5 |
| 2. | Nightjar | 22 | 4 | −81.8 |
| 3. | Black Grouse | 46 | 13 | −71.7 |
| 4. | Common Tern | 10 | 3 | −70.0 |
| 5. | Sandwich Tern (1) | 3 | 1 | −66.6 |
| 6. | Water Rail | 22 | 10 | −54.5 |
| 7. | Lesser Spotted Woodpecker | 17 | 8 | −52.9 |
| 8. | Short-eared Owl | 37 | 18 | −51.3 |
| 9. | Arctic Tern (1) | 6 | 3 | −50.0 |
| 10. | Teal | 64 | 36 | −43.7 |

(1) based on small sample size

**Table 8: Species showing largest contraction in 10km square distribution since the *Old Atlas* (top ten passerines)**

| | | *Old Atlas* | *this Atlas* | % change |
|---|---|---|---|---|
| 1. | Corn Bunting | 47 | 5 | −89.4 |
| 2. | Yellow Wagtail | 66 | 22 | −66.6 |
| 3. | Hawfinch | 24 | 13 | −45.8 |
| 4. | Twite | 1 5 | 10 | −33.3 |
| 5. | Tree Sparrow | 65 | 45 | −30.8 |
| 6. | Willow Tit | 30 | 21 | −30.0 |
| 7. | Ring Ouzel | 48 | 35 | −27.0 |
| 8. | Marsh Tit | 35 | 27 | −22.8 |
| 9. | Whitethroat | 85 | 67 | −21.2 |
| 10. | Grasshopper Warbler | 61 | 49 | −19.7 |

distribution, decline in population and international importance. This has been refined into a working document, *Birds of Conservation Concern in the United Kingdom, Channel Islands and Isle of Man* (BoCC). Unlike the original, the new list has been prioritised into species of high (Red) and medium (Amber) conservation concern; all other species are of lower (Green) concern. The list is kept under review and updated every five years.

Cumbria holds important numbers of BoCC (revised list 2002–2007) species: 21 Red-listed and 65 Amber-listed birds. Of these birds, within the county, 22 species (26%) show an increase since the first national survey, 44 species (52%) have reduced populations, and 15 species (17%) have stable populations; there were five species new to Cumbria as breeding birds. Species on the increase include some wildfowl, gamebirds and seabirds, while upland and farmland birds account for over a third of all species in decline.

**Table 9: BoCC RED list showing change in number of occupied 10km squares between the *Old Atlas* and *this Atlas***

| Occupied 10km squares in: | *Old Atlas* | *this Atlas* | % change |
|---|---|---|---|
| Hen Harrier (1 & 3) | 3 | 16 | +433.3 |
| Black Grouse | 46 | 13 | −71.7 |
| Grey Partridge | 77 | 68 | −11.7 |
| Quail (1 & 2) | 3 | 10 | +233.3 |
| Nightjar | 22 | 4 | −81.8 |
| Lesser Spotted Woodpecker | 17 | 8 | −52.9 |
| Skylark | 91 | 91 | n/c |
| Ring Ouzel | 48 | 35 | −27.0 |
| Song Thrush | 90 | 90 | n/c |
| Grasshopper Warbler | 61 | 49 | −19.7 |
| Spotted Flycatcher | 83 | 81 | −2.4 |
| Marsh Tit | 35 | 27 | −22.8 |
| Willow Tit | 30 | 21 | −30.0 |
| Starling | 88 | 88 | n/c |
| Tree Sparrow | 65 | 45 | −30.8 |
| Linnet | 88 | 88 | n/c |
| Twite | 15 | 10 | −33.3 |
| Bullfinch | 80 | 73 | −8.7 |
| Yellowhammer | 86 | 76 | −11.6 |
| Reed Bunting | 82 | 78 | −4.9 |
| Corn Bunting | 47 | 5 | −89.4 |

(1) based on small sample size
(2) sporadic breeding and unpredictable trend
(3) no successful breeding recorded in 2001

**Table 10: BoCC AMBER list showing change in number of occupied 10km squares between the *Old Atlas* and *this Atlas***

| Occupied 10km squares in: | *Old Atlas* | *this Atlas* | % change |
|---|---|---|---|
| Black-necked Grebe (1 & 3) | 1 | 5 | +400.0 |
| Fulmar (1) | 1 | 2 | +100.0 |
| Cormorant (1) | 2 | 8 | +300.0 |
| Mute Swan | 49 | 49 | n/c |
| Honey Buzzard (1 & 2) | 0 | 2 | n/a |
| Greylag Goose | 19 | 51 | +168.4 |
| Shelduck | 34 | 33 | -2.9 |
| Wigeon | 14 | 18 | +28.5 |
| Gadwall | 5 | 10 | +100.0 |
| Teal | 64 | 36 | -43.7 |
| Shoveler | 10 | 19 | +90.0 |
| Pochard | 10 | 10 | n/c |
| Eider (1) | 1 | 6 | +500.0 |
| Golden Eagle (1) | 1 | 1 | n/c |
| Osprey (1 & 2) | 0 | 8 | n/a |
| Kestrel | 88 | 84 | -4.5 |
| Merlin | 36 | 33 | -8.3 |
| Peregrine | 25 | 56 | +124.0 |
| Water Rail | 22 | 10 | -54.5 |
| Oystercatcher | 85 | 88 | +3.5 |
| Ringed Plover | 42 | 27 | -35.7 |
| Dotterel (1) | 7 | 9 | +28.5 |
| Lapwing | 91 | 84 | -7.7 |
| Dunlin | 25 | 17 | -32.0 |
| Snipe | 89 | 67 | -24.7 |
| Woodcock | 73 | 42 | -42.5 |
| Curlew | 87 | 85 | -2.3 |
| Redshank | 80 | 63 | -21.2 |
| Mediterranean Gull (1 & 2) | 0 | 2 | n/a |
| Common Gull (1) | 3 | 3 | n/c |
| Lesser Black-backed Gull | 13 | 42 | +233.0 |
| Herring Gull | 9 | 31 | +244.4 |
| Kittiwake (1) | 1 | 1 | n/c |
| Sandwich Tern (1) | 3 | 1 | -66.6 |
| Arctic Tern | 6 | 3 | -50.0 |

| Occupied 10km squares in: | *Old Atlas* | *this Atlas* | % change |
|---|---|---|---|
| Little Tern | 10 | 6 | -40.0 |
| Guillemot (1) | 1 | 1 | n/c |
| Razorbill (1) | 1 | 1 | n/c |
| Black Guillemot (1) | 1 | 2 | +100.0 |
| Puffin (1) | 1 | 1 | n/c |
| Stock Dove | 73 | 73 | n/c |
| Cuckoo | 87 | 77 | -11.5 |
| Barn Owl | 80 | 53 | -33.7 |
| Short-eared Owl | 37 | 18 | -51.3 |
| Kingfisher | 45 | 37 | -17.8 |
| Green Woodpecker | 67 | 51 | -23.8 |
| Sand Martin | 82 | 74 | -9.7 |
| Swallow | 91 | 91 | n/c |
| House Martin | 87 | 84 | -3.4 |
| Tree Pipit | 71 | 64 | -8.4 |
| Meadow Pipit | 94 | 94 | n/c |
| Yellow Wagtail | 66 | 22 | -66.6 |
| Grey Wagtail | 77 | 80 | +3.9 |
| Dunnock | 89 | 88 | -1.1 |
| Redstart | 73 | 74 | +1.4 |
| Stonechat | 40 | 56 | +40.0 |
| Fieldfare (1 & 3) | 0 | 5 | n/a |
| Mistle Thrush | 85 | 84 | -1.2 |
| Wood Warbler | 53 | 58 | +9.4 |
| Willow Warbler | 89 | 91 | +2.2 |
| Goldcrest | 76 | 80 | +5.3 |
| House Sparrow | 88 | 85 | -3.4 |
| Lesser Redpoll | 85 | 78 | -8.2 |
| Common Rosefinch (1 & 3) | 0 | 1 | n/a |
| Hawfinch | 24 | 13 | -45.8 |

(1) small sample size
(2) recent colonization and probably the nucleus of a new county population
(3) sporadic breeding and unpredictable trend

## Final remarks

Of the various groups of Cumbrian birds, the future for birds of prey in the county is still a cause of much concern for many people. In parts of the county, a jaundiced view of 'birds with hooked beaks' still holds sway – a view now long supplanted in the public mind by an appreciation of raptors as cherished and rightful inhabitants of the landscape. While the Peregrine has shown a marked increase of 124% and the Buzzard starts to regain former numbers, direct illegal harassment continues to be the greatest threat to raptorial species in Cumbria, much of it perpetrated under the spurious justification of that most objectionable term 'vermin'. Any form of wildlife which might conceivably disturb game is liable to be classed thus. One can only despair at the plight of the Hen Harriers that attempt to nest on the county's

eastern grouse-moors, where they can be subjected to persistent persecution; by the final year of this work this magnificent bird once more teetered on the brink of local extinction as a breeding species.

All we can hope is that this situation is temporary, and those empowered under the new Countryside and Rights of Way legislation will forcefully exercise the wishes of the majority and be enabled to provide better protection.

The return of the Osprey to breed in the county – re-colonizating England after an absence of 170 years – was a major milestone of this atlas period. However, its eggs will be under severe threat from collectors where not under constant surveillance, and being a raptor and a fish-eating bird it will remain at great risk from wilful disturbance. Most regrettably, information received suggests that one bird was found dead, in suspicious circumstances, at a nest in 2001; that site was not active in 2002.

Notable improvements in status involved the discovery of breeding Honey Buzzard, a species with ample opportunties to consolidate its hold on the county, given the provisos just mentioned. This is a species which harms game interests not at all.

There is always a temptation for those not closely involved with the situation on the ground to quote figures such as '12 new breeding species' as implying that the conservation picture is less bleak than is often painted. It must be pointed out that the total population of all these colonists is in a typical year not more than a few dozen pairs (ignoring the rather more numerous Reed Warbler), a number which simply cannot be set against the catastrophic losses over the years of many thousands of Cumbria's typical, and once numerous, open-country species of farmland, shore, marsh and hill, such as Grey Partridge, Lapwing, Curlew, Snipe, Skylark, and Yellow Wagtail.

There are compelling reasons why all who value Cumbria's birds should take an active part in promoting the cause of bird conservation and preservation, in surveying and reporting, in active habitat renewal work, and in education and championing of the cause.

Given the apparent willingness of government to heed calls for a refocussing of agricultural policy to target subsidies at environmental enhancement and biodiversity, rather than at mass production over all else, we may expect with cautious optimism that perhaps the worst is over, and that we may begin to see improvement. Whenever the next atlas of breeding birds is published for the county, there should be every reason to hope and expect that the status of the county's birds should receive a still more positive 'bill of health'.

# Abbreviations and references in species accounts

## Abbreviations used in the species accounts

| | |
|---|---|
| asl | above sea level |
| BAP | Biodiversity Action Plan |
| BBS | Breeding Bird Survey |
| BoCC | Birds of Conservation Concern |
| BSE | Bovine Spongiform Encephalopathy |
| BTO | British Trust for Ornithology |
| C | Celsius |
| CBC | Common Bird Census |
| CRSG | Cumbria Raptor Study Group |
| ESA | Environmentally Sensitive Area |
| EU | European Union |
| ha | hectare |
| in prep | in preparation |
| km | kilometre |
| LDNPA | Lake District National Park Authority |
| m | metre |
| MoD | Ministry of Defence |
| NCC | Nature Conservancy Council |
| PCBs | Polychlorinated bi-phenyls |
| pers comm | personal communication |
| pers obs | personal observation |
| RSPB | Royal Society for the Protection of Birds |
| SSSI | Site of Special Scientific Interest |
| WAGBI | Wildfowlers' Association of Great Britain and Ireland |
| WBS | Waterways Bird Survey |
| WBO | Walney Bird Observatory |
| WWT | Wildfowl and Wetlands Trust |

All **localities** mentioned in the accounts are listed in the Gazeteer on page 377, with a 10km square grid reference.

## Frequently cited references

A full list of references is given in the appendices. Mentions of the present work refer to *'this Atlas'*. Citations from the following are not given specific references in the accounts, except as mentioned below.

| | |
|---|---|
| Cramp *et al* 1977–93: | *The Birds of the Western Palearctic* |
| Gibbons *et al* 1993: | *The New Atlas of Breeding Birds in Britain & Ireland: 1988–1991* – referred to in the species accounts as the *'New Atlas'* |
| Hagemeijer & Blair (eds) 1997: | *The EBCC Atlas of European Breeding Birds* |
| Holloway 1996: | *The Historical Atlas of Breeding Birds in Britain & Ireland: 1875–1900* – referred to in the species accounts as the *'Historical Atlas'* |
| Sharrock 1976: | *The Atlas of Breeding Birds in Britain & Ireland* – referred to in the species accounts as the *'Old Atlas'* |
| Witherby *et al* 1938–41: | *Handbook of British Birds* |

Also: the annual reports for the county published from 1970 to 2000 under the titles *Natural History in Cumbria* (1970 to 1976); *Birds in Cumbria* (1977 to 1995); *Birds and Wildlife in Cumbria* (1996 to present). For full references to these, see under the names of: Carrier, M.; Carrier, M. & D. Clarke; Hewitt, S.; Hutcheson, M.; Moule, G.W.H.; Shield, E.; Wilson, G.

Note that fuller explanations of the methodology of the timed fieldwork and line transect survey are provided in the Introductory Chapters and the Appendices.

# Explanation of map pages

The **Distribution Map** (1) shows the geographical spread of the species using a circle to indicate its presence in a given area. The unit of area is the **tetrad**, a square of size 2km × 2km based upon the Ordnance Survey National Grid. A circle shows the presence of the species in that tetrad, and the circle size indicates its breeding status, as found by fieldwork in the years 1997–2001.

Three sizes of circle are used to indicate the highest categories of proof of breeding detected: 'possible'; 'probable'; and 'confirmed'. (See pages 25/26 for criteria.)

The **Abundance Map** (2) uses three sizes of circles to give a visual indication of the abundance of the species in each tetrad, ranked in three bands. The key on the map gives the numbers of individual birds detected during a timed visit to that tetrad. The smallest symbol is used for the lowest 50% of all tetrad counts for the species, the middle symbol is used for the middle 30% of counts, and the largest symbol shows the top 20% of counts. (The method of deriving the limits of these count bands is given on page 33.)

**NB:** In order to ensure comparability, the abundance map is based purely upon counts made during timed visits to tetrads, whereas the distribution map shows presence recorded not only during timed visits but also during supplementary and casual visits. Thus there are **some tetrads which have a symbol indicating presence on the distribution map, but which have no equivalent symbol on the abundance map**.

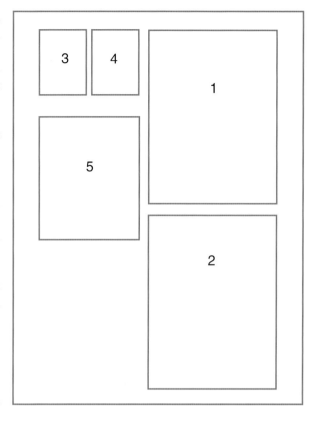

A few species were not found during any timed visits; these species therefore have **no** abundance map.

The **Small Maps** (3 and 4) allow comparisons to be made of a species' Cumbrian distribution over a 30-year time scale. They show at a 10km square level the county distribution based on (3) data presented in the *Atlas of Breeding Birds in Britain and Ireland* (1968–1972) and (4) the results of this atlas (1997–2001). The highest category of breeding (ie. 'possible', 'probable' or 'confirmed') recorded within each 10km square is plotted using three dots sizes as in the tetrad distribution map.

The **Conservation Status Box** (5) provides data on European and British status that places Cumbria in a wider context, and also suggests likely or potential county threats. Population figures for Europe, Britain and Cumbria are given. Key data from the statistical analysis of fieldwork are summarized for ease of reference.

See page 33 for further explanations.

**Birds of Conservation Concern criteria:** abbreviations used in the Conservation Status Box

| RED listing: | IUCN | Globally threatened |
|---|---|---|
| | HD | Historical population decline during 1800–1995 |
| | BDp | Rapid (50% or greater) decline in UK breeding population over previous 25 years |
| | BDr | Rapid (50% or greater) contraction of UK breeding range over 25 years |
| AMBER listing: | HDd | Historical population decline during 1800–1995, but population size has more than doubled over previous 25 years |
| | BDMp | Moderate (25–49%) decline in UK breeding population over previous 25 years |
| | BDMr | Moderate (25–49%) contraction of UK breeding range over 25 years |
| | WDMp | Moderate (25–49%) decline in UK non-breeding population over previous 25 years |
| | SPECs 2; 3 | Species with unfavourable conservation status, concentrated in Europe (2) or not (3). (W=wintering population only) |
| | BR | 5-year mean of 1–300 breeding pairs |
| | BL | 50% or more of UK breeding population in ten or fewer sites, but not BR |
| | WL | 50% or more of UK non-breeding population in ten or fewer sites |
| | BI | 20% of European breeding population in UK |
| | WI | 20% or more of NW European (wildfowl), East Atlantic Flyway (waders) or European (others) non-breeding populations in UK |
| | IUCN | Globally Threatened species assessment (Birdlife International 2000): A=Vulnerable |

# Little Grebe *Tachybaptus ruficollis*

THE Little Grebe is the smallest Palearctic grebe, its breeding dress tasteful and understated compared with its more garish cousins, and likely to draw attention to itself by its distinctive trill rather than any extravagance of its plumage. Its distribution stretches over much of the Old World, most of Africa outside the desert regions, and across Eurasia as far east as Japan and parts of Indonesia.

Widespread throughout lowland Britain and Ireland, the Little Grebe breeds in a wide range of aquatic habitats, including large lakes, small ponds, slow-moving rivers and canals, though favouring shallow waters, often less than a metre in depth, with emergent vegetation or overhanging branches in which to anchor its floating nest of decaying vegetation. Its secretive nature and preference for dense aquatic cover probably provide the reason for its loud, whinnying call. A diet of fish smaller than those required by the Great Crested Grebe, and a shorter take-off run, allow it to occupy shallower and smaller waters than its larger relative, accounting for its greater range of habitats and wider distribution. However, a more secretive nature, with birds spending much of their time concealed in emergent vegetation, leads to a lower proportion of confirmed breeding records.

The British population shows some evidence of an increase, linked to climate amelioration, since the end of the 19th century, and though the species is susceptible to hard winters, with numbers greatly affected by the severity of the winter of 1962/63, it had been thought that there had been little recent change. However, analysis of WBS data for the period 1973–98 revealed a decline of 51% and, whilst this survey is restricted to rivers and canals, thus failing to represent much Little Grebe habitat, the trend is obviously worrying and worthy of further investigation.

Little Grebes, though often shy and skulking when breeding, may be double or even triple-brooded and, whilst easily overlooked when silent, at some sites they can nest in densities of up to five breeding pairs per hectare and could be considered to be almost colonial.

In Cumbria, Macpherson (1892) commented that "they used to nest almost gregariously at Moorthwaite", and five pairs have regularly bred at Mere Tarn in recent years.

During the 19th century the Little Grebe was considered scarce as a breeding bird in the county (Macpherson 1892). However an increase, in line with national trends, was apparent in the early 20th century and by the 1960s it was regarded as "widespread and frequent, breeding on tarns, ponds and some lakes and sluggish streams up to 1,000 feet [305m asl]" (Stokoe 1962).

Despite its less restricted choice of habitat, the distribution map for *this Atlas* closely mirrors that of the Great Crested Grebe and reveals a surprisingly thinly scattered population. Although the number of occupied 10km squares shows a modest increase from 39 to 41 since the *Old Atlas,* much of the north and east of the county is sparsely populated. Birds are also absent from many larger waters, including Coniston Water, Ullswater, Ennerdale Water, Buttermere, Crummock Water and Killington Reservoir. Great Crested Grebes breed annually at some of these sites but they do not support Little Grebes, presumably due to a lack of emergent vegetation around the shoreline. Its preference for lowland waters is confirmed by the lack of records above the 300m contour, though birds breed regularly at Sunbiggin Tarn, set in moorland at around 260m asl, and which few people would regard as a lowland site.

The bulk of Cumbrian birds are concentrated on the Coastal Plain, especially Furness, and southern areas of Lakeland. The current county population estimate of 100–120 breeding pairs has been derived from count data collected during the course of *this Atlas,* supported by information available in County Bird Reports and local knowledge.

Fluctuating water levels are one of the main causes of nesting failure, with nests being either flooded or left high and dry, and predation by the apparently ever-increasing Mink population is another danger to be faced. Disturbance due to man's recreational activities

 Sponsored by Mrs Pat Curtis

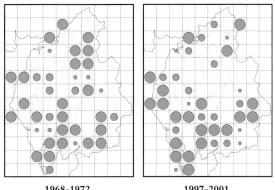

**1968-1972**  **1997-2001**

(For explanation of maps, see page 45)

**Conservation status**

European:                    Non-SPEC
UK:                          **GREEN**

**Populations**

European status:             80,000
Britain – pairs:             7,500
Cumbria – pairs:             100–120

**30-year distribution change**

|  | Old Atlas | This Atlas | % |
|---|---|---|---|
| No. of 10km squares: | 39 | 41 | **+5.1** |

| Survey data | Tetrads | % |
|---|---|---|
| Confirmed breeding: | 42 | 2.3 |
| Probable breeding: | 26 | 1.4 |
| Possible breeding: | 20 | 1.0 |
| Total: | 88 | 4.7 |

poses further risks; nests are easily swamped by the wash from a passing boat. Current climatic predictions suggest little likelihood of severe winters in the foreseeable future so these at least should pose no threat to the continued well-being of the county's Little Grebes; indeed, there would seem to be ample scope for an increase in the population, through both colonization of more waters and greater densities at existing sites. The presence of two broods in 2001 on a pond at Ayside, that had been created just a few months earlier, amply illustrates the potential for further expansion in the county presented by habitat creation.

Ian Kinley

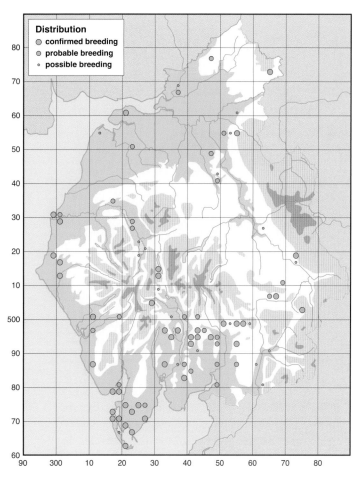

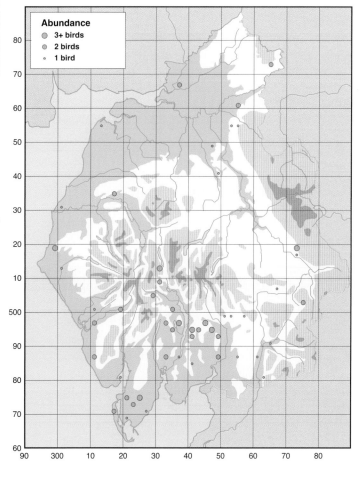

# Great Crested Grebe *Podiceps cristatus*

THE extravagant breeding plumes and bizarre courtship rituals of the Great Crested Grebe provide one of the most enchanting spectacles in nature. This elegant waterbird can be found breeding across temperate Eurasia as far as China, with other races in a few discrete populations in Africa and southeast Australia.

In Britain and Ireland, the Great Crested Grebe shows a clear preference for lowland areas, and its regional absence reflects a lack of suitably sized waterbodies. Favoured breeding habitat comprises relatively shallow standing freshwater, of at least one hectare to accommodate their long take-off runs, with ample emergent vegetation to conceal and anchor a nest. Small ponds are usually avoided. They can be remarkably tolerant of human activity, quickly colonizing newly-created sites.

The Great Crested Grebe suffered a major decline from 1851, when birds were shot on a large scale to supply the demands of the then fashionable millinery trade, and by 1860 the English population had collapsed to a mere 42 pairs. The turnround in its fortunes was entirely due to a small band of ladies who formed a movement known as 'The Fur, Fin and Feather Society', later to become the RSPB, which campaigned to abolish the slaughter of birds for their plumes. Their success led to new legislation prohibiting the killing of certain birds, including the Great Crested Grebe. The population soon began to increase and, aided by the creation of new habitats, its numbers responded accordingly: by 1931 there were an estimated 1,150 breeding pairs in England and Wales. National censuses, in 1965 and 1975, showed a

sustained increase and this was most marked in counties where new reservoirs had been constructed and mineral extraction had created new waterbodies.

In Cumbria, Macpherson (1892) knew the Great Crested Grebe only as an occasional winter visitor and the birds first bred in Lancashire North of the Sands in 1908, Westmorland in 1933 and Cumberland in 1934 (Stokoe 1962). However, numbers remained small and the censuses in 1965 and 1975 estimated a population of just 15 and 48 birds respectively (Hughes *et al* 1979).

The distribution map for *this Atlas* should present an accurate picture, given that the birds prefer fairly large areas of open water and are easy to spot, and reveals that the number of occupied 10km squares has almost doubled from 16 to 31 since the *Old Atlas,* the increase being most apparent in Lakeland. However, the species is still absent from the Coastal Plain to the north of Hodbarrow; the Solway Basin away from Longtown; the Eden Valley and the Cumbria Dales. In some areas, this absence can be explained by a preference for lowland waterbodies below 300m asl and a lack of suitable habitat, though this does not account for the failure to colonize sites such as Siddick Pond.

Nests are often conspicuous and young grebes can readily be observed, swimming or hitching a ride on the backs of their parents; hence the high proportion of confirmed breeding records. However, non-breeders are notoriously mobile, moving from one waterbody to another, and misinterpretation of birds' breeding status in spring could lead to an inflated estimate of the breeding population. The current county population of 90–110 breeding pairs is based on abundance data collected during *this Atlas* and knowledge of its Cumbrian status from available information in County Bird Reports.

In spite of the high level of leisure activities that take place, Great Crested Grebes now nest virtually colonially at Hodbarrow, identified by the results of *this Atlas* as the county's most important breeding site for this species. A rise in the population of small fish in the lagoon is believed to be the reason for a spectacular increase in the number of pairs from just two in 1994 to 16 in 2000 (S.C. Peter pers comm). Although increases have occurred at other sites, nowhere else has it been so dramatic. Bassenthwaite Lake, with up to eight pairs, is another site highlighted by *this Atlas* as a favoured Great Crested Grebe haunt.

Grebe physiology is ill-designed for walking, hence the necessity to build a nest on a floating platform stabilized by partly submerged branches or emergent vegetation. This type of construction is susceptible to changes in water levels, often the cause of failure; either because nests are flooded or left high and dry. Predation is another hazard, particularly from the habitual egg-thieving traits of Coots. However, these natural dangers pale into insignificance in comparison

Sponsored by Derek McAlone

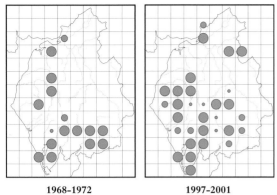

**1968-1972**          **1997-2001**

(For explanation of maps, see page 45)

*Conservation status*

European:                    Non-SPEC

UK:                          **GREEN**

*Populations*

European status:             290,000

Britain – adults:              8,000

Cumbria – pairs:              90–110

*30-year distribution change*

|  | Old Atlas | This Atlas | % |
|---|---|---|---|
| No. of 10km squares: | 16 | 31 | **+93.7** |

| **Survey data** | **Tetrads** | **%** |
|---|---|---|
| Confirmed breeding: | 36 | 2.0 |
| Probable breeding: | 17 | 0.9 |
| Possible breeding: | 25 | 1.4 |
| Total: | 78 | 4.3 |

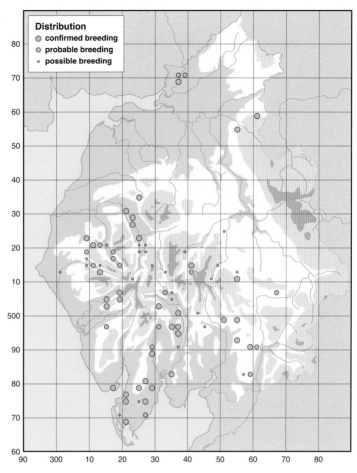

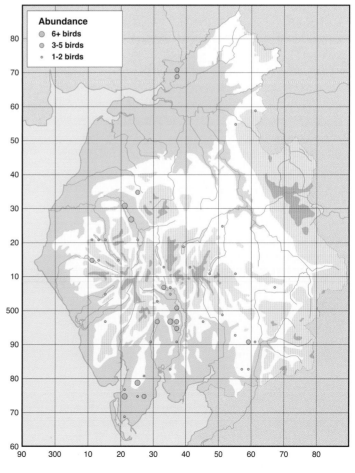

with man's ability to cause high-level and wide-scale disturbance to waterbodies through leisure activities that are bound to increase with future demands.

Though there remains scope for further increase in the Cumbrian population, through both colonization of as yet unoccupied waters and increased densities at some existing sites, it is the species' ability to cope with man-made pressures that will perhaps determine whether the entrancing courtship rituals of these delightful birds will be enjoyed more widely in the future.

Ian Kinley

# Black-necked Grebe  *Podiceps nigricollis*

**A**LTHOUGH strikingly handsome, the Black-necked Grebe can be surprisingly elusive, able to disappear into cover in a trice. In common with other grebes, it performs elaborate courtship displays in which the golden, 'fan-like' ear coverts and black neck, which gives the bird its name, are shown off in all their splendour. It also shares the captivating habit of carrying the recently hatched young on its back.

This is a widespread species with a northern hemisphere range that extends eastwards from Britain and Ireland through Europe and Asia to southeast China and into North America. Smaller populations also occur in South America and Africa. The Black-necked Grebe was unknown as a breeding bird in Britain and Ireland until the beginning of the 20th century, when nesting was first confirmed on Anglesey in 1904. This colonization reached Ireland in 1915, England in 1918 and Scotland by 1930, and was linked to massive invasions westwards, during a period of desiccation of the steppe lakes in the Caspian region of the former USSR. Although a colony – numbering over 250 pairs at its peak – existed at Lough Funshinagh in Ireland until 1959, today the bird has reverted to its former status as a scarce breeder, with the nucleus of the population restricted to a few select and mainly confidential sites in England and Scotland.

A gregarious species, nesting colonially at favoured sites, it is often to be found associating with Black-headed Gull colonies, which presumably provide an aerial 'umbrella' and protection from predators. Black-necked Grebes have a preference for shallow, undisturbed eutrophic lakes with an abundance of emergent and submerged vegetation, extensive reed fringes and little open water. The nest is a floating platform of waterweed anchored to aquatic vegetation, usually in the cover of a reed or sedge bed. A diet of insects and larvae is supplemented with molluscs, crustaceans, amphibians and small fish. In common with other grebes, it feeds feathers to its young, apparently as an aid to digestion.

First documented in Cumbria as a winter visitor during the late 19th century, in line with national trends there was an increase in sightings during the early 20th century. Birds in breeding plumage at Southwaite in May 1922 and on a moorland tarn during May 1931 culminated in the first and only proven breeding record to date, when a pair tended at least one chick on a moorland tarn in Westmorland during 1935 (Blezard *et al* 1943). Unfortunately, this early promise was not sustained and birds did not appear in suitable habitat again until 1968–75. During this period, birds were seen annually at Sunbiggin Tarn, with breeding indicated during the *Old Atlas*. However, Hutcheson (1986) asserts that, although breeding was strongly suspected in 1968, it was never confirmed. Subsequent to these sightings, the species continued to remain scarce, especially during the breeding season, although spring birds appeared briefly in suitable habitat at Sunbiggin Tarn again in May 1989 and at Urswick Tarn in May 1995.

During *this Atlas,* perhaps surprisingly, there were at least five records of birds sporting summer dress. A pair appeared on Talkin Tarn for a day in May 1998 and singles appeared at Hodbarrow in April 1998, Cavendish Dock in April 2000, and Walney Island in May 2000, though none lingered. More interestingly, a pair visited Killington Reservoir for a day in May 1997 and, later that month, what may well have been the same pair spent at least three weeks in suitable habitat at Tarn House Tarn. Although supplementary records indicate perhaps at least one breeding attempt took place, this unfortunately could not be confirmed.

Although habitat change, through drainage, or by natural vegetation succession, has resulted in the loss of some established sites, it is unclear what other factors are limiting the spread of the Black-necked Grebe in Britain and Ireland. However, predation by Pike, disturbance from boats and other water sports, and foreshore access have all been implicated in breeding failures at otherwise suitable sites.

The existence and viability of Black-necked Grebe populations in Britain and Ireland has always been precarious. Prior to 1970, it is unlikely that more than 10 pairs bred annually in Britain. However, since then, there appears to have been a steady rise in the population. During 1999, there were 24–32 breeding pairs in northern England (Ogilvie *et al* 2001), so that,

 Sponsored by a CBC Member

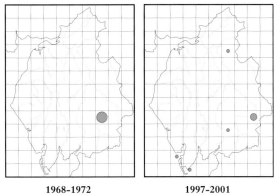

**1968–1972**        **1997–2001**

(For explanation of maps, see page 45)

*Conservation status*

| | |
|---|---|
| European: | Non-SPEC |
| UK: | **AMBER: BR** |

*Populations*

| | |
|---|---|
| European status: | 33,000 |
| Britain – pairs: | 55 |
| Cumbria – pairs: | 0–1 |

*30-year distribution change*

| | Old Atlas | This Atlas | % |
|---|---|---|---|
| No. of 10km squares: | 1 | 5 | **+400** |

| **Survey data** | **Tetrads** | **%** |
|---|---|---|
| Confirmed breeding: | 0 | |
| Probable breeding: | 1 | 0.05 |
| Possible breeding: | 5 | 0.27 |
| Total: | 6 | 0.32 |

although suitable nesting sites in Cumbria are at a premium, it is not inconceivable, given the recent increase in spring sightings, that there will be further breeding attempts in the county.

Colin Raven

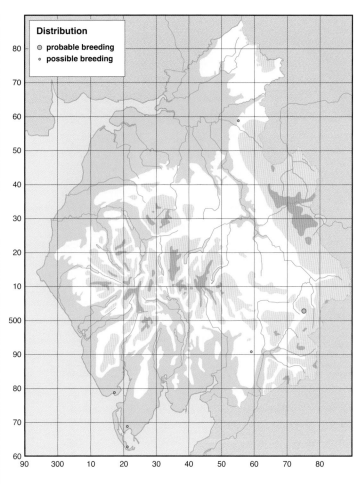

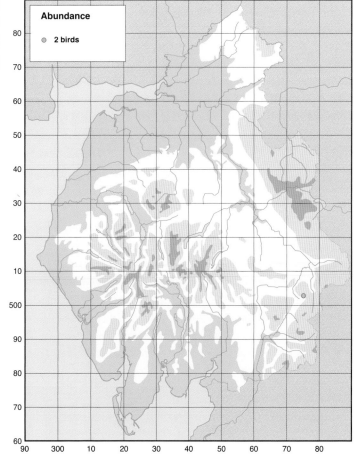

# Fulmar *Fulmarus glacialis*

IN the transparent ease with which it manoeuvres in the deepest trough of a raging sea, or in the effortless elegance displayed as it soars along a cliff-top, the Fulmar is the embodiment of ocean flight perfected. In contrast, during the breeding season the bird gives a clownish display, vociferously cackling harsh warning cries at any neighbour or intruder which ventures too close.

Over the last two centuries the Fulmar's North Atlantic range has experienced a remarkable expansion, originating in Iceland, and now reaching as far south as northwest France. It has been thought that this expansion is related to man's increased exploitation of ocean harvests, linked with innovative seabird protection laws. A more abstruse theory to explain this phenomenon postulates the appearance of a new genotype within the Icelandic population favouring range expansion (Cramp & Simmons 1977).

Until 1878, St Kilda, off northwest Scotland, was the only known colony in Britain and Ireland but following a rapid growth in population, especially over the last century, Fulmars can now be found all around the coasts wherever there are suitable cliffs. The actual nest sites are abandoned for only a few months of the year – from when the last young of the season fledge in late August or even September, to the reappearance of the adults in December to claim the better breeding ledges prior to the start of a new season of activity. Although Fulmars are now widespread, the bulk of the British and Irish population still breeds in northern Scotland.

Originally, the Fulmar's diet would have consisted mostly of planktonic crustaceans before the development of an association with fish-offal, discarded by modern factory ships processing catches at sea. Their diet and feeding behaviour does, however, vary across their North Atlantic range. Away from the rich fishing grounds plankton, squid and jellyfish are taken while surface-feeding at night. In coastal waters around Britain and Ireland, they tend to feed by day on small fish and sand-eels, and often scavenge by following fishing vessels (Furness *et al* 1984).

Macpherson (1892) deliberated why a "well-known bird in the North Atlantic did not stray at frequent intervals to the northwest coast of England." At that time very few specimens were known and those that were had been washed up along the coast in winter. Whatever the reason, its increase has certainly been very spectacular.

In Cumbria, the Fulmar has its stronghold on the red sandstone cliffs at St Bees Head, where nesting was first noted in 1940 (Stokoe 1962). A steady population expansion was evident during the second half of the 20th century with 152 nests counted in 1956, increasing to 200 by 1975. For some unknown reason this increase was not sustained. At first Fulmars chose isolated well-vegetated ledges, away from those already occupied by Herring Gulls, Kittiwakes and Guillemots. However, an increase in the numbers of breeding birds has led to greater competition for the limited nesting sites, forcing the Fulmar to nest in amongst other species (Stokoe 1962, Hutcheson 1986). Contrary to the national trend, a population decline appears to have occurred at this site with only 112 nests in 1986. Subsequently, numbers have continued to fall further, albeit with a degree of annual variation, with the population fluctuating between 26 and 65 breeding pairs. Against this background a new colony of 12 pairs has become established on cliffs between Whitehaven and Parton since 1990 (Hewitson 1998) and numbers have gradually increased to reach 15–17 breeding pairs during *this Atlas* period.

Fieldwork during *this Atlas* found no evidence of any other breeding colonies besides the known sites at St Bees Head and nearby Parton. The current county population estimate of 40–85 breeding pairs is taken from counts of these two colonies alone.

Out of the breeding season and away from the nesting colonies Fulmars are essentially marine birds with a well-dispersed distribution throughout the North Atlantic (Rankin & Duffey 1948). Fortunately, no prominent conservation issues have been identified to indicate a major cause for concern; the nomadic wanderings of Fulmars make them one of the least threatened seabirds. Any ocean bird, however, would be at risk from a serious marine pollution incident, especially one involving oil spills.

Norman Holton

     Sponsored by Jim Hewitson

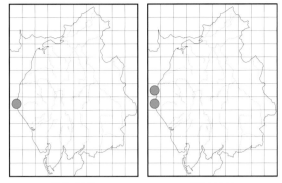

**1968-1972**          **1997-2001**
(For explanation of maps, see page 45)

***Conservation status***

| | |
|---|---|
| European: | Non-SPEC |
| UK: | **AMBER: BL** |

***Populations***

| | |
|---|---|
| European status: | 2,800,000 |
| Britain – pairs: | 539,000 |
| Cumbria – pairs: | 40–85 |

***30-year distribution change***

| | Old Atlas | This Atlas | % |
|---|---|---|---|
| No. of 10km squares: | 1 | 2 | **+100** |

| **Survey data** | **Tetrads** | **%** |
|---|---|---|
| Confirmed breeding: | 4 | 0.2 |
| Probable breeding: | 0 | |
| Possible breeding: | 0 | |
| Total: | 4 | 0.2 |

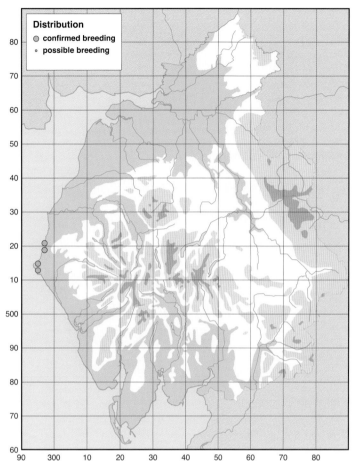

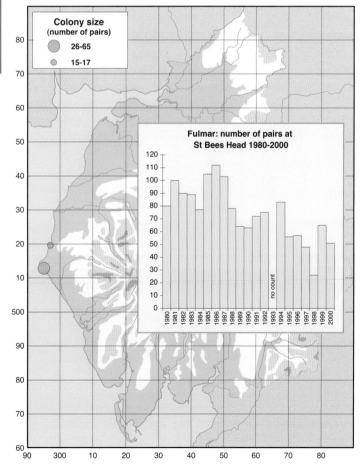

THIS large, black, conspicuous bird, almost reptilian in appearance, can often be seen perched singly or in small groups, in heraldic pose, on the skeletal branches of waterside trees, whose whitewashed limbs betray its presence. In common with other fish-eating birds, the Cormorant often excites controversy, though science can dispel erroneous hearsay.

The Cormorant is one of the most widespread species in the world, inhabiting the coastal regions of the North Atlantic, central and southern Europe, Asia east to Japan, and south to southern and eastern Africa and Australasia. Two races occur within Europe: the mainly coastal, cliff-nesting subspecies which breeds in Britain and Ireland and along Norwegian and northern French coasts, and the tree-nesting continental race which breeds mainly from the Netherlands and Denmark in the west to the Baltic and Black Sea areas in the east. British and Irish Cormorants are partly resident, but after breeding many disperse inland and southwards along the coast. Continental birds are largely migratory.

The last 30 years have seen a moderate increase in the British and Irish Cormorant population to about 11,700 breeding pairs. Most of the increase in Britain has been in southeast England where there has been a marked and rapid increase of tree-nesting birds (about 28% per annum), a proportion of which are thought to be of continental origin.

In Cumbria, historically, there was some disagreement as to whether Cormorants bred at St Bees Head. Mitchell (1885) believed they did, but this was refuted by Macpherson (1892) who stated that they used the cliffs purely as a roosting site. Birds were certainly present during the summer between the two World Wars, but breeding was not proven. Stokoe (1962) alluded to a few nesting pairs and in the early 1970s six pairs were noted in the breeding season, but no young were recorded. In 1992, two pairs raised two young and subsequently the numbers have gradually increased to 16 nests in 1997 and 31 breeding pairs in 2000.

At Haweswater, the situation is somewhat clearer. A pair attempted to nest in 1952 in a Scots pine, but the nest was destroyed by anglers. It took another 40 years before a pair successfully raised three young and a second pair built a nest in 1992. The following year 12 pairs raised 22 young and the increase continued until 1998 when there were 50 tree-nesting pairs. A small percentage, around 5–10%, are considered to have continental origins. The rapid increase in breeding birds at this site raised concerns over the Schelly, a rare fish found in these waters, and led to emergency conservation action being taken in 1998. Measures taken included temporary discouragement of nesting birds, and development of a long-term action plan.

The main Cumbrian breeding site is a derelict wooden structure, previously used as a bombing target by the RAF, in Moricambe Bay. Nesting was first confirmed in 1982, although birds were believed to have been present since the late 1960s, and the locality now holds 50–60 breeding pairs. Productivity at and dispersal from this site have been monitored annually since 1984. Results identify post-fledging survival rates as being particularly poor; mortality of juveniles within a few months can be as high as 75%. Those that do survive tend to disperse south or southeast, with recoveries from southern England, France, Portugal and Spain (pers obs). The study also shows that adults are site-faithful and there is no evidence of any interaction between this colony and neighbouring colonies across the Solway in Dumfries and Galloway.

Elsewhere in Cumbria, there has been an increased incidence in recent years of summering by non-breeding or immature birds at a number of inland sites. This presaged the colonization of one such site, Killington Reservoir, where a single pair bred successfully in 2000 and 2001. Other inland colonies may well be established in the near future, provided that any breeding attempts are allowed to proceed unhindered.

Fieldwork for *this Atlas* revealed the presence of just four breeding colonies, all of relatively recent origin, and these hold the current county population of 120–150 breeding pairs.

Cormorants become controversial birds when choosing inland sites to breed, through the perceived damage that they may cause to fish stocks; however, they remain protected under the Wildlife and Countryside Act 1981. In Cumbria, breeding numbers

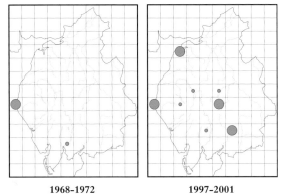

**1968-1972**          **1997-2001**

(For explanation of maps, see page 45)

---

*Conservation status*

| | |
|---|---|
| European: | Non-SPEC |
| UK: | **AMBER: BL & WI** |

*Populations*

| | |
|---|---|
| European status: | 142,000 |
| Britain – pairs: | 7,000 |
| Cumbria – pairs: | 120–150 |

*30-year distribution change*

| | Old Atlas | This Atlas | % |
|---|---|---|---|
| No. of 10km squares: | 2 | 8 | **+300** |

| Survey data | Tetrads | % |
|---|---|---|
| Confirmed breeding: | 4 | 0.2 |
| Probable breeding: | 0 | |
| Possible breeding: | 13 | 0.7 |
| Total: | 17 | 0.9 |

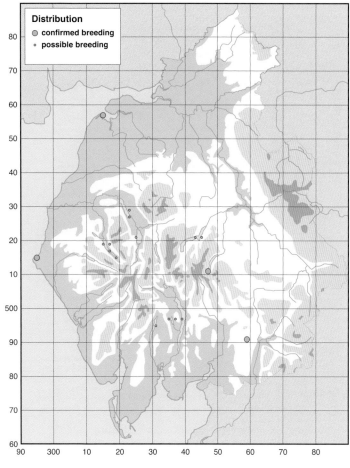

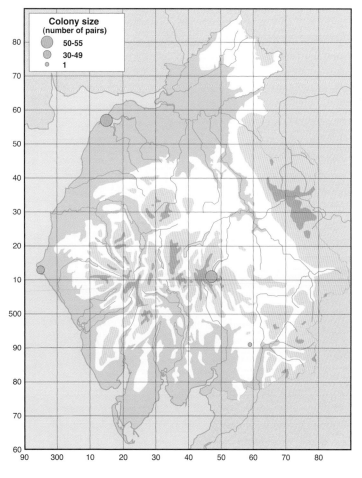

at the main freshwater site are controlled under special licence. Elsewhere in the county, conflict is often claimed but rarely substantiated. The future of the Cormorant in Cumbria will depend on its legal protection being both continued and enforced. Given the level of protection it deserves, there is no reason why both the number of occupied sites and breeding pairs should not increase.

Mike Carrier

# Grey Heron *Ardea cinerea*

THE tall figure of a Grey Heron, standing motionless for what seems an eternity in the shallows of a Cumbrian tarn before striking with lightning speed, is a timeless spectacle, hopefully to be enjoyed by many generations to come.

The range of the Grey Heron extends across much of Eurasia, east to India, and into Africa. In Britain and Ireland it occurs almost everywhere, being absent only from the most mountainous of regions. Distribution is closely linked to the availability of suitable waters for feeding and trees for nesting, although a few heronries in Britain and Ireland are to be found in reedbeds or on cliffs. Herons in Cumbria occupy traditional tree sites, with Scots pine, larch, beech and oak the most favoured species.

The first national census of the Grey Heron took place in 1928, making it the subject of the longest-running annual census anywhere in the world. Since the low point following the severe winter of 1962/63, the trend nationally has been upward and the numbers currently nesting in England and Wales are around 50% greater than in 1928. The overall pattern has been one of gradual increase, interrupted by sharp decreases and a few years of recovery after an especially icy winter, the most recent of which was in 1984/85. In recent years, the high numbers reflect the mildness of the winters and the population climbed to unprecedented levels in the 1990s, with the result that Grey Herons are now commoner than ever before in recorded history. A study of Grey Heron mortality suggests that the position would have been far less rosy had legal protection not been introduced in 1954 (Mead *et al* 1979): food for thought for those vested

interests, which, even now, call for numbers to be controlled.

Considered a "well-established resident" at the end of the 19th century with large colonies at Muncaster, Eamont, The Riddings, Greystoke, Wythop Woods and Edenhall (Macpherson & Duckworth 1886), some heronries in Cumbria have been established for centuries. In 1621 young birds from Muncaster were sent alive to the kitchens at Naworth, to be served up at the table of Lord William Howard, and the naturalist Thomas Bewick recorded the dispute over nesting territory between Herons and Rooks at Dallam Towers (Macpherson 1892). Though several heronries mentioned by Macpherson are long since defunct, Dallam is now the largest in the county and numbers have increased steadily over the years, albeit with some fluctuations, peaking at 67 nests, nearly all in beech trees, in 1992 (E. Kitchin pers comm).

The species' susceptibility to hard winters is revealed in the results of two national censuses, which produced totals for Cumberland and Westmorland of 16 heronries and 105 nests in 1954 and, following two severe winters, nine heronries and 73 nests in 1964. It took seven years for the population to fully recover nationally. Since the inception of the BTO's Heronries Census, over 100 heronries have been identified in Cumbria; however this undoubtedly involves some duplication. More recently, monitoring has revealed a relatively stable picture; although some smaller sites are deserted after a year or two, others expand and new sites become established.

Despite the steady increase in the national population, the distribution maps reveal a reduction in the number of 10km squares containing heronries from 33 in the *Old Atlas* to 25 during *this Atlas*. The decline is most noticeable in the Solway Basin, Eden Valley and Coastal Plain to the north of the Duddon Estuary and some areas of Lakeland. There has been some loss of nesting sites and illegal persecution is known to have occurred in some areas but, as neither the total number of heronries nor nests has declined, at least since the late 1980s, this reduction in range may simply be a case of birds moving to other sites within the county. Not unexpectedly, the current distribution is closely allied to bodies of water and there are obvious groupings of dots reflecting the river systems of the Kent, Lune, Duddon and Derwent as well as some of the lakes. Isolated pairs, or small groups of two or three nests, can be surprisingly easy to overlook, especially if built in conifers, so some small dots on the distribution map may represent undetected heronries, though most are likely to refer to non-breeders or feeding birds from nearby colonies.

Count data revealed 37 occupied heronries; of these, 80% held less than 10 nests, and just two, at Causeway End and Dallam Towers, both in the south of the

Sponsored by Joan Rustrick

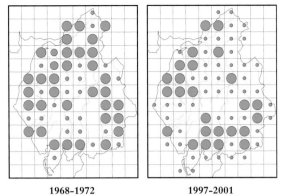

**1968-1972**        **1997-2001**

(For explanation of maps, see page 45)

*Conservation status*
European:                    Non-SPEC
UK:                          GREEN

*Populations*
European status:             122,000
Britain – nests:             10,000
Cumbria – pairs:             270–300

*30-year distribution change*
                    Old Atlas  This Atlas  %
No. of 10km squares:    57        73      +28

**Survey data**           **Tetrads**    **%**
Confirmed breeding:          37         2.0
Probable breeding:            0
Possible breeding:          322        17.5
Total:                      359        19.5

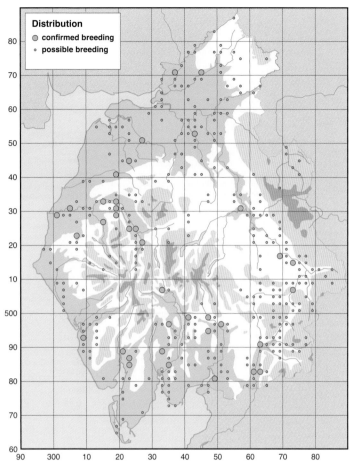

county, hosted more than 20 nests at any time during the survey period. Colonial count data from *this Atlas* suggests a current county population of 270–300 breeding pairs.

Several heronries, including such well-known and long-established ones as Causeway End, are at risk from deterioration in the state of the nesting trees and, in the absence of severe winters (predicted as a remote possibility in the foreseeable future) or pollution of watercourses, this loss of nesting sites, coupled with illegal persecution, presents the only tangible threat to the county's Grey Herons. In reality, however, their future seems secure.

Ian Kinley

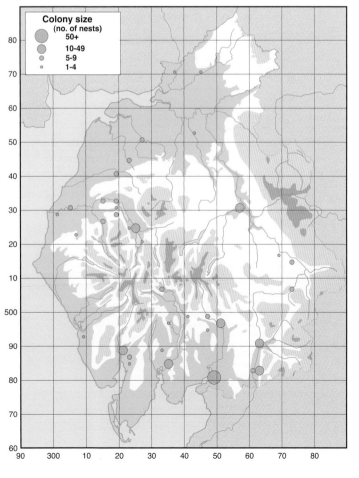

# Mute Swan *Cygnus olor*

THE belligerent approach of a male Mute Swan, surging through the water, wings arched and hissing malevolently in defence of its nesting territory, is a familiar sight, even to many non-naturalists. Mute Swans are distributed throughout western and central Europe, and have been introduced as far afield as North America, South Africa and Australia. In Britain and Ireland, this is a widespread but predominantly lowland species. Avoiding uniformly deep, unvegetated, steep-sided or oligotrophic waters, almost any other stretch of still or slow-moving water is likely to be occupied by these conspicuous birds.

Although commonly regarded as an introduction, the Mute Swan is, in fact, an indigenous species. Historically, the bird was highly prized by hunters and was perhaps only saved from extinction by its being bred in a semi-domesticated state to provide food for the medieval table prior to the 12th century. From the 13th to the 18th century, all Mute Swans were the property of the Crown and a complex system of licensing provided effective conservation of the species. After the gradual decline in 'swan-keeping' during the 18th century, the Mute Swan largely reverted to the wild state, though many remain tame urban birds. Present-day Cumbrian Mute Swans run the gamut from the bread-guzzling hordes jostling the tourists at Bowness Bay to the lone pair nesting in splendid isolation at Sunbiggin Tarn.

Estimates of the British population over the years have included 19,900–21,600 birds in 1955–56, 17,600 in 1978 and 18,750 in 1983 (Ogilvie 1986). Hard winters in the early 1960s were blamed for the decline between 1955 and 1965. Whilst during the 1970s and into the 1980s populations overall remained relatively stable, or even increased in areas where more waterbodies such as gravel pits were created, numbers declined drastically on certain rivers in England, including the Thames. The main factor was found to be lead poisoning caused by the ingestion of fishing weights, resulting in both direct mortality and reduced breeding success. The introduction of suitable alternatives and the banning of lead for fishing weights

in 1987 sharply reduced the incidence of poisoning and numbers began to recover.

Macpherson (1892) could not ascertain exactly when Mute Swans were first placed on private waters in Cumbria, other than to be sure it was not later than the 17th century. He goes on to refer to a few swans being kept on Esthwaite Water in 1787, comments on the advance in domestication of these birds in the first half of the 18th century and thought that a swan shot on Bassenthwaite, "converted into soup, and distributed to the poor of Keswick," was probably a stray Mute Swan.

In Cumberland and Westmorland, incomplete coverage in the course of BTO national censuses revealed 33 breeding pairs in 1955 and 27 breeding pairs in 1978, while there were 28 breeding pairs in Westmorland and Furness in 1983 (Ogilvie 1986). More complete coverage in 1990 produced a county total of 78 breeding pairs, 53 of which were in Westmorland and Furness. The bulk of the breeding population at that time was concentrated in the south and west of the county, particularly in Furness and around Windermere (Kinley 1991).

With its large size, striking white plumage and choice of habitat, this is surely one of the easiest species to census. The aggressive nature of breeding males and large, conspicuous nests give rise to a high percentage of confirmed breeding records. However, in all past surveys, large numbers of non-breeding birds, exceeding the breeding population, were recorded; the majority of the small dots on the distribution map for *this Atlas* are likely to represent such birds.

Generally, waters must be large enough to accommodate the birds ponderous, pattering take-off runs – though a pond at Silecroft, used during *this Atlas*, was barely 25m in diameter; presumably the birds took off from the bank. However, the most unusual nest site involved a pair that bred in the middle of the gullery on Rockcliffe Marsh in 2000. The preference for lowland waters is confirmed by the lack of records above the 300m contour, though neither Sunbiggin Tarn nor Killington Reservoir, both of which hosted breeding birds for the first time ever

 Sponsored by Grange Natural History Society

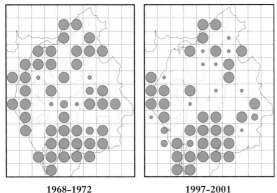

**1968-1972**     **1997-2001**

(For explanation of maps, see page 45)

**Conservation status**

| | |
|---|---|
| European: | Non-SPEC |
| UK: | **AMBER: BI** |

**Populations**

| | |
|---|---|
| European status: | 48,000 |
| Britain – adults: | 25,750 |
| Cumbria – pairs: | 100–120 |

**30-year distribution change**

| | Old Atlas | This Atlas | % |
|---|---|---|---|
| No. of 10km squares: | 49 | 49 | n/c |

| **Survey data** | **Tetrads** | **%** |
|---|---|---|
| Confirmed breeding: | 73 | 4.0 |
| Probable breeding: | 24 | 1.3 |
| Possible breeding: | 54 | 2.9 |
| Total: | 151 | 8.2 |

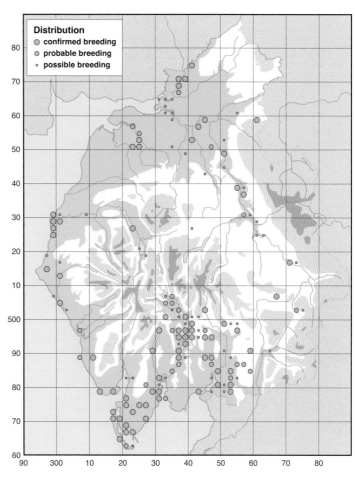

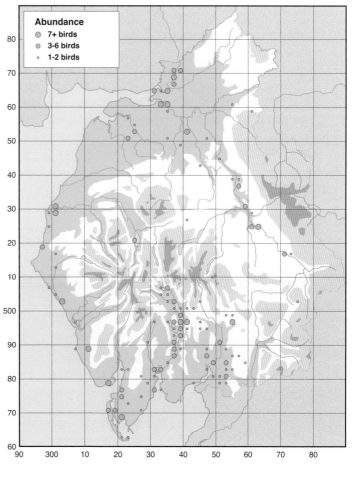

during *this Atlas,* would come under most people's description of a lowland site.

The foundation of the current county population estimate is from count data from *this Atlas,* corroborated by information from County Bird Reports. Perhaps surprisingly, in comparison to the *Old Atlas, this Atlas* shows that there has been a reduction from 42 to 34 in the number of 10km squares holding confirmed breeding pairs. Birds are now absent from previously occupied squares in the Solway Basin, the Eden Valley, some areas of the Coastal Plain and parts of Lakeland. Consequently, despite an increase in the current county population to 100–120 breeding pairs, its present distribution remains very similar to that revealed by the 1990 survey.

Despite this apparent reduction in range, there seems little threat to the continued well-being of the county's Mute Swans, and indeed there would seem to be scope for further increases.

Ian Kinley

# Greylag Goose *Anser anser*

**B**RITAIN and Ireland's only native breeding goose, the Greylag Goose is a gregarious species with a well-developed social life. Indeed, the old saying 'birds of a feather stick together' is as true of the Greylag as any other species. The readiness of Greylag Geese to react to strangers with aggression explains their value as property guards. Historically, the Greeks set cages of Greylags on city walls, as their chorus of cackling alerted many a sleeping population to furtive invaders.

The Greylag Goose breeds across Europe and Asia, from Britain and Ireland, Scandinavia and eastern Europe, across the former USSR into Mongolia and China. However, due to land-drainage, changes in farming practices and hunting, the distribution is now more disjointed than was formerly the case. A number of successful reintroduction programmes have taken place in northern Europe, including in Britain and Ireland, where feral populations are currently widely established in Scotland and England, although birds remain scarce in much of Wales and in Ireland.

Feral Greylag Geese occupy a large variety of freshwater sites including tarns, reservoirs, gravel pits and river systems. The preferred nest site is close to water on vegetated islands, but nests can also be found amongst vegetation around tarns, lakes and other waterside shores, and more recently on rocky, often inaccessible, slopes by rivers. The nest is on the ground and lined with heather, grass and moss. Nesting starts in April and during the four week incubation period the male patrols the surrounding area to fend off any would-be aggressors. Once hatched, the young goslings leave the nest almost immediately and are guarded by both parents. After a few weeks, broods often amalgamate, and at this time the adults moult and become flightless for several weeks.

Before the marshes and fens were drained for agriculture in the 17th to 19th centuries, wild Greylags bred in many parts of Britain and Ireland. However, by the early 20th century the species had retreated dramatically and was restricted to the north and west of Scotland. Here, they were subjected to persecution by crofters whose crops the birds damaged, and to excessive sport shooting on estates; by the Second World War the species was in danger of becoming extinct as a truly wild breeding bird in Scotland. However, prior to this, in the 1930s, small numbers of eggs and young were brought from South Uist to two estates in Wigtownshire – a scheme so successful that, in an effort to contain numbers, adults, eggs and young were donated to WAGBI from 1959 to found new colonies. By 1970, WAGBI had released 938 hand-reared Greylags at 33 sites in 13 English and Welsh counties. This reintroduction has proved so successful that the feral population now massively outnumbers the wild birds still breeding in Scotland and it is predicted that the gradual northwards spread of the re-established birds, coincidental with the recent increase and spread of wild birds south, will eventually lead to the two stocks interbreeding.

Cumbria was the first area to receive moulting adults and their young from Wigtownshire, with the first reintroductions made into Lakeland in 1959 and 1960. A WWT census found no Greylag Geese in Cumberland or Westmorland during 1960, such was the scarcity and localized nature of the birds at that time. Although three pairs nested in 1963, the first reintroduced birds to nest in the wild in England, and 11 pairs bred in 1965 (Harrison 1973), it took a while for a population to become established. However, the *Old Atlas* found birds in 19 10km squares, with the species widespread in Lakeland and Furness, and by 1974 with additional birds, brought as eggs from Scotland, hatched out and released at The Haws, Millom, the total population was estimated at 400 birds. By the time of the *New Atlas,* birds were found in 32 10km squares, Lakeland and Furness again holding the bulk of the population, and birds had spread into the Eden Valley. A WWT survey in 1991 produced 1194 summering birds in Cumbria with major strongholds at Derwent Water and Abbots Moss.

A comparison between *this Atlas* and the *Old Atlas* emphasizes the expansion northwards from the original release areas, with birds now present in 51 10km squares. Although still scarce on the Solway Basin and much of the Coastal Plain, there are major concentrations in the Eden Valley, Lakeland and Furness, and birds are only absent from the Border Uplands, North Pennines and Cumbria Dales. There is

Sponsored by Alcan Packaging Lawson Mardon

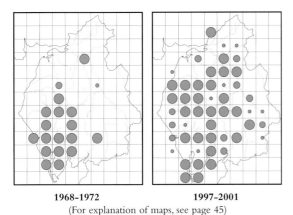

**1968-1972**          **1997-2001**

(For explanation of maps, see page 45)

***Conservation status***

| | |
|---|---|
| European: | Non-SPEC |
| UK: | **AMBER: BL, WL & WI** |

***Populations***

| | |
|---|---|
| European status: | 55,000 |
| Britain – adults: | 14,300 |
| Cumbria – pairs: | 500–600 |

***30-year distribution change***

| | Old Atlas | This Atlas | % |
|---|---|---|---|
| No. of 10km squares: | 19 | 51 | +168.4 |

| **Survey data** | **Tetrads** | **%** |
|---|---|---|
| Confirmed breeding: | 79 | 4.3 |
| Probable breeding: | 42 | 2.3 |
| Possible breeding: | 87 | 4.7 |
| Total: | 208 | 11.3 |

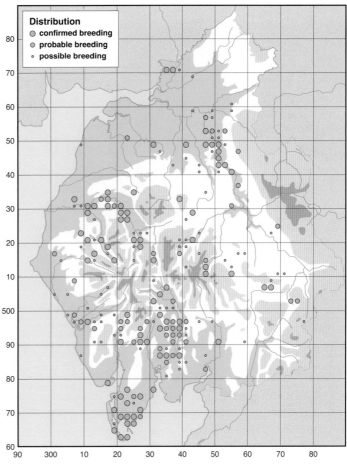

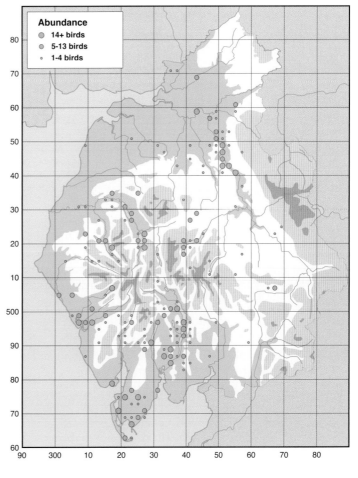

also evidence of further significant increases in the size of the feral population.

Allowing for non-breeding birds in the population a county estimate has been calculated from the BTO/WWT summer survey in 2000, which located 2,330 birds, a 95% increase since 1991. Site counts, including 596 on Windermere, 260 on Bassenthwaite, 259 on Derwent Water and 254 at Abbots Moss, suggest a current population of 500–600 breeding pairs.

Clearly the Greylag Goose is currently a very successful feral breeding bird in the county and it appears to co-exist quite happily with the Canada Goose. Modern farming practices often provide ideal habitat and good feeding areas and the species is likely to prosper for the foreseeable future. However, large flocks are unlikely to be welcomed on agricultural land and there will a constant call from some sectors for control.

Mike Carrier

# Canada Goose *Branta canadensis*

THIS bold, stately bird, with its loud, resonant flight call was first introduced into England and France during the mid-17th century to grace the private waterfowl collections of wealthy landowners. A native of North America, the species has colonized around 16 European countries and it is now one of the most widespread of introduced waterbirds. In Britain and Ireland, it occurs widely on lakes, rivers, reservoirs and gravel pits throughout much of England, becoming more localized within Scotland, Ireland and Wales. It favours waterbodies with secure nesting sites, such as islands, where the nest is usually sheltered by rank vegetation or low scrub.

Although the Canada Goose was breeding freely in scattered locations in England by the 1890s, it was not until 1938 that it was admitted to the British list. By the time of a BTO survey in 1953, the distribution of the species in Britain was still largely centred on the private lakes where it had been introduced in the 18th and 19th centuries. These groups were confined to isolated, localized sub-populations, with little movement between them and, therefore, only limited opportunities for colonization of new waters (Jones 1956). The position changed dramatically in the 1950s when, in response to complaints about the damage to cereals and puddling of fields in areas where Canada Geese were well established, the WWT and local wildfowling organizations were responsible for a policy of artificial redistribution. This involved birds being rounded up during their flightless period, in areas where they were not wanted, and taken to places where it was anticipated they would add variety to the bags of wildfowlers. As a direct result of this policy,

Canada Geese were introduced to a whole new range of breeding sites, contributing to a three-fold rise in the British population between 1953 and 1976. The Naturalized Goose Survey in 2000 indicated that the population of adult Canada Geese had increased by about three-quarters since the *New Atlas* and that much of the increase occurred in habitats that had previously held low densities (Austin 2001).

In Cumbria, a few pairs were breeding ferally on Rydal Water and Crofton Lake by the 1890s. Thereafter, no further breeding records are documented until the 1950s, despite attempts having been made to introduce the bird to Grasmere between the First and Second World Wars (Blezard 1954). Following the release of 60 birds in Westmorland during 1957, successful breeding took place at Killington Reservoir in 1958 and at a number of other localities in south Cumbria over the next two years. Nesting also occurred at Derwent Water and possibly Thirlmere in 1960, subsequent to the release of eight birds on Derwent Water in 1958 (Stokoe 1962). Further introductions followed, including the release of 21 birds at Tarns Dub in 1975. As a result of these and other introductions, Canada Geese occupied 24 10km squares by the time of the *Old Atlas*. The *New Atlas* showed a further 70% increase in distribution, with Killington Reservoir established as the main nesting site in the county, 42 pairs raising 111 young here in 1990. By the time of the 1991 WWT survey, a total of 1001 Canada Geese were located in Cumbria, with the main moulting flocks at Killington Reservoir, Grasmere, Thirlmere and Derwent Water. However, control measures were then introduced at both Killington Reservoir and Grasmere in an effort to stabilize the population.

*This Atlas* suggests that, although there has been some expansion of the Canada Goose into new areas, the species remains fairly localized with the number of occupied 10km squares actually falling slightly, from 46 to 42 since the *New Atlas*. Breeding birds are generally concentrated in a number of distinct clusters centred on Longtown, Armathwaite, Kirkby Stephen, Killington Reservoir, Derwent Water, Windermere, Grasmere and Coniston Water.

The county population estimate of 100–150 breeding pairs is based on the 2000 BTO/WWT naturalized goose survey, which happened to coincide with *this Atlas;* it located 1,615 birds, including 239 young and 253 un-aged individuals. This figure suggests a 62% increase compared with the previous count in 1991, largely attributable to an expansion of the Windermere population, with numbers at other key sites remaining relatively stable. There is a substantial proportion of non-breeding birds.

As so often the case with species transplanted artificially outside their normal range, there have been

Sponsored by Jason & Mags Bruce-Welsh

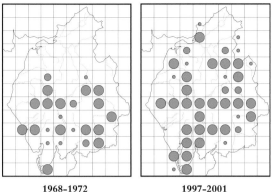

**1968–1972**     **1997–2001**
(For explanation of maps, see page 45)

*Conservation status*
European:               no criteria applied
UK:                     unspecified

*Populations*
European status:                40,000
Britain – adults:               46,700
Cumbria – pairs:                100–150

*30-year distribution change*

|  | Old Atlas | This Atlas | % |
|---|---|---|---|
| No. of 10km squares: | 24 | 42 | +75 |

| Survey data | Tetrads | % |
|---|---|---|
| Confirmed breeding: | 63 | 3.4 |
| Probable breeding: | 19 | 1.0 |
| Possible breeding: | 35 | 1.9 |
| Total: | 117 | 6.3 |

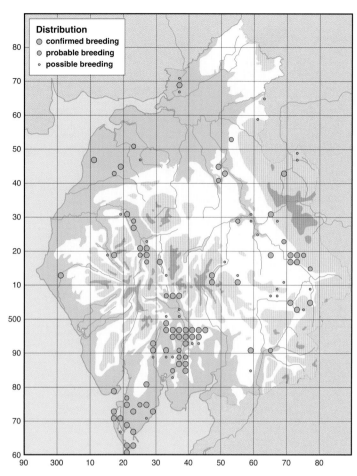

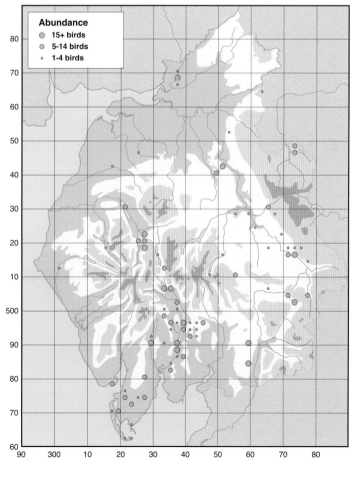

a number of unfortunate ecological side effects associated with the introduction of the Canada Goose. Because of the aggressive manner in which the bird defends its nest, it can readily dominate the wetland sites it occupies, sometimes to the detriment of indigenous species. Water eutrophication, ground erosion and destruction of vegetation are further problems which can arise as the size of the breeding population begins to outstrip the carrying capacity of the wetlands that the birds occupy.

Despite the implementation of control measures at some sites in Cumbria, away from these areas the species continues to thrive. Inevitably this will lead to calls for control at new locations, but prospects for the species are good, with a further sustained population increase in the county anticipated for the foreseeable future.

Clive Hartley

SUBTERRANEAN nesting permits the Shelduck to dispense with any need for cryptic plumage and thus become unique amongst British ducks: both sexes are adorned with similar striking plumage. Shelducks are a familiar sight on our estuaries, feeding by a distinctive side-to-side scything motion of the head, sifting mud through the lamellate bill to filter out small snails, worms and crustaceans that form the staple diet.

Its breeding range extends eastwards from Britain and Ireland to western China, although the population is split into two major geographical regions. Cumbria's birds form part of a discrete group centred on northwest Europe while the mainly Asiatic population extends from the extreme southeast of Europe, through central Asia to northern China. In Britain and Ireland birds are widely distributed, the largest concentrations occurring where there are estuaries and muddy shorelines.

A hole-nesting species, the Shelduck chooses nest-sites predominantly in sand-dunes or in rocky crevices. Rabbit-burrows are particularly favoured since Shelducks never excavate their own holes. Hollow trees, haystacks and even farm buildings are sometimes utilized, while nests on the mosses of the Solway Basin can be found in areas of dense heather, bog myrtle or gorse (Blezard *et al* 1943). The male becomes very territorial during the breeding season, vigorously defending an area, which may not contain the nest site, to the exclusion of all other Shelduck except his mate; curious behaviour, apparently serving to strengthen the pair bond and secure good feeding grounds for the pair close by the chosen nest site. Once the young have hatched, this form of territorial behaviour declines as broods amalgamate into crèches.

In Cumbria, large winter concentrations of Shelduck are found around Morecambe Bay and the Solway Firth. These disperse with the arrival of spring to breeding haunts along the coast, and inland to the mosses of the Solway Basin and several waters in Lakeland. Shelduck are renowned for their spectacular gatherings in late summer, before the majority move across the North Sea to join the rest of the European population on the Dutch Waddensee where they moult old for new feathers. During this period the crèches of young ducklings remain in the care of a dwindling number of adults.

Historically, despite a national decrease in numbers, at the end of the 19th century the species still bred commonly in the county. The coastal sand-hills of Ravenglass south to Walney Island, areas around Morecambe Bay and the Solway Basin between Mawbray and Longtown were all favoured sites (Macpherson 1892). An increase in numbers occurred during the 20th century throughout Europe, a trend mirrored by the Cumbrian population. By the 1940s it was an increasingly common nesting species along much of the Cumbrian coast. Foulshaw Moss was particularly favoured and growing numbers bred away from the shore amongst the mosses, fields and woods of the Solway Basin. Birds also began to breed around the southern end of Windermere and another inland haunt was Finsthwaite Tarn. This spread inland was presumably due to a saturation of coastal sites, and further expansion saw Coniston Water colonized in 1955–56 (Blezard *et al* 1943, Blezard 1958).

The *Old Atlas* confirmed this growth within the county and although a few Solway sites had been vacated by the time of the *New Atlas,* the breeding distribution remained relatively unchanged into the early 1990s. Again *this Atlas* shows no dramatic change, the distribution map emphasizing the species' affinity for sheltered estuarine environments, with coastal pairs only absent from the maritime cliffs and rocky shores between Whitehaven and Maryport. Although birds are continuing to increase at inland locations elsewhere in Britain, in Cumbria this is apparently not the case. A few prospecting pairs still occur around Coniston Water and Windermere but breeding was not confirmed and there has been no further growth, with birds failing to penetrate into the heart of Lakeland.

According to Yarker & Atkinson-Willes (1972), less than 50% of summering Shelducks actually breed in any one year. Evidence of this can be substantiated from the study at South Walney, where although 60

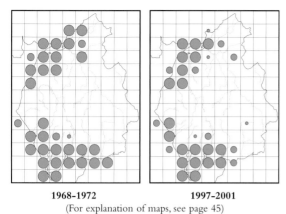

**1968-1972**    **1997-2001**

(For explanation of maps, see page 45)

***Conservation status***

| | |
|---|---|
| European: | Non-SPEC |
| UK: | **AMBER: WL & WI** |

***Populations***

| | |
|---|---|
| European status: | 41,000 |
| Britain – pairs: | 10,600 |
| Cumbria – pairs: | 700 |

***30-year distribution change***

| | Old Atlas | This Atlas | % |
|---|---|---|---|
| No. of 10km squares: | 34 | 33 | −2.9 |

| **Survey data** | **Tetrads** | **%** |
|---|---|---|
| Confirmed breeding: | 68 | 3.7 |
| Probable breeding: | 93 | 5.0 |
| Possible breeding | 69 | 3.7 |
| Total | 230 | 12.5 |

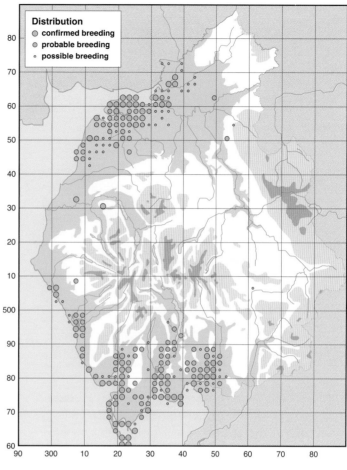

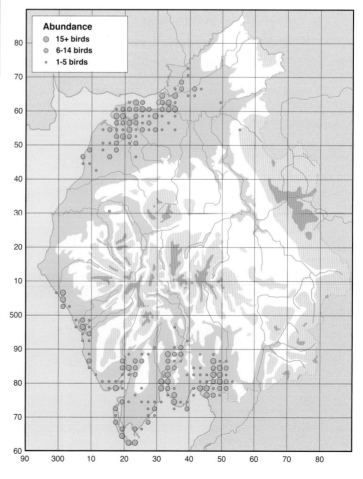

birds were present in 2001 only 12 pairs (40%) actually bred, at a density of 1.5 birds/km² (WBO 2001). This would suggest a current county population of 700 breeding pairs.

Due to its restrictive feeding methods and specialist habitat requirements, the Shelduck is at risk from sea-level rise due to global warming, and estuarine development. Barrage construction over our major estuaries would have a catastrophic impact on the species should such proposals ever become reality; fortunately the cost of such schemes is currently prohibitive. The species presently suffers from low productivity at some breeding sites, which is a real cause for concern; the large gull colony at South Walney inflicts heavy mortality on ducklings, yet this does not appear to deter breeding attempts, and as a consequence few young survive to fledging.

Colin Raven

# Mandarin Duck *Aix galericulata*

THE multi-coloured breeding plumage of the drake Mandarin Duck is one of the most spectacular and beautiful of all wildfowl and, as a result, the species was imported into Britain for ornamental purposes, from around 1745. Birds first bred in captivity in 1834 but it was not until the 20th century that a feral population, supplemented by further escapes and deliberate releases, became established. This resulted in the Mandarin Duck finally being admitted to the British list as a naturalized species in 1971.

The natural range of the Mandarin Duck extends through Japan, Korea and China to adjacent areas of the former USSR. Although small naturalized populations occur in North America, Germany and the Netherlands, the mainstay of the feral population is to be found in Britain and Ireland. Its stronghold is southern England and, although there are small numbers in Cheshire and Lancashire, whether Mandarin Ducks exist as viable feral breeders in Cumbria, has, perhaps, never been properly determined until now. Small groups seemingly become established only to apparently die out after several years.

More arboreal than our native breeding ducks, often perching on branches and shrubs and nesting in holes in trees several kilometres from water, Mandarin Ducks take readily to nestboxes; otherwise the discovery of a nest is quite by chance, which may account for the species being under-recorded. Confirmation of breeding is usually dependent on broods being observed once the young have left the nest. Lakes, ponds and rivers, surrounded by mature deciduous woodland, are the preferred habitat, with the species largely dependent on acorns, sweet chestnuts and beechmast during the winter months, although aquatic invertebrates are taken at other times of the year.

In Cumbria, breeding in the wild first occurred around 1926, when a few free-flying birds from captive stock, held in a private collection at Netherby, escaped, and thereafter bred for some years along the River Esk (Blezard *et al* 1943). There were no subsequent records, perhaps at least partially due to apathy in reporting the species, until a pair was on Esthwaite Water in 1975. However, although birds were present here up to 1979, breeding was never confirmed. From the 1980s, the Mandarin Duck was recorded almost annually in the county, with what appears to be a small breeding population established. Windermere emerged as the nucleus of this population; a drake was first recorded here in 1983 and, although numbers remained low, eight were counted in 1995. Elsewhere in the county, there is further evidence of sporadic breeding attempts. Pairs were on Heltondale Beck in 1981 and the River Bela in 1982, before an immature bird was seen on the River Lowther at Helton during 1986. This may have been of wild origin as escapees, originally from a wildfowl collection at Lowther, had been present in the area since the early 1980s. The first confirmed breeding record in recent times came from the River Eden near Appleby, the ducks having initially emanated from a collection at Appleby Castle. A female and three young were seen in 1988, and birds continued to be seen in the area until 1990 without further evidence of breeding. A pair was seen annually during the spring at Frith Wood, Haweswater between 1989 and 1991, again with breeding suspected but not confirmed. Finally, a female, which was seen to fly off Rusland Pool and disappear into adjacent woodland in 1992, could also conceivably have been nesting nearby. Further records, mainly involving drakes, came from seven sites across the county.

During this survey, the prevalence of Windermere as the main site for this species has been further enhanced. Up to eight birds were present during 1997 and fieldwork located two broods in 1998, with breeding also confirmed at nearby Esthwaite Water in 1999. Other single pairs were located at Rusland Pool, Graythwaite and Ravenstonedale.

Although the latest estimate of the British population is in excess of 7,000 birds, in Cumbria the population remains in its infancy and the secretive nature of the species makes monitoring difficult; Windermere is surrounded by large estates and private woodland with limited access and it is unlikely that all birds have been recorded. An estimation of the current county population of 5–10 breeding pairs during *this Atlas* has been taken from count data, enhanced by supplementary records.

The large amount of suitable habitat available means that there is plenty of scope for Mandarin Ducks to

Sponsored by Walney Wanderers

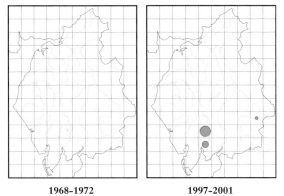

**1968–1972**  **1997–2001**
(For explanation of maps, see page 45)

*Conservation status*

| | |
|---|---|
| European: | Non-SPEC |
| UK: | Unspecified |

*Populations*

| | |
|---|---|
| European status: | Unspecified |
| Britain – individuals: | 7,000 |
| Cumbria – pairs: | 5–10 |

*30-year distribution change*

| | Old Atlas | This Atlas | % |
|---|---|---|---|
| No. of 10km squares: | 0 | 3 | n/a |

| Survey data | Tetrads | % |
|---|---|---|
| Confirmed breeding: | 2 | 0.11 |
| Probable breeding: | 2 | 0.11 |
| Possible breeding: | 1 | 0.05 |
| Total: | 5 | 0.27 |

flourish and consolidate their position as a breeding species within the county. The proposed ban on water-skiing for Windermere may prove beneficial, but the species' continued success may depend on the future levels of lakeside amenity activities and its resilience to competition for the limited nest sites from an increasing population of Grey Squirrels.

Colin Raven

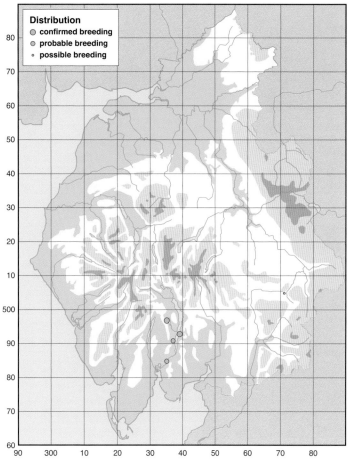

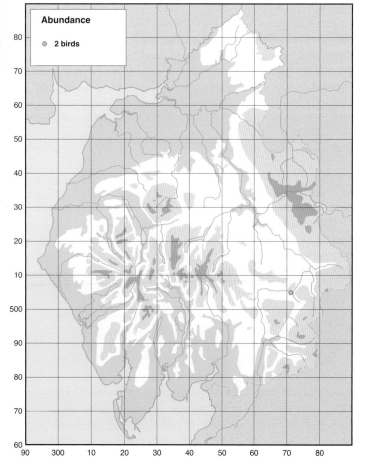

AMONGST the most abundant of European ducks, the Wigeon, with the chestnut head and striking yellow crown stripe of the drake, coupled with the high-pitched whistle, is a familiar sight and sound, frequently encountered on the saltmarshes of Cumbria throughout the winter. During the breeding season, however, it is a shy species, retiring to isolated moorland tarns to nest.

Essentially a subarctic species, the main breeding range of the Wigeon extends from Iceland and Scandinavia eastwards through the central and northern parts of the former USSR to the Pacific coast. In Britain and Ireland, although a few pairs still survive in northern England and North Wales, it is Scotland, particularly Orkney and the Outer Hebrides, that holds the bulk of the population.

As with other dabbling ducks, the nest is a hollow on the ground, lined with grass and down and well concealed amongst thick vegetation; consequently, evidence of breeding is best obtained when the ducklings appear. At this time, although the Wigeon is basically a grazer during the greater part of its life, the chironomid midge plays an important part in duckling survival, with the emerging midges a vital source of food.

The colonization of Scotland coincided with a cooler climatic phase during the 19th century, when birds were first found nesting in Sutherland in 1834. A subsequent spread southwards finally reached Cumbria in 1903, when a nest containing 10 eggs was located at Bassenthwaite Lake. Further attempts here in 1906 and 1908 were unsuccessful due to flooding. However, the status of the species in the county rapidly became clouded as a result of introductions for shooting purposes. During the period 1903 to 1908, around 30 young were reared annually from pinioned stock kept at Netherby and fully-winged birds were nesting within the confines of the estate by 1908. Although none was artificially reared during the First World War, birds were still apparently nesting regularly, as a few young were again raised from eggs gathered on the estate in 1919 (Blezard *et al* 1943). Consequently, a

female escorting a brood of ducklings on a Cumberland lough in 1922 could conceivably have come from this source. A clutch of eight eggs hatched successfully on Rockcliffe Marsh in 1938, and in the 1940s birds still nested regularly on at least one coastal moss in Cumberland. Elsewhere, summering Wigeon had become established on a number of upland tarns in Westmorland for several years before breeding finally occurred at Sunbiggin Tarn in 1944. Pairs were to nest regularly here in subsequent years and at nearby Tarn House Tarn from 1967 (Stokoe 1962, Brown 1974, Cleasby 1999).

The *Old Atlas* produced confirmed breeding in just a handful of 10km squares in the county and, apart from an isolated instance on the Coastal Plain which could be traced back to introduced birds emanating from a WAGBI reserve at The Haws, near Millom, all were moorland sites along the western edge of the North Pennines. Such sites were to hold the nucleus of the small Cumbrian breeding population throughout the 1970s and 1980s, although a pair reputedly nested in Furness in 1980. However, the *New Atlas* indicated a decline and, by the early 1990s, the species had become an irregular breeder, occurring at only three sites in the county – Sunbiggin Tarn, Tarn House Tarn and Tindale Tarn.

The results of *this Atlas* confirm the downward trend. Although summering birds were found in 20 tetrads scattered around the county, the only confirmed breeding record came from Castle Carrock Reservoir, and it is unlikely that the current county population exceeds two or three breeding pairs. Never nesting in anything other than small numbers, Cumbria has always been towards the southern edge of the regular breeding range for the species in Britain and this decline is perhaps the result of a slight decrease nationally, which began in the second part of the 20th century.

The selection of waterbody type for breeding was studied in Scotland in 1988 (Fox *et al* 1989). It appears that water acidity was an important factor governing selection, and neutral or alkaline waters were adopted

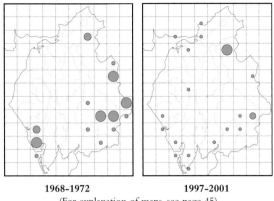

**1968-1972**          **1997-2001**

(For explanation of maps, see page 45)

*Conservation status*

| | |
|---|---|
| European: | Non-SPEC |
| UK: | AMBER: WL & WI |

*Populations*

| | |
|---|---|
| European status: | 105,000 |
| Britain – pairs: | 400 |
| Cumbria – pairs: | 2–3 |

*30-year distribution change*

| | Old Atlas | This Atlas | % |
|---|---|---|---|
| No. of 10km squares: | 14 | 18 | +28.5 |

| Survey data | Tetrads | % |
|---|---|---|
| Confirmed breeding: | 1 | 0.05 |
| Probable breeding: | 2 | 0.11 |
| Possible breeding: | 17 | 0.92 |
| Total: | 20 | 1.08 |

in preference to acidic waters. It would, therefore, seem that the species is vulnerable to water acidification as a result of acid rain and increasing afforestation. The continued presence in northern England, at several sites in Northumberland and Durham, means that the species may well continue to breed sporadically on the Cumbrian side of the border.

Colin Raven

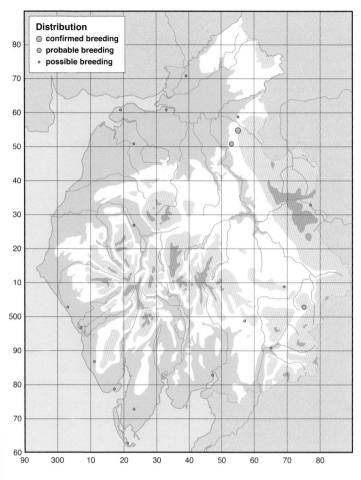

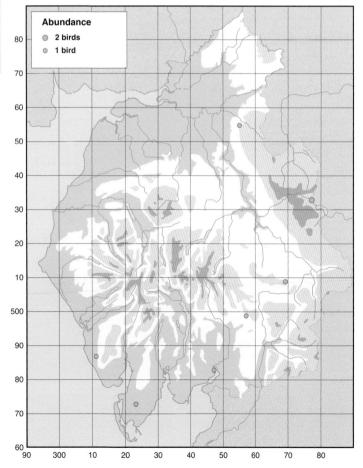

# Gadwall *Anas strepera*

GIVEN just a cursory glance the unassuming drake Gadwall appears rather bland, but closer investigation reveals it to be an exquisitely, if demurely, marked bird. Widely distributed over a large part of the northern hemisphere, in Europe it breeds farther south and east than many species of dabbling duck, with a stronghold based in the former USSR. Away from this region, it is locally distributed as a breeding bird in western Europe, although largely absent from Scandinavia and the Mediterranean.

The species underwent a westwards range expansion during the 20th century, which was accelerated, at least partly, by artificial introductions, and it is not clear how many wild birds were actually involved. In Britain and Ireland, Gadwall did not breed until around 1850 when a pair of pinioned birds was released at Narford Lake, near Narborough, Norfolk. These subsequently bred and their progeny quickly went on to colonize the surrounding area. Although substantial populations now occur in suitable habitat in Yorkshire, Lancashire and Anglesey, with isolated concentrations in Northern Ireland and Scotland, East Anglia remains the species' stronghold.

Essentially vegetarian, the species favours shallow, lowland eutrophic waters with lush emergent plant growth where it forages for submerged vegetation. The nest site is a grass-lined hollow on the ground close to the water's edge. Once hatched, the young are dependent on vegetable matter from an early age and, consequently, do not compete with ducklings of closely related species such as Mallard, which are largely insectivorous until fledging.

First recorded in Cumbria as a rare winter visitor at the end of the 19th century, the first dated sightings involved drakes on the River Eden at Grinsdale in October 1884 and on the River Lyne in January 1885 (Macpherson & Duckworth 1886). However, its existence as a breeding bird in the county, as in many areas of Britain, is generally considered to be primarily due to releases by wildfowlers, rather than natural colonization. The first such introduction occurred at Netherby where, from 1903, a few free-flying young were reared annually from pinioned stock and further birds were raised from eggs taken from Loch Leven, Fife. Feral birds were soon breeding in the wild and, by 1929, 40–50 naturalized pairs were frequenting the rearing ponds with a few pairs venturing outside the confines of the estate. A duck with five chicks frequenting a lough on the Solway Basin in June 1930 was traced to this source and one or two pairs were still in the vicinity in subsequent years (Blezard *et al* 1943). However, without any further supplements after 1926, this population slowly died out and further failed introductions were to follow. Despite the release of 900 individuals into the Lake District in 1962 (Fox 1988) and smaller schemes at The Haws, Millom and in the vicinity of Grizedale Forest during the 1970s (J. Cubby pers comm), no breeding nucleus became established in this part of the county.

Although this species generally favours lowland freshwater, the Cumbrian breeding stronghold is centred on the edge of the Pennines, around Sunbiggin Tarn at 260m asl. Initially recorded in the area during 1939, breeding was first confirmed in 1947, since when it has bred regularly in low numbers and birds now occur all year round whereas, until recently, it was just a summer visitor. Elsewhere in the county, the species remains a rare breeding bird; the only recent record away from Sunbiggin Tarn concerned a pair at Rockcliffe Marsh in 1983.

The *Old Atlas* provided confirmed breeding in three scattered 10km squares within the county, presumably a legacy of earlier releases. This had reduced to just a single square by the time of the *New Atlas*. During *this Atlas,* birds were present in 14 tetrads in ten 10km squares, although Sunbiggin Tarn was the only location proven to support nesting birds. However, pairs on a small tarn above Windermere and at Tarn Sike could conceivably have been breeding, while birds also lingered at Rockcliffe Marsh, Campfield Marsh, Mockerkin Tarn, Hodbarrow, Askam-in-Furness, Cavendish Dock and Walney Island.

Although eight pairs were recorded at Sunbiggin Tarn in 1998, count data and supplementary records from *this Atlas* suggest that the current county breeding population remains small and very localized, with 10–12 breeding pairs.

Sponsored by Philip Shirley

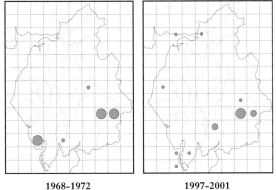

**1968-1972**          **1997-2001**

(For explanation of maps, see page 45)

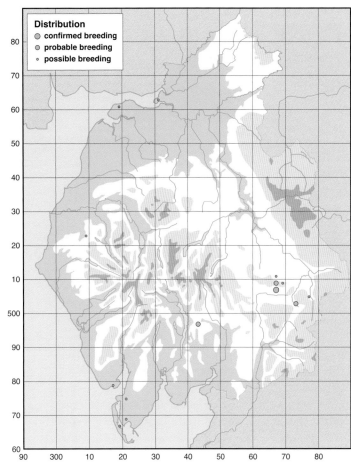

Distribution
- confirmed breeding
- probable breeding
- possible breeding

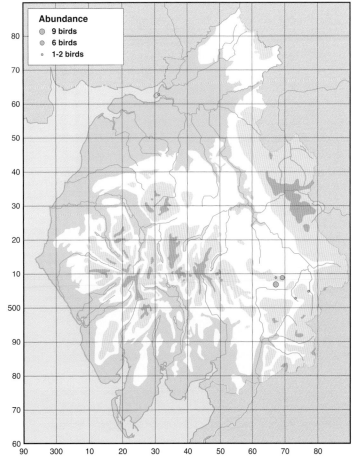

Abundance
- 9 birds
- 6 birds
- 1-2 birds

*Conservation status*

| | |
|---|---|
| European: | SPEC Cat 3 |
| UK: | **AMBER: BL & WI** |

*Populations*

| | |
|---|---|
| European status: | 23,000 |
| Britain – pairs: | 770 |
| Cumbria – pairs: | 10–12 |

*30-year distribution change*

| | Old Atlas | This Atlas | % |
|---|---|---|---|
| No. of 10km squares: | 5 | 10 | +100 |

| **Survey data** | **Tetrads** | **%** |
|---|---|---|
| Confirmed breeding: | 1 | 0.05 |
| Probable breeding: | 3 | 0.16 |
| Possible breeding: | 10 | 0.5 |
| Total: | 14 | 0.71 |

There is little doubt that the Gadwall is now a permanent part of Britain's avifauna. Latest estimates suggest 800 breeding pairs in Britain and Ireland, with a sustained population increase and range expansion. The rise in numbers frequenting Sunbiggin Tarn is perhaps the first sign that the species' steady march across England from its East Anglian stronghold is beginning to reach Cumbria. It is therefore not inconceivable that the Gadwall will prosper in the county as a breeding bird, although the dearth of suitable, undisturbed waters will perhaps limit the spread to just a handful of sites.

Colin Raven

AN early morning encounter with a group of displaying Teal on a moorland tarn is a sight and sound never to be forgotten. The drakes utter a delightful piping call as they jockey for position, continually posturing to show off their resplendent plumage to the drabber females. The smallest European duck, Teal are readily distinguished from most other species on size alone. If disturbed, birds will rise vertically from the water and the collective name 'spring' is well suited.

Although its breeding range extends eastwards from Britain and Ireland through Scandinavia, Europe and Asia to eastern Siberia and Japan, nowhere in its vast Palearctic distribution does the Teal occur in high densities and there are many areas where nesting occurs only sporadically. In Britain and Ireland, a fragmented distribution is biased towards Scotland and northern England.

A familiar species in Cumbria during the winter months, when immigrant birds augment the local population, the largest concentrations are found in lowland areas and at coastal sites, predominantly around Morecambe Bay. During the nesting season, a preference for oligotrophic waters means moorland tarns and bogs or pools on coastal peat mosses are favoured, although pairs occasionally nest on the quieter lakes with abundant marginal vegetation. Being a shy and retiring species, breeding is hard to prove: the nest site is invariably hidden amongst thick scrub within 150m of water and the female and young remain well concealed in the vegetation. As the bill is smaller than most dabbling ducks, the Teal filters smaller food particles. It is mainly a seed-eater, although animal matter is also taken with midge larvae eaten in quantity during the breeding season.

Due to its agile and rapid flight, the Teal is perhaps the wildfowler's favourite quarry. However, unlike the Mallard, it has received comparatively little attention from introduction programmes, primarily due to the species' reluctance to breed in captivity. Despite this, Teal were reared on the Netherby estate from 1889, mostly from eggs laid by pinioned stock, although some were taken from nests of birds breeding wild in the neighbourhood. Within a few years, it was the second most numerous species reared after Mallard and 1133 fully-winged birds were decoyed and 'turned down' for breeding up to 1908. Although none was raised during the First World War, rearing resumed in 1919, when a few young were hatched from eggs gathered from birds nesting in the grounds, but despite efforts being concentrated on the species until operations ceased in 1926, only small numbers were successfully reared (Blezard *et al* 1943).

Historically, Teal bred throughout the flows of Lakeland but, by the end of the 19th century, although still nesting at many sites throughout the county, it did so in reduced numbers. This decline was considered to have been brought about by changes in agricultural practice and the resultant habitat loss through land drainage and reclamation (Macpherson 1892). The early part of the 20th century saw something of a stabilization in numbers, perhaps partially as a result of introductions from schemes such as those at Netherby. Breeding birds were still present at many localities in Cumberland, Westmorland and Furness, ranging from the coastal mosses and the larger lakes to moorland tarns up to 460m asl (Blezard *et al* 1943). Indeed in the early 1970s, Teal still bred regularly in small numbers at many widely scattered locations, with strongholds amongst the Cumbria Dales and North Pennines. However, a second even more catastrophic decline was soon to occur, and, by the 1990s, the breeding population had decreased significantly. Traditional sites in the west and centre of the county were abandoned and a range contraction was apparent in former strongholds.

The *Old Atlas* suggested a Cumbrian population of around 150–250 pairs; by the *New Atlas* this had fallen to just 30–45 pairs. Although further losses have occurred since 1990, especially in the Cumbria Dales, during *this Atlas* period breeding was confirmed in ten tetrads in nine 10km squares and numbers appear to have now stabilized. Dispersing drakes – which quickly desert the incubating females to moult – and late departing or oversummering non-breeding birds are

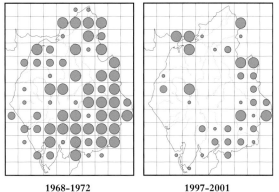

| 1968-1972 | 1997-2001 |

(For explanation of maps, see page 45)

**Conservation status**

| European: | Non-SPEC |
| UK: | AMBER: WI |

**Populations**

| European status: | 350,000 |
| Britain – pairs: | 2,050 |
| Cumbria – pairs: | 30–50 |

**30-year distribution change**

| | Old Atlas | This Atlas | % |
|---|---|---|---|
| No. of 10km squares: | 64 | 36 | −43.7 |

| **Survey data** | **Tetrads** | **%** |
|---|---|---|
| Confirmed breeding: | 10 | 0.5 |
| Probable breeding: | 17 | 0.9 |
| Possible breeding: | 26 | 1.4 |
| Total: | 53 | 2.9 |

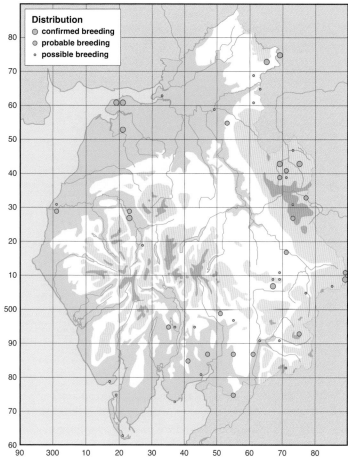

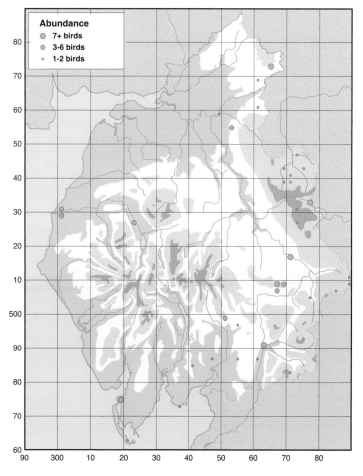

likely to be included in records of possible and probable breeding. If we ignore these, the current county population has been calculated on count data, with an assumption of an average density of three to five pairs for 10km squares where breeding was confirmed, suggesting a current county figure of 30–50 breeding pairs.

The dramatic decline recorded in Cumbria since the 1970s reflects the national trend where there is strong evidence of a considerable decline in population and breeding range during the same period. Although habitat loss, including the afforestation of upland areas, is considered to have a detrimental effect on the species, at present it is unclear whether other factors are involved in such an alarming reduction in numbers. However, climatic change, eutrophication of its breeding pools through nutrient enrichment and an increase in ground predators, such as Mink, could all be contributory factors.

Colin Raven

# Mallard *Anas platyrhynchos*

THE Mallard is certainly the most widespread and well-known of all the world's wildfowl. The handsome drake with his distinctive bottle-green head and the drabber duck are a familiar sight on any local stretch of water and they tend to congregate in quarrelsome numbers where the public go to 'feed the ducks'.

Occurring widely throughout the northern hemisphere across both the Palearctic and Nearctic regions, its European range extends northwards from Greece to Lapland, well inside the Arctic Circle. In Britain and Ireland, although widely distributed, the Mallard has a preference for lowland areas and river valleys and is consequently least abundant across southwestern England, Wales, northwest Scotland and much of Ireland. The main reason for the species' success is its adaptability and versatility, coupled with the longest breeding season of any European duck. This allows it to breed almost all year round when conditions are suitable; indeed some late breeders may include birds hatched earlier that year.

Mallards are notably catholic in their nesting habits and can be found breeding, even far from water, in a multitude of habitats, ranging from coastal mosses and remote upland moors to city centre parks. Nest sites have been known to include hollow trees, roof-top gardens, window-boxes and water tanks but the typical site is a hollow on the ground amongst dense undergrowth such as grass, nettles and brambles. It is an omnivorous and opportunistic feeder with a considerable variation in diet that is dependent upon locality and season. Generally birds feed on vegetable matter during the winter months and then switch to animal matter during the breeding season when ducklings are mainly reliant on emerging aquatic invertebrate larvae.

A ubiquitous species, not unsurprisingly the Mallard has long been the most widespread breeding duck in Cumbria. However, the introduced birds released by wildfowlers have regularly supplemented the wild population. This is adequately illustrated by the well-documented breeding activities which occurred on the Netherby estate between 1890 and 1913. In the peak seasons 8,000–10,000 birds were reared for sporting purposes, over and above the wild birds nesting in the area. In 1902 a total of 6,710 birds was shot on the estate, with a day's record of 1,317 bagged by seven guns including King George V, the then Prince of Wales. Initially many eggs were bought or exchanged, but as time went by they were gathered from clipped birds, trapped the previous autumn/winter and kept specifically for laying, with most eggs hatched under domestic hens. There can be little doubt that the population around the Solway Basin at this time was kept artificially high by these releases (Blezard *et al* 1943). Although activities have since ceased here, it is unclear just how many birds are still released across the county by shooting syndicates each year, but they probably make a significant contribution to the county's population.

The distribution map confirms that the Mallard remains widely spread throughout Cumbria with almost 60% of tetrads occupied. Although predictably absent from the barren and rocky fells of Lakeland, all the major lakes, river systems and their tributaries support breeding birds. It is also adaptable enough to be found nesting in small numbers on marginal upland sites, most notably on the North Pennines and the Cumbria Dales, as well as in remarkably small, insignificant wetland areas and apparently unfavourable localities well away from water. The abundance map shows that the greatest densities occur along the Eden and Lune Valleys and on the shallower lakes and meres, most particularly Bassenthwaite Lake, Derwent Water, Esthwaite Water and Windermere. These all have areas with well vegetated, nutrient rich, shallow margins, unlike the edges to man-made reservoirs such as Haweswater and Thirlmere, which tend to be steep-sided, and the rocky, scree strewn shores of Wast Water that are noticeably devoid of ducks.

Analysis of line transect data from *this Atlas* gives a population band of 20,000–51,000, suggesting a mean population of 32,000 birds. Although difficult to determine the origins of many, the Mallard is without question the most populous duck in the county.

The latest available BBS index indicates a stable national population between 1994 and 2000, although WBS data shows a spectacular 200% increase in

 Sponsored by Alcan Packaging Lawson Mardon

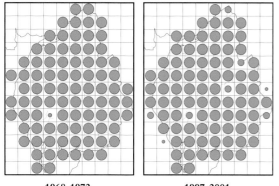

**1968-1972**          **1997-2001**

(For explanation of maps, see page 45)

**Conservation status**

| | |
|---|---|
| European: | Non-SPEC |
| UK: | GREEN |

**Populations**

| | |
|---|---|
| European status: | 2,200,000 |
| Britain – pairs: | 115,000 |
| Cumbria – pairs: | 16,000 |

**30-year distribution change**

| | Old Atlas | This Atlas | % |
|---|---|---|---|
| No. of 10km squares: | 87 | 89 | +2.3 |

| **Survey data** | **Tetrads** | **%** |
|---|---|---|
| Confirmed breeding: | 489 | 26.5 |
| Probable breeding: | 317 | 17.2 |
| Possible breeding: | 260 | 14.1 |
| Total: | 1,066 | 57.8 |

numbers between 1974 and 1996. With no recent sign of any significant decrease at local levels, Mallard population levels look set to rise further within the county as the species continues its successful exploitation of man.

Colin Raven

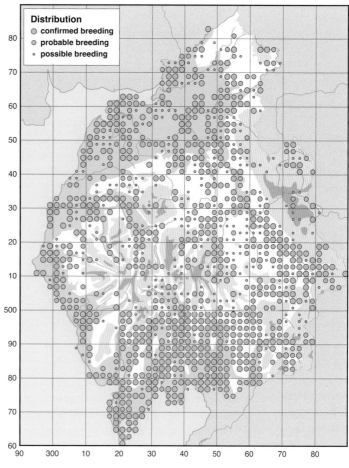

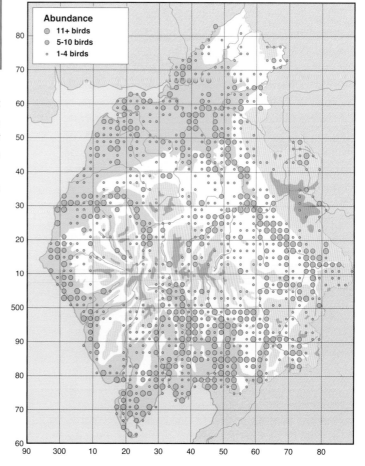

# Shoveler *Anas clypeata*

THESE striking filter-feeding ducks are immediately identifiable by the unique broad, spatulate bill. The drake Shoveler is also unusual among dabbling ducks in that it is territorial, rigorously defending the area around the nest. A widespread, but locally distributed, northern hemisphere species, the circumpolar breeding range of the Shoveler extends from Britain and Ireland across Europe to Asia and into North America. In Britain and Ireland, it is very much a localized species with the population strongholds centred on the eastern counties of England.

Dependent upon shallow, eutrophic fresh or brackish waters, the preferred breeding habitat consists of shallow margins in marshland, which support areas of good vegetative cover. The nest site is invariably a simple hollow on the ground, lined with grass and usually well hidden in thick cover, making confirmation of breeding difficult unless ducklings are seen. A varied diet contains more animal matter than that of other dabbling ducks. Freshwater molluscs are especially important, along with other crustacea and aquatic invertebrates, while small plant seeds are also taken.

During the early 19th century, Shovelers were in a perilous state in Britain; unregulated wildfowling was blamed for restricting regular breeding to East Anglia and southeast Scotland (Mead 2000). In Cumbria, the species was considered an extremely local bird, especially in the south of the county where the only confirmed record concerns a drake shot at Ayside in May 1889. Elsewhere, it appeared only rarely along the edge of the Solway Firth to the east of Silloth,

primarily as a spring migrant, and although not encountered on the Coastal Plain, it was a winter visitor to Derwent Water. As protective legislation became effective, the species began to expand as a breeding bird, and Shovelers were first proven to breed in Cumbria in 1886. A nest containing eight eggs was found on Burgh Marsh and a few pairs bred on nearby mosses in subsequent years (Macpherson 1892). A steady increase then followed, with pairs nesting on various marshes and loughs within the Solway Basin in the early 20th century. By this time, birds had also spread inland to Bassenthwaite Lake and as far east as Whins Pond. The 1940s finally saw breeding pairs become established in Westmorland, with birds, perhaps from the nearby post-war Lancashire stronghold of Leighton Moss, colonizing the marshes near Arnside and the area around Sunbiggin Tarn. Sporadic breeding also occurred at Helton Tarn, but although pools in Furness regularly held pairs in spring there is no evidence that nesting occurred there (Blezard *et al* 1943, Stokoe 1962).

A downturn in the species' fortunes, perhaps reflecting national trends, was first apparent in the early 1960s. Although still nesting widely in the county, it had become less numerous with a noticeable decline in breeding densities at favoured haunts around the Solway Basin. By the time of the *Old Atlas,* the species had disappeared from many former sites throughout Cumbria and its breeding range had become restricted to just three main areas, centred around Sunbiggin Tarn, Siddick Pond and Longtown. Despite holding only small numbers and suffering from fluctuating breeding success, these localities remained the mainstay of the Cumbrian population into the 1990s. By this time, Walney Island had emerged as a new nesting site: prospecting pairs had aroused suspicions here for several years before breeding was finally confirmed in 1986 (Dean 1990). The *New Atlas* hinted at a slight recovery, with summering birds noted at a number of other sites, especially on the Solway Basin and along the Coastal Plain, although evidence pointed to just occasional, apparently random, nesting attempts.

Although the Shoveler still remains a very localized species, *this Atlas* endorses the view of consolidation, with birds located in 24 tetrads scattered around the periphery of the county. Summering birds are still present at the traditionally favoured haunts of Sunbiggin Tarn and Longtown and confirmation of breeding came from three localities: Siddick Pond, Walney Island and North Plain Farm. The last record hints at a potential recolonization of the Solway Basin, and the presence of spring birds at sites on the Coastal Plain and in Furness also bodes well. The current estimate, derived from count data and supplementary records, suggests that the county population is unlikely to exceed 3–5 breeding pairs in any one year.

 Sponsored by Mike & Anne Abbs

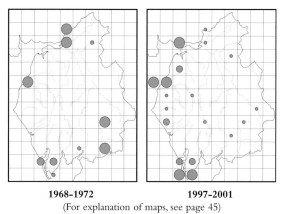

**1968-1972**          **1997-2001**
(For explanation of maps, see page 45)

*Conservation status*

| | |
|---|---|
| European: | Non-SPEC |
| UK: | AMBER: WI |

*Populations*

| | |
|---|---|
| European status: | 37,000 |
| Britain – pairs: | 1,250 |
| Cumbria – pairs: | 3–5 |

*30-year distribution change*

| | Old Atlas | This Atlas | % |
|---|---|---|---|
| No. of 10km squares: | 10 | 19 | **+90** |

| **Survey data** | **Tetrads** | **%** |
|---|---|---|
| Confirmed breeding: | 5 | 0.3 |
| Probable breeding: | 6 | 0.3 |
| Possible breeding: | 13 | 0.7 |
| Total: | 24 | 1.3 |

The Shoveler is likely to remain a marginal breeding species in the county. Suitable, shallow, eutrophic waters are now at a premium and it is perhaps no coincidence that the remaining nesting areas are all centred on nature reserves. Unfortunately, the small wetlands favoured by the species make the Shoveler very susceptible to changes in agricultural practice. Habitat and water quality are adversely affected by drainage and changes in land use, with unprotected sites particularly prone to degradation.

Colin Raven

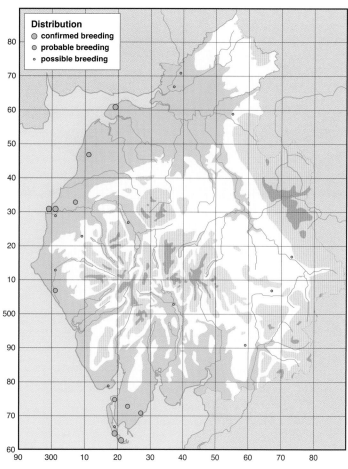

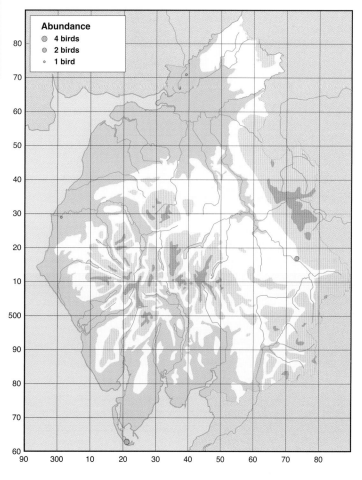

THE rich chestnut head, black breast, grey sides and black stern immediately identify the drake Pochard; even in silhouette its dome-shaped head is distinctive. As is usual amongst wildfowl, the female is less conspicuous. An Old World species nesting westwards from Mongolia, through Asia into Europe, the main population is concentrated on the freshwater lakes of the steppes. In the last 150 years it has spread further west, perhaps due to drought conditions in the breeding lakes of central Asia, to include Britain and Ireland at the edge of its range.

Prior to 1840, the Pochard was restricted to East Anglia. Although first breeding in Scotland in 1871, only during the 1900s did it rapidly spread to become established as a local breeding species throughout Britain. This range expansion coincided with the creation of artificial waterbodies as a by-product of aggregate extraction and new reservoir construction. Although aided by artificial introductions in some areas, most particularly in Hampshire, the spread was considered natural in many eastern counties (Fox 1991). In more recent years, the Pochard has consolidated its breeding distribution. The latest figures indicate that the population has stabilized after a steady rise, with an average annual total of 282–460 breeding pairs, with perhaps up to 600 pairs in a good year (Ogilvie *et al* 1999). Despite this, it is still rare in many counties away from its stronghold in the southeast, although localized concentrations now occur in northern England, Scotland and Ireland.

A shy, retiring species favouring undisturbed, lowland, eutrophic waterbodies with dense vegetation in which to breed, the sighting of ducklings is the best indicator of breeding. The nest site is usually a substantial platform of aquatic vegetation built over water or in waterlogged ground and well hidden within a reedbed. A mainly vegetarian diet consisting primarily of seeds and vegetative material, obtained by diving to a depth of 2.5m, leads to little competition with the Tufted Duck, although once hatched the young of both species feed almost exclusively on chironomid larvae.

In Cumbria, nesting was first suspected on the Solway Basin at the end of the 19th century, but it was not until 1927 that breeding was confirmed, when two nests were found at one site in Cumberland. Another nest, containing eight eggs, was discovered at the same location in May 1928 and a duck escorting several downy young was in a new Cumberland locality in July 1928 (Macpherson 1892, Blezard *et al* 1943). However, although pairs subsequently summered at a number of other sites in Cumberland and Westmorland, the species was to remain a rare breeding bird in the county. The next confirmed breeding records did not emerge until the intensive fieldwork undertaken for the *Old Atlas,* when birds were found in four scattered 10km squares. Later, a pair reportedly bred in Furness in 1979, followed by another pair with four young at Sunbiggin Tarn in 1980. Nonetheless, detected nesting attempts were to remain sporadic and it was 1989 before breeding was confirmed again, this time at Siddick Pond, where in succeeding years up to three pairs were considered to breed annually. Elsewhere, a nest with seven eggs at Killington Reservoir in 1992 was unfortunately predated, and what was presumably the same pair nested, again unsuccessfully, in 1993.

During *this Atlas* period, the dominance of Siddick Pond as the county's premier site was reaffirmed with up to two pairs nesting annually. Over Water emerged as the only other site to hold breeding birds with a single pair recorded, although it is conceivable that birds have continued to breed here undetected since the *Old Atlas.* However, although birds were located in 10 tetrads, the survey suggests that a slight decline has occurred in the county since the *Old Atlas,* which hinted at perhaps 4–8 nesting pairs. Ignoring records of late-departing and oversummering non-breeding birds, count data, enhanced by supplementary records, suggest that the current county population during *this Atlas* period is perhaps lower than previously thought, with only 3–5 breeding pairs.

It is improbable that the Pochard will become anything other than a marginal breeding species in the

Sponsored by J. B. McK. Black

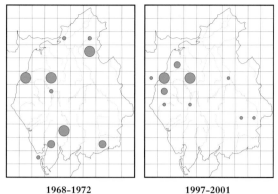

**1968-1972**　　　　**1997-2001**

(For explanation of maps, see page 45)

| Conservation status | |
|---|---|
| European: | SPEC Cat 4 |
| UK: | **AMBER: WI** |

| Populations | |
|---|---|
| European status: | 220,000 |
| Britain – pairs: | 380 |
| Cumbria – pairs: | 3–5 |

**30-year distribution change**

| | Old Atlas | This Atlas | % |
|---|---|---|---|
| No. of 10km squares: | 10 | 10 | n/c |

| Survey data | Tetrads | % |
|---|---|---|
| Confirmed breeding: | 2 | 0.1 |
| Probable breeding: | 2 | 0.1 |
| Possible breeding: | 6 | 0.3 |
| Total: | 10 | 0.5 |

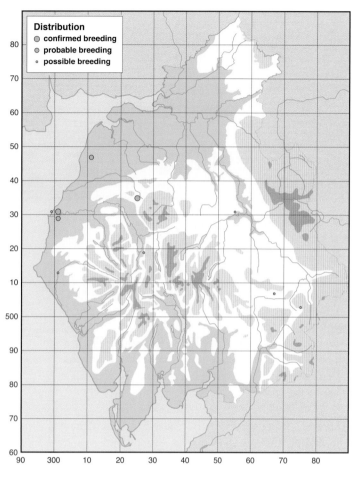

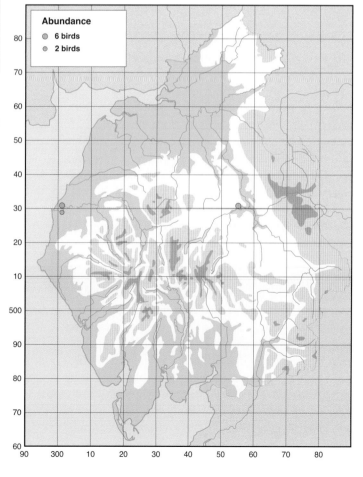

county. Generally speaking, the oligotrophic waters in Cumbria, although providing modest wintering habitat, are, in most instances, unsuitable as breeding sites. The species is usually confined to eutrophic lowland waters, rich in emergent and submerged vegetation. Water sports and intensive agriculture with intrinsic herbicide and pesticide run off are thought to be detrimental to the species' success, as it is considered very susceptible to disturbance and changes in water quality. Other factors affecting its breeding success include competition for nest sites within reedbeds with the more aggressive Coot and predation of ducklings by Pike and Mink (Fox 1991).

Colin Raven

# Tufted Duck *Aythya fuligula*

THE dapper drake Tufted Duck with black body, contrasting brilliant white flanks and long drooping crest, which gives the bird its name, has become an increasingly familiar sight, with its soberly-coloured mate, on Cumbrian waters. Ranking as one of the most successful and familiar of Britain's breeding wildfowl, it has benefited from the creation of inland waters such as reservoirs and gravel pit complexes, where it feeds by diving for freshwater molluscs and invertebrate larvae.

An Old World species, the Tufted Duck breeds widely across the northern Palearctic eastwards from Britain and Ireland through Scandinavia, Europe and Asia to Eastern Siberia and Japan. In Britain and Ireland, it is essentially a lowland species, being generally absent from the higher ground above 400m asl. The greatest concentrations occur in south and east England, the Midlands, southeast Scotland and Northern Ireland.

A westwards expansion of its range, perhaps initiated by climatic change which caused desiccation of the lakes in its nesting grounds in southwest Asia, led to birds first breeding in Britain in 1849. By the 1930s, Tufted Ducks occupied most of the suitable waters in Britain. Colonization coincided with the rapid spread of the introduced Zebra Mussel that forms a substantial part of the bird's diet. The nest site is occasionally over water, in emergent vegetation, but it is usually situated on dry ground close to the water's edge and well concealed amongst dense cover. Tufted Ducks nest considerably later than the majority of wildfowl and, consequently, broods seldom appear before July, when the ducklings feed on emerging chironomid midge larvae. A mainly animal diet and preference for shallow sites over one hectare in size leads to little competition with Britain's only other widely breeding freshwater diving duck, the Pochard.

In Cumbria, the Tufted Duck was known only as a regular, if uncommon, winter visitor to the county during most of the 19th century. Although it was suspected to have bred near Burgh-by-Sands in 1888 and on Esthwaite Water in 1911, the first confirmed breeding record came with the discovery of a nest at a tarn above Windermere in 1914. The site failed to become established, apparently due to Pike predation, but birds were nesting regularly at Sunbiggin Tarn from 1920 and further nests were found at two locations in Cumberland in 1922 (Blezard *et al* 1943, Cleasby 1999). Breeding was again suspected at Esthwaite Water in 1935 and, by the 1940s, birds were nesting annually at several sites in eastern Cumberland and Westmorland, including Sunbiggin Tarn, Tarn House Tarn, Over Water and Whins Pond, with sporadic attempts elsewhere (Brown 1974, Cleasby 1999). A population of up to five pairs first became established at North Walney in the mid-1950s and birds were also suspected to have bred on Coniston Water around this time (Blezard 1958, Dean 1990). Colonization continued apace and, by the 1970s, the species began breeding on Windermere and birds could be found in small numbers in suitable habitat throughout the county. The *New Atlas* confirmed this distribution and a noticeable increase in breeding densities was typified by the situation at Killington Reservoir, where numbers increased from a single breeding pair in 1976 to 17 broods in 1992. Further expansion, especially in the south of the county, was noted in the early 1990s, when breeding began at Fisher Tarn, Cavendish Dock and Ormsgill Reservoir.

The *Old Atlas* showed noticeable breeding concentrations in northwest and south Cumbria, with the species conspicuously absent from suitable habitat in the east. However, perhaps surprisingly, despite further consolidation and expansion elsewhere in the county *this Atlas* shows an apparent decline in the northwest. The reason for this is unclear, although habitat loss may be the principal cause. In direct contrast to this, further gains have been made in the southern strongholds and birds have spread further into the northern lakes, with Bassenthwaite Lake and Ullswater now holding nesting pairs. However, it is further east where perhaps the greatest gains have been made, with breeding birds now spread along the entire length of the Eden Valley, nesting both by still waters and by the river itself. Consequently, the majority of suitable waters in the county are now occupied, with a

Sponsored by Caron Czorny

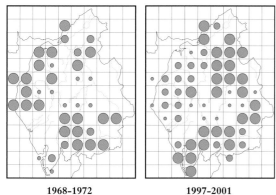

**1968-1972**    **1997-2001**

(For explanation of maps, see page 45)

*Conservation status*

| | |
|---|---|
| European: | Non-SPEC |
| UK: | **GREEN** |

*Populations*

| | |
|---|---|
| European status: | 280,000 |
| Britain – pairs: | 7,500 |
| Cumbria – pairs: | 400–550 |

*30-year distribution change*

| | Old Atlas | This Atlas | % |
|---|---|---|---|
| No. of 10km squares: | 38 | 56 | **+47.3** |

| **Survey data** | **Tetrads** | **%** |
|---|---|---|
| Confirmed breeding: | 66 | 3.6 |
| Probable breeding: | 67 | 3.6 |
| Possible breeding: | 51 | 2.8 |
| Total: | 184 | 10.0 |

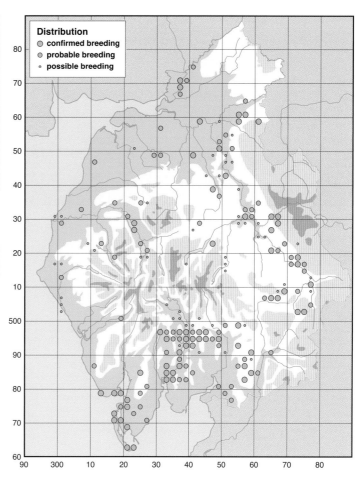

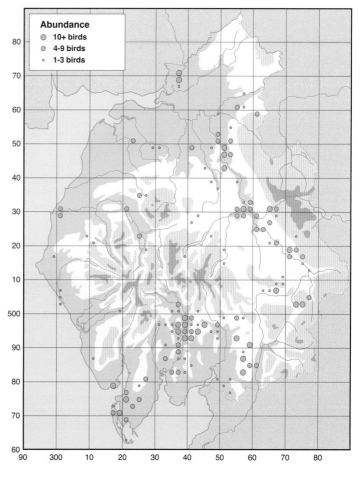

notable concentration of records in the vicinity of Windermere.

Nationally, the latest BBS and WBS data both indicate a steady range expansion. In Cumbria, although there has been some change in the species' distribution, *this Atlas* reflects the national trend and suggests that the county population is currently at an all-time high. Ignoring the presence of oversummering non-breeding birds, an estimate of 3–5 pairs in tetrads where evidence of breeding was reported would seem quite reasonable, suggesting a current county population of 400–550 breeding pairs.

Local pressures are affecting some sites in the county, most notably Killington Reservoir; 12 broods in 1997 declined to just three broods in both 2000 and 2001. However, given the sustained increase at a national level, the Tufted Duck appears set to continue to thrive as a breeding bird in Cumbria.

Colin Raven

ONE of the largest and most numerous ducks in the world, the drake Eider is unmistakable with its black and white plumage and distinctive sloping forehead, while the duck is far drabber with cryptic brown plumage. As spring approaches, activity around an Eider colony intensifies. Rafts of birds drift closer inshore and up to 30 courting drakes, displaying and calling frenetically, surround each still unpaired female in a bid to attract her attentions. After mating, the chosen male then escorts the duck ashore but takes no further part in the breeding cycle.

An essentially marine duck with a widespread Holarctic distribution which encompasses arctic and subarctic coastal regions, the Eider's breeding range extends from eastern North America, through Europe to the Pacific coast of Alaska. Britain and Ireland being at the southern edge of this range, the main concentrations are found in southwest and eastern Scotland, Orkney and Shetland. Spending most of the year at sea, it feeds extensively on molluscs, especially Blue Mussel, and, to a lesser extent, on crustaceans and echinoderms, obtained by surface diving in relatively sheltered, shallow coastal waters.

The nest site, usually a slight hollow in the ground amongst rocks or vegetation, is selected by the female and lined with down plucked from its breast. Incubation is by the duck alone, which then leads the brood to water where the ducklings mix with other broods to form crèches, in an attempt to thwart predation from marauding gulls.

In Cumbria, the population is dominated by the colony at South Walney. While the odd pair now nests further south, this remains the southernmost colony in Britain and the only one on the west coast of England. This mainly sedentary concentration, although isolated from the nearest colonies in southwest Scotland, is probably supplemented by northern birds during the winter. Records from elsewhere are scarce and relate to wandering individuals or small parties, which occasionally turn up along the coast between the Solway Firth and Duddon Estuary.

First noted at Whitehaven in about 1829, the Eider was still considered a rare visitor around the turn of the 20th century. Subsequently, there were just a handful of records, mainly from the outer Solway Firth, prior to the first nest being discovered at South Walney in 1949 (Macpherson 1892, Stokoe 1962). Numbers rose slowly at first with just 20 nests located in 1962. However, from this meagre beginning a rapid increase was to occur, culminating in the presence of 1,500 nests in 1991–92. From this nucleus, satellite groups evolved: the first nest appeared on Foulney Island in 1962, while breeding occurred at several sites along the Walney Channel and at North Walney in the late 1970s (Dean 1990). Continued growth in the mid-1980s saw birds venturing further afield. A small group penetrated Morecambe Bay to breed on Chapel Island and birds first nested at Hodbarrow in 1989. A reversal in fortunes began in 1992 when viral duck enteritis affected the South Walney population and an estimated 16% of the breeding females died (WBO 1992). Further pressures ensued: newly-arrived Red Foxes found the incubating birds easy prey and the lifting of restrictions on mussel harvesting saw an escalation in commercial activities around Foulney Island, suddenly producing competition for their main food source. These events coincided with a dramatic 45% population crash.

Although *this Atlas* revealed confirmed breeding in 13 coastal tetrads, with a slight range expansion compared to that found by the *Old Atlas,* the very localized distribution is still strikingly evident. During *this Atlas,* there were around 550–1100 nesting females *per annum,* although the population is now in freefall with numbers currently at the bottom end of this range. Despite the recent declines, the Eider remains one of our most numerous breeding ducks, with a current county population of 550 breeding females.

Despite the predation inflicted on eggs and chicks, some correlation apparently exists between the presence of large gulls and the success of an Eider colony. The growth at South Walney coincided with a large increase in Herring and Lesser Black-backed Gull numbers and many of the satellite groups have also actively sought out the company of these species. This close association,

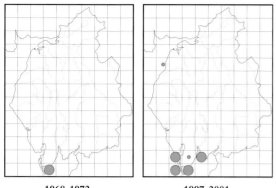

**1968-1972**  **1997-2001**
(For explanation of maps, see page 45)

| *Conservation status* | |
| --- | --- |
| European: | Non-SPEC |
| UK: | AMBER: WL |

| *Populations* | |
| --- | --- |
| European status: | 850,000 |
| Britain – females: | 31,000 |
| Cumbria – females: | 550–1,100 |

*30-year distribution change*

| | Old Atlas | This Atlas | % |
| --- | --- | --- | --- |
| No. of 10km squares: | 1 | 6 | +500 |

| **Survey data** | **Tetrads** | **%** |
| --- | --- | --- |
| Confirmed breeding: | 13 | 0.7 |
| Probable breeding: | 0 | |
| Possible breeding: | 17 | 0.9 |
| Total: | 30 | 1.6 |

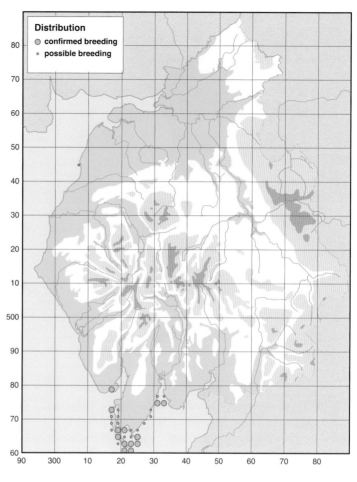

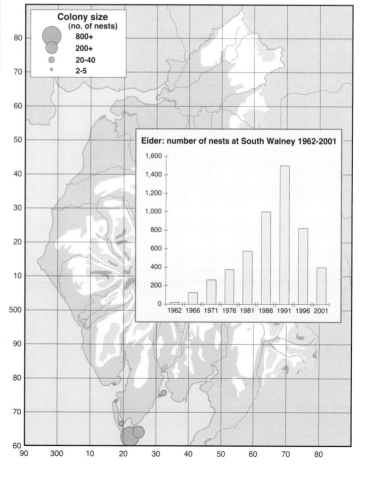

coupled with a dependence on extensive mussel beds, probably explains the limited expansion away from the Walney/Foulney complex. Being a long-lived bird enables the Eider to withstand the low productivity suffered in those years when heavy losses occur through the attentions of the gulls.

The Eider's very localized distribution in the county makes the species very susceptible to local pressures. Regular census work at the main sites gives an accurate assessment of population levels and the heavy dependence on South Walney gives particular cause for concern, with a 74% decline noted here since 1992. Whether the viability of the colony can be maintained is clearly dependent upon how it copes with the additional pressures currently being exerted. It may be that effective Red Fox control measures and a strict mussel harvesting policy have to be introduced before it is too late.

Colin Raven

# Red-breasted Merganser *Mergus serrator*

THE handsome male Red-breasted Merganser and his duller companion, with her comically scuttling young, have become an increasingly common sight on Cumbria's lakes and rivers since the mid-20th century. A ground nester, requiring substantial surrounding cover, usually woodland or scrub, it breeds by lakes, tidal coastal waters, and rivers of suitable depth and moderate current. A circumpolar breeding range encompasses northern North America, Greenland, Iceland and northern Eurasia, with isolated records farther south. In Britain and Ireland, the bird has a predominantly northern and western coastal distribution, with lesser numbers breeding inland.

Having probably bred in Scotland at least since Neolithic times, the population increased there dramatically from around 1885 to 1920. In July 1890, a half-grown brood on the River Waver was the first recorded in Cumbria, though they were considered to have crossed into the county from the Scottish side of the Solway (Macpherson 1892). A breeding record on the River Esk at Longtown in 1950 (Blezard 1954) is often quoted as the first confirmed case in both Cumbria and England, though there are records of broods on the River Esk from 1938 annually until 1950 (Brown 1974). Spreading to most of our lakes, rivers and estuaries with suitable habitat, in 1957 they first bred on Windermere where, by 1969, there were 16 pairs rearing around 120 young each summer (Atkinson 1981). By the time of the *Old Atlas,* they had further increased their range, having spread into north and south Wales and the Peak District, with Cumbria holding the bulk of the population in England.

*This Atlas* reveals that there has been a significant shift in range in Cumbria since the *Old Atlas.* There is now a striking absence of records in a swathe of 10km squares running down the east of the county. These are mainly inland river sites with Haweswater also lost as a breeding location. The 10km squares colonized since the *Old Atlas* are predominantly extensions of range in the west of the county, with the exceptions of Killington Reservoir and the River Caldew.

The reasons behind this decline in inland areas are unclear. The bird's diet brings it into conflict with game-fishing interests and destruction by man may contribute, but this is a species that managed to thrive and expand during the height of its persecution. Since 1981, Red-breasted Mergansers have enjoyed legal protection and though hundreds of licenses to destroy them have been issued in Scotland, very few have been granted in England and none at all in Cumbria. Competition with the Goosander may also play some, as yet unknown, role. The dramatic contrast in distribution between the two sawbills in *this Atlas* does reveal that Red-breasted Mergansers are much less widespread, and squares abandoned by this species are still occupied by Goosanders. Predation may also have some part to play. Red Foxes are possible culprits for their demise on Walney Island and a burgeoning gull population having some local impact at Haweswater. However, it may be that both of these former sites represent less than ideal habitats.

The distribution map for *this Atlas* shows the majority of the population is to be found around lakes and estuaries, with relatively few other riverine records and large stretches of the coast uninhabited. Of the 96 occupied tetrads, 46 contain lakes and tarns, 32 are associated with tidal waters and 18 with other inland river sites, of which only nine are further than 2km from either a lake or an estuary. Despite their history of persecution, they are surprisingly unaffected by human disturbance, with the abundance map showing that they are very successful on lakes such as Windermere and Derwent Water, two of the busiest in the Lake District. That the lakes are their main strongholds is further emphasized by the fact that the only other sites showing high abundances are Sellafield and the mouth of the River Eden. A preference for slower flowing rivers is also evident; all the river sites are at no more than 100m asl, with the notable exception of records at 200m asl on the River Caldew and the upper reaches of the River Lune. Although Red-breasted Mergansers have disappeared from sub-optimal river habitats, it is not easy to detect whether or not the overall population is also in decline.

As line transect survey methods do not produce reliable results for waterfowl, the current county population estimate of 120–150 breeding pairs has

Sponsored by Kath Atkinson

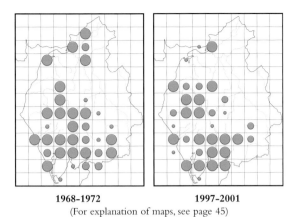

**1968-1972**          **1997-2001**

(For explanation of maps, see page 45)

***Conservation status***

| | |
|---|---|
| European: | Non–SPEC |
| UK: | **GREEN** |

***Populations***

| | |
|---|---|
| European status: | 70,000 |
| Britain – pairs: | 2,200 |
| Cumbria – pairs: | 120–150 |

***30-year distribution change***

| | Old Atlas | This Atlas | % |
|---|---|---|---|
| No. of 10km squares: | 35 | 33 | **–5.7** |

| **Survey data** | **Tetrads** | **%** |
|---|---|---|
| Confirmed breeding: | 26 | 1.4 |
| Probable breeding: | 40 | 2.2 |
| Possible breeding: | 30 | 1.6 |
| Total: | 96 | 5.2 |

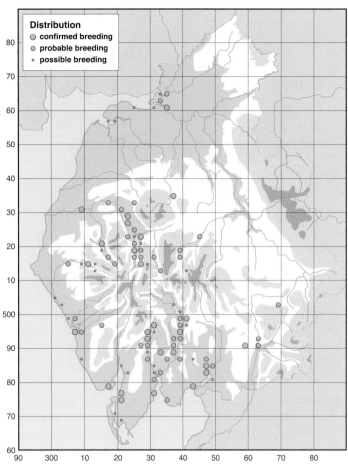

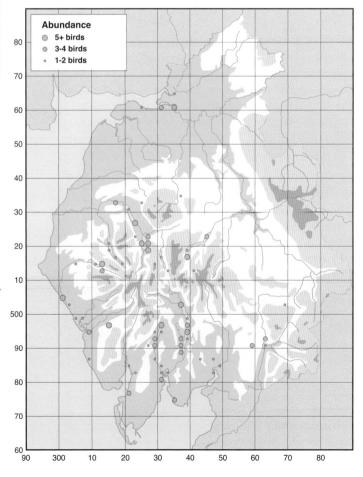

been based on count data enhanced by supplementary records and local knowledge.

Monitoring Cumbria's Red-breasted Merganser population may be important as an indicator of trends in some of our fish stocks. From 1977, there was a steep decline in the Windermere population coinciding with an epidemic disease that killed off 98% of adult perch (Atkinson 1981). Future surveys, particularly on our lakes, will detect trends and possibly predict a long-term pattern. With the national population still in the process of expanding its range, Red-breasted Mergansers should continue to flourish in Cumbria. Any future signs of decline especially on our lakes should be regarded with alarm.

Dave Piercy

# Goosander *Mergus merganser*

THIS handsome and sociable duck has become one of the most characteristic birds of the county's river systems and lakes during the last 50 years. Wary and easily disturbed, they are most often seen flying swiftly along the course of a river or, later in the breeding season, when young families form stately flotillas, exploring more secluded watercourses. The breeding population is mainly resident and unlike its smaller relative, the Red-breasted Merganser, the Goosander is almost always found on freshwater, where its diet of fish, including young salmon and trout, has raised considerable controversy from fishing interests.

The Goosander is distributed across temperate and subarctic latitudes of the northern hemisphere, favouring conifer forest and mountains. Since 1850, its range has spread southwards, the species first breeding in Scotland in 1871. Colonization of England began in 1941 and in recent decades the species has reached the south Pennines, Wales and southwest England. Few breeding birds have become established so rapidly with such success.

Goosanders favour rivers and lakes with well-wooded shores and islands, where nests are usually located in tree-holes, sometimes several hundred metres from water. In more open country, nests may be found among boulders and in riverbank cavities and, in some areas, birds have used nestboxes. Nests are often difficult to locate and confirmed breeding records mainly relate to females with broods of ducklings, although these may have moved some distance from nest sites.

Macpherson (1892) stated that "the Goosander has long been known as a winter visitor to the rivers and lakes" and went on to say "nor is it improbable that at one time a single pair of these birds may have elected to nest in the neighbourhood of Windermere, which has always been a favourite resort of this species in the colder months of the year." Summering individuals had been noted in the 1920s (Blezard *et al* 1943) but the first confirmed breeding record in Cumbria occurred in 1950 on the River Esk in north Cumberland. Stokoe (1962) commented that they then progressively occupied the rivers Eden, Lyne, Irthing and Gelt, though not necessarily in that order. Subsequently, Goosanders spread southwards as a breeding species, through the Eden Valley and central Lakeland, reaching Dentdale in the far southeast of Cumbria by 1969. However, the initial colonization was not as rapid as the parallel expansion of Red-breasted Mergansers. The reasons for such a swift and dramatic change in the breeding distribution of Goosanders are not well understood, but may relate to the increasing eutrophication of some waterbodies.

In recent decades, Goosanders have continued to expand both geographically and in numbers. The number of occupied 10km squares in the county has increased quite dramatically in the 30 years since the *Old Atlas,* almost doubling from 37 to 63. A further comparison between *this Atlas* and the *New Atlas* reveals a significant shift in the 'centre of gravity' of the breeding population, towards the south and west of the county, during the last decade. The distribution map shows Goosanders to be present on much of the available freshwater habitat, with the majority of confirmed breeding records occurring in the Derwent, Kent, Lune and Eden catchment areas. Birds are absent only on the slower rivers of the Solway Basin, the coastal fringe of Morecambe Bay and the more acidic tarns and streams of the highest areas of the North Pennines and Lakeland.

The 1987 BTO Sawbill Survey (Gregory *et al* 1997) concluded that Goosander densities were greatest on wider river stretches with relatively shallow gradients, typical of the middle reaches of Cumbria's major waterways. This survey suggested an average of one pair/4.8km of occupied river in England. A higher density of one pair/1.4km has been recorded on the lower Lune in Lancashire (Harrison *et al* 1995). Goosander broods are regularly noted on several of the main lakes in central Cumbria, supplementing the main riverine breeding population. Evidence of count data and supplementary records from *this Atlas* suggest a current county population of 300–350 breeding pairs. It is likely that the number of nesting birds in the county is similar to the number present in late winter, and this would compare favourably with the March 1991 count of 752 Goosanders in the Cumbria Bird Club Wintering Goosander Survey (Priestley 1992).

Goosanders have now exploited most suitable areas of freshwater habitat in Cumbria and potential for

Sponsored by Sheila Shuttleworth

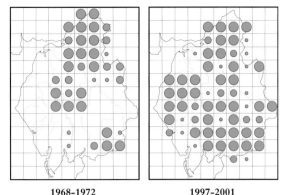

**1968–1972**        **1997–2001**

(For explanation of maps, see page 45)

*Conservation status*

| | |
|---|---|
| European: | Non–SPEC |
| UK: | **GREEN** |

*Populations*

| | |
|---|---|
| European status: | 53,000 |
| Britain – pairs: | 2,600 |
| Cumbria – pairs: | 300–350 |

*30-year distribution change*

| | Old Atlas | This Atlas | % |
|---|---|---|---|
| No. of 10km squares: | 37 | 63 | **+70.2** |

| **Survey data** | **Tetrads** | **%** |
|---|---|---|
| Confirmed breeding: | 80 | 4.3 |
| Probable breeding: | 68 | 3.7 |
| Possible breeding: | 129 | 7.0 |
| Total: | 277 | 15.0 |

further expansion in the population may be limited. The main check on population densities is undoubtedly culling of birds locally by fishing interests, legally under licence or otherwise. The debate about the actual damage to fish stocks caused by Goosanders remains unresolved; although young salmon and trout may constitute up to 80% of their diet on some river systems, predator control has not been demonstrated to have any beneficial effect on the number of returning adult fish. Nest desertion, caused by unintentional human disturbance or by predation, particularly by Mink and Grey Squirrel, can be a further problem in some areas. So far, negative factors have done little to slow the advance of this prodigious, pioneering duck.

Malcolm Priestley

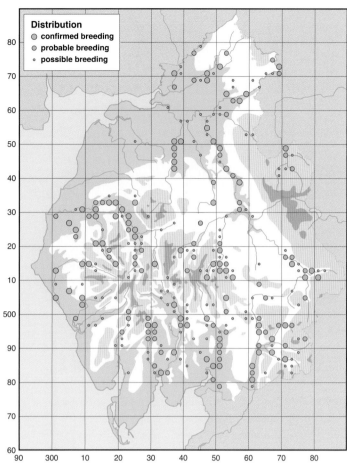

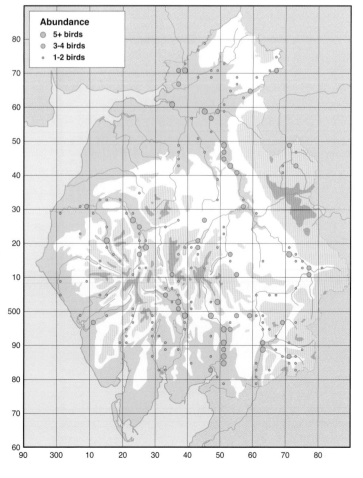

# Ruddy Duck *Oxyura jamaicensis*

THIS dumpy little diving duck, with its characteristic cocked tail, is a recent decorative addition to Cumbria's avifauna. The striking chestnut plumage, brilliant white cheeks and cobalt blue bill of the drake make it readily identifiable, while the bizarre 'bubbling' courtship display is one of the most elaborate of wildfowl rituals.

A native of North America, where it breeds principally on the northern prairies of the United States and Canada, the Ruddy Duck was first imported into Britain in the 1930s. Four drakes and three ducks, introduced to the WWT's collection at Slimbridge, Gloucestershire in 1948, were allowed to breed naturally and consequently some young avoided pinioning. An estimated 70 juveniles dispersed between 1956 and 1963 and breeding first occurred in the wild at Chew Valley Lake, Avon in 1960. However, the ensuing establishment of a feral population apparently came about more by accident than design with no evidence of deliberate introductions. The exploitation of a previously unoccupied niche in British avifauna, with no competition from native species, saw a rapid, exponential increase in numbers, which culminated in the Ruddy Duck being added to the British list in 1971.

Ruddy Ducks are predominantly nocturnal feeders, dieting on insect larvae and seeds from aquatic plants, obtained by surface diving. In the breeding season, birds prefer relatively shallow, sheltered, reed-fringed pools and small lakes, where they nest in emergent vegetation on floating structures, anchored to stems in reedbeds. An extended season means that females can produce two broods, which is unusual amongst wildfowl, and the species also benefits from parasitism. Females frequently lay eggs in the nests of other waterbirds; the ducklings are very well developed upon hatching and are quite capable of surviving alone (Hughes *et al* 1998).

Steady northwards expansion from the species' Midlands stronghold finally produced the first Cumbrian record at Longtown in 1980. This was quickly followed by the first multiple sighting of two drakes and three ducks at Standing Tarn in 1981. Perhaps surprisingly, despite the presence of spring birds at several sites in subsequent years, the species remained primarily a winter visitor and it was not until 1990 that breeding was confirmed, when a pair and six young were seen at Tarn House Tarn. Subsequent years failed to produce any further breeding records, although it is possible that nesting attempts went undetected due to the species' shy and retiring nature. Birds were found in suitable habitat at Sunbiggin Tarn, Tarns Dub, Whinfell Tarn and Whins Pond for prolonged periods during the breeding season.

During *this Atlas*, breeding was confirmed at Siddick Pond in 1997, with birds nesting here almost annually thereafter, and at Tarns Dub in 2000. Not recorded at the time of the *Old Atlas*, a comparison with the *New Atlas* shows that the species is continuing to increase with birds now found in ten 10km squares. Although Cumbrian numbers remain low, with just one regular breeding site, it appears that a small breeding nucleus is now finally becoming established. Pairs were also seen at Sunbiggin Tarn and Walney Island, with at least one unsuccessful nesting attempt considered to have taken place at the latter site. The current county population estimate, based on count data and supplementary records, seems reliable at 3–5 breeding pairs.

With the increases in Britain and Ireland, there has been a parallel rise in numbers elsewhere in Europe. First recorded on the continent of Europe in Sweden in 1965, the Ruddy Duck has been reported from around 14 European countries. Its range has now reached the breeding grounds of the endangered White-headed Duck and a number of hybrids have already occurred. Fears that the expanding population of British 'stifftails' could result in increased emigration to the continent and compound the problem have spurred the Government into action. Controversial trials to control the Ruddy Duck population in parts of the Midlands, Anglesey and Fife have been authorized and the outcome will determine whether a full-scale cull takes place.

Contrary to the experience in many other areas of Britain, the Ruddy Duck has, until now, struggled to establish itself as a regular breeder in Cumbria. At present, in terms of habitat requirements, it appears to

Sponsored by a CBC Member

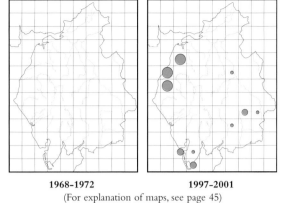

| 1968–1972 | 1997–2001 |
|---|---|

(For explanation of maps, see page 45)

***Conservation status***

| European: | no criteria applied |
|---|---|
| UK: | unspecified |

***Populations***

| European status: | 600+ |
|---|---|
| Britain – pairs: | 570 |
| Cumbria – pairs: | 3–5 |

***30-year distribution change***

|  | Old Atlas | This Atlas | % |
|---|---|---|---|
| No. of 10km squares: | 0 | 10 | n/a |

| **Survey data** | **Tetrads** | **%** |
|---|---|---|
| Confirmed breeding: | 3 | 0.2 |
| Probable breeding: | 3 | 0.2 |
| Possible breeding: | 6 | 0.3 |
| Total: | 12 | 0.7 |

have no serious competitive interaction with other breeding species in the county. However, direct competition with, for instance, Pochard, could be a possibility if numbers continue to increase (Hughes 1992). We wait to see what effect the controversial control measures will have on the situation in Cumbria.

Clive Hartley

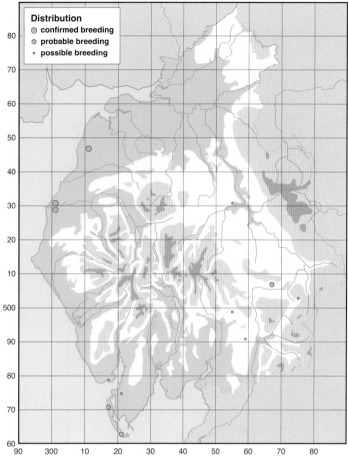

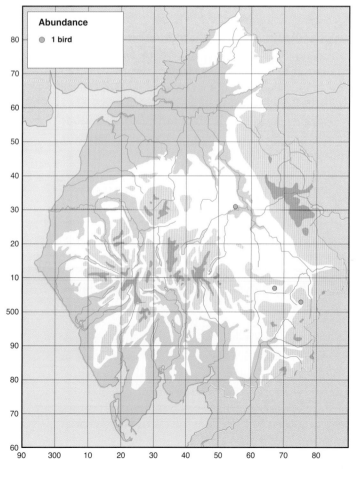

FEW British birds of prey set the pulses racing faster than the sight of a Honey Buzzard hanging for a split second on quivering wings, held high above its body. This display, in which the bird repeatedly arches its wings over its back like a giant Nightjar, and momentarily hangs in the air before swooping down, is unique amongst raptors. For many, it is not just the magical display that inspires, it is also the cloak of secrecy amongst watchers that adds an air of mystery and intrigue – understandable, given the rarity of the bird in this country. Yet in reality the species is one of the most common birds of prey in the world with a breeding range that extends from Europe eastwards into Asia. In Britain the Honey Buzzard is a summer visitor with a patchy distribution that takes in southern England, East Anglia, the Midlands, Wales, northern England and parts of Scotland. The species is absent from Ireland as a breeding bird.

Although a common bird in global terms, the Honey Buzzard is probably one of the least studied birds of prey, and until recently much of what is known about the species was based upon a small data sample. This in turn has led to an underestimation of the bird's ability to thrive in seemingly far from ideal conditions. It has always been assumed that Honey Buzzards nested in broad-leaved woodland at low altitude but recent work has demonstrated that the species will readily nest in conifers and at altitudes up to 500m asl (Roberts *et al* 1999). This study has also disproved the theory that Honey Buzzards are only likely to thrive in drier areas, where foraging for their main food item, wasp larvae, is made easier by rain-free days.

The Honey Buzzard has always been a scarce breeder in Britain with a fragmented distribution. The *Old Atlas* suggested a population of 12 pairs but the *New Atlas,* while acknowledging that data was incomplete, estimated that there may be up to 30 pairs nesting. However, Roberts *et al* (1999) indicated that the actual number of pairs could be considerably higher and this is borne out by the preliminary results of a national survey carried out in 2000, which found that there are at least 61 sites where the species bred or may have bred (Batten 2001).

Although these figures indicate a steady increase in the number of breeding pairs this interpretation should be treated with caution, given the veil of secrecy that has surrounded this bird as a result of the relentless persecution that it has suffered from the Victorian era until relatively recently. However, it is likely that there has been some population increase, and range expansion, resulting from a reduction in persecution over recent decades.

In Cumbria, Macpherson & Duckworth (1886) regarded the Honey Buzzard as a rare autumn visitor but do record that females were taken on 13th June 1783 near Carlisle and on 10th June 1857 at Schoolbank Wood, Alston. Macpherson (1892) alluded to reports that "it made its nest in high trees, and bred in the woods at Lowther." though this was never confirmed. Stokoe (1962) knew of no records after 1925, and he stated that "at least two pairs have been destroyed which might have nested, the female in the last pair, in June 1917, being nearly ready to lay." This was most likely the basis for the comment (Blezard *et al* 1943) that "the Honey Buzzard would probably nest in Cumberland if its summer visits did not usually end fatally."

The discovery of breeding Honey Buzzards in Cumbria was undoubtedly one of the highlights of *this Atlas*. In 1997 adults and a juvenile were seen at one site, and up to three pairs have been reported in the area each year since. In fact a single bird had been seen nearby as long ago as 1985 and it is possible that the species has bred unnoticed since that year. Additionally, possible breeding was recorded at another, entirely separate, location. The current county population estimate, derived from CRSG data and local knowledge, suggests 2–4 breeding pairs.

It is now known that Cumbria is as well suited to the Honey Buzzard as any other part of the country and it may well be that new breeding sites will be discovered in the future. However, the species has traditionally been regarded as a prized target for egg collectors and it is primarily for this reason that the species is closely guarded and infrequently reported. There are also other considerations, such as the effect large numbers of observers' vehicles will have on local

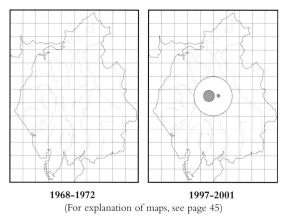

**1968-1972**          **1997-2001**

(For explanation of maps, see page 45)

---

*Conservation status*

| | |
|---|---|
| European: | SPEC Cat 4 |
| UK: | **AMBER: BR** |

*Populations*

| | |
|---|---|
| European status: | 45,000 |
| Britain – pairs: | 61 |
| Cumbria – pairs: | 2–4 |

*30-year distribution change*

| | Old Atlas | This Atlas | % |
|---|---|---|---|
| No. of 10km squares: | 0 | 2 | n/a |

| **Survey data** | **Tetrads** | **%** |
|---|---|---|
| Confirmed breeding: | 1 | 0.05 |
| Probable breeding: | 0 | |
| Possible breeding: | 7 | 0.4 |
| Total: | 8 | 0.45 |

---

traffic, and upon the attitude of landowners. Hopefully, more enlightened attitudes, combined with an increase in the county population will enable more people to enjoy the magnificent spectacle of Honey Buzzards displaying over Cumbrian skies.

Alistair Crowle

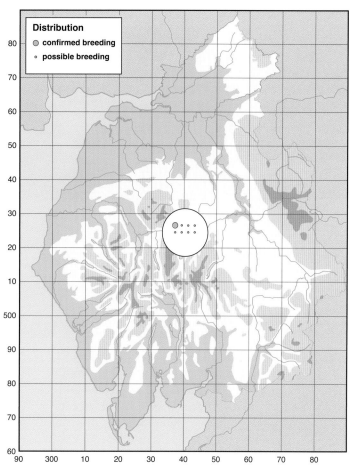

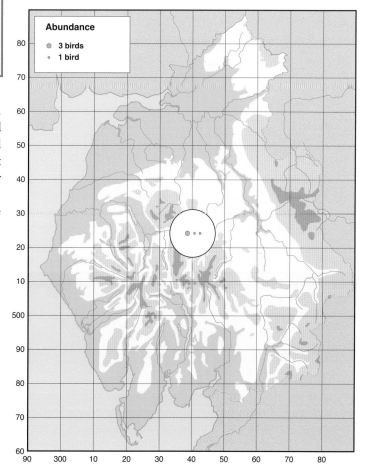

# Hen Harrier *Circus cyaneus*

REMOTE moorland is brought to life in the spring by the thrilling 'sky-dancing' display of the dove-grey male Hen Harrier. Effortlessly rising in the buoyant air above the slopes, he then casts over onto his back, and plummets in a roller-coaster of dizzying undulating loops, climbing steeply with deeply exaggerated wing-beats after each descent – an inspiring spectacle for all those privileged to witness it.

The Hen Harrier breeds across Eurasia and North America, with its main European breeding grounds in Fennoscandia, France and Spain. In Britain and Ireland, it occurs mainly in southwest Ireland, the Isle of Man and the western Highlands. In England, it is a very rare breeding bird, restricted to northern heather moorlands, and currently threatened with extinction.

18th century naturalists confronted by the presence of both 'grey' and 'brown' harriers thought them to be two species until Heysham (1796), monitoring harrier nests on Newton Common near Carlisle, proved otherwise. Prior to the Enclosures Act, and wide-scale drainage works in the 18th century, the Hen Harrier was considered common. A century later, it came into conflict with sporting interests on grouse moors. According to Macpherson (1892), large numbers of harriers were killed by gamekeepers employed by the Duke of Buccleugh and Lord Carlisle, prompting his disheartened statement "The hand of the game-preserver pressed on with the task of extermination." Then, as now, ground-nesting habits allowed for easy destruction of eggs and young, whilst bold defiance towards intruders made adults easy targets.

By the 20th century, the Hen Harrier was considered extinct in mainland Britain, a few pairs surviving only in the Outer Hebrides and Orkney. However, Graham (1993) asserts that a pair attending a nest with eggs was shot by a gamekeeper on the Bewcastle fells in 1928. Sightings, even of passage birds, were rare thereafter until a resurgence in the 1950s, the majority involving spring birds in the Border Uplands. Stokoe (1962) stated "a marked increase and spread in Scotland gives expectations of its return as a breeding bird." However, though the first recolonization in England was

acknowledged to be a pair in Northumberland in 1957, it took another three decades before the elaborate 'sky-dancing' display was again seen in the skies above Cumbria.

The *New Atlas* emphasized the rarity of Hen Harriers breeding in England with evidence found in just ten 10km squares, three of which were in Cumbria. *This Atlas* shows that the grouse moors of the North Pennines are the stronghold for the species within the county, with records outside this area considered to relate to peripatetic non-breeding birds. Indeed these moors are one of only two regular nesting areas for Hen Harriers in England.

The national Hen Harrier survey in 1998 revealed 19 territorial females in England, of which 11 reached the egg-laying stage (Sim *et al* 2001). However data from *this Atlas* shows the vulnerability of the species: although up to four territorial females bred annually in the county between 1997 and 2000, no breeding attempts were recorded in 2001.

That such a magnificent bird remains so perilously close to extinction in Cumbria at the dawn of the 21st century is shameful; there is no doubt that persecution on the managed grouse moors in the North Pennines acts as a catastrophic drain on the population. An account has been given of the activities on one such estate in 1995–1997. As part of its predator control policy, almost 1,000 birds of prey, including around 160 Hen Harriers, were killed (G. Emmerson pers comm). Sadly, this is far from an isolated occurrence – it is no surprise that several raptor species remain far below what would be their natural numbers in some of our finest landscapes. Clandestine methods are employed, even involving a cocktail of poisons. One such incident in 1998 involved dead Starlings, laced with mevinphos, being placed on a moor for one specific purpose – to bait Hen Harriers. Equally as macabre is the practice of tethering pigeons out in the heather to lure birds of prey within shotgun range.

The gravity of the situation is emphasized by the fact that in Scotland only 14% of Hen Harriers that breed on grouse moors are successful, compared with 40% on

Sponsored by Isobel Henderson & Island Holidays

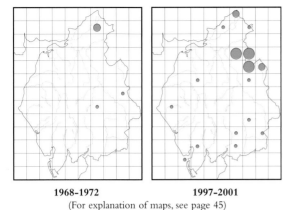

**1968-1972**          **1997-2001**

(For explanation of maps, see page 45)

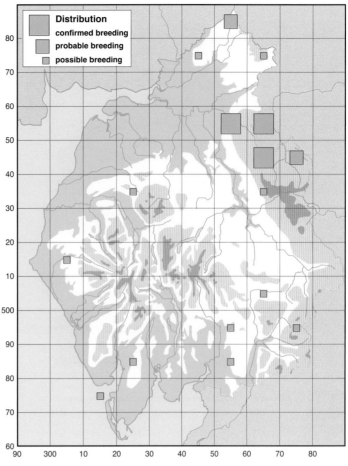

| Distribution |
|---|
| confirmed breeding |
| probable breeding |
| possible breeding |

*Conservation status*

| | |
|---|---|
| European: | SPEC Cat 2 & 3 |
| UK: | **RED: HD** |

*Populations*

| | |
|---|---|
| European status: | 9,500 |
| Britain – pairs: | 570 |
| Cumbria – pairs: | 0–4 |

*30-year distribution change*

| | Old Atlas | This Atlas | % |
|---|---|---|---|
| No. of 10km squares: | 3 | 16 | +433.3 |

| Survey data | Tetrads | % |
|---|---|---|
| Confirmed breeding: | 7 | 0.4 |
| Probable breeding: | 2 | 0.1 |
| Possible breeding: | 15 | 0.8 |
| Total: | 24 | 1.3 |

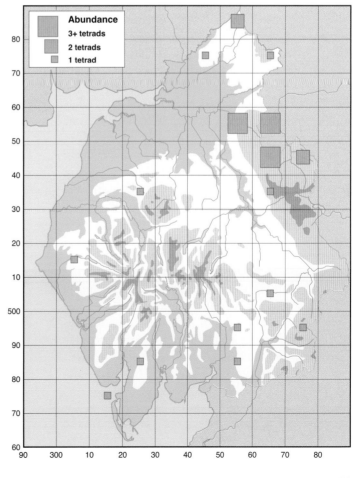

| Abundance |
|---|
| 3+ tetrads |
| 2 tetrads |
| 1 tetrad |

non-sporting estates and 66% in plantations (Etheridge *et al* 1997). Fieldwork in northern England has found remarkably similar results (Stott 1998), and on commercial grouse moors breeding ceased following the publication of a government report on *'Birds of Prey and Red Grouse'*, whereas it has fallen by just 17% on moorland with special protection schemes (Stott in prep).

The halcyon days of large grouse bags have gone forever, as the habitat availability has declined; it is unlikely that driven grouse shooting will survive if it has to resort to activities that threaten the diversity of vegetation and full suite of upland birds. Systematic, illegal killing of Hen Harriers on a few estates in the North Pennines is currently undermining any attempts to find common ground between game-shooters and conservationists. The Game Conservancy Trust estimates enough habitat to support over 200 pairs in England, so why so few?

Malcolm Stott

THE secretive, mysterious, and impressively large Goshawk is an easily overlooked species whose habits tend to keep it out of the public eye amid the quieter depths of the forest. It holds an unusual position in Britain's bird life, its population being probably wholly derived from escaped or deliberately released falconers' birds. Such introduced species are not normally afforded special protection by law, but the Goshawk is an exception. The locations of its nest sites are often carefully guarded secrets, as Goshawks are much persecuted. Some pairs have their nests illegally 'farmed' to provide birds for falconry, while adults, nests, eggs and young are destroyed in some game-rearing areas.

The Goshawk is a species of mature woodland and is found throughout the temperate and boreal zones of both hemispheres. It has both mainly resident and mainly migratory populations, and even in Britain local movements occur outside the breeding season, with established pairs not always being resident in their territories.

Although the status of the British population is blurred by secrecy, it was estimated at 400–450 pairs in 1994 (Petty 1996), twice the figure given in the *New Atlas*. Its strongholds are in Wales and the south of Scotland with smaller concentrations elsewhere, such as in East Anglia and the Derbyshire/Yorkshire border region. The Goshawk is found in both deciduous woodland and coniferous plantations with an apparent preference for the latter, which may stem from less persecution in such areas. While the species tends to be found in the larger coniferous plantations there are exceptions, such as in the Argyll forests, where

breeding has yet to be confirmed. The bulky stick nest is nearly always placed close to the main trunk; fresh greenery is added throughout the breeding season.

There is little background information available on the Goshawk's past status in Cumbria; Macpherson (1892) only mentions records from 1256 and 1849 while most recent sources fail to mention the species at all. Although Hutcheson (1986) gives 1983 as the first successful breeding season, at least one pair reared young in Cumbria in 1979 (pers obs). Birds had also been present in a wood in 1975, from where breeding was confirmed in later years, and this may better approximate to the actual first breeding date.

In spite of this fairly lengthy occupancy, the Cumbrian population has not increased greatly and numbers probably peaked during the late 1980s and early 1990s before maturing plantations began to be felled. A feature of the Cumbrian population is the number of sites which have been occupied only temporarily. A minimum total of 24 sites have been occupied since 1979 but only eight appear to have had long histories of continuous use and productivity. Some of the others have been lost through persecution, some have gone through loss of habitat and at least one has been usurped by Buzzards (pers obs). Such competition for nest sites is not unknown and the Buzzard's more catholic tastes and sedentary nature may give it an advantage over the Goshawk in the early occupancy of nest sites in the spring.

The species was recorded in 31 tetrads during fieldwork for *this Atlas* but some of these records undoubtedly referred to the same birds, given their proximity to known sites. These are widely scattered throughout the county and appear to be more closely associated with the quality of potential nesting woods than with the natural areas or a particular land class. That said, the species is absent from much of Lakeland, with some previously known sites now deserted, and is generally to be found at lower altitudes. Juveniles dispersing in the autumn often give a misleading impression of the species' distribution.

During the survey work for *this Atlas* the majority of records were of birds in outlying parts of the county, with only a handful of records from within the core area of Lakeland. The population figures are, perhaps surprisingly, low given the size of the county and the extent of apparently suitable breeding habitat. Although the number of nesting attempts may vary from year to year, for whatever reason, the current county population is estimated from data supplied by CRSG and supplementary records to be a maximum 10–15 breeding pairs in any one year.

Persecution is strongly suspected to be the major factor limiting increases in the county population, either by controlling productivity of local populations or more widely through suppression of potential

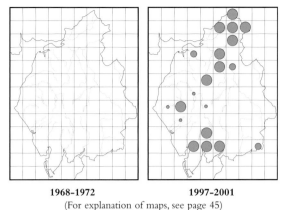

1968–1972      1997–2001
(For explanation of maps, see page 45)

| *Conservation status* | |
|---|---|
| European: | Non-SPEC |
| UK: | **GREEN** |

| *Populations* | |
|---|---|
| European status: | 75,000 |
| Britain – pairs: | 347 |
| Cumbria – pairs: | 10–15 |

*30-year distribution change*

| | Old Atlas | This Atlas | % |
|---|---|---|---|
| No. of 10km squares: | 0 | 20 | n/a |

| **Survey data** | **Tetrads** | **%** |
|---|---|---|
| Confirmed breeding: | 13 | 0.7 |
| Probable breeding: | 5 | 0.3 |
| Possible breeding: | 13 | 0.7 |
| Total: | 31 | 1.7 |

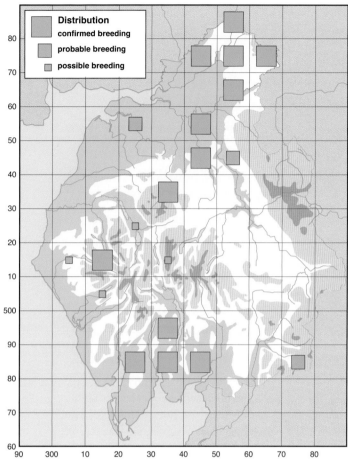

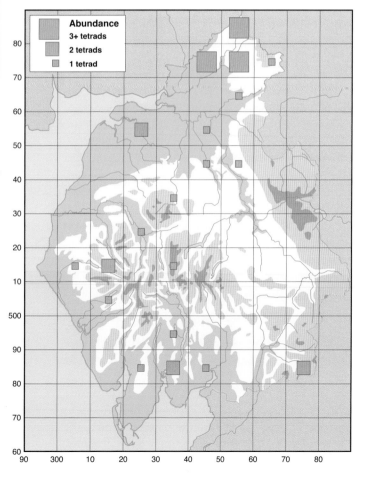

immigrant birds from peripheral areas outwith the county. In most areas where persecution can be discounted, it is believed that the most serious threats to the Goshawk in Cumbria come from competition from other species, the lack of reliable prey resources close to potential breeding areas and the loss of suitable nesting habitat, especially as commercial forestry reaches maturity and is subsequently felled.

The species may never be numerous in the county for reasons previously outlined and unfavourable spring weather often contributes to its low productivity. Few pairs that breed in Cumbria rear more than three young a season. Displaying Goshawks in the county are likely to remain rare, but if encountered by accident the spectacular sight will be one to cherish.

David Walker

# Sparrowhawk *Accipiter nisus*

THE dashing Sparrowhawk has become a familiar sight to many suburban householders, creating panic among the small birds at garden feeding stations. Its short broad wings and relatively long tail give it great manoeuvrability as it pursues its prey at speed, twisting and turning recklessly amid any obstacles.

It breeds widely over most of the Western Palearctic. In Britain and Ireland, its absence from parts of the Scottish Highlands and some of the Northern and Western Isles can be explained by lack of nesting habitat.

The bird inhabits scattered woodland and coniferous plantations, interspersed with cultivated land and open spaces. Areas of pine and spruce plantations are favoured for nesting, although deciduous trees, particularly birch, are sometimes used. The same area of a wood tends to be used each year and a large stand of woodland can hold a number of pairs. The nest is usually built just below the canopy and invariably in the upper third of the tree. An occupied nest can readily be recognized by the accumulation of down and, later, when young are present, by the copious amounts of droppings below the nesting tree.

The species is remarkably sedentary, most birds remaining close to their nesting territories. The diet consists largely of small birds, caught by stealthy approach and high-speed attack. Sparrowhawks can often be seen in suburban gardens or flying low along roadside hedges, slipping from side to side through gaps and accelerating to snatch their prey unawares. The surprise attack strategy appears a high-risk one, resulting in many fatalities to the hunter as well as the hunted. Sparrowhawk casualties, most often juveniles, resulting from impacts with windows, are a frequent source of ringing recoveries.

Sparrowhawks have largely recovered ground in eastern England lost due to the effects of the organochlorine pesticides used in the 1950s and 1960s, with the help also of lower levels of illegal persecution. Analysis of the latest available CBC data reveals a massive 188% increase since 1970, though trends may not be representative of the whole of Britain and Ireland. More recently, BBS data suggest numbers have stabilized, although with some regional variations.

Despite persecution, the Sparrowhawk remained widespread in Cumbria during the 19th century (Newton 1986). Macpherson (1892) commented that "common as this hawk must always have been in the Lakeland forests, and difficult as it is to train, early falconers appear to have held it in some estimation." Stokoe (1962) regarded it as "frequent throughout, breeding up to 950 feet [290m]." However, he also remarked on recent indications of reduced numbers and failure to breed in such areas as Low Furness and near Carlisle, though he went on to state that "compared with forests in southern and eastern England, P.A. Banks found the bird relatively numerous and successful in the spruce forests around Ennerdale in 1961." As was the case nationally, there was a dramatic decline in Cumbria during the pesticide era of the 1950s and early 1960s, when toxic residues were picked up by prey species in their food. This caused a gradual accumulation in the tissues of predators such as the Sparrowhawk and resulted in reduced breeding success and eventual mortality of the adults. Brown (1974) reported that, before 1955, 32 Sparrowhawk broods had averaged 4.15 young, but that, after this date, 16 broods had averaged just 2.18 young, with four instances of only one young being reared, a situation not recorded before 1955.

With the voluntary restrictions on the use of DDT and dieldrin during 1962–66, the population, both nationally and locally, started to make a dramatic recovery. Newton & Haas (1984) found that 30 traditional nesting sites in Cumbria showed an initial level of around 85% occupancy in 1941, this declined to a nadir of 22% in the pesticide years of 1961–65, before gradually recovering to 75% by 1978.

With birds recorded in almost all of the county's 10km squares, there is little change in distribution between the *Old Atlas* and *this Atlas*. The distribution map for *this Atlas* reveals, not unexpectedly, a lack of records from the treeless high ground of Lakeland and the North Pennines and from areas of the Solway Basin, also lacking in nesting habitat. The strongholds lie in south and west Lakeland, parts of the Coastal Plain and the Border Uplands.

Although Newton (1986) estimated densities in the Solway Basin to be in the region of 5.9 pairs/100km²,

Sponsored by Peter le Brocq

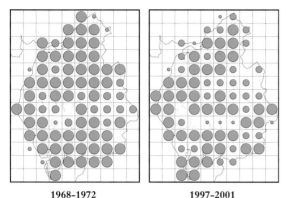

**1968–1972** **1997–2001**

(For explanation of maps, see page 45)

*Conservation status*

| | |
|---|---|
| European: | Non-SPEC |
| UK: | **GREEN** |

*Populations*

| | |
|---|---|
| European status: | 155,000 |
| Britain – pairs: | 32,000 |
| Cumbria – pairs: | 1,000 |

*30-year distribution change*

| | Old Atlas | This Atlas | % |
|---|---|---|---|
| No. of 10km squares: | 79 | 79 | n/c |

| Survey data | Tetrads | % |
|---|---|---|
| Confirmed breeding: | 84 | 4.6 |
| Probable breeding: | 166 | 9.0 |
| Possible breeding: | 205 | 11.1 |
| Total: | 455 | 24.7 |

this has perhaps fallen in response to habitat change and declining populations of some prey species. Since line transect data offers no reliable figure, the current county population figure is based on a plausible estimate from count data, enhanced by supplementary records, to suggest 1,000 pairs.

Though the future of the Sparrowhawk in Cumbria would seem secure, there is no room for complacency. Populations of some of the small birds taken by Sparrowhawks are now in decline. Some woods, particularly on the Solway Basin, which had consistently held pairs even during the pesticide era, are no longer tenanted, and larger stands of plantation which held four or five pairs during the 1980s now hold only one. The prospects for this bird in Cumbria are uncertain.

Geoff Horne

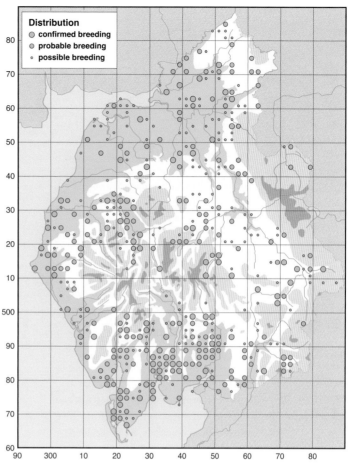

Distribution
- confirmed breeding
- probable breeding
- possible breeding

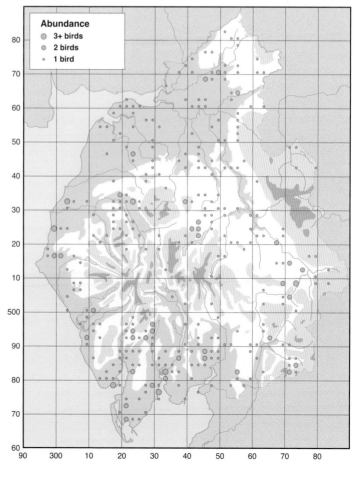

Abundance
- 3+ birds
- 2 birds
- 1 bird

# **Buzzard** *Buteo buteo*

Common Buzzard

EFFORTLESSLY soaring on broad-fingered wings, the majestic Buzzard, with its distinctive mewing calls, is often misidentified by unknowing visitors to Cumbria as the illustrious 'Lakeland Eagle'. Unlike the eagle however, which teeters on the brink of extinction as a breeding bird in the county, the Buzzard is thriving.

The Buzzard's breeding range extends almost throughout the Palearctic, north of the Mediterranean to the limit of the boreal forest, and eastwards across the boreal forest zone of Asia. In Britain, its distribution is strongly biased towards the west and north, while in Ireland it is most abundant in the northeast.

The bird breeds in both upland and lowland environments and across a broad range of land types. In woodland habitats, a bulky nest structure is built on a lateral branch of a substantial tree, close to the main trunk, but in spacious, treeless landscapes ledges on crags provide a nest platform. The Buzzard is an adept and versatile predator, taking a wide variety of prey items: mammals, particularly rabbits, are the most common, though birds, invertebrates and carrion are also frequently taken. This adaptability is the key to its success. Its resilience to changes in land use, which affect more specialist feeders, makes it less susceptible to short-term trends in agriculture. Where food is abundant, Buzzards are able to breed at very high densities; one intensively-studied population near Bristol revealed a total of 56 breeding pairs in a 75km$^2$ study area (Prytherch 1997).

In the 18th century, Buzzards supposedly bred in all British counties; however, populations diminished in a

relatively short space of time and by 1860 they were restricted to a few western districts (Newton 1979). This was no natural decline: persecution, ruthless until early in the 20th century, removed the Buzzard as a breeding species from much of Britain. More recently, the species has spread eastwards as part of a recovery from the effects of the organochlorine pesticides of the 1950s and 1960s, helped by lower levels of illegal persecution in lowland areas. Analysis of the latest available CBC data reveals a massive 350% increase since 1970, though trends may not be representative of Britain and Ireland as a whole.

In Cumbria, Macpherson (1892) observed that "the harmless character of the Buzzard did not always avail to save it from the persecution of undiscriminating churchwardens". Prestt (1965) suggested that the county population had been reduced to around 30 pairs at the beginning of the 19th century. Stokoe (1962) regarded the Buzzard as "frequent in all fell districts and adjacent wooded valleys, except in north Cumberland" and commented that it "nests in crags, commonly up to 1,500–1,750 feet [457–534m] and occasionally to 2,200 feet [671m], and in trees. Nowhere near coast, except recently on southern estuaries." The extent of subsequent recovery in more enlightened times was perhaps limited by the onset of myxomatosis in the 1950s – Stokoe mentioned breeding numbers in north Westmorland varying with fluctuations in Rabbit numbers due to myxomatosis – and organochlorine pesticide contamination of prey species in the 1960s. The county population has since shown a steady recovery, boosted by legislation outlawing the indiscriminate use of poisons in the countryside. Breeding numbers have been closely monitored in the Haweswater area for some years and the picture has been one of stability, with the number of occupied territories varying between 15 and 21 in the period 1992–2000 (Kenmir 2001).

The population increase in Cumbria has been remarkable over the 30-year time-span between the *Old Atlas* and *this Atlas,* with a marked expansion in its county range. Indeed, this has been one of the success stories of *this Atlas,* which reveals that almost all of the county's 10km squares are now occupied. The strongholds are in the Border Uplands, Eden Valley, Cumbria Dales, Lune Valley and Lakeland but the breeding range now extends to the Solway Basin and much of the Coastal Plain. However, the bird remains sparsely distributed in the North Pennines, despite much apparently suitable habitat, suggesting that this population may still be suffering from persecution on some managed grouse moors. As a result, these North Pennine moors act as a barrier against potential eastward expansion of the Cumbrian population. Optimum breeding conditions in Cumbria would appear to be open farmland for hunting, interspersed

Sponsored by Geoffrey Fryer

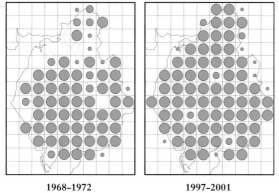

**1968-1972**       **1997-2001**

(For explanation of maps, see page 45)

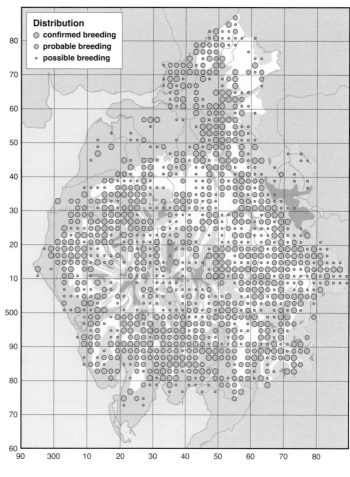

**Distribution**
- ⊙ confirmed breeding
- ⊙ probable breeding
- · possible breeding

**Conservation status**

| | |
|---|---|
| European: | Non-SPEC |
| UK: | GREEN |

**Populations**

| | |
|---|---|
| European status: | 410,000 |
| Britain – pairs: | 14,500 |
| Cumbria – pairs: | 3,500 |

**30-year distribution change**

| | Old Atlas | This Atlas | % |
|---|---|---|---|
| No. of 10km squares: | 65 | 81 | +24.6 |

| **Survey data** | **Tetrads** | **%** |
|---|---|---|
| Confirmed breeding: | 352 | 19.1 |
| Probable breeding: | 380 | 20.6 |
| Possible breeding: | 398 | 21.6 |
| Total: | 1130 | 61.3 |

with stands of relatively undisturbed woodland for breeding.

Analysis of the line transect data from *this Atlas* gives a population band of 2,000–19,000, suggesting a mean population of 7,000 birds. Note, however, the wide band limits. The highest Buzzard densities of 5.8 birds/km$^2$ occurred on peripheral wooded valleys that radiate out of Lakeland.

As an adaptable species and generalist feeder, there seems no reason why the Buzzard should not continue to thrive in Cumbria. The one limiting factor appears to be illegal persecution; hopefully, this will decline and allow this versatile raptor to extend its range still further across the county.

Bill Kenmir

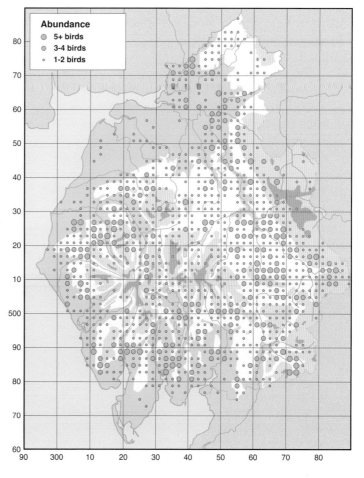

**Abundance**
- ⊙ 5+ birds
- ⊙ 3-4 birds
- · 1-2 birds

# Golden Eagle *Aquila chrysaetos*

THE King of Birds finds a special affection in the hearts of many birdwatchers. Its aloof grandeur engenders admiration, although, as the consummate predator of the British avifauna, it is able and willing to kill species varying in size from Red Deer calves to Field Voles. Often to be found perched stoically on a high ledge or cryptically positioned rowan tree, come sun or snow, the Golden Eagle is a bird of wild and harsh terrain.

It is the most widespread and numerous eagle, its range extending around the temperate regions of the northern hemisphere. Though most populations are sedentary, some migrate; however, adults seen outside the normal breeding range in Britain are almost certainly birds prospecting for potential territories rather than migrants. With only one breeding pair in Cumbria, the Golden Eagle is an extreme rarity here and is generally viewed as a typically Scottish bird.

The Golden Eagle is a generalist species, occupying a variety of habitats throughout its range. In Britain, it is mostly a bird of the uplands but it will also breed on sea cliffs and, at times, in surprisingly close proximity to enclosed farmland. In Cumbria, the remaining occupied territory includes hill farms, deer forest and grouse moor, a mixture typical of many Scottish pairs' home ranges.

Although the species is known to have formerly bred quite widely in Cumbria, as partly evidenced by the number of crags with eagle-related names, it had become extinct by the late 18th century. The exact timing of its demise is uncertain due to confusion in the records with the White-tailed Eagle but it seems likely that the Golden Eagle may have clung on longer

than the records suggest (Macpherson 1892). Although wandering individuals were recorded between times, it did not become a regular visitor again until the 1950s (Blezard 1958). This followed recolonization of southwest Scotland, part of a range expansion throughout Scotland at that time.

Eagle nests were found in Cumbria in 1957 and 1958, but eggs were not recorded until 1969 (Brown 1974). Since then, breeding has been recorded at three discrete locations, with varying degrees of success. One site is not known to have reared young (D. Hayward pers comm) but the second site reared three young during 1976–1982. The eggs laid in 1969 were found in the Haweswater territory which continues to be occupied to this day and which had, until the mid-1990s, a comparatively good breeding record, rearing 16 young from 31 breeding attempts in 32 years. Only three of these young were fledged after 1990, however, and none was reared during *this Atlas* period.

During *this Atlas,* there were no confirmed sightings of eagles away from the Haweswater territory. This follows the decline in numbers and breeding success in southwest Scotland, mainly attributed to the afforestation of foraging areas reducing the availability of food. Since it is believed that all of the recently resident Cumbrian adults originated from that source, the likelihood of new birds arriving here has thus been greatly reduced. The loss of the second established pair in 1983 followed the death of the female and the lack of a replacement.

The recent breeding failures at Haweswater may have a more fundamental cause, however, with evidence that a decline in the food supply may be preventing the adults from attaining breeding condition. Although the same two adult eagles have formed the pair since 1981, the last two clutches were not begun until approximately three weeks after the expected laying date – as late as 13th April in 2000. It is believed that changes in sheep husbandry have been the primary cause of the failing winter food supply; it is now a legal requirement to bury or remove sheep carcasses. This has been compounded by a decline within the territory of Red Grouse, which the eagles have regularly taken at times of carrion shortages. An attempt to resolve this situation was made in 2000 by a joint CRSG/United Utilities project aimed at enhancing the food supply in the months prior to egg-laying. This may have encouraged egg production that year, after a non-breeding year in 1999, although no young were hatched. Such actions are, however, not a realistic long-term solution. The best option would involve habitat enhancement work to encourage an increased natural food supply but this would probably be too long-term a project to benefit the present pair. In 2001, the outbreak of foot-and-mouth disease restricted monitoring to observations from the nearest

Sponsored by Dave Walker

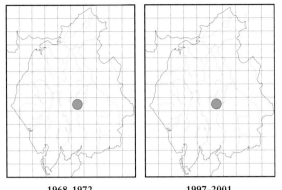

**1968–1972**　　　　　**1997–2001**
(For explanation of maps, see page 45)

| *Conservation status* | |
| --- | --- |
| European: | SPEC Cat 3 |
| UK: | **AMBER** |

| *Populations* | |
| --- | --- |
| European status: | 5,400 |
| Britain – pairs: | 420 |
| Cumbria – pairs: | 1 |

*30-year distribution change*

| | Old Atlas | This Atlas | % |
| --- | --- | --- | --- |
| No. of 10km squares: | 1 | 1 | n/c |

| **Survey data** | **Tetrads** | **%** |
| --- | --- | --- |
| Confirmed breeding: | 1 | 0.05 |
| Probable breeding: | 0 | |
| Possible breeding: | 0 | |
| Total: | 1 | 0.05 |

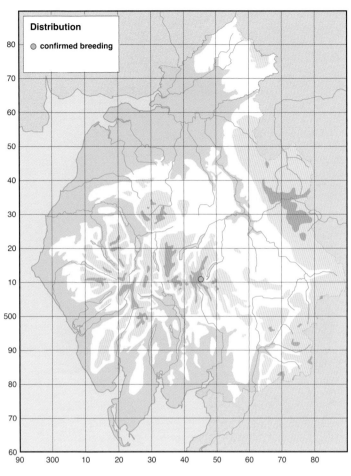

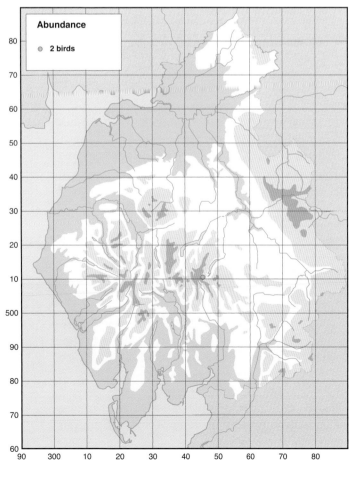

road, though the birds' behaviour suggested egg-laying failed to occur.

Even though the British Golden Eagle population is estimated at about 420 pairs, not all of these breed successfully, nor even attempt to breed, in any one year and, with the national population apparently retreating to the north and west, there is little real hope of the species re-establishing itself in Cumbria. That the bird clings on in the Lake District National Park is now something of an anachronism; yet the loss of the existing pair would be a source of great sadness to the thousands of people who have been thrilled by the marvellous sight of the English eagles over the years.

David Walker

# Osprey *Pandion haliaetus*

AN Osprey hovers over a river before plunging feet first into the water; amid a plume of spray, it emerges, a fish grasped firmly in its talons. The return of this spectacular fish-hawk, so befitting the grandeur of its Lakeland setting, during the period of *this Atlas*, was eagerly awaited, and greeted with celebration.

Ospreys have a cosmopolitan distribution, found in every continent except Antarctica. In Britain and Ireland, the core breeding area remains the old pine forests, freshwater lochs and rivers of Strathspey. The nest is a bulky structure of interwoven sticks, lined with grass, bark and moss, and situated in the top of a tree. In Scotland, pines and dead trees of various species are most frequently used.

Historically, the Osprey never featured prominently in Cumbria's avifauna and eminent ornithologists in the past doubted that it ever bred. Confusing accounts of 'Fish Eagle' and 'Sea Eagle' (*ie.* White-tailed Eagle) by earlier naturalists prompted Macpherson (1892) to investigate the available accounts. He concluded that the first authentic record of breeding Ospreys was at Whinsfield Park in 1676, and cited only two other possible nesting attempts – in the Ullswater District in 1793 and at Corby Castle in about 1831.

During much of the 20th century, the species was considered to be, at best, an irregular or scarce passage migrant in Cumbria. The *New Atlas* recorded presence in three 10km squares, and during the 1990s an upsurge in the number of passage birds moving through the county was apparent, and, more significantly, a few immature birds lingered through the summer.

During the period of *this Atlas,* the incidence of summering increased. Two immatures spent time at Bassenthwaite Lake in 1997, and in 1998 two summered at the lake. One of these, a male, had been ringed as a nestling on Speyside in 1995. It is well-known that the presence of breeding Ospreys draws others to breed nearby; to encourage nesting, nesting platforms were erected in July 1998, with imitation nests, daubed with white paint to simulate recent occupation!

In 1999 there were again two Ospreys at Bassenthwaite, but this time the male was a different, unringed, bird! In May 2000, there was real progress: Ospreys were frequently seen to mate on one of the platforms, and the birds carried sticks to the nest. However, the male seemed inexperienced, and yet again there was disappointment. The birds had departed by 10th August (Barron 2002).

In parallel with the activity at Bassenthwaite Lake, events elsewhere were proceeding apace. In 1999 a pair had been found with a nest in a natural site, but the attempt appeared to fail at the egg-laying stage. A male returned to the same site on 10th April 2000, and two females on 14th April, one of which remained to breed. Incubation began on 21st April. Confirmation of hatching came on 25th May when the female was observed tearing tiny morsels from a large trout and offering them into the nest-cup. After 53 days a single chick fledged, the first to leave a Cumbrian eyrie for around 170 years. In accordance with the wishes of the landowners no news of this event was released. At a third site, a pair built a nest through the 2000 season.

In 2001 all three of these sites were known to have completed clutches. Three chicks were reared to fledging at the site of the previous year's success. At Bassenthwaite Lake, a pair adopted one of the platforms, and at last reared a single chick from a clutch of two eggs. Once hatching had been confirmed, a viewing site was opened on the opposite side of the lake, in a welter of publicity; 25,000 people viewed the nest and birds over the following ten weeks – a great success both for the conservation movement, and for the partnership of LDNP, FC, and RSPB, and a huge boost to tourism-starved Lakeland in a year otherwise ruined by foot-and-mouth disease restrictions. Such restrictions also prevented adequate monitoring of the third site. It is known that a pair incubated, but great concern was expressed that no birds were present on two later occasions during the anticipated fledging period. Information later emerged of a bird found dead near the nest-tree; most unfortunately, since the corpse was not retained the cause of death remains unknown.

In summary, during the period of *this Atlas* the first nesting attempt was in 1999, and a total of five young

 Sponsored by Julian Hughes

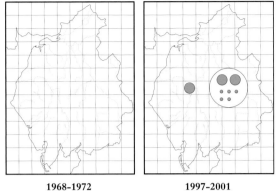

| 1968-1972 | 1997-2001 |
|:---:|:---:|

(For explanation of maps, see page 45)

**Conservation status**

| | |
|---|---:|
| European: | SPEC Cat 3 |
| UK: | AMBER: HD & BR |

**Populations**

| | |
|---|---:|
| European status: | 5,000 |
| Britain − pairs: | 136 |
| Cumbria − pairs: | 3 |

**30-year distribution change**

| | Old Atlas | This Atlas | % |
|---|:---:|:---:|:---:|
| No. of 10km squares: | 0 | 8 | n/a |

| **Survey data** | **Tetrads** | **%** |
|---|:---:|:---:|
| Confirmed breeding: | 3 | 0.16 |
| Probable breeding: | 0 | |
| Possible breeding: | 7 | 0.38 |
| Total: | 10 | 0.54 |

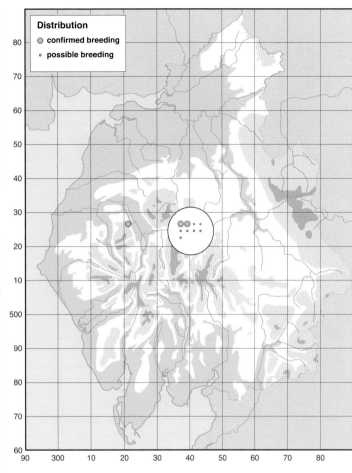

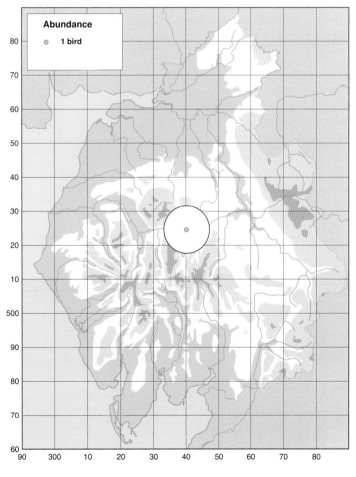

fledged from a current county population of three breeding pairs.

This recolonization reflects the continued increase in the Scottish population; numbers of nests are currently doubling every 10 years (Mead 2000). In 1999, 136 pairs nested (Ogilvie *et al* 2001). The long-term success of the Osprey in Cumbria will largely depend on a combination of dedicated protection at some sites, and secrecy at others. Undoubtedly, every eyrie will be under constant threat from the menace of egg-collectors. There is also a significant risk of interference from 'unreformed' old-style game-preservers − sadly, still all too active in parts of the county. Ospreys are high profile birds which can capture the imagination of a nation; the viewing facilities at Bassenthwaite Lake provide an opportunity to increase the public's awareness of the ongoing need for bird conservation.

Malcolm Stott

C.M. Isherwood

INSTANTLY recognizable, and immortalized in Hopkins' imaginative poem 'The Windhover', there can be few people who do not associate with the Kestrel's haunting, hovering silhouette. Its relatively recent adoption of roadside hunting habits have made it a familiar and popular bird of prey and for many years the Kestrel was the symbol of the RSPB's Young Ornithologists Club.

Distributed across three continents, the Kestrel is the most abundant raptor over much of the Western Palearctic and common and widespread throughout Britain and Ireland. Breeding occurs in all but the northernmost fringes of Europe with strongholds in Britain and Ireland, France, Germany and Russia. In many northern regions it is a total migrant wintering in southern Europe and Africa, whereas in Britain and Ireland ringing suggests that it has a partial migratory strategy. Recoveries of Cumbrian ringed juveniles have come from southwest England and northern France (Stokoe 1962 & pers obs).

The Kestrel is primarily a bird of farmland and open habitats including forest fringes and rocky areas. For such a relatively common and easily recognized species breeding birds can be surprisingly difficult to locate. Nest-site preferences include old crow nests, rock crevices, cliffs, ledges and holes in trees, and they easily take to nestboxes. All of these are readily available in Cumbria. Usually a solitary breeder, the abundance of small rodents has a marked effect on breeding numbers and success, although small colonies have been noted where food is in good supply.

Historically the Kestrel was regarded as the commonest diurnal bird of prey in Cumbria, nesting from the coastal fringe to 660m asl in the fells, and according to Macpherson (1892) they were "as much at home among the clefts of the sea cliffs as when rearing their young in the wooded valleys of Lakeland." Macpherson and Duckworth (1886) reported it as "breeding so numerously that as many as 27 Kestrels were flying in the air at once near Barron Wood but comparatively few winter with us." However, along with other predators, Kestrels were killed as vermin on game-rearing estates in the late 19th century causing serious population declines. Lack of gamekeeping during the two World Wars helped the Kestrel population to recover. However recent history suggests that in the 1950s and 1960s the species was suffering the effects of the widespread use of persistent organochlorine pesticides.

The transformation of agriculture into specialist farming has reduced the diversity in land management and where this is most intensive, such as on the Solway Basin and the lower Eden Valley, it leaves little natural habitat and reduces feeding opportunities for Kestrels. The loss of old trees, through hedgerow removal, may also have had an impact by reducing the availability of natural nest sites. High stocking rates have produced grassland that is unsuitable for voles, which may have affected their reproductive cycles. The absence of well-marked vole 'boom' years may well affect the Kestrel's ability to rear large broods, as in former years. The incidental creation of linear habitats along roadside and motorway verges, where the bird is forced to hunt in the absence of prey in the wider countryside, may lead to increased mortality, another potential source of local declines.

Although declines in the Kestrel population were highlighted in the *New Atlas,* especially from northwest Scotland and Ireland, in comparison with the distribution map in the *Old Atlas,* it remained strong in its Cumbrian range with a slight decline in the number of occupied 10km squares, from 88 to 84. The distribution map from *this Atlas* also shows little change: most valleys that radiate from central Lakeland are occupied, and there is a concentration of squares with high abundance in the triangle between Keswick, Whitehaven and Workington. The North Pennines and Solway Basin have sparse populations by comparison, and for some reason it appears to be very scarce inland between Maryport and Silloth and in the valley from Ravenglass to Eskdale.

While the long-running CBC series shows a 24% decline nationally – which may have accelerated in recent years according to BBS results – this has not been so obvious in Cumbria compared to the situation in some neighbouring counties. Analysis of line transect data from *this Atlas* gives a population band of 1,000–8,000, suggesting a mean population of 3,000 birds. However, the relatively small sample size dictates

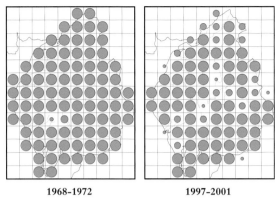

**1968–1972**  **1997–2001**
(For explanation of maps, see page 45)

**Conservation status**
European: SPEC Cat 3
UK: **AMBER: BDM**

**Populations**
European status: 280,000
Britain – pairs: 50,000
Cumbria – pairs: 1,500

**30-year distribution change**

| | Old Atlas | This Atlas | % |
|---|---|---|---|
| No. of 10km squares: | 88 | 84 | −4.5 |

| **Survey data** | **Tetrads** | **%** |
|---|---|---|
| Confirmed breeding: | 162 | 8.8 |
| Probable breeding: | 259 | 14.0 |
| Possible breeding: | 439 | 23.8 |
| Total: | 860 | 46.6 |

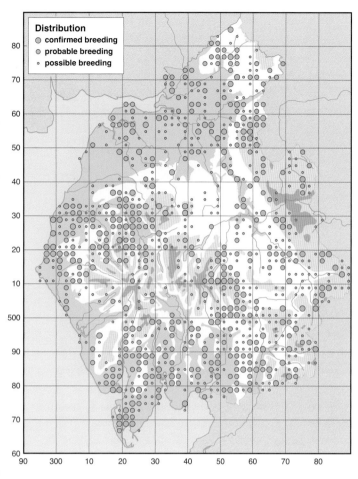

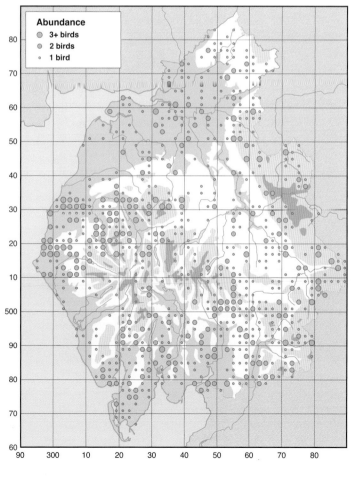

that discretion should be exercised with this estimate. The highest densities were found in the transitional zone between the arable Coastal Plain and well-wooded foothills of Lakeland.

Although the recent phenomenon of Buzzard increases has relegated the Kestrel to the county's second most numerous diurnal bird of prey, this may be temporary. Future changes in agricultural policy, perhaps with financial resources more focused towards environmental schemes, could see a return to the boom and bust cyclical populations of voles and given the Kestrel's adaptability in using man-made nest sites, the present declining trend could easily be reversed. As a key indicator of the health and diversity of our countryside its fortunes should be monitored closely by government agencies.

Pete Davies

# Merlin *Falco columbarius*

A BRIEF silhouette as this diminutive blue falcon breaks the far-distant horizon to advertise its presence, calling as it circles high above, is usually the first sighting on its breeding grounds in spring. As a scarce breeder with a preference for nesting in our least visited uplands, this dashing spirit of the moors is one of our most elusive raptors, more often encountered on our estuaries in winter.

It has a circumpolar distribution, extending throughout Fennoscandia, through central Siberia to North America. In Britain its strongholds are in mid-Wales, the Pennines, the Southern Uplands and the eastern Highlands, with an extremely sparse distribution in Ireland.

In Britain the Merlin has a preference for nesting on the ground, usually in tall heather or bracken, although it will readily adapt to trees, using old crow nests when circumstances dictate. This habit was first recorded in Cumbria during the late 1970s, following an extension of forestry plantings in the uplands. Such moorland areas would have been former traditional breeding haunts prior to the conversion to tree cover. The last cliff-nesting pair in the county was recorded from the southeast in the 1970s (Bishop 1979).

Macpherson (1892) described the bird as common during the 19th century, but threatened by persecution; their habit of perching on posts made them particularly vulnerable to being caught in pole traps placed on the moor by gamekeepers. Widespread heather loss since the 1940s (NCC 1987) and an unhealthy build up of persistent organochlorine pesticides in the 1950s and 1960s caused the population to decline sharply, from which the recovery has been slow.

Evidence suggests breeding occurred at 115 locations prior to 1980 (Shackleton 1996), including on the Solway Mosses where nesting is thought to have ceased by the 1930s (D.A. Ratcliffe pers comm). No population estimates exist for this period but peak numbers are likely to have been before the post-1940s acceleration of heather loss. Unlike today, the majority of known sites were in Lakeland, partly reflecting the greater interest from naturalists in that area, but emphasizing that the Lakeland decline has been real. During the 1930s, Sedbergh School monitored several sites in the southeast of the county, an area which today appears to hold only an odd pair.

A survey in 1983–84 located 28 occupied sites and during the 1980s 38 sites are known to have been used in at least one year. A repeat survey in 1993–94 found 42 occupied sites with a minimum total of 34 in any one year, while 59 sites have been identified as holding breeding Merlins at some time in the 1990s. Atlas methodology has its shortcomings in locating such a secretive species. Nevertheless, the *Old Atlas* confirmed breeding in 19 10km squares with presence in 17 more. The *New Atlas* showed 15 and 14 respectively. Distribution was broadly similar between the two periods; the northeastern Lakeland foothills, the North Pennines and the Border Uplands were the favoured areas, but losses were apparent from western Lakeland and on its eastern periphery around the Howgill Fells.

The Merlin in Cumbria is a well-monitored species for which detailed data are held. Additional fieldwork during *this Atlas* confirmed breeding in 17 10km squares with many more records involving nomadic non-breeding birds, some in likely breeding sites. The maximum number of 10km squares with confirmed or probable breeding during the fieldwork for *this Atlas* may have been as many as 23. While the general distribution remains similar to that of the *Old* and *New Atlases*, new evidence suggests that breeding may today occur at higher densities in the North Pennines, where a maximum of 6 pairs/100km$^2$ are recorded.

Count data and supplementary records from *this Atlas* suggest a current county population of 50 breeding pairs, a figure which complements data from a long-term study by CRSG.

Today extensive tracts of heather are confined to managed grouse moors and it is here where most Cumbrian Merlins breed. Main strongholds are on the North Pennine blanket bogs where local densities can be as high as anywhere in Britain and where nesting has been recorded up to 600m asl. A small but stable population has established itself in the Border Uplands but few pairs breed on the less extensive heather on the outlying moors of Lakeland. Although odd sites in Lakeland have recently been re-occupied, the population is sparse and widely dispersed, and many

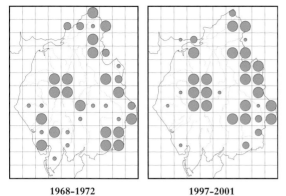

**1968–1972**          **1997–2001**

(For explanation of maps, see page 45)

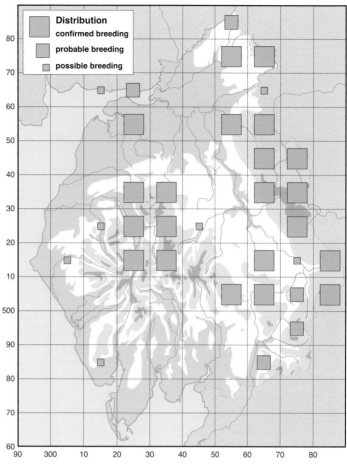

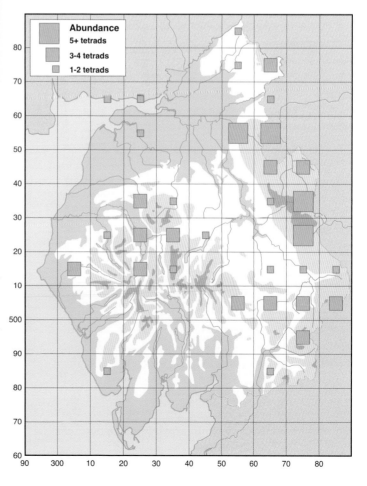

***Conservation status***

| | |
|---|---|
| European: | Non-SPEC |
| UK: | **AMBER: HD** |

***Populations***

| | |
|---|---|
| European status: | 13,000 |
| Britain – pairs: | 1,300 |
| Cumbria – pairs: | 50 |

***30-year distribution change***

| | Old Atlas | This Atlas | % |
|---|---|---|---|
| No. of 10km squares: | 36 | 33 | **−8.3** |

| **Survey data** | **Tetrads** | **%** |
|---|---|---|
| Confirmed breeding: | 44 | 2.4 |
| Probable breeding: | 12 | 0.7 |
| Possible breeding: | 41 | 2.2 |
| Total: | 97 | 5.3 |

former haunts remain unoccupied. The same is likely to be true on the eastern fringe fells around the Howgill Fells, but there are now better prospects of resumed nesting on the Solway Mosses.

Currently Merlin populations breeding on grouse moor may be close to maximum densities and should have an assured future, given that these areas are largely situated within SSSI and SPA designated areas, which afford protection to heather from overgrazing and encroachment of forestry. Elsewhere, their fate may depend on the fate of heather cover, under agri-environment schemes likely to be introduced in the wake of the foot-and-mouth disease outbreak. However, human disturbance and high populations of other raptors may also influence any expansion.

Dave Shackleton

# Peregrine Falcon *Falco peregrinus*

THIS spectacular and charismatic falcon is regarded by many as the fastest living creature. Its thrilling vertical stoops, often witnessed against a backdrop of wild mountain scenery, add to its attraction, while its display flight and strident calls during pair-bonding in early spring represent one of the first signs of life returning to the upland valleys.

The Peregrine's breeding range extends across all continents except Antarctica. It breeds widely in Britain and Ireland, though still largely absent from central, south and east England. The high fells and precipitous crags of Cumbria have always been its main English stronghold.

Macpherson (1892) commented that "the Peregrine Falcon has nested from time immemorial among the precipices of the Lake District" and cited many instances of persecution, commenting that "no species could increase in the face of such destructive measures." This is a species that has never been far from controversy: persecution by falconers, egg-collectors, pigeon-fanciers and the game-rearing fraternity was the main reason why the population remained low during the first half of the 20th century. To this day, Peregrines are illegally shot, poisoned and have their eggs or young destroyed. However, with increased legal protection, and public concern for wildlife, persecution of raptors has become unacceptable to the general public. This, together with the increase in food supply during the 1970s and 1980s as a result of the rise in popularity of racing pigeons through the county, has resulted in the healthy population of Peregrines in Cumbria today.

Historically, the main concentration of territories was in central Lakeland on land between 350m and 600m asl. Traditional nesting crags of 'first class' status were mostly remote precipitous faces, on average 60m high, in the main, facing between east and north – in fact most substantial Lakeland cliffs have this aspect. These were also the territories that held the few remnant birds during the pesticide era of the 1950s and 1960s. The effects of pesticide poisoning were first noticed nationally in the 1950s, and by the early 1960s the Cumbrian population had crashed to a mere eight pairs. Of these, only three or four pairs were rearing young in any one year and the species was on the verge of extinction in the county. Recovery occurred soon after the restrictions on the use of pesticides between 1962 and 1966. Increases from such a low level are likely to have involved movements into the county from other areas, particularly the Highlands of Scotland, which had suffered least.

The pre-Second World War estimate of 41 pairs in Cumbria has been taken as the baseline against which to measure future trends (Ratcliffe 1993). The national survey in 1971 revealed 21 territory-holding pairs in Cumbria, just over half the pre-pesticide figure. Surveys in 1981 and 1991 showed a sustained recovery in the Cumbrian population, with 68 and 94 occupied territories respectively. The latter represented a staggering 229% increase on the baseline figure. Recruitment to the Cumbrian population during the 1970s and 1980s was approximately 3.5 new pairs annually. During the initial stages of recovery, the first territories to be re-occupied were the traditional first class crags. The new birds instinctively returned to exactly the same ledges and even to the same nesting scrapes which had been used by past generations of Peregrines. As numbers continued to increase, new 'second class' territories were established. These tended to be centred on smaller, less remote crags, as well as in both working and abandoned quarries. New pairs continued to appear, now often using 'third class' sites with no previous history of occupation, such as small outcrops in lowland river valleys, and industrial slag banks close to human habitation. The 1990s saw numbers rise still further, to a total of 100 occupied territories, regarded as saturation level for the county.

Unsurprisingly, *this Atlas* reveals that the number of occupied 10km squares has more than doubled since the *Old Atlas*. Birds are now to be found breeding in previously unoccupied areas of the Coastal Plain, the Solway Basin and Border Uplands. However, it does appear that there has been a slight but discernible decline: at eight recently occupied regular breeding sites, there were no signs of occupation in 2000. One possible explanation is the reduced amount of food available as a result of fewer racing pigeons passing

Sponsored by Gary, Christopher & Andrew Henderson

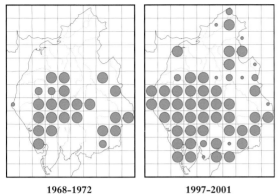

**1968-1972**          **1997-2001**
(For explanation of maps, see page 45)

***Conservation status***

| | |
|---|---|
| European: | SPEC Cat 3 |
| UK: | AMBER |

***Populations***

| | |
|---|---|
| European status: | 5,800 |
| Britain – pairs: | 1,200 |
| Cumbria – pairs: | 90–110 |

***30-year distribution change***

| | Old Atlas | This Atlas | % |
|---|---|---|---|
| No. of 10km squares: | 25 | 56 | +124 |

| **Survey data** | **Tetrads** | **%** |
|---|---|---|
| Confirmed breeding: | 127 | 6.9 |
| Probable breeding: | 13 | 0.7 |
| Possible breeding: | 74 | 4.0 |
| Total: | 214 | 11.6 |

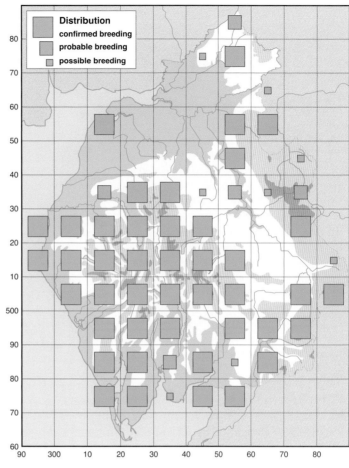

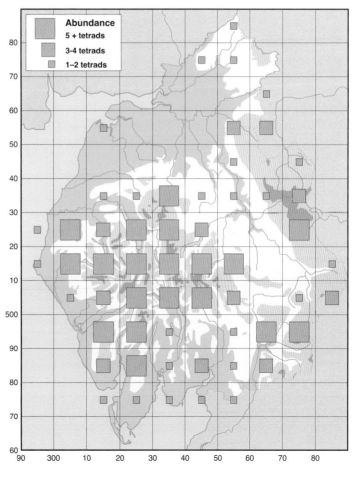

through the county. In addition, there are still high levels of illegal persecution by game-rearers and pigeon-fanciers. That said, the current county population of 90–110 breeding pairs is believed still to represent the highest density of nesting Peregrines anywhere in the world.

Cumbrian birds have been instrumental in recolonizing other parts of the country and the Peregrine has in many ways proved a classic conservation success story – thanks, in no small degree, to the efforts of dedicated enthusiasts. Nevertheless, there is no room for complacency. With just two of the 12 pairs that regularly breed east of the River Eden rearing young in 2000, no-one should doubt that we need to remain vigilant against those vested interests who, even in these supposedly more enlightened times, would strip the Peregrine of its legal protection or continue to destroy it illegally.

Geoff Horne

CONTEMPLATE a moorland landscape, desolate yet beautiful. Occasionally the stillness is punctuated by the chuckling calls of the Red Grouse, its only year-round resident. In early spring the activity increases: the moor edges seem alive with cocks rising on rigid fluttering wings in their brief display flights, the calls echoing widely over the heather.

Once considered Britain's only endemic bird species, the Red Grouse is now relegated to a subspecies of the Willow Ptarmigan. The latter has a circumpolar distribution, extending throughout northern temperate and subarctic regions. In Britain and Ireland, its derivative, the Red Grouse, has its main strongholds in Scotland and northern England with smaller populations in Wales and Ireland.

These relict populations live almost exclusively on heather-dominated moorland, managed for shooting, and maintained in a state of 'ecological arrest' by rotational burning. Historically, today's grouse moors would have been low open woodland of willow, birch and Scots pine, with a shrub layer of older, taller heather providing more cover but less food for Red Grouse. Such habitat would be similar to that now occupied by Willow Ptarmigan in Scandinavia – except for a much shorter period of winter snow cover, which presumably accounts for the failure to develop a white winter plumage, the camouflage so distinctive of other ptarmigans.

Red Grouse populations are cyclical, peaking every seventh year in the North Pennines. This oscillation in numbers may vary between moors and is attributed to the periodic build-up of a parasitic nematode worm *Trichostrongylus tenuis*. This cycle was researched in one

of the earliest studies into the fluctuations of a natural population (Lovat *et al* 1911). Large brood sizes enable the Red Grouse to increase spring populations tenfold by August, when many family groups join into packs, or coveys, making easy shooting when driven by beaters towards the waiting guns. Grouse moor management, with its regular burning regimes, has been an important land use in the uplands, maintaining almost monoculture heather landscapes that might otherwise have been lost, for instance to forestry, or 'enriched' to increase grazing. Such management is peculiar to Britain and the patchwork of uneven-aged burns is a characteristic feature of the North Pennines.

The Red Grouse is Britain's foremost sporting bird and the start of the shooting season on the 'Glorious Twelfth' has determined the date on which parliamentary commoners start their summer vacation. Macpherson (1892) remarked that, before grouse shooting became an exclusive sport, birds were killed at every season of the year. Yet, "so vast and so remote were the unreclaimed wastes of Lakeland that this failed to seriously affect numbers." By the turn of the 19th century, sporting estates in Cumbria made an economic and social contribution to rural economies that lasted until the 1950s, by which time its importance had started to diminish. Stokoe (1962) regarded the Red Grouse as "common on heather moors in north Cumberland and east Westmorland; generally rather thinly distributed elsewhere, from coastal mosses, where much reduced, up to 2,200 feet [671m]." He stated, amazing as it may seem today, that "one of the highest densities of birds noticed recently was on Kirkby Moor" and also noted the presence of several pairs on Dent Fell near Cleator Moor, Blengdale and Foulshaw Moss.

Populations in Cumbria declined sharply following a 36% reduction in heather moorland from the middle of the 20th century. Between the *Old Atlas* and *this Atlas,* its range has continued to contract, particularly in the central Lakeland hills and peripheral moorland. The results of *this Atlas* show it is now a scarce bird in the central mountains, much of its habitat having been badly degraded by sheep overgrazing. Its distribution also remains reduced in the Cumbria Dales but a few birds still inhabit the moors on the Coastal Plain and there has been an increase on the lowland mosses of the Solway Basin. The stronghold continues to be the North Pennines.

An independent measure of densities at well-studied sites such as the managed moorland at Geltsdale suggests a density of 20 birds/km², at least in 'good' years; elsewhere where heather persists densities from the count data during *this Atlas* reflect a more 'natural' level of 4–5 birds/km², suggesting a current county population at 2,500–3,000 breeding pairs.

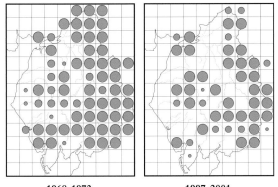

**1968-1972**          **1997-2001**

(For explanation of maps, see page 45)

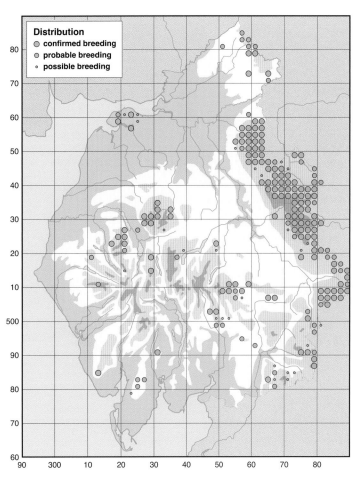

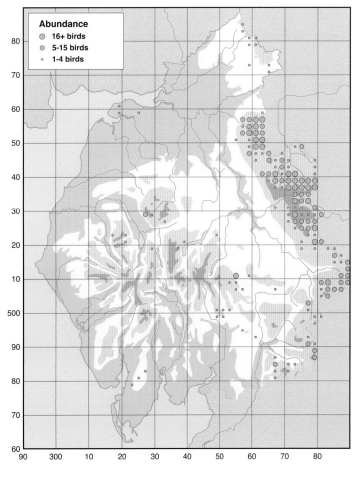

*Conservation status*

| European: | Non-SPEC |
|---|---|
| UK: | **GREEN** |

*Populations*

| European status: | 1,200,000 |
|---|---|
| Britain – pairs: | 250,000 |
| Cumbria – pairs: | 2,500–3,000 |

*30-year distribution change*

| | Old Atlas | This Atlas | % |
|---|---|---|---|
| No. of 10km squares: | 65 | 47 | −27.7 |

| **Survey data** | **Tetrads** | **%** |
|---|---|---|
| Confirmed breeding: | 139 | 7.5 |
| Probable breeding: | 46 | 2.5 |
| Possible breeding: | 27 | 1.5 |
| Total: | 212 | 11.5 |

It is debatable whether biodiversity benefits from the form of monocultural management of moorland for grouse; while some bird species do benefit, others are equally disadvantaged. For over a century, the Red Grouse has received preferential treatment, with specific management aimed at maximizing numbers, and game-keeping activities employed to minimize losses, but is this practice sustainable? Over the last few years, environmental incentives such as ESAs and Countryside Stewardship schemes have been introduced designed to maintain and enhance the distribution and growth of heather and, consequently, the wellbeing of the Red Grouse, albeit at a lower, more natural density.

Malcolm Stott

# Black Grouse *Tetrao tetrix*

CURIOUS rhythmic bubbling and strange gushing sounds announce the unmistakable presence of Black Grouse, arguably the most charismatic of our upland birds. Males habitually gather on traditional sites, known as 'leks', to perform their elaborate pre-nuptial courtship display as each attempts to exert his dominance in a bid to attract the most females (greyhens). To witness this ancient dawn ritual is one of the most memorable experiences in birdwatching.

The Black Grouse is a widespread Palearctic species with its European strongholds in Fennoscandia, Russia, Belarus and the Baltic States, and smaller populations in the Alps and Carpathian Mountains. In Britain, it is largely restricted to Scotland with isolated populations in the North Pennines and Wales. Although once widespread throughout most temperate zones of Eurasia, nearly all populations for which trends are known are in decline and those in Britain are no exception.

Neither exclusively a woodland nor moorland bird, the Black Grouse feeds on bilberry, heather, cotton grass and legumes, as well as the emergent buds and shoots of birch and rowan. This range of diet necessitates a diverse landscape supporting elements of each. The greyhen will select her nest site amongst vegetation that provides cover, and an abundance of insect food, such as sawfly larvae, for the chicks.

In Cumbria, large-scale planting of conifer forests in areas such as Kershope and Bewcastle found initial favour with Black Grouse, and some recolonization occurred in areas where birds had previously been lost. Yet soon the bird was branded the 'forester's pest' – its habit of feeding on nutritious young shoots was perceived to do damage to trees, and consequently birds were persistently persecuted. Elsewhere, populations continued to thrive on marginal farmland where small-scale cultivation was practised. Agricultural drainage grants were introduced in the mid-20th century, encouraging the conversion of hay-meadows eventually into species-poor grasslands. Agricultural intensification in marginal landscapes had a profound negative impact on Black Grouse populations in the 1950s and 1960s.

Historical introductions and reintroductions, few of which proved sustainable, cloud and confuse the bird's natural distribution in Cumbria. Heysham (1794) stated that "the Blackcock is rare in Cumberland, but most plentiful on the Bewcastle moors", an observation endorsed by Macpherson (1892). Blezard *et al* (1943) commented that "Blackgame are at present on the increase in North Cumberland, especially in the plantations around Kershope." Other indigenous populations were to be found in areas like the Solway Mosses, Lambrigg Fell and Grizedale Forest. Stokoe (1962) regarded the Black Grouse as "frequent on the moors of north Cumberland and Kentmere" but commented on a reduction in the Greystoke district and that small numbers still existed "on the Bewcastle and Gilsland moors and along the Pennine fringes from Tindale to Mallerstang". He also went on to cite Ennerdale, Blengdale, Brampton, the Barbon Fells, and the limestone uplands near Kendal and Whitbarrow, as other locations for the species.

The *Old Atlas* showed that birds had begun to disappear from traditional Lakeland sites, and a further contraction had occurred by the *New Atlas,* with birds now absent from large areas of the Border Uplands, North Pennines and Cumbria Dales. Out of 16 separate population strongholds, nine had declined to extinction by 1996. Agricultural development, afforestation and maturation of plantations have all been implicated in this countywide decline.

*This Atlas* reveals that Black Grouse have been lost from 72% of the 10km squares occupied at the time of the *Old Atlas,* three decades ago. The stronghold of today's remnant population is around Alston in the North Pennines, and small numbers still exist around Brough, Moorhouse, Kirkby Stephen, Geltsdale and Sedbergh. The reason why these have survived, while others have failed so dramatically, is perhaps the 'wilderness' aspect of these areas. The North Pennines in particular has escaped wide-scale afforestation, precluded initially by commercial shooting interests and then by designation of the area for its conservation importance.

The latest available population estimate for the whole North Pennines region is 650 males (J. Callardine pers comm), with Cumbria holding a significant proportion

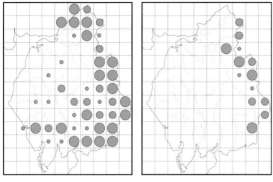

**1968–1972**        **1997–2001**

(For explanation of maps, see page 45)

**Conservation status**

| | |
|---|---|
| European: | SPEC Cat 3 |
| UK: | **RED: HD, BD & BDM** |

**Populations** – *males*

| | |
|---|---|
| European: | 700,000 |
| Britain: | 15,000 |
| Cumbria: | 185 |

**30-year distribution change**

| | Old Atlas | This Atlas | % |
|---|---|---|---|
| No. of 10km squares: | 46 | 13 | **−71.7** |

| **Survey data** | **Tetrads** | **%** |
|---|---|---|
| Confirmed breeding: | 6 | 0.3 |
| Probable breeding: | 26 | 1.4 |
| Possible breeding: | 17 | 0.9 |
| Total: | 49 | 2.6 |

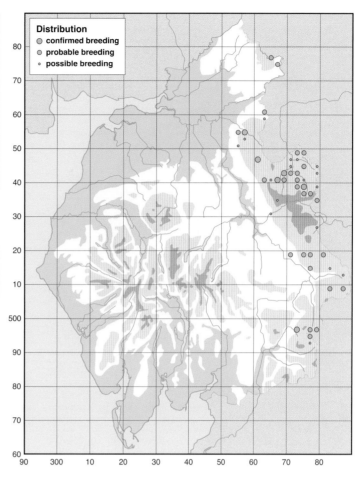

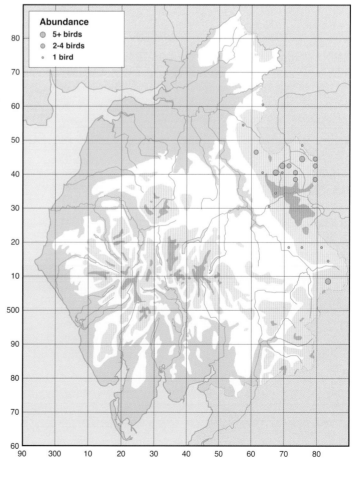

of these birds. The current county population of 185 males is taken from counts at known sites. The figure is expressed as numbers of males, since the numbers of the very secretive females cannot be known.

Black Grouse are 'biodiversity incarnate'; their presence enables us to gauge the quality of the upland environment. The North Pennines Black Grouse Recovery Project was launched in 1997, its objectives being to halt further declines and, where possible, to reverse the trend, through advocacy and habitat improvement. Judging by the number of estates and farms now entering into environmental schemes specifically targeted at Black Grouse, the project's realization looks increasingly likely. Only time will tell whether the evocative sounds of Black Grouse will remain part of the magic of the Cumbria fells for future generations.

Malcolm Stott

# Red-legged Partridge *Alectoris rufa*

A.S.W.

GAUDIER and more conspicuous than its native cousin, this colourful addition to Britain's avifauna is more readily associated with the lighter soils, cultivation and sparse vegetation of drier climates, meaning that the Red-legged Partridge is very much out of character in the Cumbrian landscape.

A Western Palearctic species, in historical times it had a much wider European distribution (Voous 1960). The current natural range extends from the Straits of Gibraltar northwards into southern and central France with a narrow belt extending east as far as northern Italy. In Britain the feral population has a strong bias towards the intensive arable regions of central and southeastern counties, with a much sparser distribution in northern England and an absence from the extreme northwest of Scotland. There are no self-sustaining populations in Ireland.

Red-legged Partridges were imported into England as early as 1673 with Charles II often credited with the first, albeit unsuccessful, introduction attempt. Subsequent endeavours also ended in failure until the first sustainable introduction followed the importation of large numbers of eggs from France – hence its vernacular name 'French Partridge'. These were hatched under chickens and released into the Suffolk countryside by the Marquis of Hertford in 1770. Although subsequent colonization stems from this source many further schemes, which continue to this day, have long supplemented the population.

The Red-legged Partridge has a preference for undulating countryside with open landscapes where sparse or low vegetation allows unobstructed views; it feeds on seeds, leaves, roots and considerable quantities of grasses and legumes, especially in winter. Pairs tend to lead a long-term monogamous life, but males can sometimes acquire two mates, and females are also known to associate with one or more males (Jenkins 1957). The clutch, of 10–16 eggs, is laid in a hollow on the ground, scantily lined with dry grasses or leaves. Within days of completing the first clutch some hens lay a second, with the pair then each incubating a clutch independently (Ricci 1983, Green 1984, Podor 1984). When two broods are produced simultaneously the young are cared for by a single parent, but otherwise they are tended by both (Johnsgard 1988).

Although accounts of historic introductions in the county are few, such events occurred at Thornthwaite in 1878 and Gosforth in 1880. However, the earliest known Cumbrian record concerns a bird feeding with poultry in a farmyard at Dykesfield in 1848, perhaps the result of an undocumented attempt to introduce Red-legged Partridges into Cumberland (Macpherson 1892). Nonetheless it seems that any releases quickly died out, and Stokoe (1962) considered that the few mid-20th century records involved introduced stock from neighbouring counties. This view was endorsed by the *Old Atlas* which showed just one occupied 10km square in Cumbria. However, soon after, a number of shooting syndicates began regularly to release birds in the county. Introductions included 25 at North Walney in 1973 and 16 at High Laverock in 1977, before the 1980s saw a significant upsurge in schemes countywide. Birds were released at sites as disparate as Longtown, Sunbiggin, Rockcliffe, Holker and Lilymere, where 60 birds were liberated in 1986. As a direct consequence of these and other undocumented releases, small populations existed in the Derwent, Eden and Kent Valleys (Hutcheson 1986). The *New Atlas* showed a spectacular 2,500% increase in the number of occupied 10km squares.

Subsequently, although there is little evidence of a 'natural' expansion in Cumbria, the population, augmented by further introductions, has continued to increase and *this Atlas* found birds in 33 10km squares. Despite the captive origins of the birds that fuelled this spread, and with further releases during *this Atlas,* the distribution map shows a widely scattered pattern of occupation, while the abundance map identifies the upper Eden Valley and lower slopes of the North Pennines as its main strongholds in the county. Unlike the Grey Partridge, this species appears to adapt more readily to, or is more tolerant of, wooded landscapes and a more omnivorous diet enables it to cope better with intensive grassland management. More interestingly it would appear to be moving into habitats occupied by the Grey Partridge; with many occupied tetrads on marginal farmed land in the much damper uplands.

 Sponsored by Warcop Army Training Area

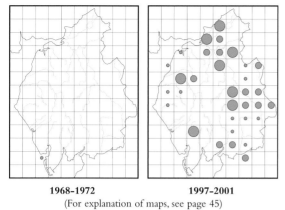

**1968–1972**     **1997–2001**

(For explanation of maps, see page 45)

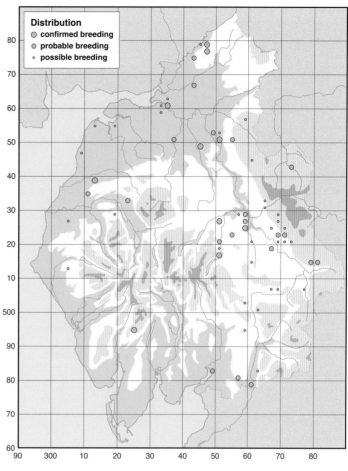

*Conservation status*

| | |
|---|---|
| European: | SPEC Cat 2 |
| UK: | unspecified |

*Populations*

| | |
|---|---|
| European status: | 3,300,000 |
| Britain – pairs: | 170,000 |
| Cumbria – pairs: | 60–80 |

*30-year distribution change*

| | Old Atlas | This Atlas | % |
|---|---|---|---|
| No. of 10km squares: | 1 | 33 | +3,200 |

| Survey data | Tetrads | % |
|---|---|---|
| Confirmed breeding: | 10 | 0.5 |
| Probable breeding: | 20 | 1.0 |
| Possible breeding: | 33 | 1.8 |
| Total: | 63 | 3.3 |

Line transect data failed to produce meaningful results for this species, and therefore the current county population estimate of 60–80 breeding pairs has been calculated from count data supported by supplementary records.

Although small numbers now breed annually in the wild, it is unclear – given the frequently inhospitable climate and generally lush vegetation – whether the current Cumbrian population is self-supporting, and would survive without the regular release of captive-bred birds. However, the prognosis of global warming may be beneficial for this species; the onset of hotter summers could produce a further range expansion and population increase over the next few decades.

Malcolm Stott

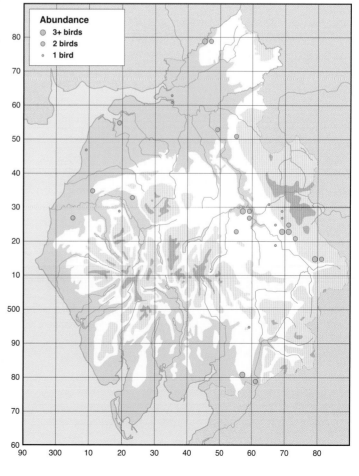

# Grey Partridge *Perdix perdix*

IN typical gamebird fashion, with a whirr of wings and a strong, low flight, the Grey Partridge skims over hedges, chases across tillage and calls from meadows in his pursuit of a mate. Once the prenuptial display has had the desired effect, the male will stay attentively by the female's side while the nest is built, typically in dense ground vegetation in the shade of a hedge.

Within its Eurasian range, temperate and steppe climatic zones are favoured, from Scandinavia south to northern Spain and Italy, east to the Kirgiz Steppes and Kazakhstan. In the south, populations become more fragmented, with distinct races being found in, for example, the Iberian Peninsula and Turkey. A native of the Palearctic, it was introduced widely into North America. It breeds in much of Britain, though largely absent from north and west Scotland, the Scottish islands and parts of Wales, and is scarce in Ireland.

The Grey Partridge is strictly a ground bird and, after the break-up of winter coveys in March, individual pairs begin to search for suitable nest sites, preferring open habitats where linear cover such as hedgerows and grass roadside verges afford concealment. It is potentially a prolific species, breeding in its first summer, and laying exceptionally large clutches averaging 15–16 eggs. However, predation of eggs and incubating hens is high, especially in areas where suitable nesting cover is limited. When the first eggs hatch, in mid to late June, the male will chaperone the precocious chicks until the female joins him later with the remainder of the clutch. The young feed on invertebrates picked off vegetation – sawfly larvae, plant bugs, grasshopper nymphs, knotgrass beetles and ant pupae in order of preference (Vickerman & O'Bryan 1979).

In Britain and Ireland, as elsewhere, the species has undergone a serious population decline, the extent of which has varied from region to region, depending on the uptake of such modern agricultural practices as intensive cultivation and the widespread use of chemicals. Some of the greatest losses have occurred on the periphery of its western range: in Ireland, and from Cornwall north as far as southwest Scotland. Analysis of the latest available CBC data reveals an alarming 84%

decline since 1970; only two other farmland species – the Corn Bunting and the Tree Sparrow – have suffered similar losses.

A hundred years ago, the Grey Partridge was one of the most numerous and familiar of birds, prospering from the conversion of swamps and mosses into 'productive land', and could be found on virtually every Cumbrian farm where tillage was practised. Whilst locally plentiful around the moorland edge, it was absent from the higher ground. The Industrial Revolution brought more mechanized methods of harvesting crops, which proved fatal to many chicks (Macpherson 1892). After the Second World War, the population declined drastically in response to changes in countryside management: intensive grassland production, increased stock-rates, the loss of hedgerows, an increased fad for 'tidiness' and a reliance on chemicals. Nevertheless, Stokoe (1962) regarded the bird as "common on cultivated ground, where not over-shot; less plentiful on higher ground, up to 1,500 feet [457m]." He commented on pairs that appeared at Grune Point in spring, both in 1959 and 1960, but were shot each year before they could breed. He also mentioned a nest on a grave mound in Lowick churchyard with 22 eggs; all but one hatched.

In Cumbria, changes are evident between the *Old* and *New Atlases,* and more vividly endorsed when compared to the results of *this Atlas.* The species has all but vanished from its former strongholds of south Lakeland, the Eden Valley and southern parts of the Solway Basin. Nowadays, it is likely to be encountered more frequently on the periphery of good farmland, where arable and small-hedged fields are close to semi-natural grasslands, such as the transitional zones in the Border Uplands, the foothills of the North Pennines and the Coastal Plain. Elsewhere in the county the population is sparse.

Analysis of line transect data from *this Atlas* gives a population band of 2,000–10,000, suggesting a mean population of 5,000 birds. Note, however, the wide band limits. The highest densities of 2.42 birds/km$^2$ were found on better-farmed land situated close to ranker vegetation. Although this figure is likely to include some

 Sponsored by Warcop Army Training Area

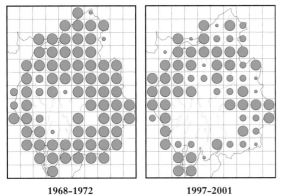

**1968-1972**     **1997-2001**
(For explanation of maps, see page 45)

*Conservation status*
European:                SPEC Cat 3
UK:                      **RED: BD**

*Populations*
European status:         2,000,000
Britain – pairs:         145,000
Cumbria – pairs:         2,500

*30-year distribution change*

|  | Old Atlas | This Atlas | % |
|---|---|---|---|
| No. of 10km squares: | 77 | 68 | −11.7 |

| **Survey data** | **Tetrads** | **%** |
|---|---|---|
| Confirmed breeding: | 82 | 4.4 |
| Probable breeding: | 129 | 7.0 |
| Possible breeding: | 61 | 3.3 |
| Total: | 272 | 14.7 |

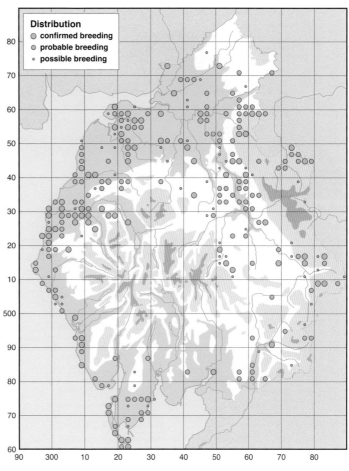

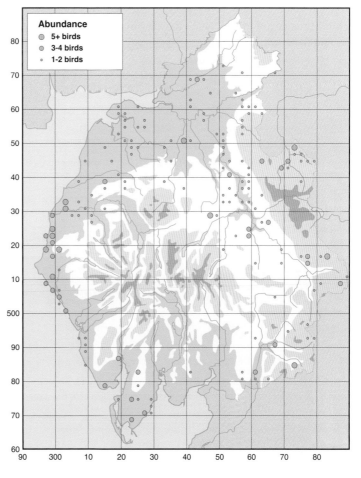

captive-hatched birds, many would have originated from wild stock.

Declines in the natural population of Grey Partridges prompted game-managers into captive breeding and releasing to supplement wild stock on estates with shooting interests. However, according to the Game Conservancy Trust, this has had, if anything, the opposite of the desired effect, by depressing productivity through the introduction of inferior quality birds and increasing the incidence and spread of potentially harmful viral diseases. Paradoxically, other farmland birds suffering similar tragic declines are afforded special conservation status, yet the fate of the Grey Partridge may lie in the hands of a few responsible sporting estates that nurture their well-being. Perhaps it is time for this species to be removed from the quarry list, if not totally, then on a regional basis, where population trends continue to spiral downwards.

Malcolm Stott

IN good 'Quail years' the easily recognizable 'wet-my-lips' call of this diminutive partridge-like bird may be heard resonating from fields with ripening ears of barley; as a master of ventriloquism, it is seldom straightforward to pinpoint the origin. The erratic irruptions of the Quail, our only migratory gamebird, lend it an enigmatic air.

Its breeding range encompasses the Western Palearctic, over-spilling into Asia. In Europe, it extends eastwards from the Atlantic seaboard, but is usually absent from the more northerly boreal regions. In Britain and Ireland, the Quail is an annual visitor to some southern counties but it is very much on the edge of its range in Cumbria, where its appearances are spasmodic. This bird has a strong affinity for open landscapes and cultivation; barley is the main cereal crop in the county and this is where it is most likely to be found – although, as a master opportunist, it will readily exploit any suitable habitat with tall vegetation.

A ground-nester, the Quail uses dry grass to sparsely line a shallow depression. The dozen or so creamy white eggs, marked with dark brown blotches, all hatch within a short period of each other and, once dry, the chicks abandon the nest. Quail can be resident in Cumbria from early May or not arrive until late July and linger into late summer. This leads to speculation that the late arrivals may be birds that have already bred further south and are moving north to attempt a second brood. However, these erratic fluctuations are still not fully understood and it has long been speculated that periodic droughts in its southern European range may trigger these otherwise inexplicable movements. Another theory is that these are young birds, hatched earlier in North Africa, which after fledging fly north and nest in their first summer.

In Britain, Quail populations during non-invasion years have been estimated at 100–300 pairs while in peak years this may be greatly enhanced to as many as 1,500–2,000 pairs. There were only five exceptional invasions during the 20th century and two of these happened to coincide with both the *Old* and *New Atlases,* the most recent being in 1989.

In Cumbria, at the end of the 19th century, Macpherson (1892) questioned if the Quail "was ever a very abundant visitor to Lakeland" though "no doubt it was always well known in some favourable localities." He regarded it as "an irregular summer visitant, thinly scattered over the cultivated parts of our area" and commented that "its trisyllabic call-note is usually heard in the neighbourhood of Allonby in the month of May: it is partial also to the valley of the Eden." He also referred to a decline around Kendal, in Furness and in the west of Cumberland; all areas where Quail were formerly not uncommon in some seasons. By the mid-20th century, Stokoe (1962) regarded it as a "now very scarce and irregular breeding visitor" and commented on records near Wigton, Winderwath, Blackwell and Grune Point.

Records show that the Quail continued to have only a token Cumbrian presence through the late 1970s and most of the 1980s, with three years in which no birds were heard, six with only one and two each with two and three records. On average only one singing male per summer was known during this period. However, the number of records during the influx of 1989 emphasized the irruptive nature of this species, with no less than 37 singing males in the county. Although most of these were in the north, from the lower Eden Valley extending westwards across the Solway Basin, records also occurred along the Coastal Plain, with some penetrating Lakeland and the North Pennines. The 1990s proved, on average, a better decade for Quail in Cumbria; in three years 12 or more singing males were found, and every year held at least one record.

The beginning of *this Atlas* coincided with another exceptionally good 'Quail year' in the county when 12 birds were recorded at eight sites. The distribution map reflects this influx; normally the few records that are received emanate from the Coastal Plain or Eden Valley, but birds were also found in the Solway Basin and southeast Lakeland. Subsequent years have seen a return to more typical summers when Quail are a novelty in Cumbria.

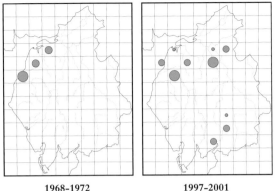

**1968–1972**    **1997–2001**
(For explanation of maps, see page 45)

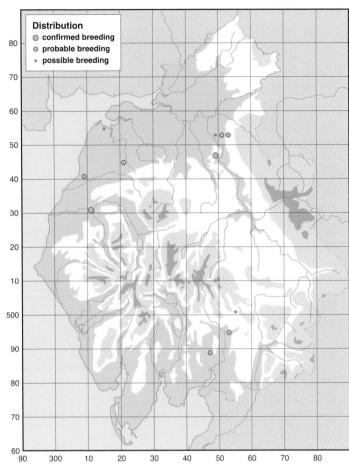

**Distribution**
○ confirmed breeding
○ probable breeding
○ possible breeding

*Conservation status*

| | |
|---|---|
| European: | SPEC Cat 3 |
| UK: | **RED: BD** |

*Populations*

| | |
|---|---|
| European status: | 720,000 |
| Britain – pairs: | 300 |
| Cumbria – pairs: | 1–2 |

*30-year distribution change*

| | Old Atlas | This Atlas | % |
|---|---|---|---|
| No. of 10km squares: | 3 | 10 | **+233** |

| Survey data | Tetrads | % |
|---|---|---|
| Confirmed breeding: | 2 | 0.1 |
| Probable breeding: | 6 | 0.3 |
| Possible breeding: | 3 | 0.2 |
| Total: | 11 | 0.6 |

During *this Atlas,* although the majority of records concerned territorial males, confirmed breeding came from the Coastal Plain and lower Eden Valley. Although the number of pairs can reach double figures in influx years, the results of *this Atlas,* based upon count data enhanced by supplementary records, suggest a current county population of no more than 1–2 breeding pairs.

At present, the threats to the Quail are hunting and trapping during its migration through the Mediterranean basin, agricultural intensification, an increased reliance on chemicals in southern Europe, and also the possibility of droughts. Although hunting returns throughout its European range have shown a downward trend during most of the 20th century, for the Quail – on the fringe of its range in Cumbria – climatic amelioration, stemming from global warming, may bring positive changes.

Malcolm Stott

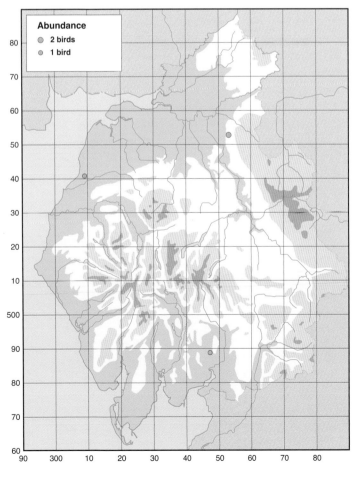

**Abundance**
○ 2 birds
○ 1 bird

WITH the first signs of spring in March, the distinctive crowing calls of the male Pheasant can be heard, as it begins to establish a harem for the season. Its metallic green head, scarlet facial mask and ecclesiastical collar make it instantly recognizable. Even in silhouette, as frequently seen on weather vanes, its shape and long tail are distinctive.

In Europe, and indeed throughout most of the Western Palearctic, the Pheasant is not an indigenous species: it was introduced from Asia Minor and later from China and Japan (Lowe 1933). In Britain and Ireland, huge numbers of captive-bred and released birds regularly supplement the feral population. This is especially true of Scotland and Ireland, where its presence is mainly restricted to the vicinity of lowland shooting estates.

The Pheasant is sedentary and catholic in its choice of habitat. Its requirements are basic: cover to nest and open ground to feed. The 10–12 olive-green eggs are laid in a sparsely lined hollow or depression on the ground, and usually tucked in dense vegetation beneath a hedge or similar location. It has an omnivorous diet: depending on the season it will eat various seeds and grain, fruits and berries, all manner of vegetable matter and invertebrates such as ants, beetles, grasshoppers, worms and grubs.

Documentary evidence suggests the Pheasant's introduction into Britain was instigated by Edward the Confessor sometime between 1042 and 1066 (Lever 1977). Although the exact date that the species became naturalized as a feral breeding bird is unknown, it was thought well enough established by the 15th century to warrant legal protection. The original 'English' race

– which lacked the white collar – appears to have been decimated by overshooting by the late 18th century (Koch 1956). This prompted the introduction of a number of races from further east, a practice that continued until the Second World War. It is probably safe to assume that all these have bred with the nominate race and now form a hybridized population in Britain and Ireland. The advent of the breech-loaded shotgun and royal patronage in the 1860s made driven Pheasant shooting fashionable. This form of shooting is reliant on the availability of high densities of gamebirds, the provision of which brought about the practice of captive-rearing. Part of this intensive management usually involves a degree of predator control, which in turn affects populations of other animals and birds.

In Cumbria, Macpherson (1892) remarked on the failure of an attempt to introduce Pheasants from Yorkshire into Lakeland some time between 1677 and 1698 and stated that this failure "appears to have damped the ardour of our sportsmen, because for the next hundred years they contented themselves with shooting Grouse and Partridges". He went on to assert that in 1784 there were no Pheasants in Cumberland, though birds were successfully introduced within the next decade and "the final years of our century witnessed the extension of its range to all the coverts of Lakeland." Stokoe (1962) had little to say other than that the Pheasant was "common where reared and preserved, otherwise sparse."

Distribution trends show little change in the 30 year gap between the *Old Atlas* and *this Atlas*. Open, mixed landscapes of cultivation and pastoral, bordered by fragmented woodland, are its preferred habitat in Cumbria, hence the scarcity of records from central Lakeland, the North Pennines and much of the Cumbria Dales, although a few may be found here in the vicinity of farmsteads. Their abundance varies greatly throughout the county's lowlands and the main concentrations today still reflect the larger sporting estates of Naworth and Netherby in the north, Inglewood and Lowther in the centre and Levens Hall and Graythwaite in the south. In such areas, captive-raised stock can dramatically bolster feral populations.

Analysis of line transect data from *this Atlas* gives a population band of 12,000–28,000, suggesting a mean population of 18,000 birds. The highest densities of 9.8 birds/km$^2$ occurred on the lowland areas of mixed farmland with small, hedged fields of the Coastal Plain.

It is difficult to determine the status of naturally sustainable populations in Britain because of the continuing practice of artificially bolstering local populations, but it is apparent that feral numbers have declined, perhaps in response to agricultural intensification. Indeed, in many parts of Cumbria, the bird cannot be properly regarded as a part of the

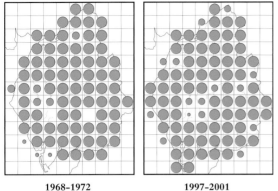

**1968–1972**          **1997–2001**

(For explanation of maps, see page 45)

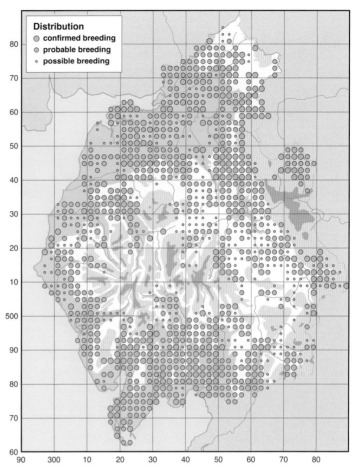

**Distribution**
- confirmed breeding
- probable breeding
- possible breeding

**Conservation status**

| | |
|---|---|
| European: | Non-SPEC |
| UK: | unspecified |

**Populations**

| | |
|---|---|
| European status: | 4,100,000 |
| Britain – females: | 1,550,000 |
| Cumbria – pairs: | 9,000 |

**30-year distribution change**

| | Old Atlas | This Atlas | % |
|---|---|---|---|
| No. of 10km squares: | 80 | 87 | +8.75 |

| Survey data | Tetrads | % |
|---|---|---|
| Confirmed breeding: | 321 | 17.4 |
| Probable breeding: | 518 | 28.1 |
| Possible breeding: | 253 | 13.7 |
| Total: | 1092 | 59.2 |

avifauna, since it would most likely cease to exist in the absence of repeated further yearly releases. In England, some 15 million poults are released annually – an astonishing figure – and each has the potential to transmit viral disease into indigenous gamebird populations. If diseases such as coccidiosis can cross a species barrier and infect other less numerous gamebirds, then Pheasant-releasing may pose a serious threat to declining populations of Grey Partridge and possibly Black Grouse. In areas of high conservation value, where native gamebirds are found in numbers, a scheme to license the release of poults may be desirable, though such legislation would prove controversial.

Malcolm Stott

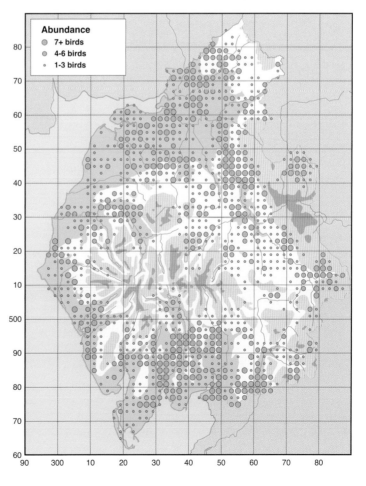

**Abundance**
- 7+ birds
- 4-6 birds
- 1-3 birds

# Water Rail *Rallus aquaticus*

THE slim, shadowy figure of a Water Rail glimpsed fleetingly as it creeps stealthily along the edge of a reedbed at dusk is the typical view for many birdwatchers of this elusive, yet intriguing, species. More likely, its presence will be betrayed solely by its distinctive, pig-like squealing emanating from the depths of apparently impenetrable vegetation.

Its distribution stretches across most of Europe, North Africa and western Asia, though the full extent of its range and population is inadequately known, due to the difficulty of proving breeding. Water Rails breed extensively, albeit sparsely, throughout much of Britain and Ireland, inhabiting a wide range of freshwater habitats, usually with areas of mud, and always with expanses of tall emergent vegetation. No aquatic vegetation is too dense. Generally feeding on exposed mud or clambering among vegetation, Water Rails are omnivorous, eating a wide variety of invertebrates and vegetable matter with amphibians, small rodents and even small birds also taken.

Building a nest platform in shallow water, choked by vegetation, has its risks and breeding attempts are constantly under threat from changes in spring water levels, when eggs, and even young, are most vulnerable. Water Rails are also susceptible to hard winters, when populations can be severely depleted, as was the case during the early 1980s.

Despite the extensive drainage of reedbed, swamp and moss from the mid-18th century, at the end of the 19th century the Water Rail was still widely distributed throughout Britain and Ireland and, in many areas, still considered a common bird. Nevertheless, even at this time, it was under pressure with the collection of eggs for the table also contributing to a reduction in breeding numbers in many counties in England and Wales. Consequently, as the 20th century progressed, gaps began to appear in the species' distribution with birds absent from much of Scotland, the Midlands, North Wales and southwest England. Although the *Old Atlas* indicated some recolonization, the population showed a further decline in numbers throughout much of its range during the period between the *Old* and *New Atlases*. More recently, a run of mild winters may have helped to increase the breeding population.

In Cumbria, at the end of the 19th century, Macpherson (1892) commented "in the old days, when so large a proportion of Lakeland was under moss, the Water Rail probably bred with us more generally than is now the case," and considered the bird chiefly a winter visitor. Nevertheless, he cites instances of eggs being taken on Rockcliffe Moss and in the vicinity of Penrith, with breeding also recorded on the River Eden. He thought it must be very local in the summer time, as its loud cry would always announce its presence. However, the "loud cry" may be rarely given once nesting gets underway, and also where birds are sparse: Macpherson surely exaggerates the ease of detection. Subsequent 20th century authors confirm that the species was a scarce or at least uncommon breeding bird, but claim that its unobtrusive habits led to the species being overlooked (Blezard *et al* 1943, Stokoe 1962).

At the time of the *Old Atlas,* birds were recorded in 22 10km squares, compared to just 10 in *this Atlas.* The distribution is now strikingly fragmented, with a notable absence from previously occupied areas in the Solway Basin. Despite the difficulties involved in censusing this species, the increased observer effort during the course of *this Atlas* would suggest this decline is real.

Crepuscular habits and a secretive nature make this a species easily overlooked by atlas fieldworkers, especially within the constraints of a timed visit. Birds are most likely to be detected as they vociferously establish territories in spring, hence migrants calling from their wintering grounds or on passage in April may falsely inflate the figures. Proof of breeding requires a lot of luck and patience and is most likely to be confirmed by sightings of adults with young – hence the paucity of recent records in the county, even outwith the constraints of atlas fieldwork. There were just four such instances during *this Atlas* period, at North Walney, Sunbiggin Tarn and on two occasions at Bassenthwaite Marsh.

Sponsored by Peter Barron

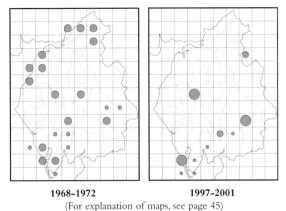

**1968-1972**    **1997-2001**
(For explanation of maps, see page 45)

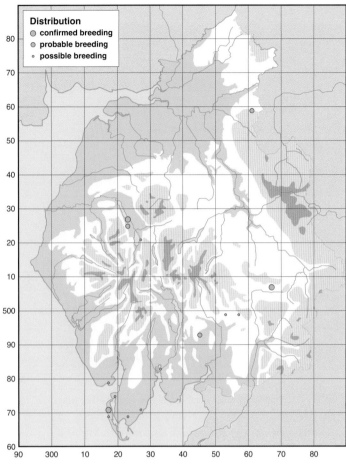

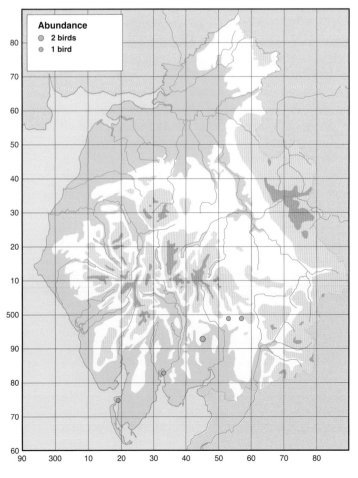

*Conservation status*
European:                    Non-SPEC
UK:                          **AMBER: BDM**

*Populations*
European:                    160,000
Britain – pairs:             700
Cumbria – pairs:             20–40

*30-year distribution change*
|  | Old Atlas | This Atlas | % |
|---|---|---|---|
| No. of 10km squares: | 22 | 10 | **−54.5** |

| Survey data | Tetrads | % |
|---|---|---|
| Confirmed breeding: | 3 | 0.2 |
| Probable breeding: | 3 | 0.2 |
| Possible breeding: | 9 | 0.5 |
| Total: | 15 | 0.9 |

The results of fieldwork for *this Atlas* are inconclusive, but using the density given by the *New Atlas* of 2–4 pairs per occupied 10km square, a baseline figure suggests a current county population of 20–40 breeding pairs.

It is difficult to predict the future of the Water Rail in the county though, hopefully, drainage of suitable habitat is a thing of the past and the latest climatic predictions indicate there is a reduced likelihood of severe winters in the future. However, global warming is also predicted to increase the chances of wetter springs which could be bad news for a species that is particularly susceptible to changes in water levels. Whether the population rises or falls, it will remain no easy task to detect any changes. A dedicated census might prove revealing.

Ian Kinley

# Corncrake *Crex crex*

THE rasping calls of the Corncrake are synonymous with hay meadows and fields of ripening corn, the monotonous sound continuing well into the night. Indeed, for centuries, the bird was as much a part of the Cumbrian countryside as the scarecrow; sadly, although both have declined the scarecrow is now probably the commoner.

Its range extends from Britain and Ireland through southern Scandinavia and France to northeast Spain, eastwards to Russia and western Siberia. The greatest densities occur in some eastern bloc countries, while it is generally scarce as a breeding bird along the Mediterranean coast. Britain and Ireland represent an isolated outpost on the northwest fringe of its range, with the main strongholds – the Western Isles, Orkney and some rural parts of Ireland – now holding 90% of the British breeding population. This remnant distribution is all that is left in the face of the northwestward march of grassland intensification over the last 50 years.

The Corncrake's breeding season is often quite protracted, since many birds are double-brooded. For this reason they require suitable habitat in the form of tall, though not dense, vegetation from May to late August. The clutch of 6–14 eggs is laid in a simple hollow, which is lined with dead leaves: often stems are pulled over the top to form a loose canopy. A traditional mix of pasture and arable farming suits their needs best; regrettably, this idyllic balance has been almost entirely supplanted by the spread of intensive grassland management, mechanization and specialist farming practices. Earlier and more frequent silage cutting, encouraged by heavy applications of inorganic

fertilizers, and the wide-scale use of herbicides and pesticides produced greater mortality of adults, nest losses and chick starvation. In addition, although the start date for cutting cereal crops has differed little, new hi-tech machinery has reduced the time taken to harvest crops by 50%, thus allowing the task to be completed much quicker, but increasing the risk of both adults and chicks being destroyed. Only when mowing is deferred until the end of July can enough young be produced to sustain the population.

In Cumbria, before the highly mechanized agricultural practices of the mid-20th century, Corncrakes were considered abundant and found in virtually every parish. Apart from the traditional hay meadows, Macpherson (1892) recorded their presence in a variety of habitats, from tall sedge meadows in some coastal districts to nettle or iris beds in Lakeland valleys. Even the odd overgrown North Pennine garden provided a suitable nest site. Although cereal crops and rushy pasture offer important feeding habitat, rarely were they used for nesting. A noticeable decline was evident from the 1950s (Brown 1974), and Stokoe (1962) considered it "generally scarce" and "a much reduced breeding visitor".

Over the last 30 years, it has become a rare and irregular summer visitor, breeding only sporadically. The *Old Atlas* revealed Cumbria as one of the last strongholds for breeding Corncrakes in England, with 40 occupied 10km squares. Yet two decades later the *New Atlas* showed only three occupied squares in the county. The National Corncrake Survey in 1993 revealed a drastic 68% decrease overall. Despite nocturnal fieldwork and use of modern technology, this survey failed to reveal any breeding birds in Cumbria. During the last decade there have only been two records of confirmed breeding in the county, both in 1990, from Rack Bridge and Abbeytown.

The results of *this Atlas* show that there has been little improvement in the situation; single calling males were recorded in just three scattered 10km squares on the Coastal Plain and lower Eden Valley. Although the secretive nature of the species meant that breeding could not be confirmed, count data suggest that the current county population is sporadic, and involves 0–2 breeding pairs.

The future looks bleak for the Corncrake, even in its eastern European strongholds. Times are changing; new, independent territories are developing policies to westernize agricultural practices. Survival hangs in a delicate balance and depends on a swift and radical reform of the Common Agricultural Policy. However, the Corncrake's problem is not just one of provincial change in land management. Its main wintering grounds lie on the savannahs south of the Sahara and its migration routes converge through Egypt, a journey across lands where the old tradition and custom of

Sponsored by Margaret Clarke

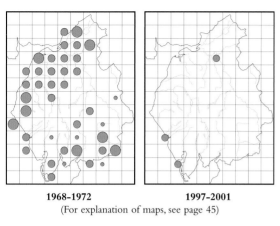

**1968-1972**    **1997-2001**
(For explanation of maps, see page 45)

**Conservation status**

| | |
|---|---|
| European: | IUCNCat A |
| UK: | **RED: HD, BD & BL** |

**Populations**

| | |
|---|---|
| European status: | 90,000 |
| Britain − pairs: | 640 |
| Cumbria − pairs: | 0–2 |

**30-year distribution change**

| | Old Atlas | This Atlas | % |
|---|---|---|---|
| No. of 10km squares: | 40 | 3 | **−92.5** |

| **Survey data** | **Tetrads** | **%** |
|---|---|---|
| Confirmed breeding: | 0 | |
| Probable breeding: | 3 | 0.2 |
| Possible breeding: | 0 | |
| Total: | 3 | 0.2 |

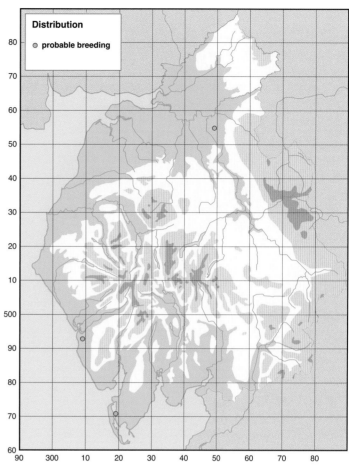

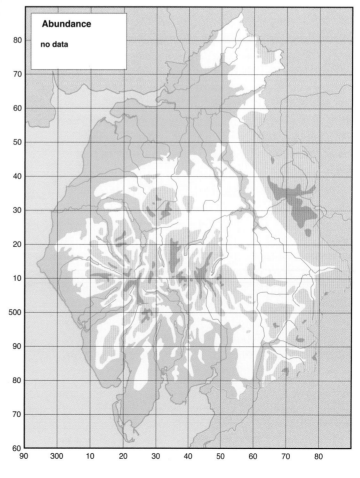

netting Quail for food causes the incidental fatality of many Corncrakes each autumn. These problems will require a great deal of educational resources to resolve.

One glimmer of hope is that, in Britain, numbers in the main strongholds have recently increased in line with BAP targets. Later cutting dates in the Western Isles and Orkney, stemming from traditional crofting practices, have, thus far, prevented Corncrakes here suffering a similar fate to birds on the mainland. Farmers in these areas receive agri-environmental payments to continue this conventional type of farming; it may be that, if these traditional methods could be adopted elsewhere across its range, they might just save this distinctive night songster from becoming a distant memory.

Malcolm Stott

# Moorhen *Gallinula chloropus*

THE Moorhen is a common and versatile resident which occurs in well-vegetated waterside habitats including lake margins, ponds, slow-moving rivers and streams, canals, wet meadows, marshes and drainage ditches. It is often conspicuous, drawing attention to itself with its constant tail flicking, and vocal, particularly in habitats with close proximity to people, although in other situations birds can be shy and secretive. It has an extensive global range and occurs in the temperate and tropical environments of all continents except Australasia, where a related species replaces it. In Britain it is one of the most familiar and widespread aquatic birds in all lowland areas though it is absent from the higher ground of upland regions. Its pattern of abundance in Ireland is more patchy.

Moorhens survive in quite diverse habitat types and pairs are often found in relatively small and isolated pockets of wetland. Birds are most successful when water conditions are eutrophic with plentiful emergent and floating vegetation providing both food and nest concealment. They are omnivorous and forage on water and land for plant and animal materials. Their nests are positioned close to the water on emergent vegetation, fallen branches and, occasionally, in bushes or trees. Unfortunately, clutches suffer high losses through predation, especially by Carrion Crows and Stoats, and repeat clutches and second broods are common (Huxley *et al* 1976) in a breeding season which may last from March to July.

The status of the Moorhen in Cumbria today has not changed dramatically since the 19th century,

when it was considered it to be "a common resident on becks and tarns, inland and near the sea" (Macpherson 1892). Stokoe (1962) commented that it "breeds by all still or quiet waters, including the smallest ponds and streams, from coastal saltmarshes up to at least 1,000 feet [305m]." Nationally, analysis of the latest available WBS data indicates a 10% decline since 1974 and, in Cumbria, a comparison of *this Atlas* with the *Old Atlas* does reveal a contraction in the geographical spread of the species – lost from 14 previously occupied 10km squares, mainly in the less favourable terrain of central Lakeland, the North Pennines and Cumbria Dales. Moorhens are vulnerable to serious population reversals during hard winters when their reluctance to vacate frozen territories can be suicidal. Fluctuations in numbers caused by adverse weather conditions make it difficult to evaluate the impact of other long-term factors undermining habitat viability. Ponds and saturated field patches lost from modern farm landscapes and the afforestation of former haunts have been detrimental in some localities. In addition, the mechanical dredging of drainage dykes and flood control measures on some rivers have damaged riparian habitats by removing vegetation for nest cover. In some parts of the county, the menace of Mink predation has also been noted. Conversely, the flooding of old mineral workings and the creation of new recreational, sporting and conservation wetlands have been compensating factors as Moorhens are adept at claiming new territory. Their natural fecundity results in a surplus of non-breeding birds with the potential to ensure rapid population recovery.

The distribution map for *this Atlas* confirms the Moorhen's preference for the nutrient-rich and slower streams and rivers of the Coastal Plain, Solway Basin and Eden Valley. Few birds penetrate far into Lakeland, where increasing stream gradients and more acidic standing waters are prohibitive. The higher ground of the Pennines is also shunned, although occasional pairs find favourable niches up to 300m asl. Many breeding sites hold only single pairs on farm and flight ponds, floodplain pools and drainage ditches. The highest population densities are found near the coast in Copeland, Furness and the Kent Valley, with over 20 breeding pairs recorded in favourable years both at South Walney, and along the 10.5km stretch of disused Lancaster Canal near Crooklands.

This is a difficult bird to census accurately and little systematic fieldwork has been attempted in Cumbria. Analysis of the line transect data from *this Atlas* gives a population band of 3,000–30,000, suggesting a mean population of 9,000 birds. Given the very wide band limits, however, this estimate should be viewed

Sponsored by Alcan Packaging Lawson Mardon

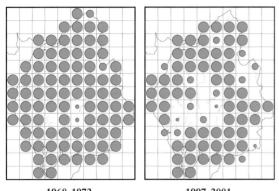

**1968–1972**          **1997–2001**

(For explanation of maps, see page 45)

**Conservation status**

| | |
|---|---|
| European: | Non-SPEC |
| UK: | **GREEN** |

**Populations**

| | |
|---|---|
| European status: | 1,000,000 |
| Britain – pairs: | 240,000 |
| Cumbria – pairs: | 4,500 |

**30-year distribution change**

| | Old Atlas | This Atlas | % |
|---|---|---|---|
| No. of 10km squares: | 87 | 73 | **–16.1** |

| Survey data | Tetrads | % |
|---|---|---|
| Confirmed breeding: | 209 | 11.3 |
| Probable breeding: | 103 | 5.6 |
| Possible breeding: | 76 | 4.1 |
| Total: | 388 | 21.0 |

with caution. The highest densities of 8 birds/km² occurred in scattered lowland locations.

The Moorhen population will remain vulnerable to temporary setbacks resulting from severe winters and further habitat loss cannot be discounted. However, the changing emphasis towards financial support for environmental objectives on farmland, more sympathetic methods of river management and the prospect of further wetland habitat creation signal a stable future for the resilient Moorhen in Cumbria.

Malcolm Priestley

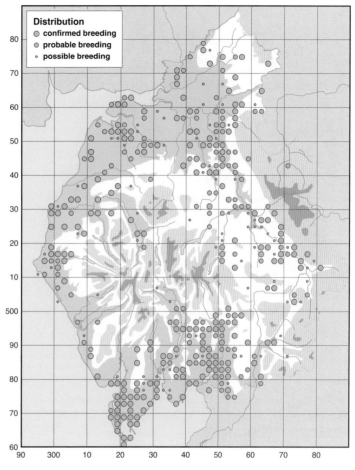

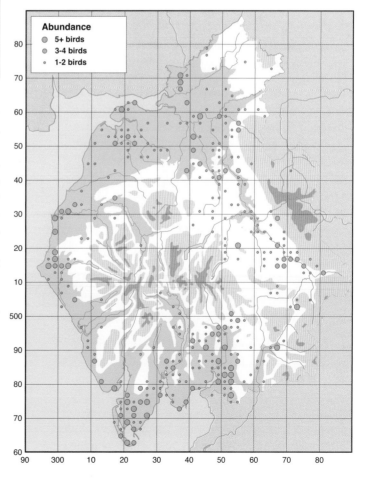

# Coot *Fulica atra*

much of their diet by diving in one to six metres of water to obtain aquatic plants, supplemented by water insects, tadpoles, newts and small fish. Nests are often conspicuous, built on trampled clumps of reed or fallen branches, relying on surrounding water rather than concealment to deter ground predators. Six eggs constitutes a typical clutch. In favourable summers, some pairs rear a second brood but one is more usual.

In Cumbria, Macpherson (1892) described the Coot as an "abundant resident" and, 50 years later, Blezard *et al* (1943) outlined the breeding distribution in Lakeland as "nesting on all lakes and many tarns, from the coastal region up to 1000 feet [305m]", a situation reaffirmed by Stokoe (1962). More recent national estimates suggest a fairly stable population in Britain, with local increases in England associated with the colonization of man-made standing waters (Marchant *et al* 1990). A similar trend is apparent in Cumbria, where birds have readily established territories on abandoned gravel pits and the numerous ponds created in recent years for fishing, shooting and conservation purposes. *This Atlas* confirms an expansion of range in the county with six additional 10km squares occupied since the *Old Atlas,* 30 years previously.

Coots are widely distributed on suitable waters in Cumbria. However, the bulk of the population is concentrated in three areas: the Coastal Plain, south Lakeland and the adjacent coastal lowlands, and the Eden Valley. Here, at low elevations and surrounded by productive farmland, wetlands are relatively nutrient-rich and well-vegetated. Most breeding sites are quite small (0.5–2.0ha) and support only a few birds, whilst several of the larger lakes and reservoirs in central Lakeland are too deep and oligotrophic to hold any attraction for the species. Tindale Tarn, Longtown Gravel Pits, Hodbarrow and South Walney are all sites with loose colonies exceeding 10 pairs. In addition, the shallower, reed-fringed bays of Windermere shelter significant numbers and, in 2000, a stretch of the disused Lancaster Canal at Crooklands held 13 pairs. Primarily a bird of the lowlands, Coot breed above the 250m contour line at Sunbiggin Tarn and Tarn House Tarn in the southeast of the county; both waters are fed by limestone springs and uniquely productive among the tarns at higher altitudes.

For such a large and obvious bird, surprisingly little is known about breeding densities locally, nationally or, indeed, in its wider breeding range. A significant stock of non-breeding birds in the county and the possible inclusion of late winter migrants in early fieldwork counts further complicate estimation of the breeding population. The species is one of those awaiting a comprehensive census in the county. However, the bird's particular habitat requirements and obtrusive behaviour mean that a relatively large proportion will have been noted during this survey;

COOT are difficult to overlook wherever they occur on open bodies of freshwater. Noisy and gregarious, often quarrelsome and aggressively territorial in the breeding season, this plump rail, with its prominent white frontal shield and bill contrasting sharply against charcoal black plumage, is unmistakable. Usually quite tolerant to human activity, birds hidden in vegetation will betray their presence with frequent loud and penetrating calls.

The species has an extensive breeding range stretching across Eurasia to China, India, Australia and New Zealand though avoiding more northerly latitudes and desert regions. It is a common resident of the wetlands of Britain and Ireland, most numerous and widespread in lowland areas, especially the Midlands, southern and southeast England and absent from most upland regions of Wales, northern England and Scotland.

Winter Coot flocks break up in February and March, when migrants return to continental breeding grounds and residents establish territories on areas of open water where there is sufficient submerged and emergent vegetation to provide food supplies, cover and nesting sites. Being very tolerant of human presence, they have become tame birds in many areas, occupying urban park lakes and readily feeding on bread provided by man. In Cumbria, the majority of the population is found on shallow lakes, ponds, reservoirs and flooded mineral workings. Smaller numbers occupy disused canals and the slower reaches of lowland rivers. Deeper lakes and reservoirs with barren shorelines, acidic tarns and more confined waterways and pools are not tenable. Coots retrieve

Sponsored by Alcan Packaging Lawson Mardon

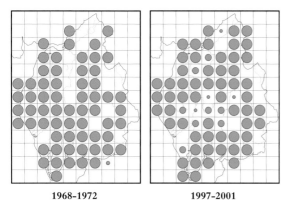

**1968–1972**       **1997–2001**

(For explanation of maps, see page 45)

*Conservation status*

| | |
|---|---|
| European: | Non-SPEC |
| UK: | **GREEN** |

*Populations*

| | |
|---|---|
| European status: | 1,200,000 |
| Britain – adults: | 46,000 |
| Cumbria – pairs: | 800–1,200 |

*30-year distribution change*

| | Old Atlas | This Atlas | % |
|---|---|---|---|
| No. of 10km squares: | 63 | 69 | **+9.5** |

| **Survey data** | **Tetrads** | **%** |
|---|---|---|
| Confirmed breeding: | 173 | 9.4 |
| Probable breeding: | 56 | 3.0 |
| Possible breeding: | 28 | 1.5 |
| Total: | 257 | 13.9 |

just over 1,000 birds were located during timed counts, and this figure can be augmented by supplementary records. The current county population is believed to be in the region of 800–1,200 breeding pairs.

The Coot seems likely to maintain its present status as one of the most characteristic of Cumbria's waterbirds. Land drainage, intensive recreational activity and canal restoration proposals pose marginal threats in the future. However, this opportunistic bird will not hesitate to pioneer new habitats as further artificial wetlands become available.

Malcolm Priestley

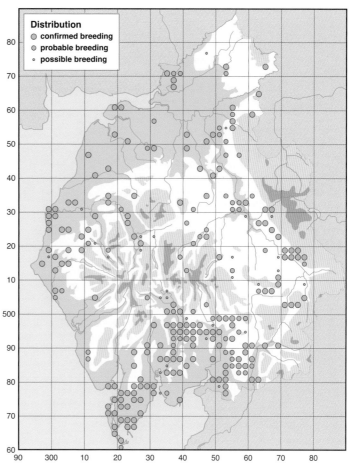

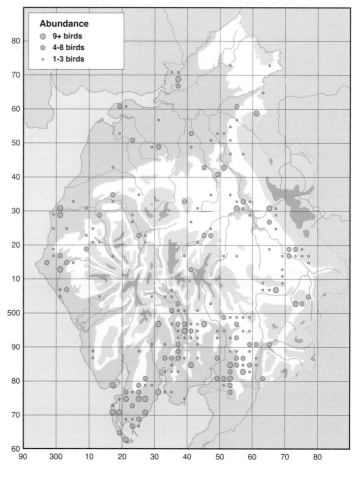

CIRCLING high, calling loudly, whether over green fields or pebbled beaches, the distinctive pied appearance and long prominent bright orange-red bill of the Oystercatcher are now just as familiar inland as on the coast. Although its characteristic piping display, in which birds run in parallel with downward-pointing bills, can be heard all year, it reaches an almost feverish pitch in spring.

The species is confined to the Palearctic, the nominate race breeding mainly along the coasts of western Europe and the Mediterranean, and increasingly occurring inland. At a time of declines in many British breeding waders, the Oystercatcher is an exception, and it is widespread throughout northwestern England and Scotland, becoming more coastal further south. Oystercatchers can be extremely long-lived birds, with a record of an individual exceeding 35 years, and show breeding site fidelity. Many inland nesting birds may leave their wintering grounds, along the coasts of the Irish Sea, as early as January to begin establishing a territory.

Oystercatchers were probably restricted to coastal breeding sites in Cumbria during the 19th century, where they favoured shingle or saltings. Walney Island, Ravenglass, Whitehaven to Silloth and the saltmarshes of Burgh-by-Sands are frequently cited as historical haunts, many of which are still occupied today. However, on at least one occasion, in 1889, they were noted to have bred inland at Gilsland, and birds also summered in the Eden Valley at Langwathby (Macpherson 1892); inland breeding was a habit that was to increase throughout the 20th century. Regular breeding on the River Eden probably started in the 1920s with birds reaching as far as Mallerstang by the mid-1930s. The Solway Basin had been colonized by the 1940s, and a decade later 15 pairs occupied a 4.8km stretch of the River Irthing below Lanercost (Blezard *et al* 1943, Buxton 1961). A pair bred at Bassenthwaite Lake in 1954 and there were several pairs near Penrith by 1960 (Stokoe 1962). Colonization in the south seems to have been slower, though this may be through less thorough documentation. In 1943 a pair was at Sunbiggin Tarn, and birds were breeding at Tebay and Killington Reservoir by 1958 (Buxton 1961).

The species has adapted to environmental change inland, not least the clearance of riparian woodland, with birds nesting on riverside shingles, grasslands and cultivated ground where they exploit the wealth of invertebrates. Unusual nest sites have included wall tops, tree stumps and industrial roofs at Carlisle, Sellafield and Barrow-in-Furness. The Oystercatcher's habit, unusual in waders, of supplying food to its young, rather than their foraging for themselves, makes rooftop nesting possible.

During 1971, about 356 pairs bred along the Cumberland coast and 116 pairs around Morecambe Bay from Walney Island to the latest defined county border with Lancashire. These figures had changed little since 1966. Inland, 69 pairs were on the River Lune (including the Lancashire reaches), two pairs on the River Derwent, one pair on the River Leven and about 133 pairs on the River Eden and its tributaries. All inland sites had shown increases since 1966 (Dare 1966, Greenhalgh 1972).

Inland breeding populations in Cumbria are believed to be on the increase. On 23 lowland, wet grassland sites where monitoring data is available, numbers rose in all but two between 1982 and 1995 (Mawby & Armstrong 1996) and at Killington Reservoir numbers have generally increased, with some annual fluctuations. Spring numbers at pre-breeding roosts in the Lune Valley increased through the 1980s and were also high in the Eden Valley by the late 1990s, with over 1,500 birds counted in 1998, many of which would be county inland breeding birds. On the coast, at Hodbarrow and South Walney, numbers appear to have remained relatively stable during the last decade.

Current distributions show a similar pattern to those of both the *Old* and *New Atlases*. Analysis of line transect data from *this Atlas* gives a population band of 8,000–26,000, suggesting a mean population of 14,000 birds. The highest densities of 10 birds/km$^2$

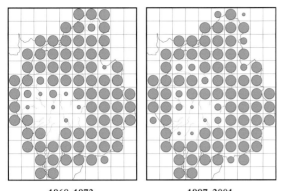

**1968–1972**          **1997–2001**

(For explanation of maps, see page 45)

*Conservation status*

European:                          Non-SPEC

UK:              **AMBER: WL, BI & WI**

*Populations*

European status:                235,000

Britain – pairs:                  38,000

Cumbria – pairs:                   7,000

*30-year distribution change*

|  | Old Atlas | This Atlas | % |
|---|---|---|---|
| No. of 10km squares: | 85 | 88 | **+3.5** |

| **Survey data** | **Tetrads** | **%** |
|---|---|---|
| Confirmed breeding: | 315 | 17.1 |
| Probable breeding: | 307 | 16.6 |
| Possible breeding: | 196 | 10.6 |
| Total: | 818 | 44.4 |

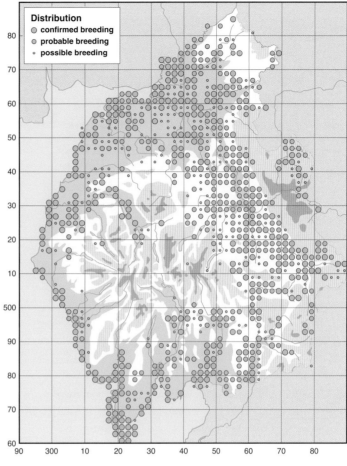

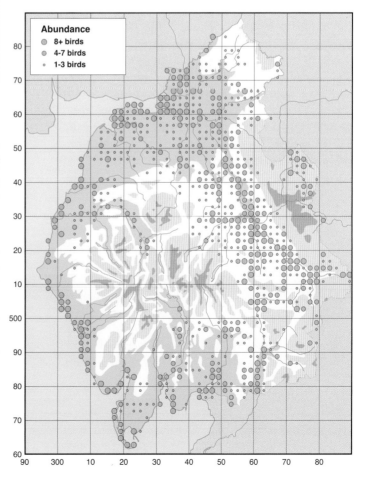

occurred on the coast and trebled those counterpart sites inland.

It remains to be seen whether room exists for further expansion. Inland, the current fashion of riparian woodland restoration, especially along the major fluvial valleys, does not bode well for this species. Changes to coastal grazing practices, particularly on saltmarshes, may be of some concern, along with an increase in recreational usage in the vicinity of present and potential breeding sites. Nevertheless, unlike most other inland waders that are dependent upon damp grassland, the outlook for the Oystercatcher in the county seems promising.

Dave Shackleton

©.M.Isherwood

SLIGHTLY smaller than a Ringed Plover with a slimmer, longer bill and distinctive yellow orbital ring, the Little Ringed Plover with its distinctive 'clockwork' running action is mostly associated with lowland sandy or gravelly freshwater margins, although coastal breeding also occurs.

A migrant ground-nesting bird, the Little Ringed Plover is found throughout Europe as far north as southern Scandinavia. In Britain, its strongholds are concentrated in England and Wales and, with one or two exceptions, Cumbria is at the northern edge of this range. There has been a pattern of population growth over the whole of western Europe since the 1930s. Britain has been part of this spread, with colonization beginning in 1938, and by 1984 there had been a notable expansion into northwest England. Ireland, with very few sightings, has yet to be colonized.

Little Ringed Plovers tend to utilize unvegetated aquatic margins with sandy or gravel banks; however, only 3% of nesting attempts in Britain occur at natural sites (Parrinder 1989). Consequently the range expansion in this species is closely associated with the increase in man-made gravel pits, a rare example of man providing, rather than destroying, suitable habitat. The males often return first and circle a territory, with a butterfly-like display flight, to declare ownership. Cumbrian birds tend to arrive relatively late, generally early to mid-May, although arrival and mating has been noted as late as early June. Once a mate is attracted, a ritualized scrape-choosing ceremony then follows with the male leading the female from one potential site to another; at one Cumbrian locality the

male took the female to three different scrapes before a final nest site was eventually adopted. The nest is a small, unlined hollow on pebbles or gravel often close to the water, and both birds share in the incubation.

Incubation is always a tense period for a species with a tendency to nest on lake shores or riverine gravel bars, where fluctuating water levels offer a constant threat of flooding; in Cumbria, this happens regularly, as it did at one site in 1998 and 2000. In dry periods they are also vulnerable to trampling: cattle frequently walk the shorelines to drink and a large sheep sat on a nest in 1997! As if this was not enough, the exposed nests are prone to predation from Carrion Crow, Red Fox and Mink. In 1998 a nest was close to a pair of breeding Oystercatcher which vigorously defended the area from potential predators such as Lesser Black-backed Gull and Grey Heron, only for both nests to succumb to flooding.

The county's first breeding record was of a pair rearing four young on a shingle bank on the River Eden in 1970; this was followed by two successful pairs that raised at least seven young on the dried-out bed of Killington Reservoir during the drought of 1984 (Hutcheson 1986). Subsequently, there were on average 2–3 pairs per annum, with an exceptional six sites occupied in 1989. The *New Atlas* reported evidence of breeding in five 10km squares and possible nesting in a further three. However, *this Atlas* confirmed breeding at only three locations although birds were recorded in a further five.

Although Little Ringed Plovers are very cryptic in their colouring and could be overlooked, it is more likely that, with Cumbria being on the northern edge of the species' range, annual population density is dependent on spring weather conditions when birds arrive back in Britain. Currently, the British population appears to be still expanding; in 1998, a non-randomized sample found that numbers had continued to increase across the country (Ogilvie *et al* 2000).

With only three known breeding sites during *this Atlas,* the Little Ringed Plover remains a rare breeding bird, although it is possible that occasional pairs breed undetected. The suggested current county population of 2–5 breeding pairs is from known numbers at monitored locations. At the most regular site, with the exception of 1999, at least two pairs have been present each year since 1995, with mixed success due to flooding and predation.

Despite the size of the county, it could be argued that 'classic' lowland Little Ringed Plover sites are not so common; gravel pits are few, and, while river and lake shingle banks are common, these are not always available due to the spring spate of many upland tributaries. The predicted climate change for Cumbria of wetter springs may seriously affect the suitability of

Sponsored by Pete Davies

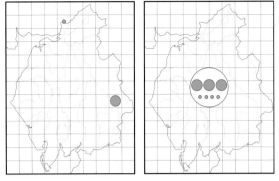

**1968-1972**          **1997-2001**
(For explanation of maps, see page 45)

| Conservation status | |
| --- | --- |
| European: | Non-SPEC |
| UK: | **GREEN** |

| Populations | |
| --- | --- |
| European status: | 75,000 |
| Britain – pairs: | 950 |
| Cumbria – pairs: | 2–5 |

**30-year distribution change**

| | Old Atlas | This Atlas | % |
| --- | --- | --- | --- |
| No. of 10km squares: | 2 | 7 | +250 |

| Survey data | Tetrads | % |
| --- | --- | --- |
| Confirmed breeding: | 3 | 0.2 |
| Probable breeding: | 0 | |
| Possible breeding: | 5 | 0.3 |
| Total: | 8 | 0.5 |

natural habitat and in future its survival as a breeding bird within the county may depend on its versatility to adapt to artificial sites such as sewage works and reservoirs which have been used in recent years.

Peter Barron

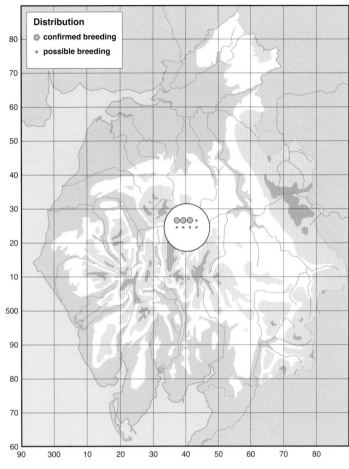

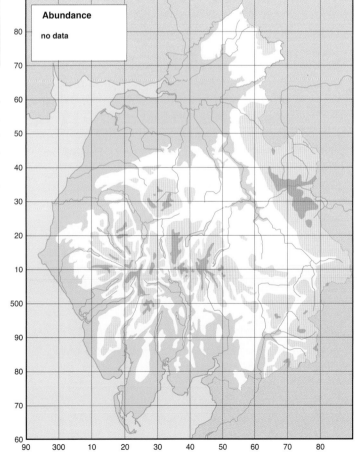

DASHING around on its 'clockwork orange' legs this smart little wader with its masked face and breast band brightens up the dullest of days. Seemingly ever alert to the possibility of food and using the 'stop-run-peck' manner typical of plovers, the Ringed Plover can cover a lot of ground in its search for sustenance.

Breeding from Baffin Island in Canada eastwards through the Palearctic to the Bering Sea the Ringed Plover is essentially a species of arctic, subarctic and north temperate coasts, although it can breed far inland where suitable habitats exist. Except for a small isolated population in Brittany, Britain and Ireland are on the southern edge of its range. In England, the greatest numbers are found on the east coast, between the Humber and Thames estuaries; they are either scarce or absent from southwest England, Wales and southern Ireland. Highest densities occur on the Western Isles, Orkney and Shetland.

In mild winters birds can be on breeding territory from mid-February, but display seldom starts in earnest until the end of March. The nest is a scrape in the ground on sand or shingle, lined with small pebbles, shells or grass, and rarely far from water. Nesting in wide-open spaces the bird's beautifully cryptic plumage and eggs are its only defence. The male makes several scrapes to tempt a female; she chooses which to use and starts laying eggs from late March onwards. Incubation usually takes 23–25 days, and once the young hatch they disperse in the vicinity of the nest until fledging after a similar period of time. During this critical phase the adults will make frenzied efforts to protect eggs and young from danger by a bold distraction display, which intensifies as the intruder approaches closer.

Although Alexander & Lack (1944) considered historic populations of Ringed Plover in Britain and Ireland stable, with no detectable changes prior to 1940, later studies revealed that a decrease had occurred in the latter part of this period, which was to accelerate over the next 30 years. Parslow (1973) attributed this decline to increases in human recreational use within its breeding habitat. Ringed Plovers habitually nest along the shingle edges of lakes, rivers and the coast, which during the breeding season brings increased potential of disturbance that causes many nests to fail. Although its numbers are diminishing it still maintains a preference for this favoured ecological niche, which is also vulnerable to flooding and, locally, trampling by livestock. Repeat clutches can be laid if the eggs are lost and in the south of its range the Ringed Plover is double-brooded. In severe winters the mortality rate for this species can be very high; following the notoriously bad winter of 1962/63 the breeding population was reduced by around 33% in England.

From Macpherson (1892) one may deduce the bird was mainly a coastal nesting species, with a few inland. His account says, "breeds numerously at Ravenglass and on Walney; some nest on gravel beds along the rivers Esk, Eden, and Irthing, occasionally on the saltmarshes and sparingly along the coastline from the Kent Estuary to Grune Point." Stokoe (1962) commented that "it nests commonly on the coast and also on shingle banks of some northern rivers and at least on one fell tarn." Although Macpherson and Stokoe had both alluded to nesting on riverside shingle, the trend of breeding inland never increased in Cumbria, as it had elsewhere in England, despite new opportunities with the creation of novel habitats such as gravel pits and derelict industrial sites. One can only speculate as to the reason; perhaps the sheer volume of visitors to Cumbria, and the Lake District in particular, means there are very few undisturbed inland areas for this species to settle – but again many artificial habitats have been created where disturbance is low! For whatever reason, inland nesting has declined since the *Old Atlas,* and today it is almost exclusively a coastal breeding bird, with the exception of two instances in the north of the county.

Due to too few contacts, the line transect data from *this Atlas* did not provide a robust estimate; consequently, the current county population of 200–250 breeding pairs has been derived from count

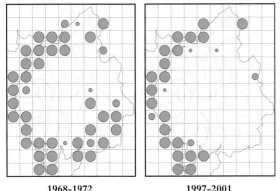

| 1968-1972 | 1997-2001 |
|---|---|

(For explanation of maps, see page 45)

*Conservation status*

| European: | Non-SPEC |
|---|---|
| UK: | AMBER: WDM |

*Populations*

| European status: | 95,000 |
|---|---|
| Britain – pairs: | 8,500 |
| Cumbria – pairs: | 200–250 |

*30-year distribution change*

| | Old Atlas | This Atlas | % |
|---|---|---|---|
| No. of 10km squares: | 42 | 27 | −35.7 |

| **Survey data** | **Tetrads** | **%** |
|---|---|---|
| Confirmed breeding: | 59 | 3.2 |
| Probable breeding: | 16 | 0.9 |
| Possible breeding: | 6 | 0.3 |
| Total: | 81 | 4.4 |

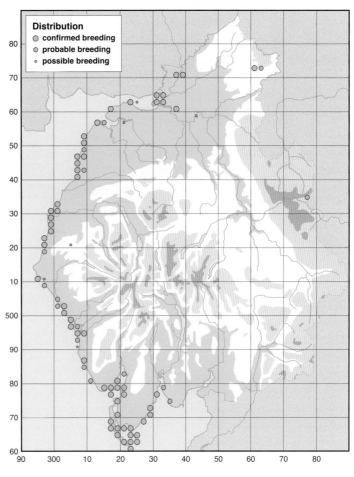

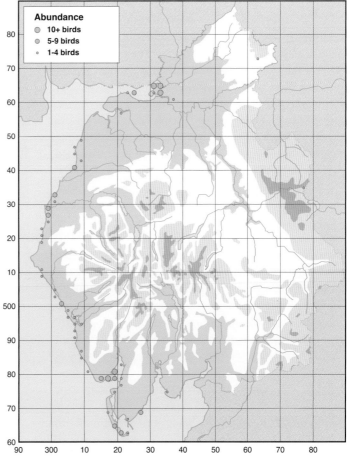

data enhanced by supplementary records.

The specific nesting requirements of Ringed Plovers leave them vulnerable to disturbance and nest-trampling. Only on protected sites such as coastal nature reserves can they maintain population levels from year to year. Even protected status does not guarantee success: South Walney in the 1960s and early 1970s had 30 successful pairs, yet this had declined to just seven pairs a decade later (Dean 1990). Today, only one or two pairs nest regularly, and these birds tend to occupy the gull-free areas of the reserve. Perhaps the relatively recent expansion of the gull colony has been the destabilizing factor, since Ringed Plovers cannot tolerate the more aggressive nature of gulls. The prognosis is not good for breeding Ringed Plovers in Cumbria, and it is unlikely that numbers will ever be as high as they were in Macpherson's day.

Arnold Strand

"THERE is only one first time": so says Nethersole-Thompson in his peerless monograph of 1973, describing how he saw his first birds "running on a great mossy lump of hill" and recalling the words of an earlier naturalist who envied those who had not seen them "for the pleasure yet to come". Their confiding nature and reluctance to fly accounts for their old Cumbrian name 'the Mossfool', as they were hunted with bow and arrow on the Solway marshes during spring migration.

With a Eurasian distribution and a preference for semi-arctic habitats, the Dotterel's summer range includes the northern limits of Fennoscandia, northern Russia, including Novaya Zemlya, northern and central Siberia, with erratic breeding in central European mountains, a relatively small population in the Highlands of Scotland, and a precarious toe-hold in Cumbria.

Dotterels are brightly coloured 'wading birds' that seldom actually get their feet wet. During the summer months they occupy well-drained stony plateaux, whilst they winter in areas of semi-desert and poor cultivation. Although occurring on coastal tundra in the Arctic, further south Dotterels are a truly montane species living in some of the most changeable and hostile summer habitats. In winter they prefer semi-arid habitats in North Africa and the Middle East.

Nesting Dotterel are extremely difficult to find due to their habit of sitting tightly on the nest and their behaviour as 'single parent families'. Laying only three eggs, Dotterels have an unusual 'reversal of sexes' breeding strategy, where the male alone incubates and tends the chicks after hatching. During incubation, the female disappears and is seldom seen again, although there are instances where well-grown chicks have been accompanied by both male and female (pers obs). There is a school of thought which believes that a reduced clutch with only a single parent attending reduces feeding competition in potentially unsympathetic habitat, offering a positive survival strategy for precocious chicks.

The *Old Atlas* estimated a Scottish population of 100 pairs; the *New Atlas* quotes an NCC survey estimate of 840 pairs in 1987–88, but gives a corrected figure for those years of 950 pairs: a seismic increase given the relatively limited range of suitable breeding habitat. The *New Atlas* reveals an increase of 21 in the number of occupied squares, with colonization of Sutherland.

Much sought after by the acquisitive Victorian zoologists and collectors and a favourite amongst fly-fishermen because of their gaudy plumage, Dotterels were in great demand during the 19th century. Subsequently, the deaths of Dotterel on both the Solway Mosses and montane breeding grounds are well documented. Nethersole-Thompson (1973) refers to the first satisfactory account of Dotterel breeding in the county, a nest with eggs on Whiteside, Helvellyn on 29th June 1835, although a clutch of eggs said to have come from Skiddaw in 1784 was held by a Carlisle magistrate! Although there are cautious estimates that as many as 75 pairs nested in Cumbria in good years, up to 1880, no more than five nests were ever found in a single season. Macpherson (1892) commented that "although suitable habitat abounds, it would be a mistake to suppose that the species has at any time bred numerously." Into the 20th century, nesting became irregular with only three nests located from 1937 to 1959. A nest was found in the North Pennines in the latter year, the first there for over 30 years. Subsequently, single nests were discovered at the same site, with two nests in both 1969 and 1970. It was not until 1974, when a male with two chicks was located on the Ennerdale Fells, that the Dotterel was found to have returned widely to its English heartland. Following this, two dedicated Dotterel enthusiasts discovered breeding on a further eight individual hills in Lakeland up to 1988, including the Helvellyn and Skiddaw Ranges and the Ennerdale and Buttermere Fells. Additionally, in 1979, five nests were found on a single hill in the North Pennines. That apart, a maximum of three nests was the most found in any one year. This apparent increase coincided with a population rise in Scotland. A cooling of the summer climate at this time was thought to be a contributing factor.

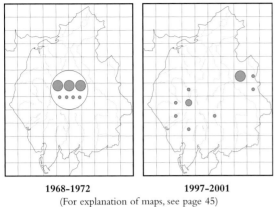

| 1968-1972 | 1997-2001 |

(For explanation of maps, see page 45)

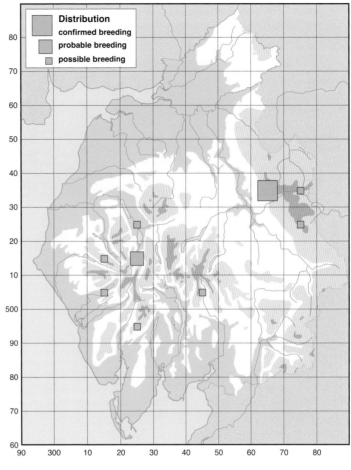

*Conservation status*

| European: | Non-SPEC |
| UK: | **AMBER: BL** |

*Populations*

| European status: | 25,700 |
| Britain – pairs: | 900 |
| Cumbria – pairs: | 1–2 |

*30-year distribution change*

| | Old Atlas | This Atlas | % |
|---|---|---|---|
| No. of 10km squares: | 7 | 9 | +28.5 |

| **Survey data** | **Tetrads** | **%** |
|---|---|---|
| Confirmed breeding: | 1 | 0.05 |
| Probable breeding: | 2 | 0.11 |
| Possible breeding: | 10 | 0.54 |
| Total: | 13 | 0.70 |

The years of *this Atlas* produced only one confirmed breeding record. In the last decade of the 20th century the weather was ameliorating strongly, and chronic over-grazing by sheep on the high plateaux reached saturation levels: together these factors may have reversed the previous trend. Migrating Dotterel often use the same traditional nesting hills for stopovers and some of the possible dots on the distribution map are likely to represent these passage birds.

Modern threats to Dotterel in Cumbria are more likely to be climatic than man-made; in fact sheep have been removed or reduced in numbers from many traditional Dotterel sites within the Lake District National Park, encouraging the re-emergence of natural vegetation.

There are presently no Dotterel enthusiasts active in the county – certainly the time and effort required is demanding, but the rewards are fabulous.

John Callion

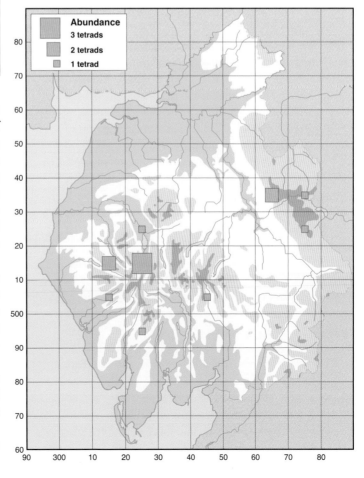

A TRUE herald of spring on the high fell, the plaintive whistling song and display of arriving Golden Plover always make a March walk on the tops worthwhile. This species is well distributed throughout high grassland and heaths of Britain and Ireland, reflecting the bird's wider Palearctic distribution from Iceland to central Siberia.

This wader breeds on flat or gently sloping grassland or heath up to around 600m asl in Cumbria. Golden Plovers are single-brooded, with up to four eggs laid into a shallow scrape from early April. Incubation is shared by both sexes, with off-duty birds feeding, often nocturnally, on invertebrates in pasture several kilometres from the nest site (Pearce-Higgins pers comm). Breeding grounds are vacated from early July, with birds dispersing south and west to coastal grassland for the winter.

The distribution across the central and southern parts of its European range contracted during the last century, climate change, afforestation and peatland drainage playing a part. This was reflected in Britain and Ireland with breeding birds lost from many historic haunts, as the *Old Atlas* shows. Changes within Cumbria are more difficult to document although the *Historical Atlas* does refer to Golden Plover breeding more frequently on the mosses within the Solway Basin early in the 19th century. Macpherson (1892) suggests that breeding both on the Solway mosses and high moors of Lakeland was at low density, but recognized the Solway Firth as an important post-breeding and wintering site for large flocks of birds. Stokoe (1962) commented that "breeding birds are more local and generally less numerous than perhaps ten years ago; remains common on some Pennine moors up to 2,900 feet [884m], but reduced on Border moors and some inland mosses; sparse in central fells and gone from the coastal mosses." He goes on to remark that "a reduction in the numbers in the Skiddaw group of fells and in the Helvellyn range has been noticed since about 1950" and that "in the Pennines and elsewhere there are probably fewer too and distribution is irregular, but local concentrations with maintained numbers are still to be found."

Post-1945 intensification of upland use, both in sheep farming and forestry practice, also affected the birds' distribution with notable range contractions in the Borders, Dumfries and Galloway, as is evident from the *New Atlas*. Contractions in range and population decline are reflected in the bird's Red list status in the BoCC. There is no doubt that both factors will have had a significant impact on Cumbria's population, with increases in sheep numbers across the county after World War II, coupled with moorland drainage, together with the establishment of the Border Forest complex. Equally, air pollution, in the form of acid deposition, generated by heavy industry since the industrial revolution, has already been implicated in the loss of Sphagnum moss from mires in the south Pennines (Lee *et al* 1988). Such habitat change may well affect suitability for breeding Golden Plover. The intensification of our use of the uplands for recreation may also have affected the bird's status on fell ground popular with walkers (Yalden & Yalden 1988).

Comparison of Golden Plover distribution during *this Atlas* and the *Old Atlas* reveals very little obvious change. The North Pennine massif is the bird's county stronghold, with the Cumbria Dales and Border Uplands also making a major contribution. Analysis suggests any small gains in the North Pennines are balanced by losses in the Cumbria Dales. A few pairs still breed on the fells of central Lakeland.

The population is currently experiencing small changes in range across the county but overall numbers appear to be stable. Analysis of line transect data from *this Atlas* gives a population band of 1,000–8,000, suggesting a mean population of 3,000 birds. However, given the relatively small sample size, a degree of discretion should be exercised with this estimate. The highest densities of 3.9 birds/km$^2$ occurred, perhaps predictably, in the North Pennines.

The future of Golden Plover will be influenced by several anthropogenic factors. Sustainable use of the uplands, for forestry, agriculture, electricity generation and recreation, is paramount for this bird's Cumbrian future. The long-term impact on this species of any

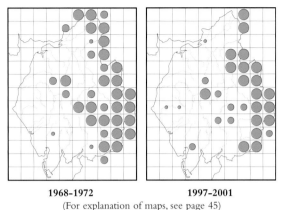

**1968-1972**     **1997-2001**

(For explanation of maps, see page 45)

**Conservation status**

| | |
|---|---|
| European: | SPEC Cat 4 |
| UK: | **GREEN** |

**Populations**

| | |
|---|---|
| European status: | 550,000 |
| Britain – pairs: | 22,600 |
| Cumbria – pairs: | 1,500 |

**30-year distribution change**

| | Old Atlas | This Atlas | % |
|---|---|---|---|
| No. of 10km squares: | 37 | 30 | −18.9 |

| **Survey data** | **Tetrads** | **%** |
|---|---|---|
| Confirmed breeding: | 84 | 4.6 |
| Probable breeding: | 43 | 2.3 |
| Possible breeding: | 15 | 0.8 |
| Total: | 142 | 7.7 |

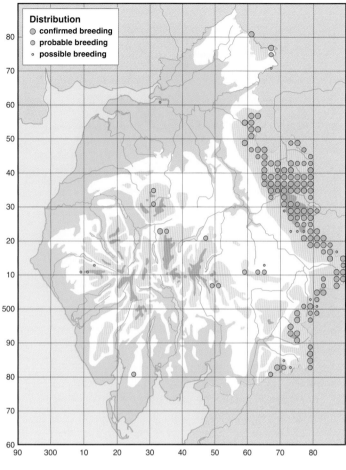

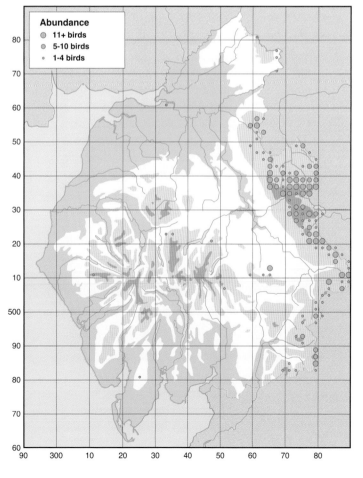

changes in farming practices following foot-and-mouth disease is difficult to predict, although opportunities may exist for habitat restoration in the Cumbria Dales and Lakeland. Recent widespread uptake of agri-environment schemes across the county's uplands, such as ESA and Countryside Stewardship schemes, has the potential to restore areas of suitable grassland and heath to a favourable condition. Continued support and reform of these schemes may assist strengthening of populations across the county.

Global climate change predictions for this century suggest that significant temperature and precipitation increases may compound the effects on British and other north European populations in years to come. The outcome for Golden Plover is difficult to predict, but wetter and wilder spring weather, together with potential changes in vegetation may have a real influence on this characteristic species of our wonderful uplands.

Nick Mason

RECOGNIZED as much by the evocative call as its acrobatic display flight, the Lapwing is essentially a bird of open countryside and personifies spring in Cumbria just as much as Wordworth's daffodils. On the ground the long, erect crest, dark glossy-green upperparts, contrasting with brilliant white underparts, readily identify the bird.

A common and familiar Palearctic species with a range that stretches eastwards from Ireland to Siberia, in Britain and Ireland its stronghold is in northern England and Scotland which hold 66% of the remaining breeding birds.

Also known as the Peewit or Green Plover, the Lapwing returns to its breeding grounds as early as February if the weather is favourable. In Cumbria these extend from the coastal saltmarshes, through the farmland belt to the moors along the edge of the North Pennines. Although usually avoiding the highest Lakeland peaks, it has been recorded breeding at 893m asl on the summit of Cross Fell, where a day old nestling was ringed in June 1936 (Brown 1974). The nest site is generally a scrape on the ground with the eggs laid in April or May and the young hatching after 19–34 days. The Lapwing has a catholic diet, consisting mainly of ground-living invertebrates, and is useful to the farmer in destroying more wireworms, tipulid and lepidopterous larvae than carnivorous insects and worms (Coward & Barnes 1969).

Although the Lapwing was met with in the county during the 17th century, it had become significantly more abundant as a breeding bird by the early 19th century. This was thought to be due to changes in the character of the landscape: vast areas of flow country had been drained and brought under the plough, providing ideal nesting habitat (Macpherson 1892). Indeed towards the end of the century the Lapwing was still considered to breed in vast numbers (Robinson 1888), but nationally it was already suffering from man-made pressures. Losses due to agricultural change and the systematic collection of eggs for the table caused enough concern to see the introduction of the Lapwing Protection Bill in 1926.

Subsequently numbers recovered until after the Second World War, but the continued change from traditional farming methods again put pressure on the species and this was compounded by the severe winter of 1962/63. In Cumbria this decline was typified by an area of farmland near Carlisle where 51 pairs of Lapwing were found in 1937; the same area held just three pairs in 1966 (Brown 1974).

Although the *Old Atlas* recorded Lapwings in 91 10km squares in Cumbria, by the *New Atlas* birds had begun to disappear from marginal habitat in the heart of Lakeland with three squares unoccupied. *This Atlas* shows Lapwings have now deserted seven 10km squares and even where breeding was confirmed, densities are well down on previous years. Indeed, from the distribution map it can be seen that the Lapwing is almost totally absent from the valleys and moors of central Lakeland. The current strongholds are areas of the Solway Basin, North Pennines, Coastal Plain and Eden Valley.

The latest CBC index shows a national decrease of 40% since 1970. However the trend from previous years shows an even more catastrophic decline of over 50% and supporting this is a 1998 BTO/RSPB survey which suggests a fall of 47% since 1987. The Cumbrian results of this survey show an even greater cause for concern: out of 34 tetrads that were surveyed in both years the figures indicate a 60% fall. In 1987, there were 367 breeding pairs located but this had dropped to 148 breeding pairs in 1998. In 12 tetrads (35%), Lapwings had died out completely and in one tetrad, where there had been 20 pairs, none was found in 1998.

Analysis of line transect data from *this Atlas* gives a population band of 17,000–40,000, suggesting a mean population of 23,000 birds. The highest densities of 17.6 birds/km² occurred in intensively farmed areas on the alluvial flood plain of the Solway Basin and lower Eden Valley, where mixed arable, grassland and pasture is widespread.

Agricultural intensification, at least in part brought about by subsidies, has had a seriously detrimental

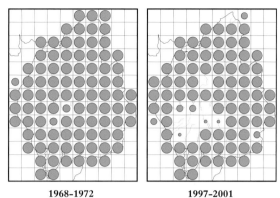

| 1968–1972 | 1997–2001 |
|:---:|:---:|

(For explanation of maps, see page 45)

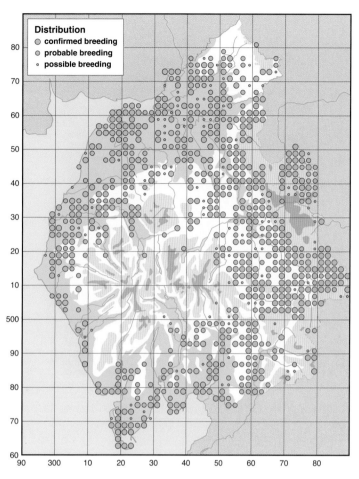

**Distribution**
- confirmed breeding
- probable breeding
- possible breeding

**Conservation status**

| | |
|---|---|
| European: | Non–SPEC |
| UK: | AMBER: BDM & WI |

**Populations**

| | |
|---|---|
| European status: | 1,300,000 |
| Britain – pairs: | 126,300 |
| Cumbria – pairs: | 11,500 |

**30-year distribution change**

| | Old Atlas | This Atlas | % |
|---|---|---|---|
| No. of 10km squares: | 91 | 84 | −7.7 |

| Survey data | Tetrads | % |
|---|---|---|
| Confirmed breeding: | 458 | 24.8 |
| Probable breeding: | 253 | 13.7 |
| Possible breeding: | 99 | 5.4 |
| Total: | 810 | 43.9 |

impact on the species. The change to autumn-sown cereals, increased areas of silage, 'improved' grassland and higher stocking levels have all put pressure on the Lapwing. Although the outlook is bleak, it is still not too late to reverse the trend. Encouraging 'set-aside' schemes, introducing financial incentives for environmentally sensitive management, and increasing public demand for organically grown crops which do not require insecticides and herbicides, could all help to ensure that the Lapwing remains a familiar species within the county.

Arnold Strand

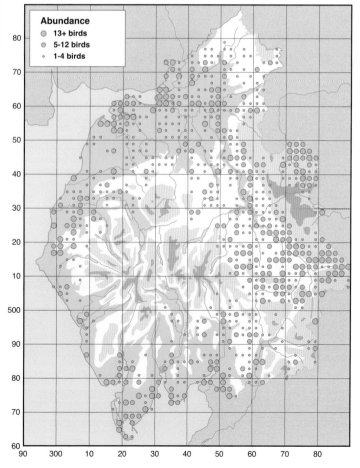

**Abundance**
- 13+ birds
- 5-12 birds
- 1-4 birds

# Dunlin *Calidris alpina*

THOSE birdwatchers fortunate enough to be on the high, wind-swept moors or coastal saltmarshes in spring will delight in the trilling 'song' of the Dunlin, often given in an ecstatic fluttering display flight. When the observer enters its territory, the bird may perch on a tussock, beady-eyed and anxious, craning up for a better view, and showing off the resplendent breeding plumage, strongly reddish-brown above, and with diagnostic black belly. A single Dunlin will often accompany a single Golden Plover on the moors – giving rise to an old name, 'Plover's Page' – but the purpose of this behaviour is unknown; suggestions that the taller bird gives an early warning of intruders are speculation: if this were so, why is such behaviour not apparent in many other pairs of larger and smaller birds?

The Dunlin has a Holarctic distribution, with its Western Palearctic breeding range stretching eastwards from Iceland to the coasts of the Kara Sea. Britain and Ireland are on the extreme southwestern edge of this range, and consequently it is absent as a breeding bird from much of England, Wales and Ireland, with the highest densities found in the North Pennines, Grampians, northern Scotland and the Northern and Western Isles.

Its choice of nest site depends on location: on moorland, rough vegetation is used, usually close to bog pools, whereas on the coast the clutch of four eggs is hidden in a very well-concealed shallow scrape or depression on the ground, or in a tuft or tussock, usually near water. High tides and heavy rains during the breeding season can cause many nest failures due to flooding. However these are often replaced with a second clutch. The Dunlin shows atypical behaviour in that it is the female that is left to raise the chicks, unlike many wader species in which the male rears the young. On the breeding grounds birds feed mainly on small invertebrates such as dipteran flies, beetles, caddisflies, wasps, sawflies and mayflies.

In Cumbria, the Dunlin is found nesting in remote moorland areas as well as the sea-washed turf of coastal districts. Indeed one short paragraph written over 200 years ago firmly fixed this dual habitat existence: "The Dunlin appears the first or second week in May and breeds on our moors. On 19th June 1783, I shot several old ones on Rockcliffe Marsh" (Heysham 1794). Almost 100 years later, a few pairs nested upon the eastern fells, especially in the Bewcastle and Alston districts, but the stronghold of the species was on Rockcliffe Marsh. Smaller numbers also nested on Burgh Marsh, Glasson Moss, Bowness Flow, Wedholme Flow, Skinburness and in the vicinity of Ravenglass. However, birds were wholly absent from the mountains of Lakeland (Macpherson & Duckworth 1886). By the 1940s coastal populations were in decline. Both Blezard (1946) and Brown (1974) noted a considerable reduction in breeding Dunlins on the Solway saltmarshes and mosses in their time. Stokoe (1962), whilst also alluding to the decline along the Solway, mentions the continued existence of nesting birds on Arnside and Meathop Marshes in the Kent Estuary and that the species "breeds locally on the Pennine and Border fells". Although the *Old Atlas* reaffirmed the presence of breeding birds in the North Pennines, Border Uplands, Cumbria Dales, the marshes of the Solway Firth and on the southern estuaries, by the time of the *New Atlas* birds had largely disappeared from southern coastal habitats.

*This Atlas* confirms that Rockcliffe Marsh is now the only known coastal breeding site in Cumbria. This one time premier county site previously held double figures of nesting birds, but sadly they can now be counted on the fingers of one hand. Elsewhere, the Dunlins that choose to nest at higher altitudes, especially in the North Pennines and Cumbria Dales, have fared better. These discrete populations have maintained higher numbers, even if not all of their former range, since birds are now almost totally absent from the Border Uplands as a result of afforestation. The results of a survey carried out in 1998 confirm the presence of 10 pairs on moorland near Appleby and 4–6 pairs are regular on the high fells at Geltsdale (P. Ullrich, M. Stott pers comm).

The restriction in land class occupation and few contacts makes analysis of the line transect data from *this Atlas* meaningless for this species. The county population of 15–25 breeding pairs has been estimated by attendance of birds at established breeding sites.

Upland and especially coastal breeding populations

Sponsored in memory of Arthur & Betty Stott

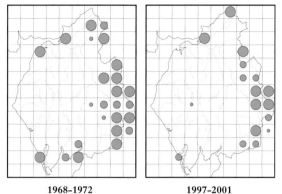

| 1968-1972 | 1997-2001 |

(For explanation of maps, see page 45)

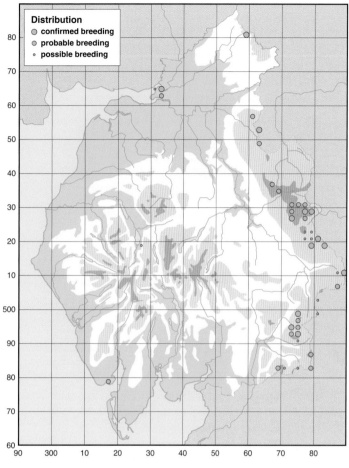

**Conservation status**

| European: | SPEC Cat 3 (W) |
| UK: | AMBER: WDM, BL, WL & WI |

**Populations**

| European status: | 350,000 |
| Britain – pairs: | 9,500 |
| Cumbria – pairs: | 15–25 |

**30-year distribution change**

| | Old Atlas | This Atlas | % |
|---|---|---|---|
| No. of 10km squares: | 25 | 17 | –32 |

| **Survey data** | **Tetrads** | **%** |
|---|---|---|
| Confirmed breeding: | 13 | 0.7 |
| Probable breeding: | 18 | 1.0 |
| Possible breeding: | 12 | 0.7 |
| Total: | 43 | 2.4 |

both show a long-term decline and general contraction in range. Coastal development and agricultural reclamation are often cited as the main causes. Had the Dunlin continued to nest in any numbers in coastal areas it would certainly have been vulnerable to rising sea levels. However, the effects of global warming on its upland habitats are less predictable. An increase in the height of vegetation, a drying out of bog pools, or changes in invertebrate life cycles might all contribute to the demise of the Dunlin in Cumbria.

Arnold Strand

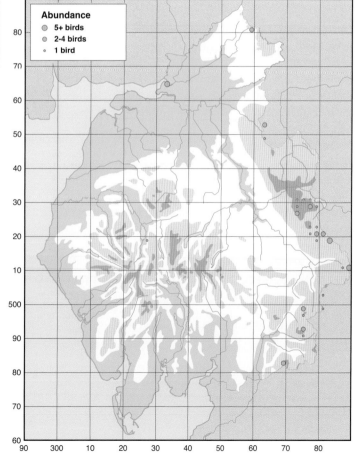

THE drumming of the Snipe, produced by the vibrating tail feathers, as it displays over its breeding territory, has long been a familiar sound associated with damp pastures and bogs across the temperate zone of the Western Palearctic and as far north as the arctic tundra. The bird's breeding habitat consists of marshy areas of all kinds, where there is ground cover for nesting and soil conditions sufficiently damp for adult birds to probe for soil invertebrates close to the nest and where chicks can feed themselves on surface invertebrates soon after hatching. In Britain and Ireland, these conditions are most widely met with on the moorland bogs and marshy pastures of northern England, Wales, Scotland and Ireland. The Snipe also occurs, more locally, in lowland areas, where it nests on fens, alluvial meadows and coastal grazing marshes.

In common with many other parts of Europe, the number of Snipe breeding in Britain fell significantly during the 20th century. This decline was initially concentrated in areas of the Midlands and southeast England which the Snipe had colonized during the late 19th and early 20th centuries (Parslow 1973). However, the decline extended into northern England and southwest Scotland during the 1960s and has continued since, with a dramatic drop in numbers during the 1990s. The Snipe is currently on the BoCC Amber List, due to a 90% decline revealed by analysis of CBC data for the period 1972–96, although this drop is not necessarily representative of the overall population.

In Cumbria, Macpherson (1892) regarded the Snipe as "a plentiful bird in Lakeland" though he commented on the "large portion of snipey ground" that has been reclaimed even in the dreariest and most remote portions of our area." Notwithstanding this, the bird remained a widespread and fairly common breeding bird in the county up until the 1960s. Stokoe (1962) described it as "common and widespread; nests from coastal saltmarshes up into the fells, occasionally to 2,600 feet [793m]" though he did comment that "drainage and other factors have brought about a reduction in numbers in some parts." Since then, the numbers of Snipe breeding within the county have fallen significantly. The bird disappeared from 22 10km squares between the *Old Atlas* and *this Atlas,* a drop of nearly 25% in occupied squares over a period of 30 years, with the largest declines taking place in the Eden Valley and on the lowland grasslands of the Solway Basin and the Coastal Plain.

Snipe are conspicuous birds during the breeding season and are easy to locate by the distinctive drumming or by their loud *'chip-per, chip-per, . . .'* calls, often uttered from conspicuous perches at any time of day or night. Data from *this Atlas* show that the distribution is becoming increasingly localized. Apart from some relatively small pockets on the Solway mosses and around Morecambe Bay, breeding Snipe are now almost entirely confined to the rough pastures of the North Pennines, Cumbria Dales and Lakeland and the unafforested parts of the Border Uplands. It was found to be most abundant on grass moorlands and enclosed upland pastures in parts of the North Pennines, particularly around Alston and on the arc of land between the headwaters of the Rivers Eden and Lune, stretching from Warcop Fell to the Shap Fells. Good numbers are also still to be found around Borrowdale and Coniston in Lakeland and Spadeadam in the Border Uplands.

Analysis of the line transect data from *this Atlas* gives a population band of 3,000–19,000 birds, suggesting a mean population of 8,000 birds; note, however, the wide band limits.

Much of the decline in Snipe numbers over the last 30 or 40 years can be attributed to changes in land use and land management practices, particularly the drainage and increased fertilization of land associated with conversion to arable farming, productive grassland and commercial forestry (Mason & Macdonald 1976, Baines 1988). These activities have resulted in a direct loss of habitat. They have also had an indirect effect by reducing the availability of food for adults and chicks and by enabling animals and machinery to be brought onto the land some weeks earlier in the year than would otherwise be the case, resulting in increased trampling by cattle, destruction of nests and eggs by machinery and curtailment of opportunities for repeat nesting. Other contributory factors include the effects of natural predators (the

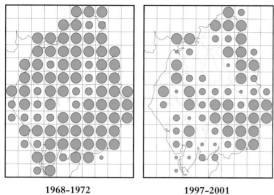

**1968-1972**                    **1997-2001**

(For explanation of maps, see page 45)

| Conservation status | |
|---|---|
| European: | Non-SPEC |
| UK: | AMBER: BDM |

**Populations**

| European status: | 920,000 |
|---|---|
| Britain – pairs: | 55,000 |
| Cumbria – pairs: | 4,000 |

**30-year distribution change**

| | Old Atlas | This Atlas | % |
|---|---|---|---|
| No. of 10km squares: | 89 | 67 | −24.7 |

| Survey data | Tetrads | % |
|---|---|---|
| Confirmed breeding: | 73 | 4.0 |
| Probable breeding: | 151 | 8.2 |
| Possible breeding: | 82 | 4.4 |
| Total: | 306 | 16.6 |

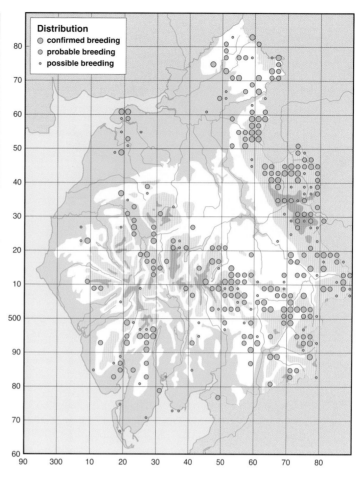

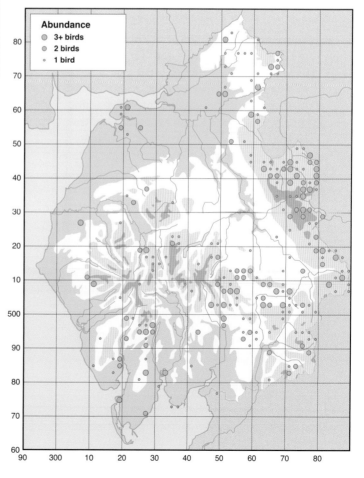

most important cause of egg loss) and of shooting activity.

Any long-term recovery in Cumbria will depend on wide-scale changes in the way the countryside is managed. New initiatives, more radical than the ESA schemes currently running in the Lake District and Pennine Dales, are needed if we are to take full advantage of the opportunities presented following the recent foot-and-mouth disease crisis, to reshape the countryside to provide a better future for Snipe.

Clive Hartley

# Woodcock *Scolopax rusticola*

C.M.Isherwood

THE spectacular, crepuscular aerial ballet of roding Woodcock on spring evenings provides for most observers the only chance to observe this secretive and mysterious bird, whose woodland habits are unique amongst British waders. The Woodcock's breeding range covers most of Europe's woodland and scrub, at increasing altitude southwards, and the species occurs right across northern Eurasia. It is widespread throughout Britain, with notable gaps only in areas of high ground and low-lying areas such as the fens. In Ireland, its distribution is much patchier.

This bird nests on the ground in open canopy woodland, where an understorey of scrub is available, up to 500m asl. Woodland types used range from mixed deciduous ancient woodland, through upland oak and birch and early rotation conifer woodland. Densities do appear highest where woodlands are damp, offering an excellent feeding resource (Kalchreuter 1982). There are still gaps in our knowledge of the species' breeding biology, with the promiscuous and polygynous systems and subsequent behaviour poorly understood. In winter, our Woodcock numbers are swollen by annual influxes of Scandinavian birds fleeing freezing conditions.

Macpherson (1892) noted that Woodcock were recorded in the county as early as 1618, being a favourite dish at the table of Lord William Howard during the autumn and winter months. Records suggest enormous numbers of Woodcock were trapped or snared for food during this time. Cumbrian breeding is first alluded to in correspondence from 1831, with more widespread records from later in the 19th century. Stokoe (1962) commented that the species "nests in woods throughout the area and most commonly in the south; sometimes above the tree limit in the Pennines and to 1000 feet [305m] in the central fells."

Until the early 19th century recorded only as an English breeder, the Woodcock's range did, however, continue to expand north throughout the 19th and early 20th centuries from strongholds in southern Britain and the Midlands. This expansion may have been aided by the cessation of summer Woodcock shooting and the rise of Pheasant breeding and associated woodland management (Blezard *et al* 1943). Nationally, analysis of the latest CBC data indicates a worrying 71% decline since 1970, though CBC monitoring takes little account of extensive afforested areas in the north and may not be an accurate reflection of population levels. The *New Atlas* suggests Woodcock abundance is declining across Britain and Ireland, with habitat lost as post-war afforested areas reach maturation and become less suitable for breeding. This long-term decline sets this species on the Amber list of BoCC, although accurate assessment of national status is difficult due to poor monitoring coverage in northwest Britain and low detectability by standard methods.

In Cumbria, *this Atlas* suggests that the county population is declining in line with national trends, with the number of occupied 10km squares reduced since the *Old Atlas*. The current distribution in the county is patchy, with hotspots around Derwent Water, Bassenthwaite Lake, the southern side of Windermere and Geltsdale. Densities in these areas were as high as 2 breeding pairs/km². Records from the northern half of the county have reduced, particularly when comparing *this Atlas* with the *Old Atlas;* previous haunts in several 10km squares from Silloth east to Armathwaite now appear unoccupied. This could be linked to increased agricultural intensification in this area. With records in only 5% of tetrads, this thin distribution may also reflect the low detectability of this species in standard surveys without dusk visits. Skulking habits, cryptic plumage and a well-concealed nest make detection during daylight hours unlikely unless the bird is flushed at close quarters, and assessing breeding status is even more problematic.

Estimation of the county population is by no means straightforward; the *Old* and *New Atlases* based estimates of densities on 10–25 breeding pairs/100km². Cumbria's large areas of quality habitat would justify this range of densities, giving some confidence in the suggested county population estimate of 600–1,000 breeding pairs.

The main influence affecting the Woodcock's future in Cumbria will be management of the county's woodland resources. Semi-natural broad-leaved woodland in the county is extensive, with most of the

Sponsored by Tommy Holden

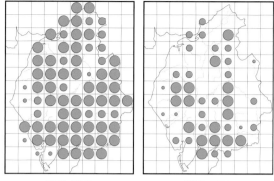

**1968-1972**    **1997-2001**
(For explanation of maps, see page 45)

| *Conservation status* | |
|---|---|
| European: | SPEC Cat 3 (W) |
| UK: | AMBER: BDM |

| *Populations* | |
|---|---|
| European status: | 600,000 |
| Britain – pairs: | 15,000 |
| Cumbria – pairs: | 600–1,000 |

*30-year distribution change*

| | Old Atlas | This Atlas | % |
|---|---|---|---|
| No. of 10km squares: | 73 | 42 | −42.5 |

| **Survey data** | **Tetrads** | **%** |
|---|---|---|
| Confirmed breeding: | 21 | 1.1 |
| Probable breeding: | 118 | 6.4 |
| Possible breeding: | 23 | 1.2 |
| Total: | 162 | 8.7 |

19,700ha located in the south and west (Kelly &
Perry 1990). Many of these remaining fragments
make up more than 100 woodland SSSIs. Grant-
aided broad-leaved woodland planting is
currently popular in the North Pennines and
Cumbria Dales, with Woodcock a potential
beneficiary. Continued restructuring of
coniferous plantations may also offer potential
new habitats as maturing woodland is harvested.

Nick Mason

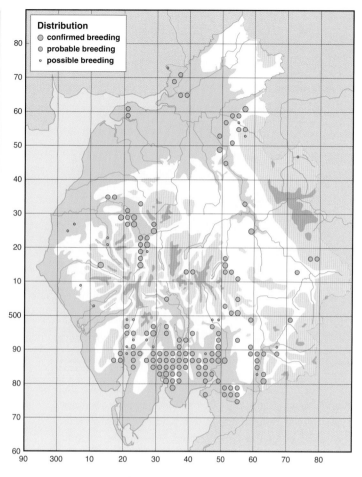

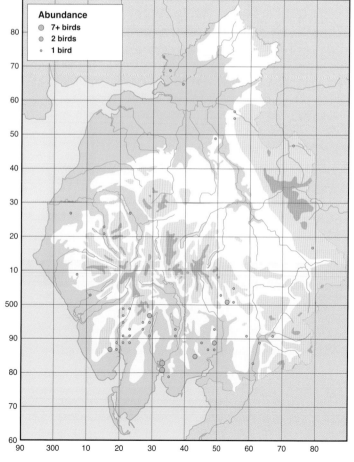

THE song of the Curlew, that intense crescendo of fluid bubbling, epitomizes wild open country. Its evocative notes rise to fever pitch – a welcome sound of spring in Cumbria, as the bird alternately rises steeply on vigorously flapping wings, and then drifts in wide circles over moorland, pasture or saltmarsh.

Widely distributed throughout the northern Palearctic, the Curlew's main requirements are for damp soils and wide uninterrupted views – given these, the birds will nest on bogs, marshes, pastures, meadows, and moorland. Although scarce through much of continental Europe, and in southeast England, it is still tolerably common over much of Britain and Ireland, reaching very high densities in the North Pennines and Southern Uplands.

The nest is a scrape on the ground, lined with grass and a few feathers, usually within a tussock amongst rough grassland and always in open country. After hatching, the female deserts the brood at 12–14 days, leaving the male to complete the task of rearing the chicks. Perhaps surprisingly, broods use relatively small home ranges between hatching and fledging; in one study, the mean maximum distance the young moved from the nest was 374 metres (Grant 1997). The young feed exclusively on invertebrates picked off vegetation, not by probing in soft ground, while adults have a wider, more omnivorous diet involving seeds, berries, crustaceans and worms, up to larger prey items such as toads, lizards and even small birds.

Once regarded as a typical upland bird in Britain, this is not true today since it enjoys a more diverse range of grassland habitats. In Cumbria its breeding haunts extend from the high wind-swept fells, where

birds have been found breeding on Skiddaw at 762m asl and the North Pennines at 792m asl (Brown 1974), to the coastal saltmarshes. This extension of its Cumbrian breeding range, as elsewhere in Britain, began during the early 20th century.

However, post-Second World War drainage and intensive grassland management, coupled with a heavy dependence on a cocktail of chemicals, were probably all factors that conspired to stem the rate of expansion by the late 1950s. Although Stokoe (1962) considered it to be still common and widespread, Brown (1974) recorded an area of farmland near Carlisle holding 12 pairs in 1937 that had declined to a single pair by 1968. At the same time increased stocking densities, particularly sheep numbers on the fells, were having a deleterious affect on the vegetation and creating unsuitable conditions for nesting Curlews. Another factor which has seriously impacted on the availability of traditional breeding habitat has been afforestation in the uplands; Philipson (1952), referring to the northeastern moors around Bewcastle and Spadeadam, commented that Curlews had declined by as much as 50% in 30 years following the loss of open country to Forestry Commission plantations.

Recent surveys suggest that Britain and Ireland hold at least 30% of the European population of breeding Curlews. However, the breeding range is probably contracting and marked declines have occurred in some areas, particularly Northern Ireland. In 1995–96, research was carried out in the North Pennines to determine habitat requirements and breeding success on marginal farmland. The study area contained both moorland and non-moorland habitats in a region where much of the land is managed for Red Grouse. Despite control of generalist predators, primarily Carrion Crow, Red Fox and Stoat, predation still accounted for 20–30% of nest failures, with a majority taken by Stoats. Trampling by cattle and chick starvation were found to be the other main causes contributing to a productivity rate of 0.59–0.61 fledglings/pair (Grant 1997).

Although *this Atlas* detects little change in distribution at the 10km square level since the *Old Atlas,* the maps clearly demonstrate an eastern bias to the Curlew's range and abundance. The Lune Valley, upper Eden Valley and North Pennines hold important populations, with birds showing a strong preference for managed moorland. Elsewhere, it is more sparsely distributed, with a noticeable lack of records from much of central Lakeland.

Analysis of line transect data from *this Atlas* gives a population band of 15,000–31,000 birds, suggesting a mean population of 21,000 birds. The highest densities of 4.8 birds/km$^2$, perhaps not surprisingly, occurred in the North Pennines.

The latest available CBC index shows a national

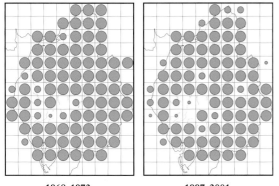

**1968–1972**          **1997–2001**
(For explanation of maps, see page 45)

*Conservation status*

| European: | SPEC Cat 3 (W) |
|---|---|
| UK: | **AMBER: BI & WI** |

*Populations*

| European status: | 135,000 |
|---|---|
| Britain – pairs: | 35,500 |
| Cumbria – pairs: | 10,500 |

*30-year distribution change*

| | Old Atlas | This Atlas | % |
|---|---|---|---|
| No. of 10km squares: | 87 | 85 | −2.3 |

| **Survey data** | **Tetrads** | **%** |
|---|---|---|
| Confirmed breeding: | 503 | 27.3 |
| Probable breeding: | 563 | 30.5 |
| Possible breeding: | 178 | 9.7 |
| Total: | 1,244 | 67.5 |

decline of 30% since 1970, which is not sufficient for inclusion on the new BoCC Red List. From the North Pennines study it is evident that rough grasslands and other relatively unimproved habitats such as wetlands and remaining moorland are of the greatest importance to Curlews breeding on marginal farmland. Despite the removal of capital grants for agricultural improvements, which were available in the 1970s and 1980s, land improvement continues in the uplands. This will only change given a fundamental reform of the Common Agricultural Policy, shifting the focus of agricultural support from production towards payments designed to meet environmental and social objectives.

Arnold Strand

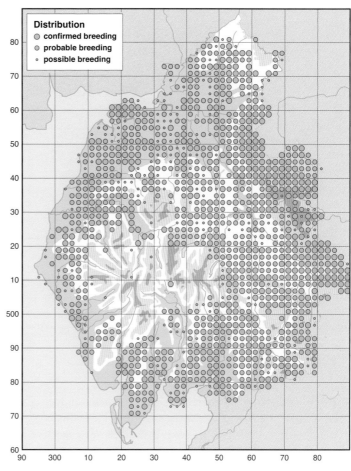

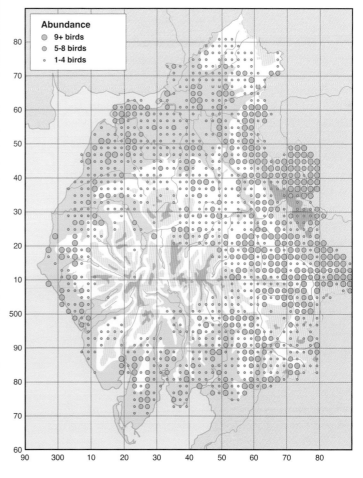

C. M. Sherwood.

THE old names of 'watchdog of the marsh' and 'yelper' are very appropriate as this eternally vigilant, noisy and restless wader is usually the first to indicate the approach of any intruders with its scolding alarm call. With its diagnostic white trailing edge to the wing the Redshank is easily recognized in flight.

Essentially a bird of temperate and steppe latitudes, the Redshank breeds only sporadically in continental Europe and the Balkans, becoming more common further north and east. It breeds in Iceland and above the Arctic Circle in northern Scandinavia, and the range stretches as far east as Siberia. In Britain and Ireland it is almost entirely absent from southwest England and is sparsely distributed in Wales and Ireland. The greatest concentrations are in northwest England, south and northeast Scotland and the Northern and Western Isles.

In Cumbria, as elsewhere, the Redshank breeds on coastal saltmarshes, damp marshes and meadows and along moorland edges, reaching a height of 500m asl in the North Pennines. It is one of the earliest waders to return to its breeding grounds, often appearing at the end of February. The nest site is on the ground, often hidden in a tussock with the leaves entwined into a canopy to provide shelter; however it can also be a scrape lined with grass on saltmarsh or shingle. The clutch, usually four eggs, is laid from early April onwards. A large number of prey species have been recorded in the Redshank's diet but it feeds mainly on crustaceans, molluscs Trind polychaete worms on estuaries, with earthworms and cranefly larvae taken inland.

The Redshank suffered a huge decline in Britain during the early part of the 19th century, chiefly attributed to extensive land drainage, and in 1840 its distribution was limited to the counties bordering the North Sea. However, from 1865 it began to spread back westwards towards Cumbria and had become well established on the Solway marshes by the 1880s, with some hundreds of eggs collected from Rockcliffe and Burgh Marshes every season, for sale as 'plovers' eggs' (Robinson 1888). From being a chiefly coastal nesting species in the latter part of the 19th century by the 1940s the Redshank had become a common nesting bird in suitable habitat throughout Cumbria. However, as farming practices intensified, the expansion ground to a halt and the draining of marshes and 'improving' of pastures caused a catastrophic decline, especially on the Coastal Plain and Solway Basin. At the time of the *Old Atlas,* although in decline, Redshanks were still widespread in the county being absent from just 13 10km squares, yet by the time of the *New Atlas* the species had disappeared from a further nine squares, mostly in Lakeland.

The current situation in Cumbria gives rise for serious concern, with a fourfold reduction in distribution between the *Old Atlas* and *this Atlas*. Results from *this Atlas* show that 30 10km squares are now devoid of Redshanks. As can be seen from the distribution map it is now almost totally confined to the periphery of the county with the main concentrations on the Solway Basin, Eden Valley, North Pennines and southern Coastal Plain. Moreover the saltmarshes that have long been a stronghold of this species have also suffered from the decline; Rockcliffe Marsh, the premier site for this species in Cumbria, boasted 112 breeding pairs in 1993 but this had fallen to just 40 in 2000.

The analysis of line transect data is not robust on account of the small sample size, although the calculated figure coincides with a more subjective estimate for the current county population of 250 breeding pairs, derived from count data. With two major estuarine habitats bordering the county, the densities found on Cumbrian saltmarshes were surprising low.

Like most other wader species, the Redshank has been the victim of man's relentless 'march of progress', with little thought being given to the long term health of the environment. Nationally, the CBC index shows a 72% drop between 1972 and 1996 and this is backed up by the latest WBS information which shows a fall of 34% in the 22 years to 1999. These surveys consistently point out the tragedy of a declining species, what the causes are, and what must be done to reverse the trends before it is too late. However, nature

Sponsored by Ray Downes

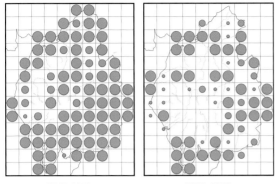

**1968-1972**          **1997-2001**

(For explanation of maps, see page 45)

*Conservation status*

| | |
|---|---|
| European: | SPEC Cat 2 |
| UK: | **AMBER: BDM** |

*Populations*

| | |
|---|---|
| European status: | 350,000 |
| Britain – pairs: | 32,100 |
| Cumbria – pairs: | 250 |

*30-year distribution change*

| | Old Atlas | This Atlas | % |
|---|---|---|---|
| No. of 10km squares: | 80 | 63 | **−21.2** |

| **Survey data** | **Tetrads** | **%** |
|---|---|---|
| Confirmed breeding: | 84 | 4.6 |
| Probable breeding: | 67 | 3.6 |
| Possible breeding: | 56 | 3.0 |
| Total: | 207 | 11.2 |

can also take its toll: Redshanks are susceptible to harsh weather and in severe winters can suffer huge losses. Furthermore, on the saltmarshes nests and eggs are often lost to high tides and although replacement clutches can be laid, in some years complete failure occurs. The additional threat of global warming and consequent rise in sea levels means that one of the species' final refuges is in danger of being lost.

Arnold Strand

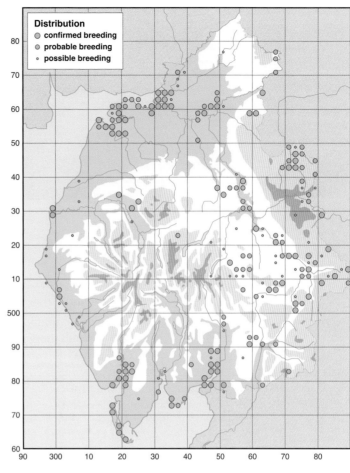

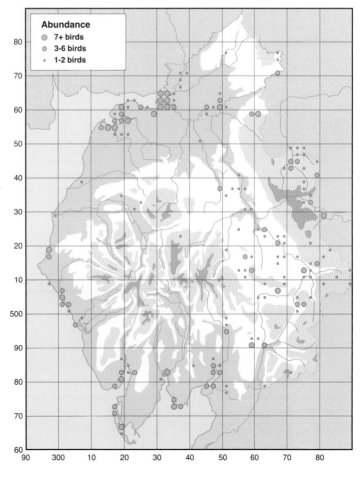

# Common Sandpiper *Actitis hypoleucos*

SKIMMING over the water on stiff, flickering wings, calls ringing out eerily through the mist hanging low over the water on a still Cumbrian morning, the Common Sandpiper, or 'Willy Wicket' as it is known locally, is an excitable summer visitor found frequenting rivers and lake shores.

An Old World species, its distribution extends eastwards from Ireland, through Europe to the Pacific coast with the majority of the European population found in Fennoscandia. Britain and Ireland hold only a fraction of the totals and a northwestern bias sees few breeding to the south of a line drawn between the Severn and Humber estuaries. Its strongholds are in upland areas, most particularly in Scotland.

In Cumbria, numbers at some traditional sites fluctuate from year to year with weather conditions dictating arrival dates, which in a normal year will be from mid-April; frosts in late April or early May can raise mortality rates in newly-arrived birds. After an all-too-short three months, post-breeding flocks of up to 20 birds begin to assemble in late June, and by mid-July the breeding areas are largely deserted.

The nest scrape can be up to 100m from the water's edge. On Bassenthwaite Lake and Derwent Water nests are usually 3–50m from water, hidden in a clump of vegetation such as sedge or nettles. Shingle is a requirement of the young birds rather than the adults as it provides the necessary invertebrate food supply and cover when threatened. Common Sandpiper densities tend to be higher on watercourses with a shallow gradient and territories are generally associated with shingle shores and banks, which the birds defend vigorously. At Langstrath, three or four pairs breed annually on a long stretch of beck with large gravel bars and an easy gradient of only 20m/km, at a breeding occupancy rate of one pair/km; however, birds are never found on steeper sections of the same beck. Breeding density varies greatly with differing habitat but comparisons can be made with studies in the Sedbergh area which found frequencies of 1.05 pairs/km (Cuthbertson *et al* 1952). A survey at Bassenthwaite Lake in 1995 found 22 territories on 13km of suitable lakeshore habitat giving a frequency of 1.7 pairs/km (Barron 1996).

In Cumbria, there are indications that a range contraction is occurring from fringe areas, including the fell becks, with birds preferring the larger rivers and lakes. At the turn of the century, Common Sandpipers were "one of our most widely distributed birds, nesting in the neighbourhood of most of the lakes, tarns and rivers within our area" (Macpherson 1892). However, Stokoe (1962) noted that the species "has declined as a nesting bird, at least in north Cumberland." A 1951 survey along 100km of river and fell becks, including the River Lune, was repeated in 1993 and found a 43% reduction in numbers. The River Rawthey showed the most marked decline from 1.15 pairs/km to 0.3 pairs/km over a 21km length. The largest areas of decline coincided with sections of river where recreational disturbance had increased significantly but the virtual disappearance from mainly undisturbed fell becks has raised the probability of a general decline with birds now concentrated on rivers with a richer choice in food supplies and breeding sites (Cleasby 1994).

Although a slight range contraction appears to have occurred between the *Old Atlas* and *this Atlas,* especially in more marginal habitats along the Coastal Plain, the greatest change is likely to have involved population densities. During *this Atlas* the strongholds remain the North Pennines, Lune and Eden Valleys and Lakeland with a noticeable lack of records from the western Solway Basin.

Analysis of line transect data from *this Atlas* gives a population band of 5,000–20,000, suggesting a mean population of 10,000 birds. This high figure might be explained by the number of extensive, high quality, river systems within the county; however, a subjective estimate gives a considerably lower figure.

Increased disturbance, poor water quality affecting food supplies and increasing rainfall patterns are all factors which may affect future populations. The Common Sandpiper is a bird of riverine and lake-shore habitat popular with recreational users such as

Sponsored by Peter Barron

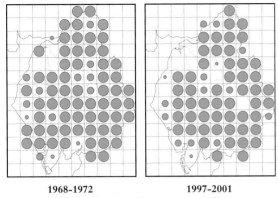

**1968–1972**  **1997–2001**
(For explanation of maps, see page 45)

*Conservation status*

| | |
|---|---|
| European: | Non-SPEC |
| UK: | **GREEN** |

*Populations*

| | |
|---|---|
| European status: | 570,000 |
| Britain – pairs: | 15,800 |
| Cumbria – pairs: | 5,000 |

*30-year distribution change*

| | Old Atlas | This Atlas | % |
|---|---|---|---|
| No. of 10km squares: | 76 | 67 | **–11.8** |

| **Survey data** | **Tetrads** | **%** |
|---|---|---|
| Confirmed breeding: | 147 | 7.8 |
| Probable breeding: | 149 | 8.0 |
| Possible breeding: | 60 | 3.3 |
| Total: | 356 | 19.1 |

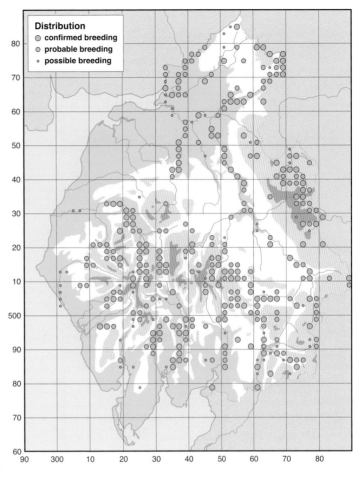

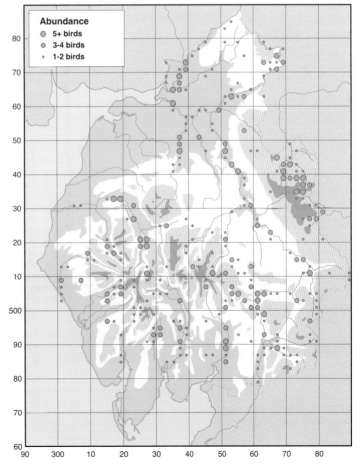

anglers and walkers. These are leisure pursuits that have increased over the last 30 years and they are likely to have had a significant effect on a species sensitive to regular disturbance. Synthetic sheep dips used in the uplands can destroy invertebrate life if even very small quantities enter watercourses. Although new disposal regulations have been introduced, Cumbria has been the worst affected county in England for pyrethroid sheep dip pollution, with 200km of affected river since 1996. Acid rain, a problem identified over 30 years ago, is thought to be diminishing, as regular testing of watercourses has shown a return to expected levels (Environment Agency pers comm). Finally, increasing rainfall patterns due to climatic changes associated with global warming may affect food resources and cause more frequent flooding of nest sites.

Peter Barron

# Mediterranean Gull *Larus melanocephalus*

THIS is one of the most attractive of all gulls, particularly in summer, when its scientific name is justified by its jet-black hood, which contrasts vividly with a bright red bill and almost translucent white wings. At this time of the year, its distinctive, far-carrying and rather nasal call attracts attention amid the higher-pitched screeching of a chaotic Black-headed Gull colony.

Mediterranean Gulls now breed through much of Europe, eastwards to the former USSR and Turkey. In the 1940s and 1950s, the bulk of the world population, estimated at fewer than 40,000 pairs, was to be found in colonies around the Black Sea coast of the Ukraine. Numbers in this region increased dramatically – reputedly to more than 300,000 pairs in 1983 – but subsequently declined to 50,000–75,000 pairs in recent years. During this period of rapid increase, the species became much more widespread throughout central and western Europe, where breeding populations are now firmly established and both the number of colonies and the size of the population are increasing annually. Eastward expansion has also occurred, with birds reaching the Caspian Sea by the late 1980s. Extensive colour-ringing programmes in a number of countries have revealed that individual birds may breed at widely separated sites in successive years, moving, for instance, from the Mediterranean to the North Sea (Kearsley 1999).

The first breeding record in Britain occurred in 1968, when a pair nested in a colony of over 10,000 pairs of Black-headed Gulls in Hampshire. Since 1979, breeding has been annual. Though the British population was a modest 60–79 pairs in 1999, this represented a further rise in the number of both localities and pairs, following the largest increase reported in a single year in 1997 (Ogilvie *et al* 2001). In Ireland, the first successful breeding was in Wexford in 1996, although eggs were laid in Antrim in 1995 (Mead 2000). Occurrence within existing colonies of Black-headed Gulls is normal though in Scotland there have been several instances of birds summering amongst Common Gulls. Its diet during the breeding season consists largely of insects, both terrestrial and aquatic, though at other times of the year the wide variety of recorded food reflects the diversity of habitats in which birds are found.

The population increase and range expansion has been reflected in the dramatic rise in Cumbrian sightings since the first county record on Arnside Marsh in July 1976. The vast majority have occurred outside the breeding season, however, with particular peaks in late summer/early autumn, and to a lesser extent in spring. Sightings of colour-ringed individuals have revealed several birds of Dutch and Belgian origin, and one from Hungary.

The first sighting in the county in any way suggestive of breeding involved an adult at Killington Reservoir on 16th–17th June 1989, though there were no further developments of any significance until the period of *this Atlas,* when birds appeared at two Black-headed Gull colonies. These handsome gulls still attract the unwanted attentions of egg-collectors and, for this reason, the sites have not been named and the dots on the distribution map have been centrally placed.

At the first site, a first-summer male and an adult male held territory and displayed separately for several weeks in 1998 and the adult male returned and behaved in a similar fashion in 1999. Nesting then seemed certain when this bird attracted a mate and the pair set up territory, with a second-summer bird also present, but then the adults vanished and the immature lost interest. No birds were seen there in 2001. Meanwhile, at a second site, two birds flying round calling and apparently prospecting near another Black-headed Gull colony on 18th April 1999 were followed, in 2000, by a pair, consisting of an adult male and second-summer female, which set up territory and displayed vigorously. However, though both birds remained well into July, no eggs were laid.

These events culminated in the first instance of confirmed breeding in the county in 2001, when what were presumed to be the same birds, now both adults, returned and set up territory in exactly the same spot. They were observed on a nest in mid-May but, sadly, deserted in early June, around the time when hatching was due to occur. The nest was found to contain two eggs and the cause of failure remains unknown. Though usually described as a shallow depression lined with grass and some feathers, this sole Cumbrian nest

 Sponsored by Ian Kinley

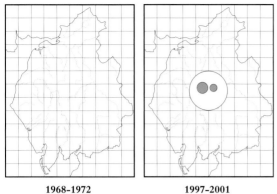

| 1968-1972 | 1997-2001 |
|---|---|

(For explanation of maps, see page 45)

*Conservation status*

| | |
|---|---|
| European: | Non-SPEC |
| UK: | **AMBER: BR** |

*Populations*

| | |
|---|---|
| European status: | 250,000 |
| Britain – pairs: | 54 |
| Cumbria – pairs: | 1–2 |

*30-year distribution change*

| | Old Atlas | This Atlas | % |
|---|---|---|---|
| No. of 10km squares: | 0 | 2 | n/a |

| **Survey data** | **Tetrads** | **%** |
|---|---|---|
| Confirmed breeding: | 1 | 0.05 |
| Probable breeding: | 1 | 0.05 |
| Possible breeding: | 0 | |
| Total: | 2 | 0.1 |

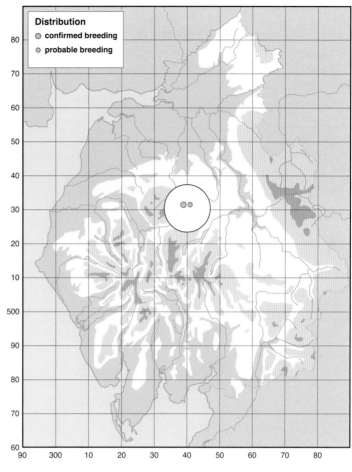

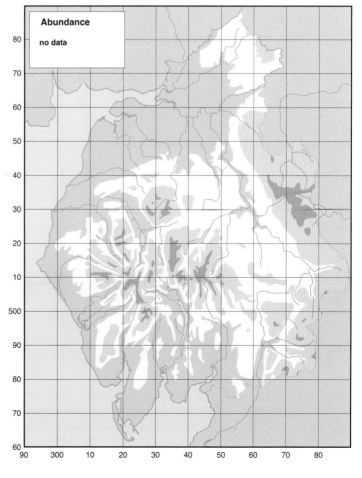

was a bulky affair, constructed largely of rushes, with a few leaves.

Although the majority of the British population still breed in southern England, numbers are increasing and birds are spreading northwards: in 1999, a total of three to five pairs nested in Lancashire and Yorkshire and an adult held territory as far north as Orkney (Ogilvie *et al* 2001). So, despite these initial disappointments, it seems certain that there will be further breeding attempts in Cumbria in the future and, hopefully, this delightful gull will establish itself as a regular breeder in the county.

Ian Kinley

# Black-headed Gull *Larus ridibundus*

A VISIT to a sizeable Black-headed Gull colony is an impressive experience, as the entire population rises in a white cloud, calling furiously, to mob the intruder, only to settle quickly once the danger has passed.

The species is widely distributed across the Palearctic, from Iceland, Britain and Ireland, northern and central Europe, through Russia, to China and Korea. Over the last 20 years or so, small colonies have become established in Spain and Italy. It breeds throughout Britain and Ireland, though sparsely in southwest England. This is the most widespread gull in Europe and has successfully exploited all manner of inland sites, whether following the plough for food, nesting on gravel pits or roosting on reservoirs.

The Black-headed Gull breeds on coastal saltmarshes and dunes, and inland by lakes, tarns, and gravel pits, up to an altitude of 700m asl. It also nests on drier sites, particularly on moorland or amongst heather. The nest, often a substantial structure, is constructed of grass or sedge, or whatever material is readily available.

The species suffered a prolonged and steady decline in England during the 18th and 19th centuries – remarkably, almost to the point of extinction. This was due in the main to agricultural change and the drainage and enclosure of marshes, coupled with a systematic plundering of eggs; at one stage in excess of 14,000 eggs were taken annually from a single colony in Norfolk. The situation in the far north of England and in Scotland was somewhat different, the bird not being subjected to the same pressures.

At the start of the 20th century, the situation improved due to the creation of suitable new habitats, such as sewage works, gravel workings, and reservoirs, and at the same time there was a marked reduction in persecution and egg collection, allowing for more young to hatch and fledge successfully. The estimated population in England and Wales in 1938 was 35,000–40,000 pairs; by 1973, the figure was in excess of 100,000. Paradoxically, around this period, there was evidence of a decline in northern England and Scotland, due in part to the same sorts of land-use change which had previously caused such a catastrophic decline further south.

At the end of the 19th century, Macpherson (1892), commenting on Walney Island as being the most southerly coastal site and referring to "the ancient" colony at Ravenglass, implied that no breeding colonies existed within the interior of Lakeland. Other significant colonies at this time included Sunbiggin Tarn, Cliburn Moss, Greystoke, Denton Fell and Bolton Fell, while Moorthwaite, which held 1,000 pairs in 1889, was considered to be the largest colony in northwest England. However, colonies such as those at Wedholme and on the Bowness and Solway Mosses had been greatly reduced as a consequence of systematic disturbance. In 1938, 31 colonies were noted in Cumbria, with Walney Island and Ravenglass supporting the largest numbers (Witherby *et al* 1938–41). By 1958, Walney Island had been largely deserted, yet the county population had increased significantly to 16,250–19,250 pairs, spread over 32 colonies. Ravenglass held a massive 13,000–16,000 pairs, while other significant colonies included Sunbiggin Tarn with 1,200 pairs and North Scales, Heads Nook with 1,000 pairs, though the latter had been abandoned by 1961 (Stokoe 1962).

The pattern of 'boom and bust' continued to be a feature of Cumbrian colonies during the second half of the 20th century. Prior to 1957, there was a large colony on Foulshaw Moss that was then abandoned. More recently, Rockcliffe Marsh supported 2,657 pairs in 1976 and Foulney Island 1,100 pairs in 1983, but a steady decline has since occurred at both. Even long-established colonies are not immune: Ravenglass still held 10,000 pairs in 1972, but the colony was soon to collapse; numbers at Sunbiggin Tarn reached 8,000 pairs in 1990 but had fallen to 1,400 pairs by 1996. However, the tale is not entirely one of abandonment; relatively new colonies at Hodbarrow and Killington Reservoir held, respectively, 1,200 pairs in 1991 and 3,700 pairs in 1996.

Data gathered during the course of the survey involved counts at 51 colonies; currently, the largest colony is at Killington Reservoir, with 3,200 pairs. No other site supported more than 1,000 pairs during *this Atlas;* indeed, numbers at some formerly significant colonies continued to fall; for example, Sunbiggin Tarn

 Sponsored by Jack & Angus Gould

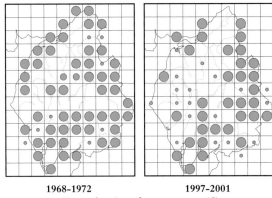

| 1968-1972 | 1997-2001 |

(For explanation of maps, see page 45)

***Conservation status***
| European: | Non-SPEC |
| UK: | **GREEN** |

***Populations***
| European status: | 2,100,000 |
| Britain – pairs: | 167,000 |
| Cumbria – pairs: | 6,000 |

***30-year distribution change***
| | *Old Atlas* | *This Atlas* | *%* |
|---|---|---|---|
| No. of 10km squares: | 58 | 52 | **−10.3** |

| **Survey data** | **Tetrads** | **%** |
|---|---|---|
| Confirmed breeding: | 51 | 2.8 |
| Probable breeding: | 0 | |
| Possible breeding: | 76 | 4.1 |
| Total: | 127 | 6.9 |

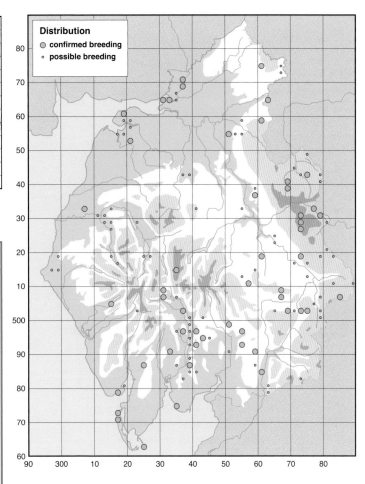

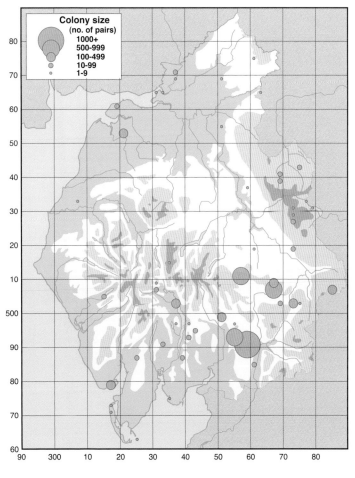

held a meagre 46 pairs in 2000. In contrast, a totally new site near Shap contained 500–700 nests in 1999. The current county population of 6,000 breeding pairs derives from the sum of the colonial counts.

Black-headed Gull colonies vary greatly in size from year to year and, in some cases, are completely deserted for no apparent reason, or inexplicably suffer a total breeding failure. It may be that the site is affected by changes in water levels, by disturbance or predation, particularly by Red Fox or Mink. Though Black-headed Gulls are long-lived birds and are usually sufficiently productive to maintain a stable population, the decline at some of Cumbria's major colonies over recent years, coupled with the fall in numbers overall, gives cause for concern for the future prospects of this species in the county.

Mike Carrier

THIS small, elegant gull is a familiar sight in Cumbria for much of the year, whether busily feeding on fresh green pastures in spring, wheeling and tumbling in white clouds behind the autumn plough or flying in to roost on our estuaries or inland lakes in winter. Despite its name this bird is not the commonest of our gulls, either inland or around the coasts. The majority that occur in Cumbria are passage or wintering birds.

Europe holds the bulk of the world population of Common Gulls, breeding throughout the western Nearctic and northern Palearctic with Fennoscandia the main stronghold. Large numbers are also found in Denmark and Scotland. Declines have been noted in Denmark and Norway but elsewhere the population is stable or increasing (Tucker & Heath 1994). In Britain and Ireland, Common Gulls are widespread in winter, accompanying Herring and Black-headed Gulls to their feeding places around the coast and towns. Huge numbers also feed in pastures and playing fields. However, as breeding birds their range is limited. They breed throughout the Scottish Islands and Highlands and more locally in southwest Scotland and northern and western Ireland. During the late 20th century it has under gone a range expansion southwards and now breeds in small numbers in Northumberland and Durham, with some pairs even reaching the English southeast coast (Lloyd *et al* 1991).

Favoured breeding habitats include islands or shingle spits in lakes, rivers and coastal inlets, upland heaths and lowland bogs. They usually breed in small colonies but often pairs will nest alone. Associations with other small gulls or terns at breeding sites are not uncommon. In Scotland colonies have recently become established on heather moorland adjacent to agricultural land, where they feed on the readily available supply of invertebrates. Nests are constructed on the ground using local material in which a clutch, usually of three eggs, is laid; both adults share incubation that takes around 26 days. The chicks are tended by both parents. They leave the nest in the first week, and fly after four or five weeks. They will feed on whatever is close to hand – edible refuse, shellfish, earthworms, small mammals, and small birds and their eggs. In some circumstances, especially at lakeside tourist attractions, some birds have developed a feeding habit of their own; waiting until a bolder Black-headed Gull has taken food from a human's hand, they dart in and attempt to rob the other bird.

Macpherson (1892) cast doubt on nesting records from Cumberland and Westmorland in the 18th and 19th centuries, while acknowledging that nesting had occurred on the Scottish side of the Solway by 1871. Breeding has never been anything other than occasional in Cumbria and probably involved no more than one pair at any one site. The first fully documented instance was of a single pair on Long Newton Marsh in 1914 (Dunlop 1923). This was the second breeding record for England and the first for the mainland, the first being on the Farne Islands. A pair returned to nest at this site in 1923 and again in 1924. A pair was strongly suspected of having bred on Rockcliffe Marsh in 1931 and other single pairs were recorded at Ravenglass in 1932 and 1940, presumably in the Black-headed Gull colony (Blezard *et al* 1943). The next documented evidence of nesting was in 1977 when a pair bred at Easedale Tarn, a site that may have been used regularly around that time. A pair nested on a small rock in Thirlmere in the early 1980s and breeding may have occurred there intermittently ever since (G. Horne pers comm). It would seem likely that the species has been under-recorded over the years, as both the *Old* and *New Atlases* revealed at least one pair possibly breeding in Cumbria; however, this cannot be substantiated by county records from that time. Although the *Old Atlas* showed confirmed breeding at two inner Solway 10km squares, both these are likely to have been from outside Cumbria and probably involved the same Scottish nesting squares as recorded in 1914.

The scarcity of Common Gulls breeding in the county is highlighted by the few 10km squares from which records were received for *this Atlas*. The possible records can safely be dismissed as late passage birds, while the one probable record came from an unlikely nesting site in Lakeland. This leaves just one single record of confirmed breeding on a moorland tarn at 750m asl and represents the current county breeding population.

# Lesser Black-backed Gull *Larus fuscus*

THE slaty-grey upperparts, dazzling white underparts and striking bright yellow legs and bill make the Lesser Black-backed Gull a handsome bird during the breeding season. However, guano-splattered visitors to the large colony at South Walney, ducking hastily to avoid the dive-bombing attacks of territorial birds, may dispute this view.

Breeding widely across northern Europe, its range extends eastwards from Britain and Ireland, Iceland and Spain to Norway and the Baltic. The Lesser Black-backed Gull is strongly migratory, moving southwards in autumn. British birds tend to winter around the coasts of Iberia and west Africa, but the pattern is changing, and increasing numbers now overwinter in Britain.

A relatively large gull, its opportunistic habits lead to a rather catholic choice of breeding sites. At times occurring in dense colonies of many thousands of pairs, it nests on estuaries and open coasts, and inland it is associated with lakes, reservoirs, moorland and mosses. The nest, often merely a scrape in the ground, is lined with grass or seaweed. The bird's association with man has been strengthened by the relatively new habit of nesting on rooftops.

At the end of the 19th century, although persecuted in some areas, Scotland was the species' stronghold and it was considered locally common in Wales and Ireland. In England, besides Cumbria, small numbers bred in Devon and Cornwall and elsewhere along the south coast, while the main east coast colony was on the Farne Islands. In response to a reduction in persecution after the Second World War, a considerable population expansion took place throughout Britain and Ireland.

Although several smaller colonies existed in Cumbria in the 19th century, by the 1890s these had dispersed to leave five main colonies on the grouse moors of Foulshaw Moss, Roudsea, Bowness Moss, Solway Moss and Butterburn Flow (Macpherson 1892). In the mid-20th century small groups or isolated pairs still bred on the county's saltmarshes, mosses and moorlands, but the colonies on Foulshaw Moss and Roudsea had become extinct by 1947 through a combination of egg collecting and persecution from gamekeepers (Oakes 1953, Stokoe 1962). By this time, South Walney and Rockcliffe Marsh had emerged as the main breeding sites. At South Walney, nesting was first recorded in 1926. In the ensuing years, the colony increased rapidly: 500 pairs in 1947, 9,500 pairs in 1965, 17,500 pairs in 1969, and 21,000 pairs in 1974, by which time the colony was estimated to hold 33% of the British and Irish population. Thereafter, although numbers fluctuated, the population remained fairly high with 19,000 pairs in 1978 and 22,000 pairs in 1996 (Dean 1990, WBO 1996). The first positive breeding record from Rockcliffe Marsh was of a single nest in 1925. There were 16 nests the following year, and 250 by 1933. Numbers subsequently rose with 600 in 1967, well in excess of 1,000 in 1972, and 7,640 pairs counted in 1995.

By the time of *this Atlas,* a noticeable range expansion had occurred, with breeding confirmed in 17 10km squares compared to just nine in the *Old Atlas.* Although some losses have occurred in the Solway Basin and around Ravenglass, there have been gains in the vicinity of St Bees Head and at a number of inland sites, including in the heart of Lakeland. There are thriving colonies of 700 pairs in the grounds of Haverigg Prison and 125 pairs at Wood Howe Island on Haweswater. In common with national trends, there has also been an increase in rooftop nesting – sites during *this Atlas* include Sellafield with 50 pairs and Barrow-in-Furness with 150 pairs, and around 360 pairs on the disused RAF base at Carlisle.

The current county population, estimated at 32,000–35,000 breeding pairs, is derived from counts at 24 colonies, ranging in size from several with just a single pair, to 7,660 pairs at Rockcliffe Marsh and a massive 22,000 pairs at South Walney.

The advent of landfill sites – rich feeding grounds for this omnivorous gull – and changes in agricultural practices, both increasing food availability, are possible reasons to explain such dramatic increases. Nationally, the species had become so successful by the 1970s that it was regarded as a pest in some areas and suffered further persecution. Alleged interactions on grouse moors led to conflict with sporting interests, and conservation bodies perceived the birds as a direct

Sponsored by a CBC Member

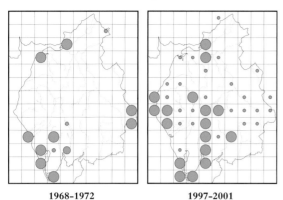

**1968–1972**  **1997–2001**
(For explanation of maps, see page 45)

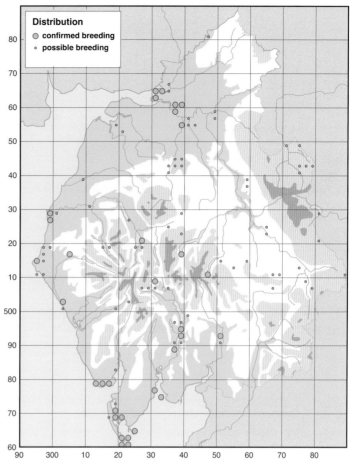

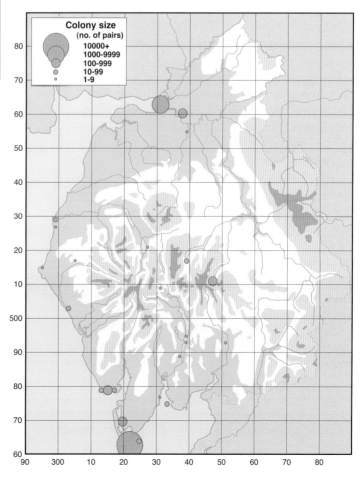

***Conservation status***
European:                                    SPEC Cat 4
UK:                        **AMBER: BI & BL**

***Populations***
European status:                          220,000
Britain – pairs:                            83,000
Cumbria – pairs:                        32–35,000

***30-year distribution change***

|  | Old Atlas | This Atlas | % |
|---|---|---|---|
| No. of 10km squares: | 13 | 42 | **+233** |

| **Survey data** | **Tetrads** | **%** |
|---|---|---|
| Confirmed breeding: | 33 | 1.8 |
| Probable breeding: | 0 | |
| Possible breeding: | 71 | 3.9 |
| Total: | 104 | 5.7 |

threat to other species, especially terns. Where they moved into urban areas they caused great annoyance and disturbance, leading to calls for culling, and birds were also blamed for bacterial pollution to water supplies at some reservoirs. These fears were used to justify the introduction of routine control measures at many large colonies.

Although such measures have been little used in Cumbria, there are indications that the population may have peaked. The huge colony at South Walney is not secure: gravel extraction continues to reduce space for nest sites, and productivity may be falling as a result of botulism – in 1998 an especially virulent outbreak caused high mortality rates in both adults and chicks (WBO 1998).

Mike Carrier

161

# Herring Gull *Larus argentatus*

ANYONE living near or visiting the coast can hardly ignore the Herring Gull. Love or loathe it, the species makes its presence felt with its loud, somewhat musical, calls often delivered from rooftops. Through over-familiarity, it is easy to overlook the bird's clean and aerodynamic lines, the clear greys and whites of its plumage, and those cool and calculating eyes. In many respects its success is due to its propensity to associate with man.

Both a Palearctic and Nearctic species, the Herring Gull occurs in two distinct groups of subspecies. The northern group occupies a wide belt across northern North America, and in Europe from Britain and Ireland through northwest France, Holland and throughout Scandinavia and the Baltic regions. The southern group, now generally regarded as a separate species, the Yellow-legged Gull, can be found in Spain, through central Europe to Mongolia. Expansion of the latter's range northwards up the Atlantic coast of France (nesting alongside Herring Gull without hybridization) has already seen birds starting to breed in southern England. It may be only a matter of time before this gull breeds in some of Cumbria's colonies of Herring and Lesser Black-backed Gulls.

Herring Gull colonies are found in a wide variety of places, including rocky or sandy sea coasts, large estuaries, islands and inland lakes. Additionally, they share with the Lesser Black-backed Gull the habit of nesting on buildings. The first such records were made in the 1920s in coastal towns, but the habit has spread inland over the years. Although the first such event passed unrecorded in Cumbria, substantial numbers now nest on buildings in Whitehaven, Workington,

Barrow-in-Furness and inland north of Carlisle, with smaller numbers elsewhere.

Historically, Herring Gull populations nationally were very much lower than was the case in the 20th century. Whilst there was some increase prior to the Second World War, a population explosion occurred between the end of the war and the early 1970s. It is likely that a marked reduction in persecution and the greater availability of food were the main causes. Herring Gulls are capable of eating anything organic, and have therefore benefited from their exploitation of increasing quantities of refuse from town centres, rubbish tips, fish docks and sewage outfalls. Between 1945 and 1972 the population increased at 13% per annum and this was coupled with a very high chick survival rate.

Success can bring its problems and starting in the 1970s there were strident calls for control measures to be introduced. It was alleged that other bird species were suffering, that public health was at risk and where birds were nesting in towns they soon fell from favour due to noise, aggression and the fouling of gutters and walkways. Consequently, 19th century persecution was replaced by 20th century control: initially by destruction or pricking of eggs, and later by culling of adults. This had its effect, and whilst there may have been other reasons, the population around the coasts of Britain and Ireland fell dramatically from a high of 343,600 pairs in 1969 to 190,900 pairs by 1987. The decreases were most marked in northern Scotland, Wales and the southwest of England.

St Bees Head has hosted Herring Gulls since records began, and probably long before that, making it the oldest known colony in Cumbria. Macpherson (1892) alludes to the presence of several hundred nests. The number of occupied nests had increased to 1,670 in 1956, with nesting noted fifty metres inland from the cliff-tops in subsequent years (Stokoe 1962). By 1979, numbers had risen to 2,000 pairs. The first evidence of a decline was noted in the 1980s and this continued into the 1990s with the population falling to just 540 pairs in 1996. A second site, at South Walney, saw sporadic nesting from 1904 (Oakes 1953), with birds securely established by 1928, 35 pairs in 1934, a rise to 120 nests by 1945, 9,500 pairs in 1965 and an astonishing 25,000 pairs in 1977. Thereafter a noticeable reduction saw the population fall to 12,000 pairs in 1984 and 8,000 pairs in 1988 (Dean 1990). These events were not an change of nesting behaviour particular to Cumbria, but followed national trends.

More recently, other colonies in the county included those inside the Whitehaven Chemical Works, where 649 pairs were counted in 1990, and Rockcliffe Marsh where numbers increased from just 12 pairs in 1967 to 1,935 pairs in 1995. Similarly, a colony inland on Wood Howe Island, Haweswater progressed from a

Sponsored by a CBC Member

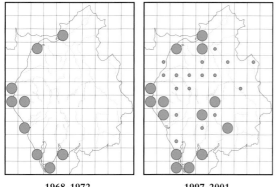

**1968-1972**    **1997-2001**

(For explanation of maps, see page 45)

**Conservation status**

| | |
|---|---|
| European: | Non-SPEC |
| UK: | **AMBER** |

**Populations**

| | |
|---|---|
| European status: | 790,000 |
| Britain – pairs: | 160,000 |
| Cumbria – pairs: | 10–13,000 |

**30-year distribution change**

| | Old Atlas | This Atlas | % |
|---|---|---|---|
| No. of 10km squares: | 9 | 31 | +244.4 |

| **Survey data** | **Tetrads** | **%** |
|---|---|---|
| Confirmed breeding: | 35 | 1.9 |
| Probable breeding: | 0 | |
| Possible breeding: | 42 | 2.3 |
| Total: | 77 | 4.2 |

handful of pairs in 1984 to 97 pairs in 1998.

During *this Atlas* breeding was confirmed in 14 10km squares compared with nine at the time of the *Old Atlas*. The current county population estimate of 10,000–13,000 breeding pairs is taken from counts at around 26 colonies, ranging in size from several with just a single pair, to Rockcliffe Marsh with 2,300 pairs and South Walney, by far the largest, at 9,560 pairs.

Despite the downturn in fortunes, confirmed by *this Atlas*, the Herring Gull remains an extremely familiar bird in the county. The main colonies at South Walney and Rockcliffe Marsh appear relatively stable, although botulism and Red Fox predation give some cause for concern and ongoing gravel extraction at South Walney continues to reduce the area available for nesting.

Mike Carrier

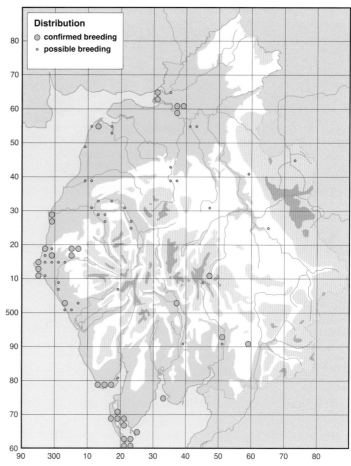

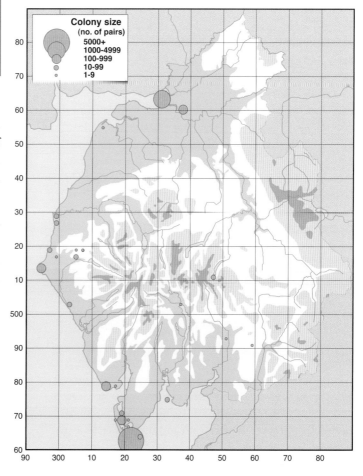

# Great Black-backed Gull *Larus marinus*

A.S.W.

AS an opportunist scavenger or ruthless predator, the Great Black-backed Gull is a fearsome species, given respect and space by others in feeding frenzies and occupying prime elevated or protected positions in mixed gull colonies.

The species breeds around the North Atlantic from France and Scandinavia to Greenland and the eastern coasts of Canada and the USA. In Britain and Ireland, nesting sites are mostly coastal with birds breeding singly or in mainly small colonies in northern and western areas. There is a striking absence from British south and east coasts between the Isle of Wight and the Firth of Forth. Up to three eggs are laid on the ground in grassy, rocky or stony areas with pairs often found among larger numbers of Herring or Lesser Black-backed Gulls. At some sites, the species derives most of its food from neighbouring birds and their eggs and chicks although it is widely omnivorous and may feed extensively on fish and other seafood, refuse at landfill sites or even plant material.

During the 19th century, Great Black-backed Gulls bred in Cumbria on the Rusland Fells, Devoke Water and Solway Mosses, including Wedholme Flow. However, they were considerably persecuted for their habit of betraying the presence of punt-gunners. A few, curiously, were trapped to "lend attractiveness to garden lawns" (Macpherson 1892). Blezard *et al* (1943) knew of breeding birds at a number of additional sites including Foulshaw, Meathop, Roudsea and Foxfield Mosses. A colony also existed on Bowness Moss with one or two pairs relocating to Rockcliffe Marsh in 1928, numbers rising to a peak of 64 pairs in 1996. Vast numbers are said to have bred at South Walney during the 17th century (Mitchell 1892) though their recent history at the site began in 1946 with continual occupation from 1955 (Dean 1990). The population here built up gradually at first with 18 pairs in 1975 but, 20 years later, numbers had rocketed to 105 pairs to become one of the largest colonies in England. Elsewhere, most colonies appear to have been of only temporary existence with Stokoe (1962) noting that Walney Island and Rockcliffe Marsh had become the only occupied sites. The latter part of

the 20th century saw a continuation of this pattern although the *New Atlas* recorded additional breeding sites at St Bees Head, Whitehaven, Hodbarrow and Chapel Island in the Leven estuary.

During the survey period, South Walney and Rockcliffe Marsh remained the primary sites. At South Walney the population peaked at 120 pairs in 1998 before falling back to 80 pairs in 2000, whilst the Rockcliffe Marsh colony declined to 39 pairs in 2000. Elsewhere, two pairs nested on Foulney Island and at Haweswater, with single pairs recorded at Hodbarrow, St Bees Head, Whitehaven and on Chapel Island. A development in 2000 involved three pairs breeding on roofs in the BAE Systems complex at Barrow-in-Furness. This seems to be a rare phenomenon, with a countrywide survey reporting just 11 roof-nesting pairs in 1994 (Raven & Coulson 1997). The current county population estimate of 130–180 breeding pairs derives from colony count data.

The South Walney birds nest within the large colony of Herring and Lesser Black-backed Gulls whilst those at Rockcliffe Marsh form an essentially discrete colony close to large numbers of Lesser Black-backed Gulls. In all likelihood, the Great Black-backed Gulls have benefited from gaining at least some of their food by piratical methods from their smaller neighbours as well as by predating their eggs and chicks. The protection from human persecution and relative freedom from disturbance offered to birds at these nature reserve sites undoubtedly led to their steady growth in numbers. The recent decline in numbers at South Walney has probably been caused by winter gravel extraction work reducing many of the island and narrow spit areas within the gravel pools favoured as nest sites by this species. Indeed the roof nesting birds in Barrow-in-Furness must surely originate from displaced South Walney pairs. Fluctuations at Rockcliffe Marsh are harder to explain, though the dramatic rise in the early 1990s coincided with rapidly expanding numbers of Lesser Black-backed Gulls at the site. Recent declines may be linked to the stabilization of Lesser Black-backed Gull numbers and possibly, therefore, a reduction in their output of eggs

Sponsored by a CBC Member

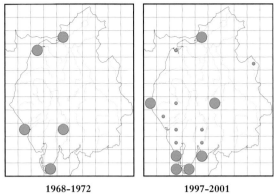

**1968-1972**                    **1997-2001**

(For explanation of maps, see page 45)

*Conservation status*

| European: | SPEC Cat 4 |
| UK: | **GREEN** |

*Populations*

| European status: | 105,000 |
| Britain − pairs: | 19,000 |
| Cumbria − pairs: | 130−180 |

*30-year distribution change*

| | Old Atlas | This Atlas | % |
|---|---|---|---|
| No. of 10km squares: | 5 | 15 | **+200** |

| **Survey data** | **Tetrads** | **%** |
|---|---|---|
| Confirmed breeding: | 13 | 0.7 |
| Probable breeding: | 0 | |
| Possible breeding: | 15 | 0.8 |
| Total: | 28 | 1.5 |

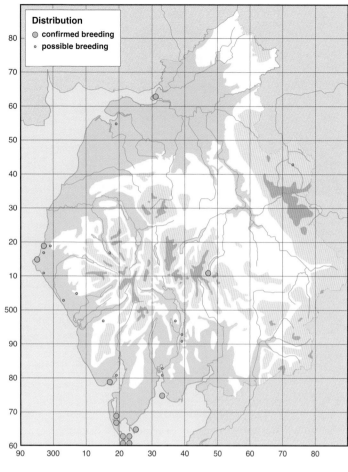

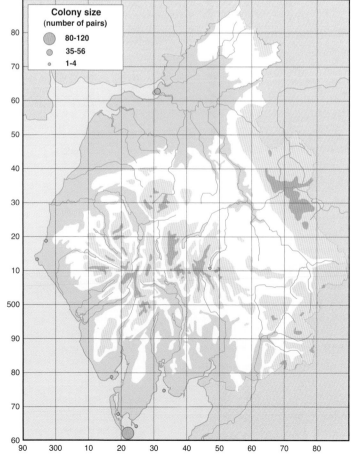

and chicks as a food resource.

Great Black-backed Gulls and their nests and eggs can be legally controlled by landowners or occupiers under a General Licence. The predatory tendencies of these birds can have a considerable impact on colonies of coastal breeding species perceived to be more desirable, especially terns. Control of nesting attempts can limit establishment or population growth at these sites and, during the period of *this Atlas,* accounts for the discontinuation of breeding at Foulney.

The presence of this bird as a Cumbrian breeding species seems to be relatively secure for the time being although high dependence on just a couple of sites does leave it vulnerable to local environmental changes. If the roof nesting birds in Barrow-in-Furness are tolerated it will be very interesting to see if the population there can expand to become a significant proportion of the Cumbrian total.

Nick Littlewood

WHETHER battling tirelessly in the face of a winter gale or following trawlers for scraps of offal, the Kittiwake is truly a 'sea-gull'. Its brightly coloured gape and tongue are used to the best effect when initiating pair-bonding by a rhythmic 'choking' call with upward-pointing bill.

The species has a broad circumpolar distribution extending southwards to Portugal. Of an estimated world population of 6–8 million pairs, Britain and Ireland holds 7.9% (Lloyd *et al* 1991), with a high proportion of the population breeding in northern Scotland, southwards along the North Sea coastline to the Humber. However, colonies can be found on most coasts, although these are thinly scattered in the southeast. Inland records are uncommon and breeding colonies are on coastal cliffs or, occasionally, man-made cliff-like structures such as harbour walls or warehouse window ledges, although such sites are not utilized in Cumbria. The nest is a compacted accumulation of grass, seaweed and mud attached to a narrow ledge and into which are laid one to three eggs.

The red sandstone cliffs at St Bees Head provide the only suitable cliff-nesting site in Cumbria and the Kittiwake's history as a breeding bird in the county is rather a brief one. Macpherson (1892) recognized the suitability of St Bees Head but noted that the species did not happen to breed there at the end of the 19th century. Subsequent county avifaunas do not record when the species first colonized the site but Blezard *et al* (1943) noted some 20 pairs nesting in 1932 and that this figure was gradually increasing. Stokoe (1962) reported further increases with a count of 1,651 pairs of nesting birds in 1956. This appears to be the highest

count made before a decline to around 810 pairs in 1984 (Hutcheson 1986). Subsequently, the breeding population recovered to a high of 1,630 breeding pairs during 1994.

The colonization of St Bees Head occurred during a time of sustained increase in the British breeding population. A national enquiry into the status of Kittiwakes in Britain and Ireland in 1959 revealed the rate of increase in England, Wales and the Isle of Man between 1900 and 1959 to have been between 3% and 4% per annum (Lloyd *et al* 1991). A likely factor contributing to this increase was the introduction of the Seabirds Protection Act in 1869. Prior to this many colonies were systematically depleted as the millinery trade demand for 'white plumes' increased. Kittiwakes were shot in large numbers and climbers also supported their incomes by the annual harvest of eggs that were sold for human consumption. Food supply has also played a role in determining changes in numbers and distribution. Kittiwakes are normally plankton feeders but have adopted a strategy of feeding on discards from fishing vessels. The expansion of the fishing industry in British waters since the 1940s is likely to have increased this food availability. The relative stability of the population at St Bees Head in the latter half of the 20th century is in contrast to the national trend and whilst the limiting factors are unknown, food supply is likely to be significant.

During the survey, the colony at St Bees Head has fluctuated markedly; a proportion of birds not breeding in some years may account for the wide range in population counts. For example, a low count in 1998 reflected similar reductions at other colonies that year, which were attributed to non-breeding rather than high over-winter mortality (Thompson *et al* 1999). The current county population of 1,000–1,500 breeding pairs during *this Atlas* is based on annual seabird counts at St Bees Head.

The recent trend in Cumbria suggests a degree of relative stability. The breeding site is secure from disturbance and inaccessible to land-based predators. Ravens are known to be predators of Kittiwake nestlings and Peregrines will take both adults and young. Both species are present at St Bees Head but their impact has not been quantified.

As already mentioned, Kittiwakes have taken to nesting on man-made structures. This adaptability was further demonstrated in 1998 when this became the first species to be recorded breeding successfully on a fuel rig off the coast of Britain. A single pair bred that year on a gas platform in the Irish Sea, followed by several pairs in 1999 (Thorpe 1999). Expansion of the species within Cumbria, away from St Bees Head, is unlikely unless the population again undergoes a significant increase in numbers. However if this occurs, the harbour areas of Workington and Whitehaven

Sponsored by K Shoes

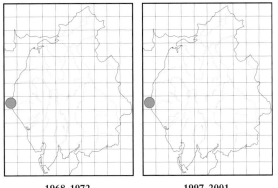

**1968-1972** **1997-2001**

(For explanation of maps, see page 45)

***Conservation status***

| European: | Non-SPEC |
|---|---|
| UK: | **AMBER: BL** |

***Populations***

| European status: | 2,350,000 |
|---|---|
| Britain – pairs: | 490,000 |
| Cumbria – pairs: | 1,000–1,500 |

***30-year distribution change***

| | *Old Atlas* | *This Atlas* | % |
|---|---|---|---|
| No. of 10km squares: | 1 | 1 | n/c |

| **Survey data** | **Tetrads** | **%** |
|---|---|---|
| Confirmed breeding: | 2 | 0.1 |
| Probable breeding: | 0 | |
| Possible breeding: | 0 | |
| Total: | 2 | 0.1 |

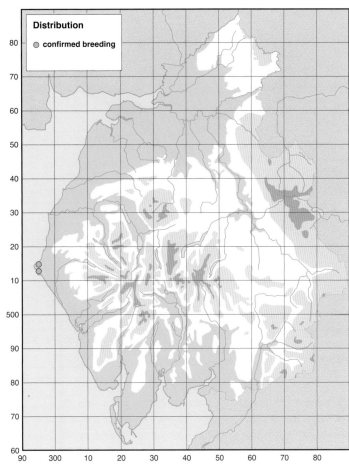

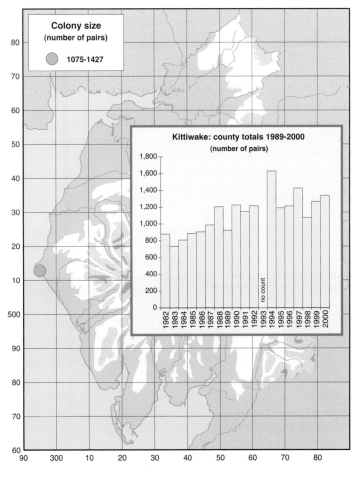

would seem to be the most likely candidates for colonization.

Trends in Kittiwake populations within Britain have varied from region to region over the last 15 years. Declines are evident in Shetland, southeast Scotland, southeast England and Wales whilst other areas show either no significant change or a slight increase. The Cumbrian colony would appear large enough to overcome short-term population fluctuations. The effect of longer-term factors, such as changes in the fishing industry, may be more significant, although difficult to forecast.

Nick Littlewood

# Sandwich Tern *Sterna sandvicensis*

RAUCOUS grating calls indicate the presence overhead of the first Sandwich Terns of the spring. Birds arrive back in the county from mid-March onwards and breeding activity soon begins in earnest. One or two eggs are laid in a shallow scrape on shingle, bare ground or short vegetation, often amongst taller herbaceous plants, with young fledging from late June onwards.

Sandwich Terns breed in most coastal European countries and east to the Caspian Sea. There are also colonies in eastern North America, the Caribbean and Atlantic coasts of South America. The distribution is highly aggregated with most birds breeding in large colonies often mixed with other tern species and Black-headed Gulls. In Britain and Ireland, colonies are widely scattered around the coastline, with notable absences from much of western Scotland, Wales and the east and southwest of England. Birds remain in northern waters later than other tern species, with records in November not unusual, before migrating south to winter along the coast of West Africa.

This species has a reputation for fickleness in its choice of nesting places, and furthermore colonies will readily shift in response to disturbance. Breeding has only ever been confirmed at a few sites in Cumbria. The first documented colonies were on Walney Island; birds were breeding at the north end by 1843 with numbers peaking at 40 pairs in 1880 before heavy persecution finally saw the site abandoned in 1889. By this time birds were also breeding at South Walney, where nesting was first noted in 1879; the population probably peaked in 1930 when 535 young were ringed. This site held the majority of the Furness

population, though with some years of absence, until breeding first took place on Foulney Island in 1958. Numbers here reached 1,600 pairs in 1984, but a steady decline followed and a total breeding failure in 1995 led to the cessation of nesting in Furness (Dean 1990, Littlewood 1996).

Elsewhere in the county, a few pairs were breeding amongst the marram-clad sand-dunes of Ravenglass by 1884. Although the exact date for the foundation of this colony is unclear, it was thought that the pioneers involved birds escaping the persecution on Walney Island. Numbers rose steadily to 400 pairs in 1930, 480 pairs in 1955 and 708 pairs in 1976, before breeding was last recorded in 1977 (Macpherson & Duckworth 1886, Stokoe 1962, Hutcheson 1986). A small colony was also noted at Roanhead in 1912 and a single pair bred at Rockcliffe Marsh in 1926 (Blezard *et al* 1943, Brown 1974).

The population size in Cumbria has fluctuated greatly but following a general increase through much of the 20th century a recent downward trend is evident. Some inter-colony movement of birds between Ravenglass, South Walney, Foulney Island and latterly Hodbarrow is thought to have taken place. The magnitude of these fluctuations indicates a degree of recruitment of adults into and emigration of birds out of the breeding population.

The most recent, and only surviving, colony is at Hodbarrow. Nesting birds were first documented here in 1989 and 120 pairs raised around 20 young in 1990 – the first successful fledging. Although 520 pairs were present in 1991, in recent years the population has been lower and, during *this Atlas* has remained remarkably stable, with colony counts ranging between 300 and 380 breeding pairs, with moderate breeding success.

Sandwich Terns are vulnerable to the same pressures from coastal development, disturbance and predation as other species of terns. Predation seems to be the main reason for the abandonment of Ravenglass and, after heavy losses to Red Foxes led to a total breeding failure in 1995, the cessation of nesting at Foulney Island (Littlewood 1996). Breeding numbers may also be adversely affected by the trapping of birds by man on the wintering grounds although this is difficult to quantify. A further crucial factor affecting the distribution of this species in the county is its close relationship with Black-headed Gulls. At former colonies on Walney Island, Foulney Island and Ravenglass, and at the current stronghold at Hodbarrow, birds have elected, given that the gulls lay earlier, to nest in association with Black-headed Gulls where they are afforded some protection from larger marauding gulls and other predators. Although some tern eggs and chicks are lost to the Black-headed Gulls, which also steal food from adult birds coming

 Sponsored in memory of Frank Roberts

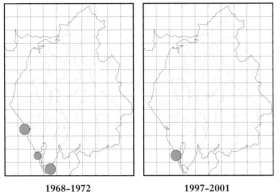

**1968-1972**　　　　**1997-2001**
(For explanation of maps, see page 45)

*Conservation status*

| | |
|---|---|
| European: | SPEC Cat 2 |
| UK: | **AMBER: BL & BI** |

*Populations*

| | |
|---|---|
| European status: | 125,000 |
| Britain – pairs: | 14,000 |
| Cumbria – pairs: | 300–380 |

*30-year distribution change*

| | Old Atlas | This Atlas | % |
|---|---|---|---|
| No. of 10km squares: | 3 | 1 | **−66.6** |

| **Survey data** | **Tetrads** | **%** |
|---|---|---|
| Confirmed breeding: | 1 | 0.05 |
| Probable breeding: | 0 | |
| Possible breeding: | 0 | |
| Total: | 1 | 0.05 |

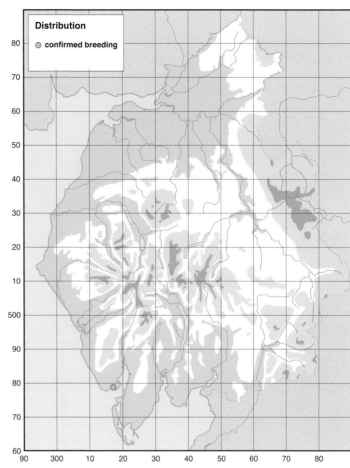

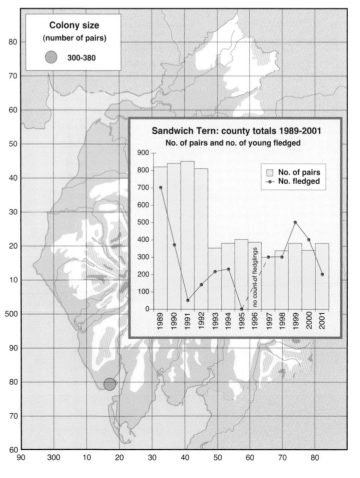

into the colony to feed their chicks, the arrangement leads to overall increased breeding productivity for the terns (Veen 1977). Indeed, the desertion of Foulney coincided with the demise of the Black-headed Gull colony there.

The future of this bird in the county depends on the continued management of coastal nature reserves. The habit of this species of switching colonies underlines the importance of maintaining a series of such sites around our coast and the provision of wardening should birds colonize or recolonize a site. Recent breeding success of both this species and Black-headed Gulls at Hodbarrow could soon lead to recruitment of new breeding birds into the population of each species. Recolonization of Foulney Island, South Walney or even Ravenglass might then become a real possibility.

Nick Littlewood

# Common Tern *Sterna hirundo*

A VERSATILE and widespread species, the Common Tern is as adept at exploiting sheltered man-made nesting habitats as it is at battling through a roaring ocean gale. Masses of Common Terns congregate at established sites in spring: their noisy attacks follow any intruder through the colony, like a 'mexican wave' of aerial bombardment, as pairs defiantly defend their chosen nest site.

The global breeding distribution is essentially Holarctic, extending southwards patchily to West Africa and the Caribbean. The species breeds at scattered sites across Britain and Ireland, though with few locations in Wales or the southwest. In many parts of England, the Common Tern is the most familiar of the breeding *Sterna* species, thanks to its adoption of inland waters as nesting sites. In Cumbria, however, it remains entirely coastal, sometimes forming mixed colonies with Arctic Terns, on shingle, sand and, especially, grassy areas. It also shares a reputation with the Arctic Tern as a long-distance migrant, and whilst its journeys normally take it only as far as the coasts of western and southern Africa, ringing recoveries show that Common Terns venture well into the southern oceans, with one bird reaching Australia (Hume 1993).

Nationally, during the 19th century, numbers undoubtedly decreased as a result of egg-gathering for food and shooting for sport. Following the Seabirds Protection Act of 1869, numbers had increased, particularly in England, by the beginning of the 20th century. From the 1930s, a slow decline set in, although following the Second World War an increasing number of birds began to breed inland. This increase was a result of suitable waters being created by gravel extraction and reservoir construction.

Common Terns are usually site-faithful but colonies will move, especially following seasons with poor breeding success. In Cumbria, towards the end of the 19th century, the principal colonies were at Walney Island, Ravenglass and Rockcliffe Marsh (Macpherson 1892). These sites, and several smaller colonies, including Skinburness, survived into the mid-20th century (Blezard *et al* 1943, Stokoe 1962). However,

breeding soon became less regular at South Walney, with substantial numbers moving to Foulney Island from 1955 (Dean 1990) and breeding was last recorded at Ravenglass in 1988. The *Old Atlas* showed confirmed breeding in ten 10km squares in the county; by the time of the *New Atlas* this had declined to five.

The numbers of birds at each of the major colonies have fluctuated markedly since records began. At South Walney, the 911 young ringed in 1935 must have represented a substantial colony although the actual number of pairs is not recorded. A maximum of 600 nests was recorded at Foulney Island in the 1960s. Since 1980, combined totals for both sites have exceeded 100 pairs only once, in 1984 (Dean 1990, Littlewood 1996). Breeding was last recorded at South Walney in 1992 and at Foulney Island in 1996. The Rockcliffe Marsh colony contained about 150 pairs in 1934 (Blezard *et al* 1943) while Stokoe (1962) estimated 40–50 pairs in a normal year.

The distribution map shows that *this Atlas* recorded confirmed breeding in just four tetrads within two 10km squares. The three tetrads in the north of the county represent the same peripatetic colony at Rockcliffe Marsh, where the population has varied during *this Atlas* between 20 and 47 pairs with moderate breeding success noted. The most significant colony, however, is at Hodbarrow. Numbers here have been fairly stable, with 40–52 pairs nesting, and productivity has been encouragingly high since the bulk of the colony moved to the long and narrow 'ski bank' in 1997. The current county population of 60–100 breeding pairs is derived from counts at the two breeding colonies.

Common Terns are apparently better able to tolerate human presence close to their breeding grounds than other species (Lloyd *et al* 1991) as demonstrated at Hodbarrow, where they seem unaffected by regular use of the adjoining water by water-skiers, although actual nesting sites obviously need to be free of continual disturbance. The situation, however, is made very different by the presence of predators at a site: the

 Sponsored in memory of Joe Spurrs

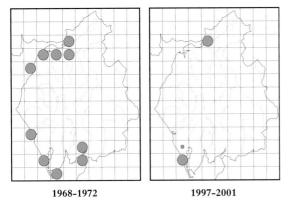

**1968-1972**          **1997-2001**

(For explanation of maps, see page 45)

**Conservation status**

European:                    Non-SPEC
UK:                          **GREEN**

**Populations**

European status:             210,000
Britain – pairs:              12,300
Cumbria – pairs:              60–100

**30-year distribution change**

|                      | Old Atlas | This Atlas | %   |
|----------------------|-----------|------------|-----|
| No. of 10km squares: | 10        | 3          | **-70** |

| Survey data          | Tetrads | %    |
|----------------------|---------|------|
| Confirmed breeding:  | 4       | 0.22 |
| Probable breeding:   | 0       |      |
| Possible breeding:   | 1       | 0.05 |
| Total:               | 5       | 0.27 |

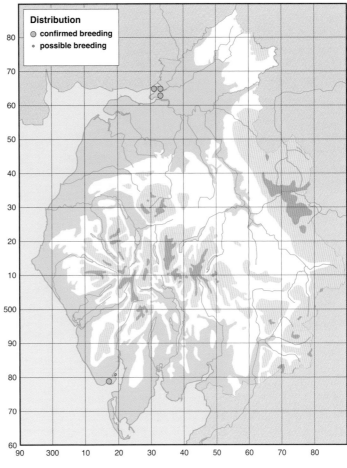

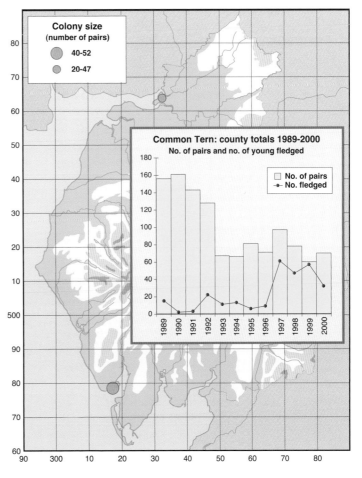

complete failure of colonies to rear young is a striking feature in some years. Following heavy losses to Red Foxes in 1995, Foulney Island was deserted by the bulk of its breeding birds the following season. A similar situation arose at Hodbarrow where Red Foxes were thought to be the cause of total breeding failure for several years in the early 1990s. At Rockcliffe Marsh, the most persistent site in the county, breeding success has been adversely influenced in some years by high tides flooding the marsh and washing out nests.

Despite the occasional use of a variety of sites, the future prospects for the Common Tern in Cumbria would appear to be dependent on coastal nature reserves where the birds are given a degree of protection by wardening schemes. Any newly colonized or recolonized sites will need to be afforded similar protection if nesting is to persist and bolster the county population.

Nick Littlewood

# Arctic Tern *Sterna paradisaea*

COMBINING aerial grace and elegance with the strength and resilience of an oceanic survivor, the Arctic Tern is truly the greatest traveller of the avian world. From its circumpolar breeding distribution around the coasts of northern Europe, Canada and Russia, the species migrates to the edge of the antarctic pack ice. Ringing recoveries have involved birds of European origin even as far as Australasian waters.

The distribution within Britain and Ireland has a distinctly northern bias with about 30,000 of the estimated 46,500 pairs breeding at the time of the *New Atlas* being in the Northern Isles. Nesting occurs in coastal colonies, with up to three eggs being laid on shingle, sand or rocky shores. Colonies are aggressively defended from potential predators and blood can be drawn from the scalp of human intruders. Birds feed mainly by plunge diving for fish, especially sand-eels, herrings and sprats.

In Cumbria, Macpherson (1892) records that the species "has always nested on Walney Island" but the earliest documented record concerns four nests found at North Walney in 1864 (Harting 1864). The colony increased to around 40 nests the following year, but the birds had moved to the south end by the 1890s, where 50 pairs bred in 1905 (Dean 1990). Ravenglass was colonized early in the 20th century and breeding occurred on Rockcliffe Marsh from at least 1923 with nearly 20 pairs noted in 1934. The species was also noted in a Common Tern colony at another Solway site in 1938 (Blezard *et al* 1943). During the second half of the 20th century, the distribution contracted considerably. The *Old Atlas* confirmed breeding in six

coastal 10km squares between Foulney Island and Rockcliffe Marsh. During the *New Atlas,* confirmed breeding was recorded from just four sites: South Walney, Foulney Island, Rockcliffe Marsh and Drigg Dunes where the last pair bred in 1988. Foulney Island, where breeding has occurred since at least 1955, is now used in preference to South Walney where birds last bred in 1988.

At the species' historical and current strongholds of South Walney and Foulney Island, numbers have fluctuated markedly and both sites have been successively colonized, abandoned and recolonized. The peak at South Walney in the first half of the 20th century was probably the 100 nests counted in 1913 whilst in the second half 150 pairs nested in 1971 (Dean 1990). At Foulney Island, following the initial colonization, the population rose rapidly at first to 229 nests in 1957, although successive years saw fewer pairs (Stokoe 1962). An average of 68 pairs bred at Foulney Island in the 1980s decreasing to 44 pairs by the 1990s, although this may be misleading with the recording of 'nests' instead of 'pairs' during the early 1980s producing a slightly inflated figure for that decade (Littlewood 1996).

During the survey period for *this Atlas* confirmed breeding was recorded from Foulney Island where the population ranged between 33 and 55 breeding pairs. In spite of intensive wardening schemes the breeding success was rather low, averaging 14 young per year. In addition, possible breeding was reported from two sites: at Hodbarrow, where two birds were seen frequently in the Common Tern colony in 2000, and in the north of the county, where the species has virtually disappeared from the inner Solway, just a single summering bird was at Rockcliffe Marsh in 1999. The current county population estimate of 60 breeding pairs is based on colony count data.

Arctic Tern colonies are vulnerable to coastal development, recreational activities and the attention of predators. All current confirmed and possible nesting sites in the county are on nature reserves that are likely to be relatively safe from threats of inappropriate development and where wardening may minimize disturbance from recreational activities. Predators on the other hand can have a significant impact on breeding success whether on a nature reserve or not. At Foulney Island egg and chick losses in recent years have been attributed to Herring Gull, Red Fox and possibly Kestrel. Remarkably, a Little Owl was recorded taking adult birds in 1964 and 1996 (Dean 1990, Littlewood, 1996). This habit was also noted at South Walney in 1986 when corpses of nine adults were discovered having suffered a similar fate. Furthermore, high tides frequently cause failures on Foulney Island when beach nesting birds are inundated

Sponsored by David Hirst

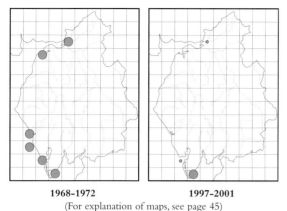

**1968-1972**          **1997-2001**

(For explanation of maps, see page 45)

***Conservation status***

| | |
|---|---|
| European: | Non-SPEC |
| UK: | **AMBER: BL** |

***Populations***

| | |
|---|---|
| European status: | 520,000 |
| Britain – pairs: | 44,000 |
| Cumbria – pairs: | 60 |

***30-year distribution change***

| | Old Atlas | This Atlas | % |
|---|---|---|---|
| No. of 10km squares: | 6 | 3 | **–50** |

| **Survey data** | **Tetrads** | **%** |
|---|---|---|
| Confirmed breeding: | 2 | 0.1 |
| Probable breeding: | 0 | |
| Possible breeding: | 2 | 0.1 |
| Total: | 4 | 0.2 |

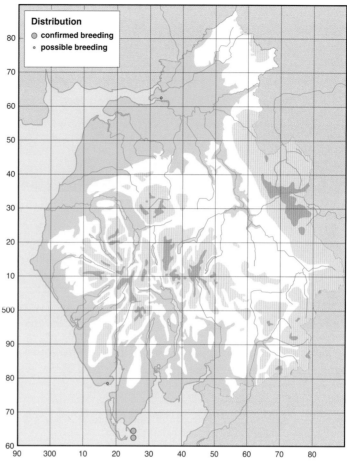

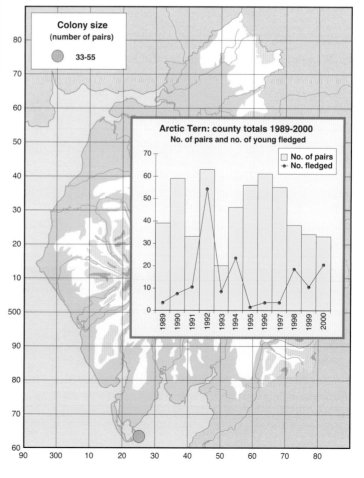

by rising water. Although intervention by moving eggs further up the beach may be successful, such action is not ideal and increases disturbance in the colony.

The status of this species in the county is clearly a cause for concern. Arctic Terns are long-lived birds and have a long association with sites in the south of the county, though their small population at a single site leaves them perilously vulnerable to local extinction. Their continued presence depends not only on the maintenance of nature reserves that are sufficiently free from the attention of predators and pressures of recreation, but also on wider environmental factors such as food availability and sea levels.

Nick Littlewood

# Little Tern *Sterna albifrons*

ASECLUDED shingle beach, the sound of crunching pebbles underfoot, while overhead the persistently loud, harsh calls, '*kyrrik-ik, kyrrik-ik, kyrrik-ik*' penetrate the consciousness: these are the sights and sounds that typify a Little Tern colony. The fast, jerky wingbeats, white forehead and yellow bill make these diminutive birds distinct from all other British terns.

The Little Tern is part of a group of closely allied species that breed in every continent in the world except Antarctica. In many parts of its range, especially Russia, the Little Tern breeds extensively inland along rivers and by lakes but in Britain and Ireland the species is almost exclusively coastal and inland records are very rare indeed. Although colonies tend to be widely distributed, southeast England is the stronghold, with the coast between Lincolnshire and Hampshire holding around 75% of the national population. Birds return from West Africa in late April or early May to breed in small loose colonies or even singly on shingle or sandy beaches, often sharing these beaches with holidaymakers. Two or three eggs are laid and the species will readily lay replacement clutches, frequently at a new site, if the first attempt fails.

The mobility of this species as a breeding bird has resulted in records of nests from most parts of the Cumbrian coast between Foulney Island and the Solway Firth. Macpherson (1892) cites colonies at Walney Island and Ravenglass, whilst also referring to breeding near Allonby and Skinburness. Blezard *et al* (1943) adds Foulney Island, Roanhead and "other localities along the Cumberland coast northward to Skinburness" whilst Stokoe (1962) records that small colonies bred between Walney Island and Grune Point. The *Old Atlas* maps confirmed breeding for nine 10km squares in the county, covering much of the coast between Foulney Island and Grune Point with the exception of the maritime cliffs between St Bees Head and Workington. The *New Atlas* shows a more patchy distribution: confirmed breeding reduced to seven 10km squares, and a loss of sites between Netherby and Silecroft.

The distribution map for *this Atlas* shows a further decline. Breeding was confirmed in just eight tetrads: Foulney Island and Hodbarrow in the south of the county and a further six sites along the coast between Siddick and Grune Point. These tetrads all lie within five 10km squares and when compared with the results of the *Old Atlas,* a contraction of range is evident. The main losses involve sites in the south of the county, with the entire coastal stretch northwards from Hodbarrow to Siddick now lacking breeding Little Terns.

Movement of Little Terns between nesting sites is a well-established habit. The causes are varied and not well understood. In some instances there are clear reasons linked to human disturbance or excessive predation, but in other cases no clear explanation is apparent. The former colony at Ravenglass was evidently abandoned when the site became unsuitable following changes to the vegetation. The breeding productivity of the species also fluctuates widely. At Hodbarrow, a wardened colony, breeding success was very poor indeed between 1986 and 1994 with an average annual fledging rate of less than 0.1 chicks/pair. Predation was considered to be the main reason for failure, with Stoat and Red Fox particularly active on the site. Since then, protection measures for the main colony area seem to have paid some dividends. With the erection of an electric fence around the colony, the average annual fledging rate for 1995 to 1999 was 0.25 chicks/pair; still perilously low but an improvement on the previous situation (Peter 1999). The scattered sites in the north of the county are less intensively studied. Some pairs breed at sites popular with beachgoers and at Mawbray the breeding area has been fenced off in some years to deter casual disturbance. It is unclear, though, if this is effective or if the fence attracts further unwanted attention.

Although it is generally assumed that the breeding population in the county has fallen during the 1990s, from a peak of 65 pairs in 1993, no systematic colony counts have been undertaken and the degree of under-recording in this period makes it impossible to make an accurate assessment. Indeed, the combined total of pairs contained in seven colonies located during *this Atlas*

 Sponsored by Solway Offshore Ltd

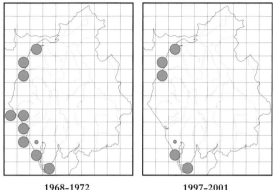

**1968–1972**          **1997–2001**

(For explanation of maps, see page 45)

**Conservation status**

| | |
|---|---|
| European: | SPEC Cat 3 |
| UK: | AMBER: BL |

**Populations**

| | |
|---|---|
| European status: | 21,500 |
| Britain – pairs: | 2,400 |
| Cumbria – pairs: | 70–80 |

**30-year distribution change**

| | Old Atlas | This Atlas | % |
|---|---|---|---|
| No. of 10km squares: | 10 | 6 | **–40** |

| **Survey data** | **Tetrads** | **%** |
|---|---|---|
| Confirmed breeding: | 8 | 0.4 |
| Probable breeding: | 0 | |
| Possible breeding: | 3 | 0.2 |
| Total: | 11 | 0.6 |

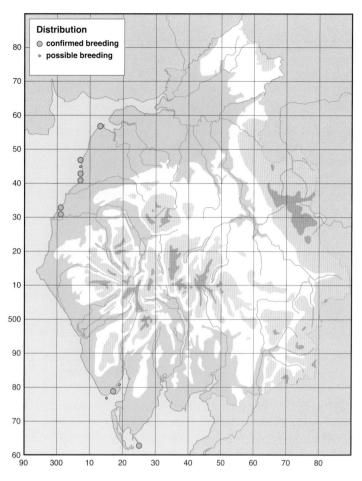

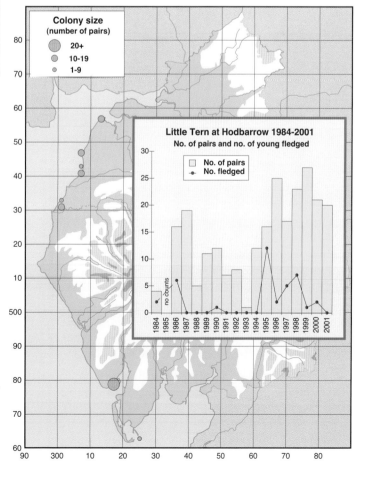

actually suggests an increase. Whilst there is always the possibility that some inter-colony movement of nesting birds during the five year period of *this Atlas* has inflated the figures, under-recording in earlier years is much more likely. The current county population estimate of 70–80 breeding pairs is based upon counts at colonies.

Hodbarrow is now the most important county site for this species, but with continued low breeding productivity the colony cannot be sustained without recruitment from elsewhere. High productivity at some Little Tern colonies in the county is not unknown. For example, 32 young fledged from 24 pairs at Siddick in 1988, but such occurrences have become increasingly rare (Peter 1999). The future, though difficult to predict, may depend on the continued perseverance of these birds at a small nucleus of protected sites along our coastline and their ability to adapt to rising sea levels.

Nick Littlewood

175

EVENING sunlight in May accentuates the great buttresses of red sandstone, stippled with the white fronts of innumerable seabirds, and glints on the Guillemot-dappled sea beneath. The sight and sound of a seabird colony at this time of year is a most thrilling experience – the cacophony a result of thousands of voices proclaiming ownership of each tiny piece of vertiginous ledge. Feeding time for the chicks is a period of great excitement and, in the summer twilight, the July cliffs are alive with gargling calls.

The Guillemot's breeding range spans the North Atlantic and North Pacific Oceans and occupies adjacent southern arctic waters; the Atlantic birds disperse southwards in autumn to the region of the North Atlantic Drift current. In Britain and Ireland, it has a widespread, though discontinuous, distribution, occurring wherever suitable cliffs allows breeding. The largest colonies tend to be in the more isolated and wilder regions, with Scotland holding the bulk of the British population. In England, the largest concentrations are in the northeast and southwest, with none breeding between Flamborough Head and the Isle of Wight. In Cumbria, the species has a very localized distribution during the breeding season, with the substantial red sandstone cliffs of St Bees Head home to the only auk colony in northwest England.

Guillemots make up the principal component of the North Atlantic seabird colonies and, being gregarious birds, they nest in overwhelming numbers, assembling on inaccessible, open cliff ledges in the avian equivalent of towering tenements. First-time breeders are usually relegated to the outer, less favoured, edge of

the colony where they are rarely successful. Guillemots lay a single egg, its pyriform shape preventing it from rolling off the narrow exposed ledges. After the young hatch, although gorged on sandeels and sprats brought to them by their parents, they live a precarious life. The young leave the ledges at about a third grown, and, incapable of proper flight, they launch themselves from considerable or even colossal heights into the void, relying on their rudimentary wings to avoid the rocks and crashing waves below. This leap, in blind faith, usually happens at dusk, so as to evade the attentions of predatory gulls. On the water below, they somehow manage to reunite with their parents and learn to feed and fend for themselves. This strategy of leading the part-grown young to sea and feeding them there has its advantages; it is safer and more economical in effort for adults whose flight is costly in energy and which prefer to feed well offshore.

The steep climb from Fleswick Bay and short walk above the cliff-tops on a summer's day to laze and gaze at the spectacle below is one of Cumbria's true jewels. However, it has not always been this tranquil: birds were indiscriminately shot for food and pleasure during the 19th century until the first bird protection act in Britain made this an offence in 1869. Macpherson (1892) referred to the great numbers of Guillemots, which "in company with a lesser number of Razorbills, rear their young on the cliffs at Sandwith", while Macpherson & Duckworth (1886) reiterated tales of breeding birds being taken at St Bees Head in 1675. Stokoe (1962) quoted a total of 2,009 breeding pairs at St Bees Head in May 1956, but commented that up to 20% of the population may have been missed due to the counting methods employed. Regular counts have taken place since 1980, with the population revealed to be stable, averaging 5,259 birds in the 1980s and 5,249 birds during the 1990s.

During the period of *this Atlas,* counts have shown a year on year growth, with the number of birds using the colony increasing from 5,620 in 1997 to 7,340 in 2000 (access restrictions due to foot-and-mouth disease prevented any counts in 2001). The current county population of 6,540 adults is based on a mean for the years 1997–2000 from seabird monitoring counts of birds on ledges.

Although the recent increase in numbers at St Bees Head is encouraging, man's activities continue to cause great problems for many seabirds. It is calculated that 3–5 million tonnes of oil are lost in the world's oceans each year, whilst incidents involving the flushing out of supertankers at sea are all too common. The effects can be catastrophic, especially for auks; in many oil incidents, over 50% of all casualties are Guillemots. Drift netting is another major hazard that accounts for a calculated 20,000 auk deaths each year in Galway

Sponsored by Steve Percival, Ecology Consulting

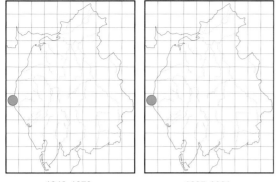

**1968-1972**          **1997-2001**
(For explanation of maps, see page 45)

***Conservation status***

| | |
|---|---|
| European: | Non-SPEC |
| UK: | **AMBER: BI & BL** |

***Populations** – adults*

| | |
|---|---|
| European: | 2,000,000 |
| Britain: | 1,050,000 |
| Cumbria: | 6,540 |

***30-year distribution change***

| | Old Atlas | This Atlas | % |
|---|---|---|---|
| No. of 10km squares: | 1 | 1 | n/c |

| **Survey data** | **Tetrads** | **%** |
|---|---|---|
| Confirmed breeding: | 2 | 0.1 |
| Probable breeding: | 0 | |
| Possible breeding: | 1 | 0.05 |
| Total: | 3 | 0.15 |

Bay alone. Altogether an estimated 1.5 million Guillemots worldwide die annually at man's hand. This is more than the population can withstand. More locally, any prospect of more supertankers using the Irish Sea increases the risk for our sole auk colony.

Malcolm Stott

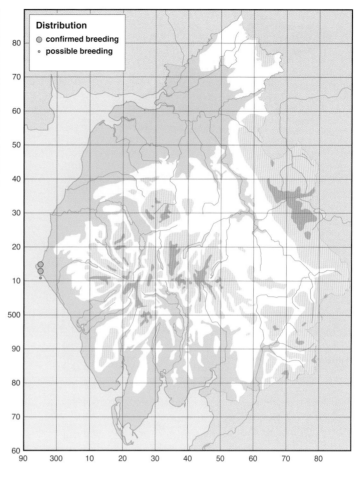

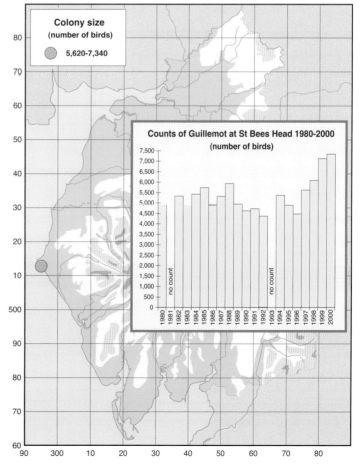

# Razorbill *Alca torda*

THE ceaseless activity of an auk colony cannot fail to impress even the non-birdwatcher – a privileged insight into another world. If not mesmerized by the swarm of birds swirling below, it is possible to separate the Razorbills even at a distance from the chocolate-brown Guillemots by their much blacker upperparts; closer views might be needed to see the much heavier bill with diagnostic markings and a white line that extends to the eye.

A truly marine species, confined to the cooler temperate and boreal coasts of the North Atlantic and adjacent Arctic Oceans, the Razorbill has a less extensive distribution than the Guillemot. In the Western Palearctic, the northern limits of this distribution reach Bear Island and Svalbard, the main range extending from Murmansk, around the Baltic coast, to Iceland and the Faeroe Islands, and southwards to Britain, Ireland and northwest France. In comparison to the Guillemot, and outside of the Icelandic population, Razorbill numbers are small, with about 70% of these breeding around the coastline of Britain and Ireland. The bulk of this population is to be found in northwest Scotland, although a discontinuous distribution extends the entire length of the west coast of England and Wales, with Yorkshire the southernmost limit down the east coast. In Ireland, it can be found on most suitable cliff habitats. During autumn dispersal, large movements of this auk, en route to wintering grounds as far south as the Straits of Gibraltar, may be witnessed off the Cumbrian coast.

All seabirds are dependent on land to breed and generally nest in comparatively inaccessible parts of the coastline. Razorbills return each January to inspect their natal ledges, prior to the breeding season, but they never occur in Guillemot-like concentrations, although breeding alongside them. The use of cliffs for breeding protects vulnerable eggs, and later young, from ground predators. The quality of the nest site can also have a considerable effect on the breeding performance. Unlike Guillemots, Razorbills prefer to nest individually or in more dispersed groups, with the single sub-elliptical egg usually laid on a wide, sheltered ledge or in a rocky crevice or cavity; only rarely are exposed situations utilized. A staple diet of fish, mainly sandeels, sprats, herring and capelin is caught by surface diving, with crustaceans also taken.

Cumbria's only colony at St Bees Head has been long established – indeed Macpherson (1892) commented that birds had probably existed there from time immemorial. The continued presence of these birds during the 20th century is well-documented, although very little evidence is available on colony size, until Stokoe (1962) reported the presence of 60 pairs in 1956. However this was considered to be an underestimate with "most nests hidden in crevices and many are not readily discoverable". In 1975, 600 birds and 200 occupied sites were counted, and this had increased in 1978 to 250 pairs, though numbers declined to 150 nests a year later. Birds have been monitored almost annually since 1980 and the seasonal population for 1980–1996 averaged 237 individuals, with only four counts recording less than 200 birds.

During fieldwork for *this Atlas,* regular colony counts have produced a population band of 200–300 birds. The current county population estimate is based upon a mean of 242 adults occupying ledges during seabird monitoring counts.

Despite the obvious difficulties of seabird monitoring, a judicious review of past records, from colonies that have been regularly and systematically counted, can often provide a comprehensive insight into current trends. At St Bees Head, the mean population during the 1980s was 230 birds; this had increased to 246 birds in the 1990s, equivalent to a 7.0% rise. During *this Atlas* period, although the rate of growth has slowed, there was a further 2.1% rise over the mean since regular counts were started. These figures suggest that the Razorbill population in Cumbria is currently relatively stable.

Razorbills, however, remain highly vulnerable to marine pollutants such as oil and toxic waste, and there are further hazards to contend with: discarded plastics, monofilament drift netting and the over-exploitation of fish stocks by man continue to put the population at great risk.

Malcolm Stott

 Sponsored by a CBC Member

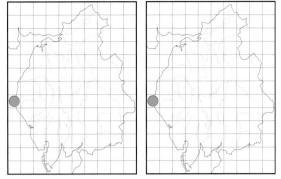

**1968-1972**          **1997-2001**
(For explanation of maps, see page 45)

*Conservation status*

| | |
|---|---|
| European: | SPEC Cat 4 |
| UK: | AMBER: BL |

*Populations* – *adults*

| | |
|---|---|
| European: | 480,000 |
| Britain: | 148,000 |
| Cumbria: | 242 |

*30-year distribution change*

| | Old Atlas | This Atlas | % |
|---|---|---|---|
| No. of 10km squares: | 1 | 1 | n/c |

| **Survey data** | **Tetrads** | **%** |
|---|---|---|
| Confirmed breeding: | 2 | 0.1 |
| Probable breeding: | 0 | |
| Possible breeding: | 1 | 0.05 |
| Total: | 3 | 0.15 |

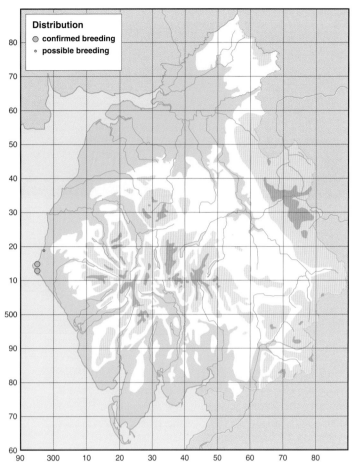

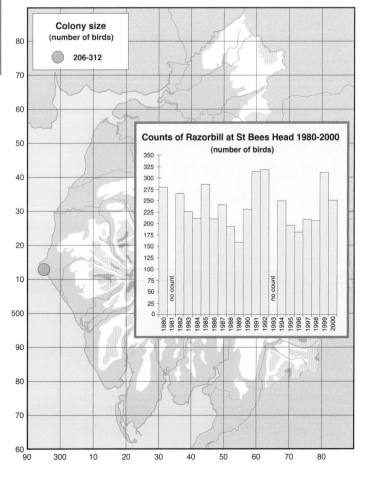

**Counts of Razorbill at St Bees Head 1980-2000**
(number of birds)

# Black Guillemot *Cepphus grylle*

THE crimson legs, vermilion gape and dazzling white blur of the Black Guillemot's wing patches attract attention to this most lovable seabird, which is often called by its Nordic name 'Tystie'. This can be the most elusive of the auks; the boulders at the base of the St Bees Head cliffs provide its sole Cumbrian breeding haunt.

The Black Guillemot has a circumpolar distribution, breeding along rocky shores in the Arctic Ocean and on both sides of the Atlantic with Britain and Ireland forming the southernmost limit of its range. In Britain they occur mainly on the Northern and Western Isles and along the western coast of Scotland. Until 1938 they were found on both the east and west coasts of England but since the demise of the Yorkshire population, Cumbria hosts the only colony south of the Scottish border.

Birds can be seen displaying from April onwards as they gather, in early morning, on the sea adjacent to the colony. This usually involves a certain amount of head-bobbing, communal bathing and standing on the water vigorously flapping their wings. Pairs then pirouette around each other, head to tail, and uttering a shrill but rather feeble *'peee'*. From a cliff-top vantage point they can also be seen energetically chasing each other just below the surface of the water, their white wing patches and red feet most obvious. Unlike the Guillemot, which lays only one egg on an exposed ledge, Black Guillemots will normally produce two eggs. These are laid in a well-sheltered crevice amongst stones or boulders at the base of the towering cliffs. The chicks stay concealed and comparatively safe in this well protected site, not usually venturing from the nest until fully grown and able to look after themselves.

The earliest documented record in Cumbria concerns two adults in breeding plumage, shot in the neighbourhood of St Bees in 1862 (Macpherson & Duckworth 1886). However, despite single birds being seen at St Bees Head in April 1921 and July 1932, and the presence of two birds on the sea below the cliffs in July 1935, it was not until 1940 that the first nest was discovered (Stokoe 1962, Brown 1974). Subsequently, three pairs were present in June 1949 and by the 1960s, one to three pairs were considered to breed annually. Since 1980, this small population has remained remarkably stable; annual monitoring has revealed between four and seven pairs. In addition, intriguingly, a juvenile accompanied by two adults was seen off Walney Island on 25th August 1980.

Black Guillemots are generally sedentary, and most Cumbrian birds choose to remain close to their breeding grounds for much of the year, favouring the more sheltered waters around the boulder-strewn beach of Fleswick Bay. Here the shallower water provides good feeding areas where the birds forage for fish and invertebrates close to the seafloor. Outside the breeding season a few birds annually visit the relatively sheltered waters in the mouth of Morecambe Bay, where they prefer the shallow tidal channels around Walney and Foulney Islands. Birds occasionally remain in this vicinity throughout the breeding season raising speculation that pairs may sporadically breed amongst the boulders found on the rocky shoreline of Piel Island. In the north of the county, the outer reaches of the Solway Firth also provide a few winter records. The small number of birds involved at these sites suggest that these are probably dispersed individuals from the breeding colony at St Bees Head.

Nesting as they do among rocks and boulders, rather than cliff ledges, there is always the possibility that Black Guillemots may breed elsewhere in the county, other than St Bees Head. Fieldwork for *this Atlas* failed to reveal any such records, though birds were again present during the breeding season in the Walney/Foulney Island area. Consequently, with no new breeding sites located, the distribution remains unchanged since the *Old Atlas* and the current county population of eight birds is based on seabird monitoring counts.

All birds are vulnerable to food shortages and none more so than seabirds, given the modern over-exploitation of sea-fish, in particular by 'vacuum' factory ships. Even more insidious is the high risk of

 Sponsored by Pete, Di, Kristy and Daisy Clark

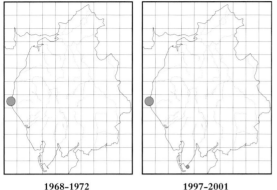

**1968-1972**     **1997-2001**

(For explanation of maps, see page 45)

---

***Conservation status***

| | |
|---|---|
| European: | SPEC Cat 2 |
| UK: | **AMBER** |

***Populations*** – *adults*

| | |
|---|---|
| European: | 100,000 |
| Britain: | 36,500 |
| Cumbria: | 8 |

***30-year distribution change***

| | Old Atlas | This Atlas | % |
|---|---|---|---|
| No. of 10km squares: | 1 | 2 | **+100** |

| **Survey data** | **Tetrads** | **%** |
|---|---|---|
| Confirmed breeding: | 1 | 0.05 |
| Probable breeding: | 0 | |
| Possible breeding: | 2 | 0.1 |
| Total: | 3 | 0.15 |

---

oil pollution, especially if it happened to coincide with the breeding season. It need not necessarily be a major incident on the scale of that at Sullom Voe which wiped out almost the entire breeding population in that part of Shetland in 1978; the small number of birds that breed at St Bees Head are probably at most risk from a passing vessel flushing its ballast tanks close to the colony.

Norman Holton

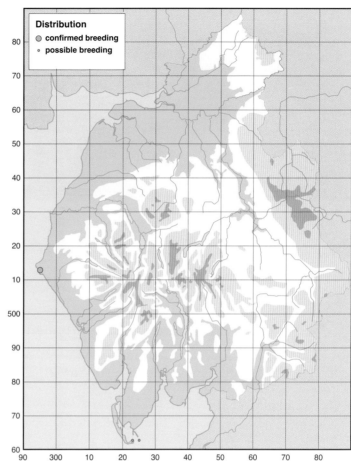

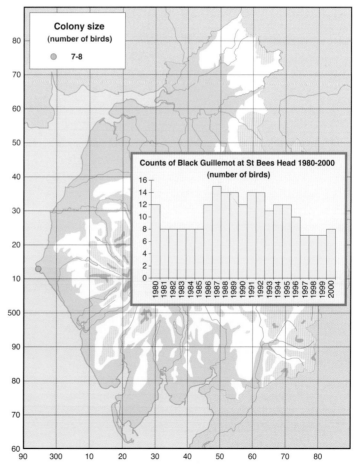

STANDING upright and alert atop a thrift-covered cliff-top with its multi-coloured beak crammed with glistening fish is everyone's vision of the Puffin. This charming 'sea-parrot' is probably as popular with non-birdwatchers as is the Robin, though few ever see it in life.

The Puffin is one of the most abundant species of seabird in the Northern Atlantic. An estimated world total of some 6.5 million pairs breeds from Brittany northward to Greenland and Svalbard, with the largest numbers being found in Iceland, Norway, northwest Scotland and the Faeroe Islands (Webb *et al* 1990). In England, the main concentrations are found in the northeast, where the Farne Islands, Coquet Island and Bempton hold around 28,000 breeding pairs.

The largest Puffin colonies are generally located on offshore islands where they nest in deep burrows either excavated by the birds themselves or purloined from Rabbits or Manx Shearwaters. Smaller colonies exist on mainland cliffs, and where these lack a soil cap to burrow into Puffins will occupy cracks in cliff-faces and holes under boulders. Both birds play an active part in their courtship displays at sea, which involve much clashing and rubbing of their colourful bills and comical bouts of head bobbing. Pair-bonds will have already been established by the time the birds return to the frenzied activity of the breeding colony. Their call, a long growling croak, is uttered in various situations and, like other auks, Puffins spend much of their time on the water, diving in pursuit of prey. They feed their chicks on small fish, in particular sandeels, clupeids and gadoids. The food of the adults is less well known, but is predominantly fish, with crustaceans and other marine invertebrates also taken in winter (Harris 1984). Chicks do not leave the nest until they are capable of being independent and by the end of August the colony is largely deserted.

Macpherson (1892) stated that "the Whitehaven fishermen assure me that even in the breeding season they see few Puffins off St Bees Head, and the description of their orange bills leaves no room for doubt as to the species; but though the grassy ledges of St Bees are suggestive of Puffin burrows, in point of fact the species does not nest there." Stokoe (1962) failed to mention when Puffins first nested at St Bees Head but did comment, "the breeding birds at St Bees Head are unusual in that although earth-topped buttresses, fairly secure at least from human access, are available, most nests are placed under fallen blocks on ledges or in cracks in the sheer face of the cliff". He also stated that eight pairs were found nesting in 1956 and rather more than this in subsequent years with about 20 birds counted in 1961. Hutcheson (1986) considered the population at St Bees Head to be 12–15 breeding pairs.

Restricted in Cumbria to St Bees Head, even here the lack of suitable nest sites limits Puffin numbers. Monitoring the breeding population is normally based on a count of occupied burrows, which is often difficult especially when Puffin excavations undermine unstable cliff-top vegetation, or nests are hidden amongst boulders. Alternatively counts are made of individual birds on the water beneath the colony to get an indication of breeding numbers. This technique has been used to survey the breeding population annually over the last 21 years as part of the National Seabird Monitoring Programme.

During the period 1980–89 the population yearly mean was 10.9 breeding pairs, with a maximum of 15 pairs in 1980 and 1981. For the years 1990 to 1999 the average had dropped to 5.7 breeding pairs with a maximum count of 12 pairs during that period. Puffin numbers have shown declines at colonies elsewhere and these have been attributed to various factors, including human disturbance, introduction of Brown Rats and predation by larger gulls, none of which are thought to be adversely affecting the small population at St Bees Head. This apparent decline in Cumbria coincided with the end of full-time wardening on site, and a change in survey methodology from 1993 onwards, with surveys restricted to a few counts each year as opposed to the intensive daily monitoring that used to occur. Comparisons between these two periods should therefore be treated with caution, since

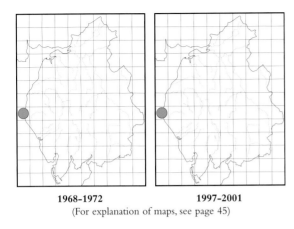

**1968-1972**          **1997-2001**

(For explanation of maps, see page 45)

*Conservation status*

| European: | SPEC Cat 2 |
| UK: | AMBER: BL |

*Populations – adults*

| European: | 5,400,000 |
| Britain: | 898,000 |
| Cumbria: | 10 |

*30-year distribution change*

| | Old Atlas | This Atlas | % |
|---|---|---|---|
| No. of 10km squares: | 1 | 1 | n/c |

| **Survey data** | **Tetrads** | **%** |
|---|---|---|
| Confirmed breeding: | 1 | 0.05 |
| Probable breeding: | 0 | |
| Possible breeding: | 0 | |
| Total: | 1 | 0.05 |

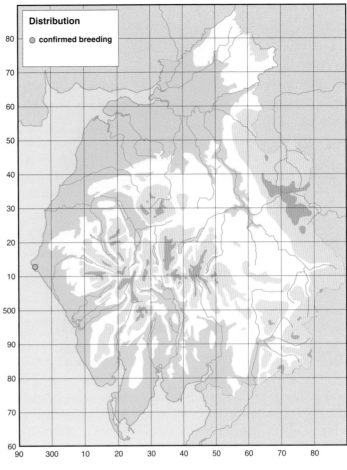

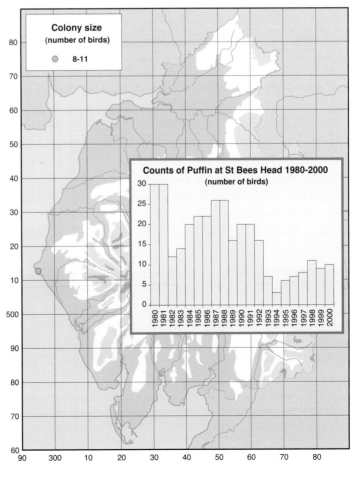

they are not directly comparable.

Fieldwork for *this Atlas* found no additional breeding sites, and hence no change to the county distribution of Puffin since the *Old Atlas*. The current county population of ten adults is derived from seabird monitoring counts.

Outside the breeding season Puffins habitually disperse to the open seas and are rarely seen from the coast during the winter months. This oceanic existence involves a degree of risk in the 21st century, with an increased volume of oil transported by fewer super-tankers leaving a proportion of the population vulnerable to oil spillage. Populations are also at risk from modern commercial fisheries, particularly those utilizing modern techniques to harvest large quantities of sandeels; reductions in these food stocks have affected breeding numbers in some areas (Tucker & Heath 1994).

Norman Holton

# Feral Pigeon *Columba livia*

ONE of the most prolific pest species, the Feral Pigeon is renowned for its ability to despoil our towns and villages. Flocks will also take to the fields during the harvest to grub for spilt corn and patrol the farmyards in the hope of an easy meal. The haunts of the ancestral species, the Rock Dove, are primarily coastal cliffs, and the species has made a remarkable transformation into the town pigeon. The traditional nesting places of sea cliffs have been replaced by railway stations and town halls and the majority now forage on bare pavement and concrete instead of the closely cropped pasture of their past.

The change from wild to feral has been a long process, with intermediate stages present throughout, and this has greatly blurred the species distribution worldwide. The Rock Dove itself has a wide distribution across the Palearctic, outside of North Africa and east Asia, but the details of the original range are obscured by the long history of domestication, and the current range is similarly confused by the unknown extent of the admixture of feral birds into the wild population. By contrast, the Feral Pigeon is to be found in most, if not all, of the large towns and cities of the world. As a result of domestication and introduction, its range is, not surprisingly, closely linked to that of humans. In Britain, it is safe to say that few pure bred Rock Doves exist away from the Western Isles. Even in the Highlands and Islands, feral birds, which have more-or-less reverted to wild-type plumage, exist to confuse the issue. The *New Atlas* suggested that the feral form had impinged even further on the range of the wild Rock Dove in Scotland since the *Old Atlas*.

Few people would today think of the Feral Pigeon as a quarry species for the pot; the town pigeon is seen as a dirty bird, even though its rural counterparts may live as healthy a lifestyle as any other wild bird. Domestication, however, would have originated through birds of wild origin being bred in the confinement of dovecotes to provide a ready source of protein. Once habituated, the birds would be allowed to range for themselves, returning to the dovecote for roosting and breeding. Murton (1971) considered the use of dovecotes to have declined during the late 18th century, when agricultural improvements made the production of wheat more valuable for bread than for feeding stock. With domestication being known from ancient Egypt and before, a feral population was probably established long before this decline in importance.

The situation in Cumbria is also confused, at least part of the problem being a general lack of interest in feral species shown by naturalists. While Macpherson and Duckworth (1886) considered that a few pairs of Rock Doves continued to breed at Sandwith, Macpherson (1892) believed all Lakeland breeding birds to be of the feral form. Although the Rock Dove has been reported in Cumbria since then, the possibility that any birds of pure stock have occurred in the county during the 20th century is remote.

Comparing the *Old Atlas* with *this Atlas* reveals some variation in distribution, the number of occupied 10km squares having increased slightly from 53 to 60. The figures reflect a combination of gains and losses, with no overall pattern. Any local declines are probably the result of several factors, including improvements in farming efficiency and the redevelopment, improvement and sanitizing of towns and villages. As with several other species, barn conversions may also be depriving the Feral Pigeon of potential nest sites.

The Feral Pigeon's Cumbrian population appears strongest in the Solway Basin, the Coastal Plain and in the Eden Valley but the species has a scattered distribution which can be more strongly linked to the human population than geographical or habitat features. While it is present in the larger towns and villages, it is also found in hamlets and on individual farms. Even so, it is apparently absent from a large part of the county. It may have been under-recorded during *this Atlas,* however, especially away from the towns, due to the difficulty of distinguishing truly feral – and thus recordable – birds from domestic stock. Exhausted, disorientated and abandoned racing pigeons are known to join flocks of feral birds. Further confusion may ensue from the recent practice of locating pigeon lofts on some grouse moors – areas in which domesticated pigeons would not occur naturally – to divert birds of prey away from the game species.

Sponsored by a CBC Member

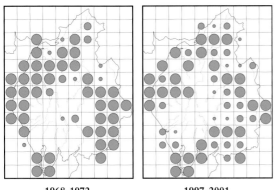

**1968-1972**    **1997-2001**
(For explanation of maps, see page 45)

*Conservation status*

European:            Non-SPEC
UK:                  GREEN

*Populations*

European status:     5,400,000
Britain – pairs:     200,000
Cumbria – pairs:     4,500

*30-year distribution change*

|  | Old Atlas | This Atlas | % |
|---|---|---|---|
| No. of 10km squares: | 53 | 60 | +13.2 |

| Survey data | Tetrads | % |
|---|---|---|
| Confirmed breeding: | 61 | 3.3 |
| Probable breeding: | 73 | 4.0 |
| Possible breeding: | 90 | 4.9 |
| Total: | 224 | 12.2 |

Analysis of the line transect data from *this Atlas* gives a population band of 1,000–48,000, suggesting a mean population of 9,000 birds. However, the very wide band limits may imply a degree of caution with this estimate. The highest densities of 35.4 birds/km² occurred in coastal habitats.

By the very nature of its existence, and its rapid diluting of the pure species, the Feral Pigeon is unlikely to attract much serious study except when considerations of human health are involved. Given its symbiotic relationship with mankind in the past, its abandonment now seems an unwarranted change of attitude. The Feral Pigeon is the same species as its wild counterpart, it just happens to have adapted to our way of life.

David Walker

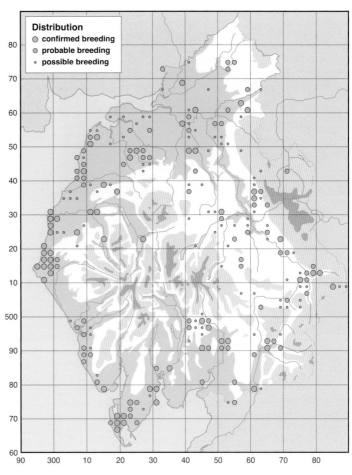

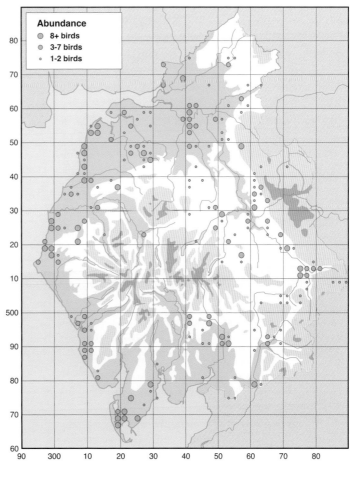

VERY much a retiring species, the Stock Dove is easily, and often, overlooked by birdwatchers and casual observers alike. The absence of the Woodpigeon's white warning flashes in the wings often sees the Stock Dove dismissed as a Feral Pigeon when seen in a pair or small family group in a stubble field or when gathered around a feed trough. Seldom seen in groups larger than the family party during the breeding season the Stock Dove has neither the cachet of an exotic nor the spectacle of a flocking species to attract many devotees. Nonetheless, its demure demeanour, compact shape, and – in a rare close view – the shimmering green and vinous neck-patches all lend it a certain charm.

This is a western Eurasian species with the easternmost populations being migratory. Although widespread in Britain and Ireland, but by no means common, the Stock Dove extends northwards to the Highland line. However, this distribution has seen expansions and contractions; increases were linked to the spread of arable farming while a steep decrease during the 1950s coincided with the introduction of organochlorine seed dressings. This decline had been reversed by the late 1960s and the latest available CBC data shows an impressive 108% increase since 1970. Its nest sites include holes in trees, quarries, old buildings and cliffs, while squirrel dreys, old nests and even nestboxes are also used. In Cumbria, one of the earliest breeding records involved a pair nesting in a Rabbit hole (Macpherson 1892).

In Cumbria, perhaps surprisingly, the species was thought to be merely a winter visitor 200 years ago, with the first documented breeding record at Irton in

1840. Thereafter the species quickly spread and was considered locally common by the end of the 19th century with Cockermouth, Drigg, Kirksanton and St Bees Head all noted as breeding sites (Macpherson & Duckworth 1886, Macpherson 1892). This expansion continued into the 20th century; Stokoe (1962) considering it to be "widespread and fairly common, breeding from the coastal cliffs and sand-dunes up to the lower fell crags." However a downturn in fortunes was evident by the 1990s, and a comparison between the *Old* and *New Atlases* shows a slight retreat from peripheral areas, with confirmed breeding in two fewer 10km squares.

*This Atlas* reveals a continuing decline with confirmed breeding in eight fewer 10km squares than in the *New Atlas*. Although there is some fluctuation in distribution away from the species' stronghold, birds have been lost from much of the southwest, where eight 10km squares with confirmed breeding in the *Old Atlas* have been reduced to just four. Although, at first glance, the declines in Cumbria would appear to be against the national trend, CBC plots are concentrated in the arable rich areas of southeast England and may not be representative of Britain as a whole. Indeed, closer scrutiny reveals that a long-term range contraction in northern and western Britain has occurred since the *Old Atlas*.

The distribution map shows a distinct northeasterly bias, the species avoiding the more industrial and mountainous areas. The current population strongholds are in the Eden Valley and the Solway Basin, where Stock Doves are closely associated with the mixed and arable farmland found on the fertile alluvial plains. Although birds still occur in small numbers in some of the outlying valleys, possibly because of agricultural change being slower there, its general absence from the Coastal Plain is somewhat puzzling. The area holds a landscape similar to the Solway Basin but breeding records are sparse and the abundance map shows only small numbers of birds: a shortage of potential nest sites may be a factor. In the south of the county, where arable farming is less commonplace, the species retains a fragmented distribution along the river valleys.

Analysis of line transect data from *this Atlas* gives a population band of 6,000–24,000, suggesting a mean population of 12,000 birds. The highest densities of 6.9 birds/km² occurred on alluvial flood plains with intensively farmed and productive grassland such as those found in the lower Eden Valley.

While the more fertile farming areas in the county continue to offer potential nesting sites, mainly through the breadth of choice available, opportunities in some parts are being lost and it is possible that there will be further declines, especially in marginal habitats. Dead and dying trees in hedgerows or on field

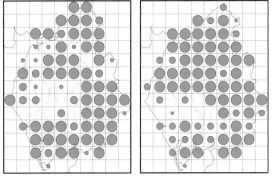

| **1968-1972** | **1997-2001** |
|:---:|:---:|

(For explanation of maps, see page 45)

**Conservation status**

| European: | SPEC Cat 4 |
|---|---|
| UK: | **AMBER: BI** |

**Populations**

| European status: | 510,000 |
|---|---|
| Britain – pairs: | 240,000 |
| Cumbria – pairs: | 6,000 |

**30-year distribution change**

| | Old Atlas | This Atlas | % |
|---|---|---|---|
| No. of 10km squares: | 73 | 73 | n/c |

| **Survey data** | **Tetrads** | **%** |
|---|---|---|
| Confirmed breeding: | 124 | 6.7 |
| Probable breeding: | 279 | 15.1 |
| Possible breeding: | 206 | 11.2 |
| Total: | 609 | 33.0 |

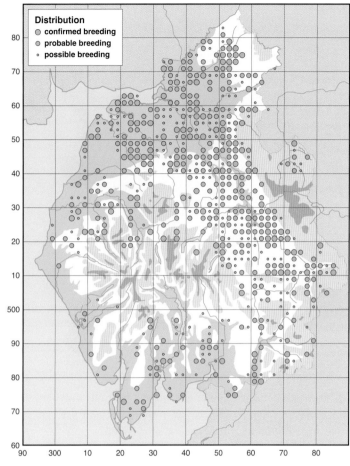

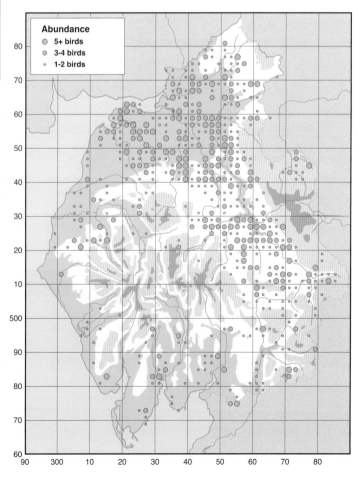

boundaries are quickly felled and broken limbs are cleaned and made safe as the countryside becomes more 'sanitized'. A commonly-used nesting alternative is also being lost as old barns are demolished, converted into dwellings or simply renovated. Brown (1974) noted regular breeding in quarry sites but there are no recent records from within the county and nestboxes are apparently only rarely used. The loss of nest sites, coupled with agricultural change, is probably an important factor in the declines that have been witnessed in Cumbria over recent years and, as there is now little tolerance for an unkempt landscape, it is a process that is unlikely to be reversed.

David Walker

IN spite of its name, the Woodpigeon is probably best known for its habit of flocking in the fields after the harvest. Although highly gregarious at this time – post-breeding flocks can number thousands in some areas – this is a territorial species which breeds in isolation from its neighbours. The implication in its name of a woodland life also belies its presence in town parks and leafy suburbs, where its song and wing-clapping display flight have become increasingly familiar to many who do not venture into the woods.

Although apparently suitable habitat exists across Eurasia, the species range does not extend far beyond continental Europe, although migratory populations exist towards western central Asia and it is also found in parts of North Africa. There is also some movement within, and out of Britain, with large daily movements recorded at coastal sites in the autumn and in response to harsh winter weather. In Britain and Ireland, the Woodpigeon is a widespread species found in all but the most mountainous and treeless areas. It is most abundant in arable farming areas, especially in central, southern and eastern England.

The nest will be as familiar to many as is the song, the flimsy, half-made, jumble of twigs often balanced precariously in a roadside bush. Its natural breeding haunt is in the woods, however, and the species will occur in coniferous plantations as well as in deciduous stands, copses and spinneys, if it has easy access to the fields for feeding. It is more a bird of the woodland edge, although it will nest in the centre of large stands of trees. The breeding bird, and its nest, are not always conspicuous and, while the shed downy feathers

attached to ground and vegetation alike often indicate its presence, it is the sudden clatter of wings and sticks, as the bird takes flight, that gives confirmation.

It is difficult to assess the historical status of such a common species. Nationally, Woodpigeons declined in the 1960s and early 1970s, due to a combination of cold winters, chemical seed dressings, weed control and a switch to autumn-sown cereals. However, the species adapted by breeding earlier and exploiting the newly available oil-seed rape crop, and the latest available CBC data shows an 88% increase since 1970. In Cumbria, little specific interest was shown in the bird, other than as an agricultural pest and a quarry species, but it is likely that the Woodpigeon has always been widespread, within the limitations imposed by the absence of nesting habitat and feeding-grounds. As could be expected, it was absent from the treeless upland areas, though Macpherson (1892) notes a ground nest amongst heather near Shap in 1843 and Murton (1965) also mentions such nest sites elsewhere in Britain.

During *this Atlas,* birds were absent from just five 10km squares within the county, suggesting little or no change in distribution from that recorded in the *Old* and *New Atlases.* The tetrad maps, however, with their greater resolution, clearly illustrate an absence from the higher ground in the North Pennines, Cumbria Dales and Lakeland.

Although the species has a broad dependency on arable farmland this is not clearly demonstrated by the maps. The Woodpigeon is most abundant along the lower reaches of some of the larger Cumbrian rivers, especially in areas with alluvial flood plains, and probably best reflects a landscape of intensive arable farming with ample hedgerows and copses of mature trees. It is also found breeding far into the Lakeland valleys, but the more pastoral, and thus open, nature of much of the Cumbrian countryside suits only lower nesting densities. Perhaps more surprising is the comparatively low number of tetrads where breeding was confirmed, especially in the mixed farmland in the Solway Basin. With a preponderance of suitable nesting habitat available, this area would appear to offer favourable conditions for breeding. Perhaps the sparsely occupied areas outside the main clusters represent sub-optimal habitat and their chosen strategy is to nest in loose colonies on the periphery of good feeding-grounds.

Analysis of line transect data from *this Atlas* gives a population band of 81,000–130,000, suggesting a mean population of 100,000 birds. The highest densities of 30 birds/km² occurred, perhaps predictably, in the well-farmed lowland country with many hedgerows and small woods for nesting, mainly arable with a mixture of good grassland and pasture for feeding.

Sponsored by a CBC Member

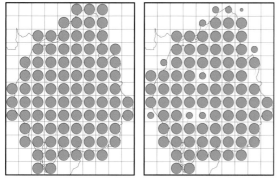

| 1968-1972 | 1997-2001 |
|-----------|-----------|

(For explanation of maps, see page 45)

**Conservation status**

| | |
|---|---|
| European: | SPEC Cat 4 |
| UK: | **GREEN** |

**Populations**

| | |
|---|---|
| European status: | 10,000,000 |
| Britain – pairs: | 2,350,000 |
| Cumbria – pairs: | 50,000 |

**30-year distribution change**

| | Old Atlas | This Atlas | % |
|---|---|---|---|
| No. of 10km squares: | 89 | 89 | n/c |

| **Survey data** | **Tetrads** | **%** |
|---|---|---|
| Confirmed breeding: | 627 | 34.0 |
| Probable breeding: | 632 | 34.8 |
| Possible breeding: | 176 | 9.5 |
| Total: | 1,435 | 78.3 |

It is unlikely that shooting has a major effect on the Cumbrian population even though it is viewed as a pest species in some areas, mostly for its feeding habits and attraction to autumn sown crops. Murton (1965), however, has shown that organized pigeon-control effectively only removes the surplus birds that may have been lost naturally from the population. Woodpigeon shooting is not as well organized as game shooting and, in many places, the pigeons are barely troubled at all. Ongoing changes in agricultural policies and practices may see the species targeted even less in future years and its range expansion into closer association with human habitation may further increase its familiarity as a town bird.

David Walker

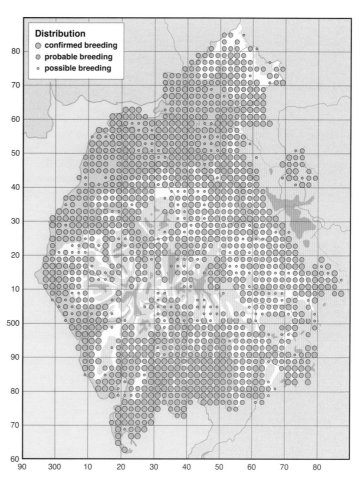

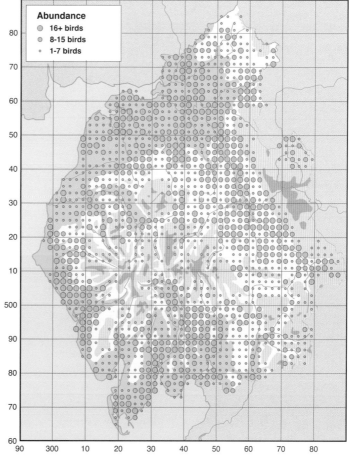

# Collared Dove *Streptopelia decaocto*    Eurasian Collared Dove

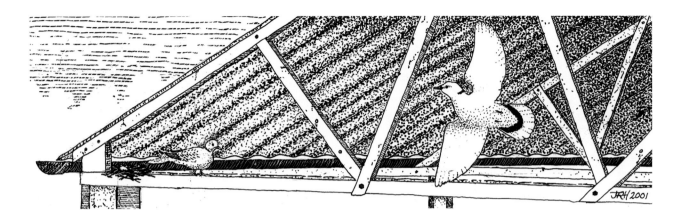

THE monotonous song of this slight dove can be heard at most times of the year and is well known to most people; likewise there will be few who are unfamiliar with its soft, sandy-coloured plumage. A confiding bird, its wing-clapping display flight is obvious as it loops from perch to perch; it also has a deep fondness for perching in pairs on television aerials and lamp-standards.

Originally a bird of the Indian subcontinent and parts of central and eastern Asia, the Collared Dove was hardly known in Europe prior to the 1930s but has since undergone a spectacular range expansion to occupy much of continental Europe, even reaching the Faeroe Islands. First reported in Britain from Lincolnshire in 1952, although the legitimacy of this was questioned, the earliest confirmed breeding record was at Overstrand, Norfolk in 1955 (Palmer 2000). By the end of the following year there were at least 16 Collared Doves in that area and it had also been recorded in Suffolk and Surrey (Hudson 1965). Birds reached Scotland in 1957; Ireland was colonized two years later, with birds breeding in Dublin and also, far to the west, in Galway; and Wales had its first in 1961 (Mead 2000). The species' spread across Britain continued unabated and, by the time of the *Old Atlas,* birds were widely distributed throughout Britain and Ireland, even reaching the Northern Isles.

Largely a bird of the suburbs, there will be few parks and tree-lined avenues without a pair of Collared Doves. This bird may even be in the process of superseding the Feral Pigeon as the 'town pigeon' of our landscaped city centres. Collared Doves show more confidence when visiting gardens, whilst nesting in trees, rather than old buildings, gives them easier access to the richest pickings. In the more rural areas they will even form loose breeding colonies to take advantage of a food source and make best use of the available habitat. The nest can often be found quite low down in roadside trees or on lofty structures in modern cattle buildings, and where food is plentiful they seem capable of breeding at almost any time of the year.

The first Collared Doves arrived in Cumbria in 1959, when birds appeared at Coniston (Hardy 1979) and Anthorn, with one pair at the latter site fledging a single youngster – the first confirmed breeding record (Stokoe 1962). In spite of a continuing presence in the north of the county, subsequent colonization was initially slow with no records from Westmorland until 1963, when three birds were seen at Appleby. However, birds also reached Walney Island in 1963 and by the mid-1960s birds were breeding successfully at sites as diverse as Skinburness, Dalston, Sedbergh and Arnside. The *Old Atlas* indicated that a rapid range expansion had occurred, with birds found in 65 10km squares spread throughout the county. Although absent from much of the North Pennines, Border Uplands and Lakeland, birds had become established in low-lying areas such as the Solway Basin, Eden Valley, Coastal Plain and Lune Valley. The *New Atlas* showed further consolidation; although birds were still noticeably absent from the North Pennines and much of central Lakeland, the Border Uplands had recently been occupied and the highest densities were found across the Solway Basin.

*This Atlas* continues to suggest a smaller population in the south than in the north. As could have been predicted, the maps show a distribution that is largely associated with human habitation, and away from the more upland parts of the county. Surprisingly, the Collared Dove's range has still not extended far into the Lakeland valleys, even where there are small towns and villages. This is possibly due to the lack of arable and cattle farms in these areas: the preponderance of sheep farming results in little spilt grain or loose feeds that would enable the bird to expand its range along these valleys.

Although, compared with the *Old Atlas,* the number of 10km squares where breeding was confirmed has increased by 60%, a slight decrease in range is detectable between the *New Atlas* and *this Atlas.* This would suggest a possible redistribution locally, especially around the fringe of Lakeland where breeding records remain sparse.

    Sponsored by Keith & Moyna Clark

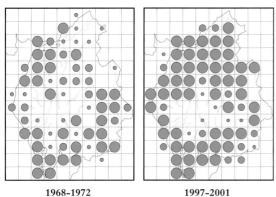

| 1968-1972 | 1997-2001 |

(For explanation of maps, see page 45)

*Conservation status*

| | |
|---|---|
| European: | Non-SPEC |
| UK: | **GREEN** |

*Populations*

| | |
|---|---|
| European status: | 7,000,000 |
| Britain – pairs: | 200,000 |
| Cumbria – pairs: | 8,500 |

*30-year distribution change*

| | Old Atlas | This Atlas | % |
|---|---|---|---|
| No. of 10km squares: | 65 | 72 | +10.7 |

| **Survey data** | **Tetrads** | **%** |
|---|---|---|
| Confirmed breeding: | 216 | 11.7 |
| Probable breeding: | 316 | 17.1 |
| Possible breeding: | 113 | 6.1 |
| Total: | 645 | 34.9 |

Analysis of line transect data from *this Atlas* gives a population band of 10,000–30,000, suggesting a mean population of 17,000 birds. The highest densities of 12 birds/km² occurred on the intensively farmed alluvial plains of the lower Eden Valley, Solway Basin and parts of the Coastal Plain where arable farming is dominant.

The latest available CBC index shows a 638% rise since 1970, and with the species' westward spread still continuing unabated there seems little reason to doubt that the Collared Dove will continue to thrive in the county, at least for the foreseeable future.

David Walker

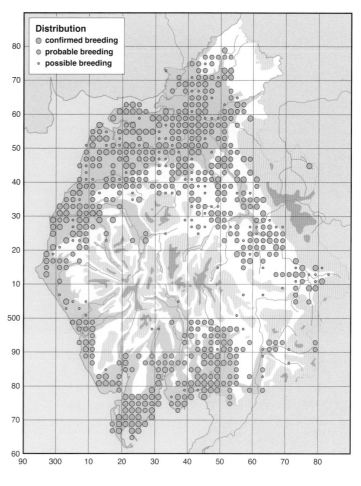

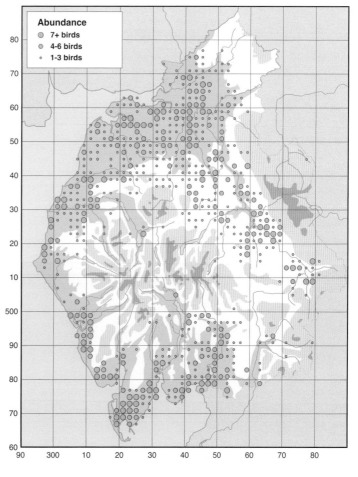

C.H.Isherwood

FROM the comforts of the 21st century, we can look back, not so very far, to a time when life was slightly less certain and our existence and economy were more closely affected by the comings and goings of the seasons. Then the Cuckoo featured largely as the welcome harbinger of spring and the season of new fresh life. Even now, as more of us retreat into an urban lifestyle, there can be few birds that have such a widely recognized call as the Cuckoo and it continues to provoke contributors to write letters to the popular press.

An Old World species with a widespread distribution, the Cuckoo is a migrant, spending the winter in Africa and returning to much of the Palearctic to breed. In Britain and Ireland, in the extreme northwest of its European breeding range, birds are found throughout with the largest concentrations in southern and eastern England. Cuckoos are extremely catholic in their choice of habitats and can be found in marshes, coastal dunes, heaths, reedbeds, farmland, hedgerows, open country with scattered trees, parkland, and coniferous or broad-leaved woodland with scrub. The common element throughout is an abundance of prey, almost entirely insects and mostly hairy caterpillars. In Cumbria, the male has returned by late April and is delivering his far-carrying call from an elevated perch. Shortly after, the female's unmistakable bubbling call may be heard, often from the same locality in consecutive years. Following mating, the ever-watchful female scrutinizes the progress of potential foster birds and deposits her egg and evicts one of her host's, when the opportunity arises.

There are three principal hosts: the Reed Warbler, Dunnock and Meadow Pipit. The first-named has a very restricted breeding range within the county, and while the last two are widespread, it is perhaps the Meadow Pipit which inadvertently fosters most young Cuckoos in Cumbria. However, this supposition is not borne out by Macpherson (1892) who lists as hosts Whinchat, Robin, Pied Wagtail, Reed Bunting, Chaffinch, Yellow Bunting (Yellowhammer), Hedge Sparrow (Dunnock), Linnet and Twite yet remarkably fails to mention Meadow Pipit.

Historical authors are unanimous in their statements of the species' status within Cumbria. Macpherson (1892) describes the bird as abundant upon the moors of the Lake District, while Mitchell (1892), and referring only to the Lancashire portion of Cumbria, alludes to the species being "universally distributed and equally common". However, by the 1960s, Brown (1974) while considering the species "still plentiful about the fells", noted a decline in most lowland areas. Spencer (1973), again referring to Lancashire North of the Sands, hints at the future picture by stating that the Cuckoo is "widespread and moderately numerous though commonly agreed to be declining".

Comparisons with both the *Old* and *New Atlases* and *this Atlas* are illuminating and confirm Spencer's belief. Both previous atlases indicate occurrence in all of Cumbria's 10km squares and clusters of abundance around Lakeland, but additionally, the *New Atlas* portrayed a small coastal decrease within the county. This work also affirms a huge decline in Ireland and, in smaller numbers, throughout the rest of Britain except for a marginal increase in the northwest. This general decline is also reflected in the latest CBC index which shows a 31% fall since 1970.

In line with national trends the species does appear to be declining in the county. Unlike in the *Old Atlas* the Cuckoo was not recorded in all of Cumbria's 10km squares during *this Atlas*. In fact it is now absent from ten inland 10km squares and was represented in no more than two tetrads in a further 18 10km squares. Away from open moorland habitats, some correlation exists between Meadow Pipit and Cuckoo distribution. It is thinly distributed around the southern section of the North Pennines, northern Lakeland and most of the Coastal Plain and Cuckoos are very poorly represented throughout the Eden Valley, northwards to the Solway Basin, and southwards through the Lune Valley and Cumbria Dales. Many of these areas support only small Meadow Pipit populations. However, significant clusters were found on the unimproved mosses of the Solway Basin around Bowness-on-Solway and Wigton and, in line with previous atlas results, the species remains faithful to southern and central Lakeland, and the Border Uplands.

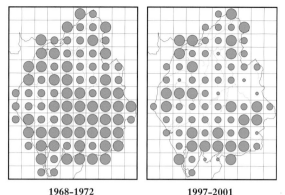

**1968-1972**       **1997-2001**

(For explanation of maps, see page 45)

**Conservation status**

| | |
|---|---|
| European: | Non-SPEC |
| UK: | AMBER: BDM |

**Populations**

| | |
|---|---|
| European status: | 1,600,000 |
| Britain – pairs: | 19,500 |
| Cumbria – pairs: | 1,000 |

**30-year distribution change**

| | Old Atlas | This Atlas | % |
|---|---|---|---|
| No. of 10km squares: | 87 | 77 | −11.5 |

| **Survey data** | **Tetrads** | **%** |
|---|---|---|
| Confirmed breeding: | 50 | 2.7 |
| Probable breeding: | 382 | 20.7 |
| Possible breeding: | 152 | 8.2 |
| Total: | 584 | 31.6 |

Analysis of line transect data from *this Atlas* gives a population band of 700–5,000, suggesting a mean population of 2,000 birds. However, given the small sample size and wide band limits, the estimate should be viewed with caution. The highest calculated densities of 1.25 birds/km² were on the seaward fringe of the Coastal Plain.

The Cuckoo's main item of prey is hairy caterpillars. Predicted global weather patterns may have already begun to affect the abundance and availability of these invertebrate species, and their consequent decline may have already impacted upon the Cuckoo. In addition habitat loss from agricultural intensification and the associated reduction in insect food supply may be compounding the problem.

Tim Dean

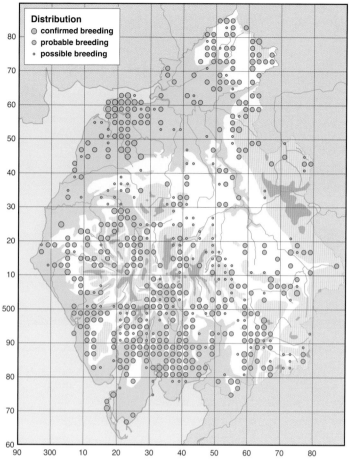

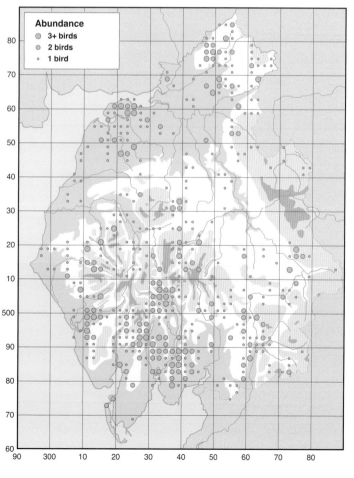

# Barn Owl *Tyto alba*

THIS denizen of the night, with its blood-curdling screech, heart-shaped face and pale plumage, is one of the most recognizable and fondly regarded of birds. Mostly encountered at dusk, the Barn Owl appears as a ghostly white apparition, quartering over fields or caught fleetingly in the glare of car headlights as it silently hunts its prey.

The Barn Owl has a global distribution and is the most widespread land bird in the world. In Britain and Ireland the population is biased towards south and eastern England, Wales and southern Scotland, while Cumbria and Lancashire support the mainstay of the northern England population.

Usually nesting in buildings, predominantly in barns, a handful still nest in trees, quarry faces or walls. Unusual Cumbrian sites include a modern garage on the edge of a housing estate, a village hall and a grain silo. In the past, Barn Owls used river cliffs, dovecotes and, once, an abandoned Otter holt (Macpherson 1892, Bunn *et al* 1982). Feeding mainly on Common Shrews, Wood Mice and Field Voles, with whose cyclical fortunes it is closely linked, the species has a protracted breeding season that extends from February to October, during which time incidences of double-brooding occur. Although data collected from a sample of nest sites in Cumbria since 1992 suggest an average brood of just under three chicks, some areas are more productive than others and a site in the Solway Basin has fledged 50 young since 1986.

Once a familiar sight in Cumbria's agricultural landscape, the Barn Owl's decline began in the mid-19th century with persecution cited as the prime cause (Macpherson 1892). In 1932 an estimated 745 pairs bred in Cumbria and, in contrast to the rest of Britain, the species was considered to be increasing (Blaker 1933). At this time, birds occurred in high densities in some areas with three pairs nesting on one farm in the Lyth Valley. However, local fluctuations were reported throughout the 1930s, with rodenticides already responsible for a decline in east Westmorland (Blezard *et al* 1943). Harsh winters in 1947 and 1962/63 severely reduced the population, and recovery was hindered by the wide-scale use of organochlorine chemicals during the 1950s and 1960s (Shawyer 1998). The loss of rough grasslands through farming intensification, and of nest sites from conversion of traditional buildings, summer droughts and further harsh winters, hindered a full population recovery. By the 1980s the Cumbrian population was at its lowest ebb since the pesticide era (Bunn *et al* 1982). In 1987, only 120 sites were known, indicating a 84% decline since 1932 (Shawyer 1987).

Although the *Old Atlas* recorded Barn Owls in 80 10km squares spread throughout Cumbria, this had decreased to 39 squares by the *New Atlas,* with birds having largely deserted the southeast and centre of the county. *This Atlas* shows a welcome improvement with 53 occupied 10km squares, and birds recorded from 217 tetrads. Of these, 164 sites in 155 tetrads were identified as holding breeding pairs. The majority of sites held single pairs but three tetrads held three pairs while 16 held two pairs. During the 1960s, 79% of Cumbria's 10km squares held Barn Owls, falling to 41% by the late 1980s and recovering to 56% today. The current strongholds are the Solway Basin, western Border Uplands, lower Eden Valley and the northern portion of the Coastal Plain. Birds have largely disappeared from the upper Eden Valley, North Pennines, Lune Valley, eastern Lakeland and the fringes of Morecambe Bay. Although the fells of central Lakeland have probably never held many pairs, nesting was recorded at 450m asl in 1932 (Coombes 1932). The current highest known site is at 280m asl, with 40% of sites below 50m asl, and 70% below 100m asl.

While it is likely that daytime surveys will always under-represent a largely nocturnal species such as this, it would appear from the long run of data available that the bird is presently increasing, perhaps in response to a series of mild winters. During the last decade, 152 sites are known to have held breeding Barn Owls in at least one year; in addition the survey revealed 12 previously unknown sites to hold birds. The current county population of 150–200 breeding pairs is derived from CRSG and count data from *this Atlas,* enhanced by supplementary records, and reinforced by local knowledge.

Sponsored by a CBC Member

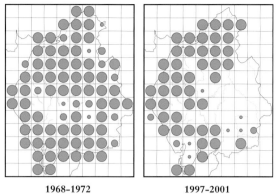

**1968–1972**          **1997–2001**

(For explanation of maps, see page 45)

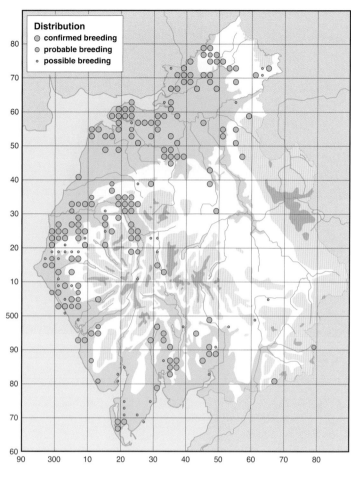

| *Conservation status* | |
|---|---|
| European: | SPEC Cat 3 |
| UK: | **AMBER: BDM** |

| *Populations* | |
|---|---|
| European status: | 140,000 |
| Britain – pairs: | 4,400 |
| Cumbria – pairs: | 150–200 |

*30-year distribution change*

| | Old Atlas | This Atlas | % |
|---|---|---|---|
| No. of 10km squares: | 80 | 53 | −33.7 |

| **Survey data** | **Tetrads** | **%** |
|---|---|---|
| Confirmed breeding: | 155 | 8.4 |
| Probable breeding: | 18 | 1.0 |
| Possible breeding: | 44 | 2.4 |
| Total: | 217 | 11.8 |

Whilst unfavourable weather brings about short term fluctuations in numbers, it is habitat loss and fragmentation which has caused the long term decline and low population levels evident today. Cumbrian Barn Owls do not disperse far, so the present range extension from existing population centres, whilst encouraging, is slow. Strategic positioning of nestboxes has proved highly successful in the northwest of the county (71% of breeding pairs, where nest type is known, now utilize boxes). The species can exist in intensively farmed landscapes and afforested areas, provided there are sufficient rough grassland corridors on which to hunt. The crucial element in Barn Owl conservation is the extension of these rough grasslands which could come about through agri-environment schemes designed to promote a more diverse range of habitats. However, measures to reduce road casualties and prevent the misuse of rodenticides are also needed.

Ian Armstrong

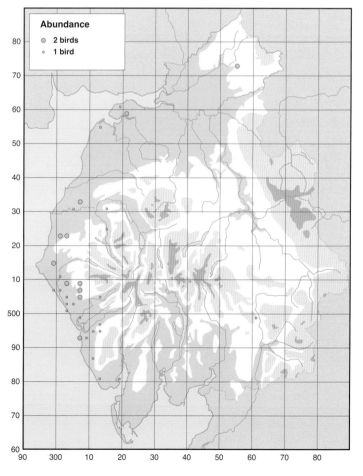

# Little Owl *Athene noctua*

**O**FTEN seen during the day, perched prominently atop a telegraph pole or fence post, when approached Little Owls perform a curious bobbing display before finally flying off with a rapid, low, undulating flight. The species takes its scientific name from an association with the goddess Pallas Athene. Although she inherited war-like qualities from her father Zeus and mother Metris, it is as a symbol of wisdom that Greek artists portrayed the Little Owl on the shoulder of Athene.

Little Owls breed from western Europe and North Africa across Asia to the Pacific. In Britain, birds are found throughout England and Wales, northwards to the Borders region of Scotland. It is absent from the Isle of Man and Ireland. The preferred nest site is a tree hole but holes in walls, buildings, cliffs and quarries are frequently used and it is not unknown for the species to nest in rabbit burrows.

The species is not indigenous to Britain. During the 19th century attempts were made to introduce the bird from the continent and after a somewhat inauspicious start they fairly quickly became established as a breeding resident. Following a number of failed attempts, from as early as 1842 in Yorkshire, successful introductions occurred in Kent from 1874 and Northamptonshire during 1888–90 with the first nest found in Kent in 1879.

Why so many attempts were made to naturalize the Little Owl in Britain is open to question. It has been suggested this was done for no other reason than that they were considered an ornamental addition to the countryside; more likely it was because continental horticulturists appreciated the bird's usefulness in controlling pests, due to its ability to consume large quantities of insects, snails, slugs and rodents. What was perhaps not realized at the time was the species' ability to feed extensively on small birds, particularly in the breeding season. A fearsome and fearless hunter, it will even tackle birds as big as itself; at South Walney in the 1980s birds dieted on Little, Arctic and Common Terns (Dean 1990).

As the Little Owl spread north it was only a matter of time before the species occurred in Cumbria. The first documented record came from Westmorland in 1856 (Macpherson 1892). Thereafter birds were recorded several times during the early 20th century before the first nest was found at Waberthwaite in 1944. Spread continued with pairs breeding at Durdar in 1950, Boot in 1954, St Bees in 1955, Aspatria in 1956, Ulverston in 1957, Salta and Southwaite in 1958, Aglionby in 1959, Calder Bridge and Helton Tarn in 1961 (Blezard 1958, Stokoe 1962). By the time of the *Old Atlas,* birds were widespread but thinly distributed around the periphery of the county, while the *New Atlas* indicated expansion into new areas in the Coastal Plain and Solway Basin, where high levels of abundance were found.

During *this Atlas,* there is evidence of a slight decline, particularly in the north, where abundance levels have apparently fallen in the Solway Basin since the *New Atlas.* In common with other areas of Britain, most Cumbrian breeding sites occur in areas of open country, primarily lowland farmland which still supports extensive hedgerows and small copses, with few birds to be found above 250m asl. Consequently, the species is absent from much of the higher barren, treeless landscape found in the North Pennines, Cumbria Dales and central Lakeland. Although birds are now only thinly distributed along the Eden Valley, Solway Basin and parts of the Coastal Plain, there are still pockets holding reasonable numbers, particularly in Furness and southeast Lakeland. Inevitably, as the Little Owl is an inconspicuous species, there will have been some breeding pairs overlooked.

How many owls sit motionless, inconspicuously observing the surveyor as he passes beneath unaware of their presence? As with all nocturnal species, standard survey techniques often offer inconclusive answers. Until a countywide survey of this species is undertaken, the best subjective estimate of the current county population is 250–500 breeding pairs.

The species has had, and continues to have, problems. Historically, its reputation became controversial and there are examples of Little Owls being killed as they were perceived as a threat to game-rearing. Its name was eventually cleared and today it is often actively encouraged by farmers. However, there is recent evidence of a national decline: the *New Atlas* indicated an 11% drop in distribution and the latest

 Sponsored by Lillian Strand

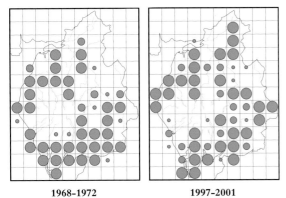

**1968-1972**　　　　**1997-2001**

(For explanation of maps, see page 45)

| Conservation status | |
|---|---|
| European: | SPEC Cat 3 |
| UK: | unspecified |

| Populations | |
|---|---|
| European status: | 250,000 |
| Britain – pairs: | 9,000 |
| Cumbria – pairs: | 250–500 |

**30-year distribution change**

| | Old Atlas | This Atlas | % |
|---|---|---|---|
| No. of 10km squares: | 47 | 53 | +12.7 |

| Survey data | Tetrads | % |
|---|---|---|
| Confirmed breeding: | 53 | 2.9 |
| Probable breeding: | 66 | 3.6 |
| Possible breeding: | 49 | 2.7 |
| Total: | 168 | 9.2 |

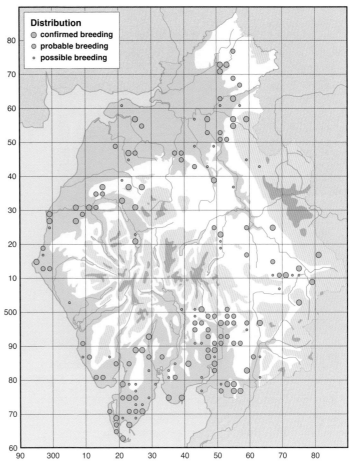

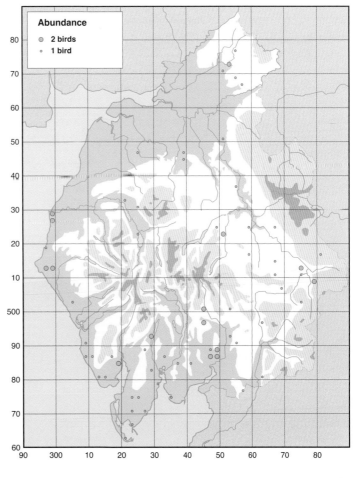

available CBC data shows an 18% population fall since 1970. The reasons for this are unclear but possible causes are losses during severe winters, habitat loss due to agricultural intensification, a shortage of suitable food through the general use of pesticides and a reduction in suitable nest sites. The destruction of hedgerows and the demolition or renovation of farm buildings may have contributed to the decline.

Given the fall in national levels and the fact that Cumbria is at the northern limit of the species' range in Britain, it is likely that – unless changes in agricultural practices take place – the recently detected decline in the county population will continue, especially in less favoured marginal habitats.

Mike Carrier

# Tawny Owl *Strix aluco*

THERE are probably many people who have never seen an owl in the wild, but who nevertheless recognize the familiar wavering hoot of the Tawny Owl. The species is not uncommon and can be found even in many parts of suburbia and the centres of major cities. It is quite extraordinary how Tawny Owls evade detection by human beings at their daytime roosts, even while being mobbed by smaller birds.

A Palearctic species, its distribution extends through Eurasia, to western Siberia. In Europe, it ranges from Britain to the boreal regions of Scandinavia and Russia, and southwards to the Mediterranean. In Britain, birds are absent from the Northern and Western Isles and Isle of Man. The species does not breed in Ireland.

Open broad-leaved woodland is the preferred habitat, although Tawny Owls can also be found in well-timbered parks, gardens and in the centres of large towns and cities. Generally monogamous, and pairing for life, Tawny Owls are strictly resident, with the male most vociferous in late winter in defence of his territory, and the young dispersing locally. The nest site, normally in a large hole in a tree, is chosen by the female, which will also readily take to using a nestbox. In Cumbria, productivity studies at Grizedale Forest show that 40% of the boxes provided are occupied, with a 76% hatching success and less than 1% of chicks failing to fledge. Ground nesting is not uncommon, especially in conifer plantations in southwest Scotland (D. Watson pers comm); in the absence of mature timber, and therefore suitable nest holes, a typical nest would be at the base of a conifer tree hidden amongst the root bole. Macpherson (1892) refers to a pair

nesting on Lupton Moor in Westmorland in 1886 – an unusual site – and makes reference to the habit of using rabbit burrows, and also to birds nesting amongst rocks.

Tawny Owls are catholic in their diet: prey species range from beetles, frogs, mice and voles, to include Rabbits and birds as large as pigeons. The remains of a Merlin were found alongside that of Ring Ouzel and Grey Wagtail at one Geltsdale nest in 1944 (Blezard 1946). Productivity in many species tends to fluctuate between years, depending on food availability, but in Tawny Owl populations this is not as obvious as in most. Their ability to feed on a wide variety of prey ensures plentiful food items in most years.

Historically Tawny Owls were much persecuted; apart from the prejudices of gamekeepers, young owlets were often taken and captive reared as pets and the adults shot as specimens for the local taxidermist to mount. A widespread national increase took place between 1900 and 1930, perhaps reflecting a decrease in persecution with an absence of gamekeepers during and after the First World War. Despite short-term losses, due to hard winters, this continued into the 1950s, and the species began to extend its range, moving into urban parks and utilizing new conifer plantations. Thereafter the population appears to have been relatively stable. The CBC index shows little change since 1970, a trend confirmed by the latest BBS data.

In the late 19th century, the Tawny Owl was considered "an abundant resident, nesting freely in wooded districts" (Macpherson & Duckworth 1886). Macpherson (1892) considered that, although large numbers were killed by gamekeepers, the species was continuing to hold its ground, and that it "endeavours to breed from Roudsea northwards." By the mid-20th century, in line with national trends, the Tawny Owl had increased to such an extent that it had taken over many haunts vacated by Long-eared Owls and was breeding up to 450m asl (Stokoe 1962, Brown 1974). The *Old Atlas* confirmed a widespread distribution with a range that was to remain relatively unchanged into the 1990s, although the *New Atlas* showed minor losses from coastal districts.

Tawny Owls, although nocturnal, can be readily surveyed: the territorial hoot of the male, breeding call of the female and food soliciting calls of recently fledged young are characteristic night sounds. Despite night-time coverage being limited in some areas during *this Atlas,* sufficient tetrads were visited to give an insight into its distribution. Although further losses have occurred in peripheral areas since the *Old Atlas,* especially along the Coastal Plain, birds remain widely scattered throughout the county. The strongholds are in sheltered, wooded valleys and there is an obvious absence from the more exposed, treeless landscapes of

 Sponsored by Mary Abbot

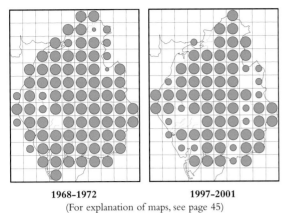

**1968-1972**       **1997-2001**

(For explanation of maps, see page 45)

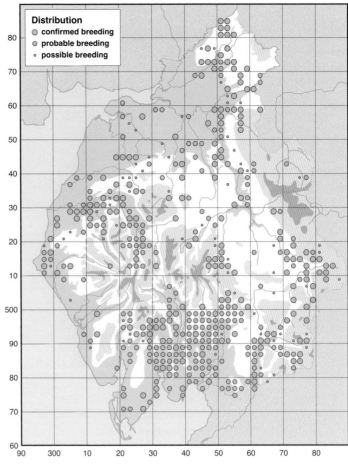

| *Conservation status* | |
|---|---|
| European: | SPEC Cat 4 |
| UK: | **GREEN** |

| *Populations* | |
|---|---|
| European status: | 470,000 |
| Britain – pairs: | 20,000 |
| Cumbria – pairs: | 5,000 |

**30-year distribution change**

| | Old Atlas | This Atlas | % |
|---|---|---|---|
| No. of 10km squares: | 84 | 72 | **−14.2** |

| **Survey data** | **Tetrads** | **%** |
|---|---|---|
| Confirmed breeding: | 196 | 10.6 |
| Probable breeding: | 207 | 11.2 |
| Possible breeding: | 66 | 3.6 |
| Total: | 469 | 25.4 |

the higher fells of central Lakeland and the North Pennines.

Calculating countywide population estimates for any nocturnal species is always going to be unsatisfactory, without species-specific survey. However, population estimates can often be derived from local studies. At Stapleton one such study, over five years, found a mean density of 1.5 birds/km² (M. Stott pers comm) in a typical rural landscape, which suggests a current county population of 5,000 breeding pairs.

Although susceptible to prolonged periods of harsh winter weather, the speed at which the Tawny Owl can adapt and modify its ecology in response to a changing environment, not only in rural areas but in towns and cities, will ensure that the most eerie and easily recognizable of night sounds will remain with us well into the future.

Norman Healy

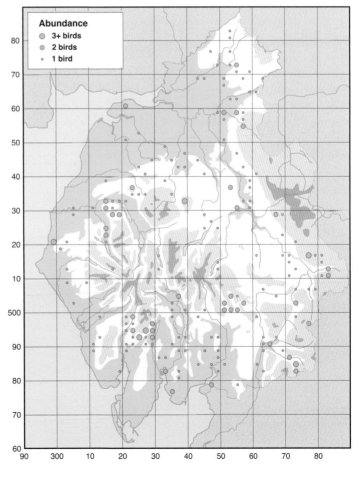

# Long-eared Owl *Asio otus*

THE Long-eared Owl is perhaps the most elusive and under-recorded of Cumbria's breeding birds. This highly nocturnal species is easily overlooked in its daytime roost perched motionless close to a tree trunk and seldom seen flighting before late dusk. The male's feeble triple hoot may betray territories in early spring or, more strikingly, the haunting and penetrating food calls of the young carrying through the night in late June or July confirm the presence of breeding pairs.

Resident birds are fairly sedentary, although passage migrants and wintering owls supplement numbers outside the breeding season. Long-eared Owls have a circumpolar Holarctic distribution extending from northwest Africa to the northern coniferous forests across Eurasia and North America. Its breeding range in Britain and Ireland is widespread but extremely irregular, with the majority of birds occurring in the eastern portions of both islands.

Long-eared Owls require woodland for roosting and nesting with access to open country, productive in potential prey, notably Field Voles and other small mammals, amphibians, beetles and roosting birds. Coniferous woodlands, including fellside plantations and shelter belts up to 350m asl, are particularly favoured when surrounded by moorland, rough grassland and marginal farmland. Carr woodland and thorn scrubland also provide suitable habitat in association with heathland, coastal dunes, marshes and lowland mosses. The old nests of Carrion Crows, Magpies, Sparrowhawks, Buzzards and Woodpigeons are used as nesting platforms, as occasionally are squirrel dreys or man-made sites. Ground-nesting pairs are also found.

Historically, the species has never been common in Cumbria. Macpherson (1892) described the Long-eared Owl as "a resident, breeding sparsely in fir plantations, becoming more numerous towards the Scottish borders". Blezard *et al* (1943) refers to the bird's "preference for the woods bordering the mosses" but emphasized a sharp decline in the Solway region and the Cumberland Plain. Stokoe (1962) stated "although resident, a much decreased species in its former haunts and now generally sparse; frequents scrub and remote woods on mosses, moors and fell slopes, breeding up to 1,200 feet [366m]." The impact of tree felling, especially during wartime, and the intensification of agriculture, damaging lowland habitats, have most probably contributed to a decrease in the species' range and numbers in the county. Furthermore, the larger Tawny Owl has enjoyed a population increase since the relaxation of the persecution of Victorian times, suggesting that competition for food, space and nest sites may be more than coincidental with the decline of the Long-eared Owl in Cumbria and other parts of Britain. The high density of the latter's population on the Isle of Man and in Ireland, in the absence of its larger relative, adds weight to the significance of interspecific rivalry.

Fieldwork for *this Atlas* revealed the presence of Long-eared Owls in only 12 tetrads (0.6%), most occurring in typical habitat of upland conifer plantations with adjacent expanses of unimproved grassland and moorland. No owls were observed in the coastal mosslands of the Solway Basin or Morecambe Bay. Breeding was confirmed in three distinct districts; Geltsdale and the Irthing Valley in the northeast, the Killington Fells and Dentdale in the southeast and Thornthwaite Forest and Calder Bridge in the far west. A comparison with the *Old Atlas* shows an apparent loss of 28% in terms of occupied 10km squares during the last three decades. However, there is little correlation in the distribution of occupied squares in the two survey periods for a species with known site fidelity. Records in the years preceding *this Atlas* suggest a more widespread population, including breeding pairs or birds on suitable territory, at sites in the Eden Valley, Shap Fells, Winster Valley, Greystoke Forest, Glasson Moss and a few locations on the western fringes of Lakeland.

Based on count data from *this Atlas,* enhanced by supplementary records alone, the current county population estimate of 10–15 pairs in Cumbria would be a conservative estimate. Most records refer to known perennial territories, as accidental encounters are unusual, given the remote location of much suitable habitat and the late hour of Long-eared Owl activity.

Warburton (1979) found little evidence that extensive plantations in Lakeland provided new niches

 Sponsored by Lakeland Pavers

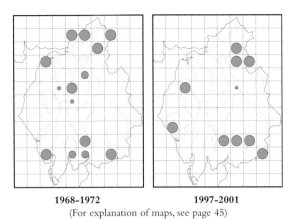

**1968–1972**                    **1997–2001**

(For explanation of maps, see page 45)

**Conservation status**

| | |
|---|---|
| European: | Non-SPEC |
| UK: | GREEN |

**Populations**

| | |
|---|---|
| European status: | 205,000 |
| Britain – pairs: | 2,350 |
| Cumbria – pairs: | 10–15 |

**30-year distribution change**

| | Old Atlas | This Atlas | % |
|---|---|---|---|
| No. of 10km squares: | 14 | 10 | −28.5 |

| **Survey data** | **Tetrads** | **%** |
|---|---|---|
| Confirmed breeding: | 9 | 0.5 |
| Probable breeding: | 0 | |
| Possible breeding: | 3 | 0.2 |
| Total: | 12 | 0.7 |

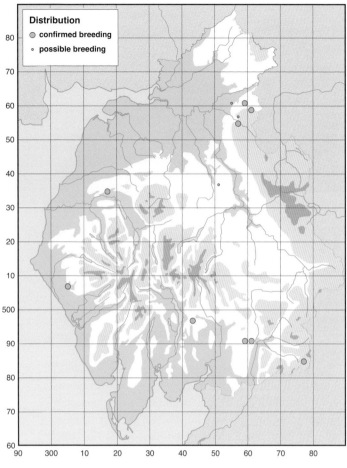

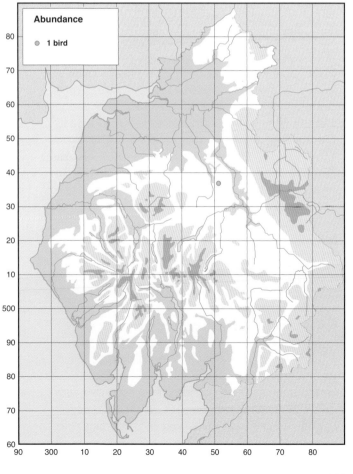

for the Long-eared Owl as trees matured. Nevertheless, more diversified forestry programmes and the restoration of lowland mosslands may have positive effects on future populations of this species. In addition, the provision of wicker nesting baskets has achieved encouraging occupancy rates in areas of prime habitat (Garner & Milne 1996). Any further surveys of Long-eared Owls will be complicated by fluctuations in numbers corresponding to cyclical changes in vole populations. However, the status of the Long-eared Owl in Cumbria remains uncertain and can only be resolved by a systematic investigation in the years ahead.

Malcolm Priestley

# Short-eared Owl *Asio flammeus*

BUOYANT and purposeful wing-beats characterize the graceful charisma of this unique owl as it quarters its spacious landscapes. An aerial wing-clapping display is a trait of the Short-eared Owl in the breeding season; the wings are brought together beneath the body with a soft beat audible at close range, as the bird performs shallow undulating flights to advertise its presence.

Principally this species has a circumpolar Holarctic distribution, with a discontinuous range that reaches the Neotropics. Although widespread throughout central and southeastern Europe, its population is now sparse following agricultural improvements and the loss of large expanses of wet grassland habitats. Its Western Palearctic range extends from Iceland, through Fennoscandia, to parts of Russia. Britain holds a good proportion of the European population, mostly in Scotland and northern England; it also breeds irregularly in Ireland.

The Short-eared Owl is unlike any other regularly breeding species of British owl. It is a ground-nesting species that frequents open, treeless country, especially grassland and heather moorland, and hunts mostly during the day using its eyes rather than its ears to locate prey. Its main food in Britain is the Field Vole, whereas in northern Europe lemmings form the staple diet. It also differs from other owls in being highly nomadic, both in summer and winter. This stems from the violent fluctuations in local vole populations and its strategy of moving in search of better hunting grounds, increasing its chance of survival (Lack 1966).

The availability of suitable prey items is critical to Short-eared Owl populations. When voles are most abundant, the owls may lay a clutch twice the size of that in normal years. Similarly, as with all species that have cyclical populations, the number of breeding pairs in any one year is dependant on food availability, which in good years may be double that of years when vole populations are low. A study in Scotland showed that in one vole plague, 30–40 pairs settled on 1400ha of moorland recently planted with conifers. By June, vole numbers had crashed and nearly all the owls departed, the two remaining breeding pairs holding much-enlarged territories (Lockie 1955).

In Cumbria, accounts from the 19th century mainly refer to birds killed by gamekeepers. Macpherson (1892) recalled finding no fewer than six Short-eared Owls on a gibbet near Cardurnock. These were, presumably, birds killed outside the breeding season as, although sporadic breeding occurred on coastal mosses following large winter influxes, the only references to regular nesting are accounts from the remote upland areas around Bewcastle and Brampton. Stokoe (1962) regarded the Short-eared Owl as "scarce and irregular as a breeding bird. Most often on Border hills and Solway mosses, elsewhere low moors, young plantations and sand-dunes may be frequented."

Comparison between the *Old Atlas* and *this Atlas* reveals a significant decline of over 50% in the number of occupied 10km squares, most evident in Lakeland, the Coastal Plain and the Border Uplands. Although the extreme northeastern part of the county was once a stronghold for the species, today there is more tree-covered fell than heather moorland, which probably accounts for its demise – no breeding records were forthcoming from *this Atlas*. The county distribution now shows a strong bias towards the eastern grouse moors, where, sadly, antipathy towards anything with a 'hooked bill' means that they are not tolerated. Its main breeding haunt nowadays is the North Pennines, where higher nesting densities tend to reflect a greater ratio of grassland to heather.

During the survey work for *this Atlas*, Short-eared Owls were recorded in 52 tetrads, though many of these records would refer to nomadic non-breeding birds. A density of 2.4 birds/100km², taken from a study in the North Pennines, together with count data and supplementary records from *this Atlas*, provide the basis for estimating the current county population at 15–30 breeding pairs.

Although Short-eared Owls are attracted to breeding in newly-forested areas, these are transitory habitats and soon become unsuitable once the tree canopy closes. Cumbria has over 35,000ha of rotational forestry, but there is little evidence of this habitat being used within the county. The cyclical population fluctuations of voles

Sponsored by Michael Williams

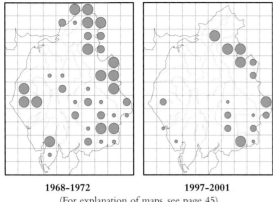

| 1968-1972 | 1997-2001 |
|---|---|

(For explanation of maps, see page 45)

**Conservation status**

| European: | SPEC Cat 3 |
|---|---|
| UK: | **AMBER** |

**Populations**

| European status: | 17,000 |
|---|---|
| Britain – pairs: | 2,250 |
| Cumbria – pairs: | 15–30 |

**30-year distribution change**

| | Old Atlas | This Atlas | % |
|---|---|---|---|
| No. of 10km squares: | 37 | 18 | **−51.3** |

| **Survey data** | **Tetrads** | **%** |
|---|---|---|
| Confirmed breeding: | 12 | 0.6 |
| Probable breeding: | 20 | 1.1 |
| Possible breeding: | 20 | 1.1 |
| Total: | 52 | 2.8 |

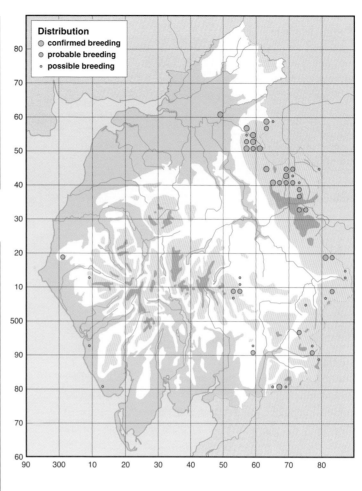

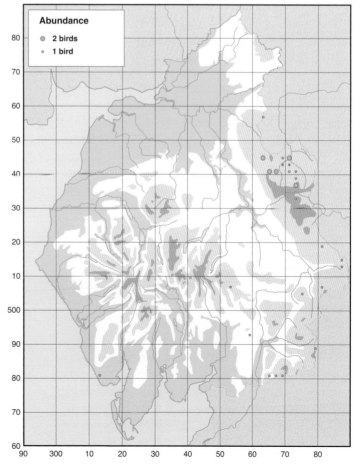

are reflected in similar fluctuations in the owl population. At Geltsdale, in a 'good' vole year, densities of owls can be 5–6 pairs with just half that in 'poor' years. However, since many breeding birds are removed through illegal persecution on grouse moors each year, the natural carrying capacity may never be attained.

With apparently suitable habitat available along the Coastal Plain and in the numerous mosslands, why Short-eared Owls are restricted to the east of the county during the breeding season is a mystery. Vole abundance in these areas could be the determining factor. The Short-eared Owl appears to occupy a moorland edge habitat similar to that favoured by Black Grouse. Good work is presently ongoing to improve habitat quality and reverse the fortunes of the latter species; away from the commercial interests of grouse moors this type of habitat management could also prove beneficial for this diurnal spirit of the moors.

Malcolm Stott

THE Nightjar's low-pitched, rhythmic churring, rising and falling on the still night air, is one of the most evocative sounds of summer. The slow, silent, moth-like flight of its long-tailed, shadowy form, glimpsed at dusk as it hunts for crepuscular insects over grass heaths or in woodland clearings, adds to the perception of the bird as a ghostly figure of the night.

A summer visitor to much of Europe and Asia, its breeding range covers the warm temperate and warmer boreal zones of the Western Palearctic from North Africa to southern Sweden, Finland and Russia, just south of the Arctic Circle. It nests in a variety of habitats where dryish open ground is covered with dead leaves, twigs or similar debris. This includes areas of open-canopy broad-leaved, mixed and coniferous woodland; forest edges and clearings; heathland and grass steppes with scattered trees; birch and poplar scrub; and scrubby areas of steppe and semi-desert.

In Britain, the Nightjar is strongly associated with transitional habitats, nesting on land up to about 450m asl, where clear felling, coppicing, grazing or burning have resulted in areas of sparse woodland or scrub. Dry heath in the early phases of regeneration by birch and pine has traditionally been favoured, particularly within the bird's stronghold in the south of England. Large plantations, during the early planting stage and the restocking period after felling, have become of increased importance in recent years, particularly within East Anglia and the north and west of Britain.

In common with much of western Europe, the Nightjar population of Britain underwent a dramatic contraction in both numbers and range during much of the 20th century, most markedly between the end of the Second World War and the early 1980s (Stafford 1962, Morris *et al* 1994). In recent times, there has been something of a renaissance in response to new opportunities provided by heathland management in the south and east of England and enlightened forestry practice in other parts of Britain. Numbers of churring males increased by an estimated 62% between the national surveys of 1981 and 1992. While currently on the BoCC Red List, the Nightjar appears to be well on

the way to meeting the BAP target of 4,000 pairs by 2003.

In Cumbria, the Nightjar was relatively common towards the end of the 19th century, with its distribution ranging from "the mosses which fringe the Solway Firth to the Westmorland moors" (Macpherson 1892). Stokoe (1962) described it as "rather local and sparse, on dry ground and clearings with low cover" and stated that it "breeds from Solway mosses and lower slopes of fell valleys to about 1,000 feet [305m] and perhaps nesting to 1,500 feet [457m]." He also said that it "has decreased markedly in several regions," commented on declines on the Solway mosses and on the fells around Coniston Water, but stated that "several pairs continue to breed on limestone hills near Arnside, Milnthorpe and Beetham" and that "in 1959 and 1960, good numbers were present in the Winster valley". There were brief periods in the 1960s and late 1970s when churring males colonized young forestry plantations in the north and west of the county. However, the bird had disappeared from the North Pennines, Eden Valley, east Lakeland, Lune Valley and the Cumbria Dales by the time of the *Old Atlas*. This was followed by a further dramatic decline, with the *New Atlas* locating birds in just three of the 22 previously occupied 10km squares. The 1992 BTO survey revealed just five churring males at two sites in the south of the county.

*This Atlas* reveals that the Nightjar still has no more than a tenuous foothold in the county. Birds were located in just four 10km squares and the species is restricted to long-established haunts on the raised bogs of the Leven and Duddon, a lowland moss on the Solway Basin and an area of clear-fell in a south Lakeland forest. Although the current county population of 2–6 breeding pairs is known from sites with an established occupancy, the Nightjars' crepuscular habits mean that special effort is required to locate them and it is to be hoped that the situation is not so bleak as it appears.

As with most long distance migrants, a combination of factors, involving the bird's breeding grounds, stop-over sites and winter quarters, is likely to have contributed to the Nightjar's decline. The complex and inter-related

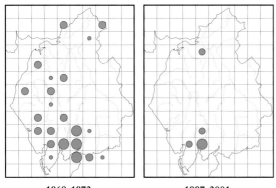

**1968-1972**    **1997-2001**
(For explanation of maps, see page 45)

***Conservation status***

| | |
|---|---|
| European: | SPEC Cat 2 |
| UK: | **RED: BD** |

***Populations***

| | |
|---|---|
| European status: | 240,000 |
| Britain – pairs: | 3,400 |
| Cumbria – pairs: | 2–6 |

***30-year distribution change***

| | Old Atlas | This Atlas | % |
|---|---|---|---|
| No. of 10km squares: | 22 | 4 | −81.8 |

| **Survey data** | **Tetrads** | **%** |
|---|---|---|
| Confirmed breeding: | 2 | 0.1 |
| Probable breeding: | 3 | 0.2 |
| Possible breeding: | 1 | 0.05 |
| Total: | 6 | 0.35 |

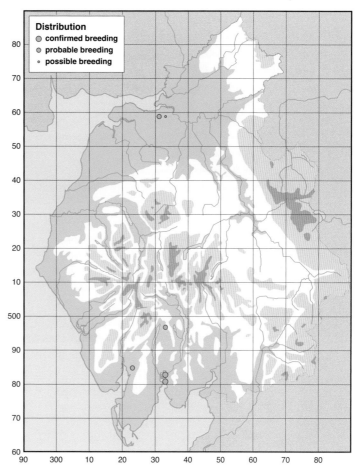

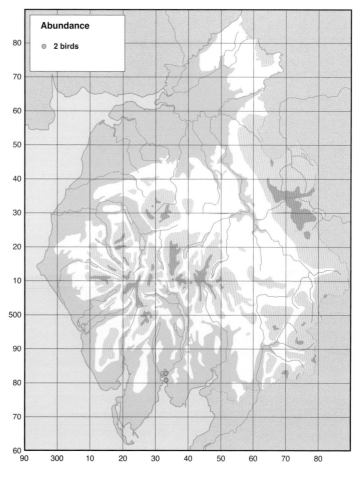

nature of the factors involved indicates how difficult it will be to work out comprehensive programmes for Nightjar conservation. In Cumbria, felling and restructuring operations currently underway in the coniferous forests of the Border Uplands could provide new habitat at Kershope and Spadeadam during the next few decades. The creation of a patchwork of forest blocks of different age groups within some of the larger plantations, in conjunction with the introduction of sustainable clear-fell management systems, could assist successful colonization. The prospects may be further enhanced by adopting creative habitat management techniques, such as leaving clearings of dry, bare ground for nesting and a few stands of timber for song posts, linked to feeding areas of open bracken, grass heaths or low intensity grazing relatively close to potential nest sites (Morris *et al* 1994, Scott *et al* 1998).

Clive Hartley

SCYTHING, shearing and screaming silhouettes chasing above villages and towns, Swifts are a brief but indelible image of our short summers. Rarely arriving in large numbers until early May, the 'Deviling', as it used to be known in Westmorland, is with us in Cumbria for barely three or four months, but in that limited period, its presence encapsulates all that a typical summer should be. My own perennial memory of them is of their noisy aerial pursuits on a steamy May evening dashing between the gaunt and austere Victorian industrial buildings of the 'Dolly Blue' factory in Backbarrow.

A widespread summer visitor to much of the Palearctic, in Britain and Ireland the Swift is commonest in the warmer and drier south and east of Britain, the species becoming progressively scarcer in the colder, wetter northwestern areas of its range. After spending the winter on or south of the Equator in Africa, the Swifts' return coincides with a burgeoning British supply of their prey, chiefly flying insects and small airborne spiders. Weather conditions determine whether the prey will be taken two or 1,000 metres above the ground. Wherever it is taken, Swifts find great difficulty in operating successfully in windy, wet and cold conditions when prey is understandably hard to obtain. During such instances, young Swifts can survive without food for several days and become torpid, resulting in a prolonged fledging period.

The species' other main requirement is abundant nesting sites. Although nesting occurs in holes in trees and away from man-made sites in parts of Europe, Swifts in Britain and Ireland almost exclusively choose old buildings, usually in areas of long-standing human occupation. The nest site is most commonly under the eaves or in some similar small crevice. Preferred locations are at least five metres above the ground in order that birds can drop from the nest and have enough time to gather velocity. Modern housing rarely affords nesting opportunities and consequently Swifts are most at home in old urban areas of high human population.

Mitchell (1892) and Spencer (1973) both describe the Swift as being a common and widespread summer

resident in Cumbria. In addition, Oakes (1953) relates an instance of the species nesting for several years in old copper-mine galleries at the foot of the Old Man of Coniston. Stokoe (1962) repeats this information and embellishes it with reference to a colony nesting naturally in the cracks of a red sandstone crag in the Eden Valley near Armathwaite.

Swifts were recorded in all of the county's 10km squares during both the *Old* and *New Atlases*. The *Old Atlas* confirmed breeding in 84 (90%) 10km squares while the *New Atlas* showed a similar pattern. Furthermore, the *New Atlas* reflects the species' preference for sections of the Coastal Plain, Eden Valley, Solway Basin and south Lakeland, all areas of relatively high human population – at least in a Cumbrian context – with the more sparsely populated areas of the county holding few birds.

*This Atlas* again portrays the expected dependence upon human habitation and the absence of the species from the wilder moors and high fells of the North Pennines, Border Moors and central Lakeland where the human population is very sparse. The strongholds remain those sections of the Coastal Plain, Eden Valley, Solway Basin and southern Lakeland which support high densities of human habitation. However, there is also a distinct paucity of records on the Coastal Plain between St Bees Head and Millom and between Maryport and Burgh-by-Sands in the southwest section of the Solway Basin. This dearth of records is possibly due to the sparseness of human populations, leading to a lack of appropriate nest sites, and perhaps an increased exposure to the worst of the west coast weather, causing food to be less freely available than at more sheltered inland sites.

A satisfactory assessment of the county population awaits a species-specific survey. Given the mobile nature of feeding birds, and the highly localized breeding distribution, analysis of line transect data is of only limited value. A population band of 4,000–30,000 was suggested, with a mean of 11,000 birds. The highest densities of 6.1 birds/km² occurred in the south of the county, in the large, sprawling conurbations around

Sponsored by a CBC Member

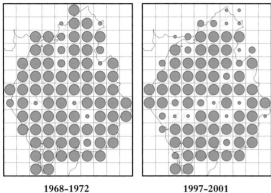

**1968-1972**          **1997-2001**

(For explanation of maps, see page 45)

*Conservation status*
| | |
|---|---|
| European: | Non-SPEC |
| UK: | **GREEN** |

*Populations*
| | |
|---|---|
| European status: | 4,300,000 |
| Britain – pairs: | 80,000 |
| Cumbria – pairs: | 5,500 |

*30-year distribution change*
| | Old Atlas | This Atlas | % |
|---|---|---|---|
| No. of 10km squares: | 84 | 85 | +1.2 |

| Survey data | Tetrads | % |
|---|---|---|
| Confirmed breeding: | 206 | 11.2 |
| Probable breeding: | 205 | 11.1 |
| Possible breeding: | 400 | 21.7 |
| Total: | 811 | 44.0 |

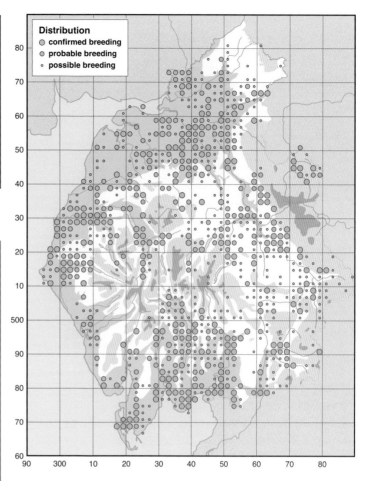

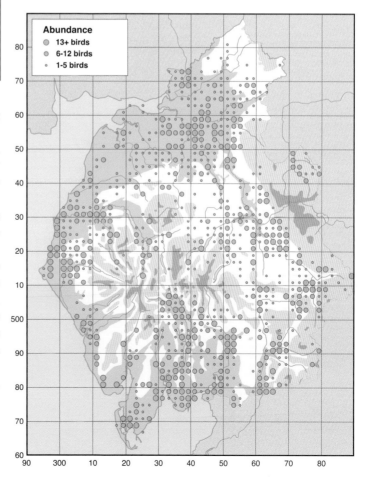

Kendal. A total of over 6,500 birds was seen during the timed visits.

Swifts have benefited from tighter control on atmospheric pollution, which has increased prey availability, and thus colonies can now thrive close to the centres of large conurbations. However, many birds are excluded from their breeding holes by demolition and restoration work. Perhaps we should be taking a leaf out of Amsterdam's book, where it has been made illegal to re-roof buildings unless access for Swifts is retained. Climate change predictions point to windier and wetter conditions, and the consequent effects upon invertebrate populations and availability may mean that Swifts find prospering in Cumbria more difficult in the future.

Tim Dean

# Kingfisher *Alcedo atthis*

FRUSTRATINGLY, a flash of turquoise accompanied by a loud and penetrating *'zeeee'* is often all you get. For such a brightly-coloured bird, good views of Kingfishers can be decidedly difficult to obtain, although anglers, all too often, delight in recounting instances of birds using their fishing rods as hunting perches.

Usually to be found in the vicinity of ponds, lakes, flooded gravel pits and slow-flowing rivers, the Kingfisher is found wherever there is clear ice-free water, abundant food and suitable soft and vertical banks in which to excavate its nesting burrow. Within the Western Palearctic it occurs throughout most of Europe, though totally absent north of latitude 60°N. In much of Europe, where population densities are generally lower than in Britain and Ireland, breeding birds are forced to migrate due to the severity of continental winters. These two factors reinforce the importance of the British and Irish populations in European terms. Prolonged icy conditions take their toll, but with a lengthy breeding season (March to mid-September) coupled with a high productivity potential, recovery can be swift.

Nationally, the Kingfisher suffered from almost ceaseless destruction throughout the 19th century. As early as 1860 it was decreasing in numbers, birds being killed for the production of fishing flies and fashion accessories from the plumage, or in the belief that they ate trout and salmon fry. It is also likely to have suffered from the pollution of its watercourses during the Industrial Revolution. Following a reduction in persecution, the 20th century saw something of a recovery although the severe winters of 1946/47 and

1962/63 acted to slow this increase.

In Cumbria, at the end of the 19th century, according to Macpherson (1892), "A few Kingfishers haunt our northern streams and backwaters". He also cites the occurrence of birds on the River Eden and near Ulverston and concludes, "Kingfishers live for weeks on the creeks of our saltmarshes". Mitchell (1892) mentions breeding birds on the rivers Winster and Duddon and, like Macpherson, alludes to saltmarshes being a favoured feeding locality. By the mid-20th century, Oakes (1953) considered it to be moderately numerous near Coniston and Broughton Mills, although Stokoe (1962) remarks on a substantial reduction in numbers in Westmorland, with other declines in the Crake valley and around Carlisle. The *Old Atlas* showed that birds were still well represented in suitable habitat across the county. However, by the time of the *New Atlas* some thinning in distribution was apparent, with losses in the Solway Basin, upper Eden Valley and southern Lakeland.

During the survey period for *this Atlas,* the species was found to be still widespread, although locally distributed, with birds recorded in 79 (4.3%) tetrads. The strongholds are the Solway Basin and the Eden and Lune valleys, where its preferred habitat of slow-moving rivers occurs. The distribution map also illustrates the scarcity of the species on the Coastal Plain north of the Duddon, and in particular, the absence of birds from the valleys of the Esk, Irt and Mite, occupied at the time of the *Old Atlas.*

The Solway Basin holds the highest population with confirmed breeding coming from the King Water, River Irthing, River Eden at Carlisle and River Wampool. The Eden valley saw confirmed breeding at two sites, while the River Lune produced three confirmed breeding records. Records from Furness come from the Ulverston area, mirroring Macpherson's 19th century account, Barrow-in-Furness and the west side of the Cartmel peninsula.

Kingfishers are notoriously difficult to census, being easily overlooked unless conducting a specific species survey: there is a strong suspicion that *this Atlas* does not fully reflect the bird's distribution in the county. Some sites in the south and west of Cumbria, which historically and over substantial time periods have held breeding birds, are not represented on the map.

As for most species with linear habitat preferences, the type of BBS line transect survey carried out during *this Atlas* does not generate reliable results for Kingfisher. Following the assumption of 3–5 pairs per occupied 10km square used in the *Old Atlas,* but taking into account different related densities shown by the timed counts of the *New Atlas,* a current county population of 50–100 pairs can be estimated. This is perhaps the only reliable measure to hint at what the county population may hold, until a dedicated survey

Sponsored by Helen Spencer & K Shoes

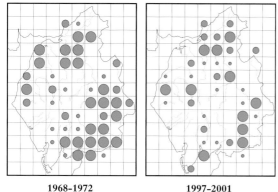

**1968-1972**          **1997-2001**

(For explanation of maps, see page 45)

*Conservation status*

| European: | SPEC Cat 3 |
| --- | --- |
| UK: | **AMBER** |

*Populations*

| European status: | 52,500 |
| --- | --- |
| Britain – pairs: | 4,400 |
| Cumbria – pairs: | 50–100 |

*30-year distribution change*

| | Old Atlas | This Atlas | % |
| --- | --- | --- | --- |
| No. of 10km squares: | 45 | 37 | **−17.8** |

| **Survey data** | **Tetrads** | **%** |
| --- | --- | --- |
| Confirmed breeding: | 16 | 0.9 |
| Probable breeding: | 23 | 1.2 |
| Possible breeding: | 40 | 2.2 |
| Total: | 79 | 4.3 |

can be carried out.

Pollution of watercourses from agricultural run-off and industrial contamination affects the Kingfisher's principal prey items, freshwater fish and aquatic insects. Improved water quality in tandem with stricter legislation should favour the welfare of this species in the future, already evidenced by an increase in the Scottish breeding populations along the rivers Clyde and Tay and in the Great Glen.

The Kingfisher's future as a breeding species within Cumbria looks hopeful. It is unable to cope with harsh icy winters. However current predictions of climate change due to global warming indicate a wetter and warmer regime. This assumption, and the continued betterment of water quality, would indicate improved prospects for the Kingfisher.

Tim Dean

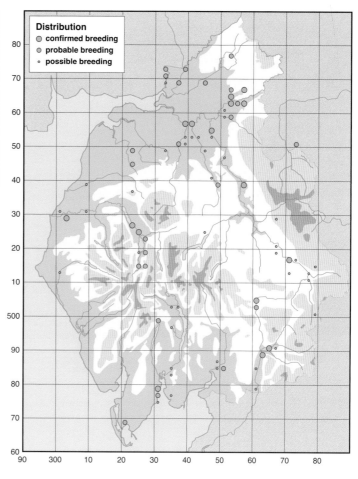

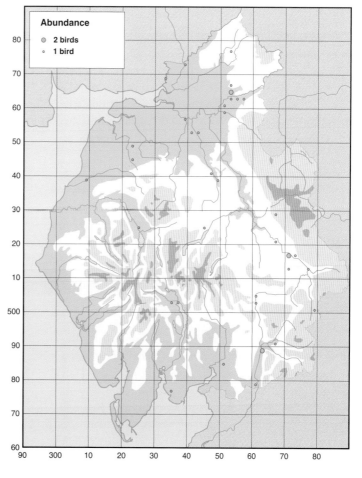

# Green Woodpecker *Picus viridis*

WITH its striking green and yellow plumage and bright red cap, the Green Woodpecker is a conspicuous, almost exotic bird. The loud and distinctive, far-carrying 'yaffling' call can be heard echoing through Cumbrian woodlands in spring and according to folklore is a portent of rain; hence one of its local names, 'Rainbird'.

A Palearctic species, it is found throughout Europe from Spain, Italy, Greece and Turkey northwards to Sweden and western Norway and then eastwards into the former USSR and Iran. Within Britain, the species has a mainly southerly distribution, being particularly common in southern Wales and England, from the Midlands southwards, and noticeably absent from large areas of Scotland. It does not breed in Ireland.

A bird of open or broken deciduous woodland, it is equally at home in well timbered farmland, parkland and even large gardens. It is often to be found out in the open feeding on the ground in fields and meadows especially where there is a plentiful supply of ants which form a substantial part of the bird's diet. The nest chamber is usually sited 2–6 metres off the ground in the main trunk of a mature tree, with oak, ash and birch the preferred species.

The Green Woodpecker's distribution in Britain has not always been as it is today. Though generally doing well in the south, numbers have fluctuated considerably in the north. During the early 19th century Northumberland was the northern limit with a very few records from Cumbria, although a pair was considered to have bred at Edenhall in 1887 (Macpherson 1892). The national range then contracted southwards and recolonization of the county did not occur until 1918 when birds bred in Westmorland (Witherby *et al* 1938–41). A few pairs bred in Cumberland in the 1940s and the first nest in Lakeland was found in 1945 (Temperley & Blezard 1951). From then on, it increased considerably, becoming widespread in the south of the county and also expanding northwards. Indeed, Stokoe (1962) commented "from a distribution restricted only 20 years ago to a few favoured districts, most suitable habitats are now occupied." Although widespread at the time of the *Old Atlas,* being absent only from the mainly treeless areas of the Solway Basin, by the *New Atlas* a decline was evident with losses in the Solway Basin and much of the Eden Valley. A Cumbria Bird Club survey in 1994–95 showed that the decline in the north and east of the county was continuing unabated. Afforestation was considered partly to blame for this decline; some previously suitable habitat had been lost as areas planted with conifers are of little value to the Green Woodpecker. Although a few birds were still present in commercial forestry in areas such as Ennerdale and Whinlatter, they were thought to be nesting in nearby deciduous stands (Atkins & Callion 1997).

*This Atlas,* although still indicating a strong correlation between the bird's presence and river valleys, underlines this gradual decline especially in the north of the county, with the map showing few records to the north of Lakeland. Despite the presence of some large and apparently very suitable woodland areas, the species is now notably absent from much of the Solway Basin, Border Uplands and Eden Valley, while a comparison with data from the 1994–95 Cumbria Bird Club Woodpecker and Nuthatch Survey also shows evidence of a slight decline in the west of the county. The species' stronghold is now centred on the woodlands of south Lakeland, where the valleys hold good areas of grassland surrounded by open woodland, copses and hedgerows. Similar areas on the northwest periphery of Lakeland, around Bassenthwaite Lake and Derwent Water, in the lower Eden Valley and Border Uplands also hold fragmented, isolated populations.

Although nearly 300 birds were located during timed counts, too few were encountered during the line transect fieldwork to produce a meaningful figure. The current county population estimate of 250–300 breeding pairs is a subjective assessment, based on count data enhanced by supplementary records, and would agree with the finding of the 1994–95 survey, which concluded the population "would be in the lower region of the 101–1000 pairs" band.

The strong link between Green Woodpeckers and ants may be a factor in their decline within the county. There has been a significant loss – 65% between 1940 and 1970 (NCC 1987) – of unimproved lowland

 Sponsored by Denis White

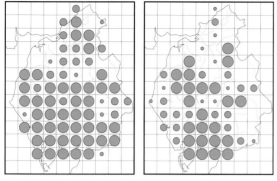

| **1968-1972** | **1997-2001** |

(For explanation of maps, see page 45)

**Conservation status**

| European: | SPEC Cat 2 |
| UK: | **AMBER** |

**Populations**

| European status: | 670,000 |
| Britain – pairs: | 15,000 |
| Cumbria – pairs: | 250–300 |

**30-year distribution change**

| | Old Atlas | This Atlas | % |
|---|---|---|---|
| No. of 10km squares: | 67 | 51 | −23.8 |

| **Survey data** | **Tetrads** | **%** |
|---|---|---|
| Confirmed breeding: | 70 | 3.8 |
| Probable breeding: | 140 | 7.6 |
| Possible breeding: | 61 | 3.3 |
| Total: | 271 | 14.7 |

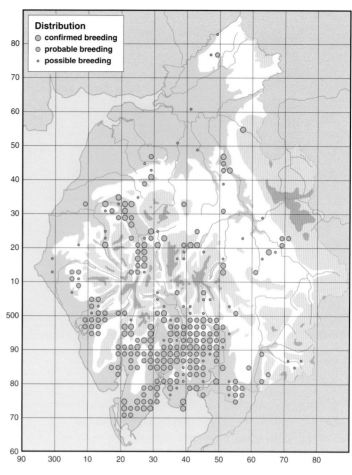

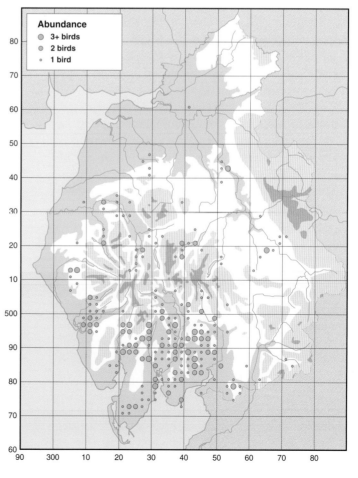

grassland, the main habitat of the Yellow Meadow Ant which forms a substantial part of the bird's diet. It is possible that this ant, which favours warmer, south-facing meadows, is doing better in the south of the county and this is reflected in the relatively high numbers of Green Woodpeckers still found there.

The decline in ants, coupled with afforestation and the improvement of lowland grasslands could all be contributing to the current range contraction of this species within Cumbria. However the latest CBC data reveal a 90% increase nationally since 1970, so hopefully, if the existing policy of integrated mixed woodland is continued in forestry management, this trend will become apparent in Cumbria in the not too distant future.

Roy Atkins

# Great Spotted Woodpecker *Dendrocopos major*

THE pied plumage, augmented with a splash of red, makes the Great Spotted Woodpecker a handsome bird, while the increasingly regular habit of visiting garden feeding stations has brought the species to the attention of a wider audience. The far reaching, resonant drumming, so evocative of Cumbrian woodlands in spring, is one of the few territorial 'songs' not actually made vocally. Its presence is also betrayed by the frequent *'tchick'* call, while a wide range of sounds are made during aerial chases at the height of the breeding season.

An Old World species, the Great Spotted Woodpecker is found throughout Europe, where its range extends from Britain through Norway and Sweden eastwards to the former USSR, and southwards through Spain and Italy into North Africa. Although widespread throughout Britain, it is most abundant in much of southern England and Wales, becoming scarcer in Scotland. It remains unknown as a breeding species in Ireland, the Isle of Man and the Outer Isles.

Although generally associated with mature deciduous woodland, the species is actually more adaptable than many realize, also being found in coniferous woods and plantations as well as gardens and hedgerows. Woodland holding standing dead wood is of great importance, both for feeding and providing nest sites, though Great Spotted Woodpeckers are quite capable of creating holes in living wood too. Feeding mainly on invertebrates, primarily wood boring insects such as beetle larvae, they also eat a wide variety of nuts and seeds.

Nationally, the species declined dramatically in the 18th century, particularly in the north of Britain, disappearing from Scotland and most of northern England by the beginning of the 19th century. From about 1870, it began to spread back north and continued to increase until around the 1950s. Numbers then stabilized until, possibly as a result of Dutch Elm disease which created a wealth of dead wood in the 1970s, a further increase was noted. Since then, numbers have continued to rise, with the latest available CBC data showing a 102% increase since 1970.

In Cumbria, at the end of the 19th century, Macpherson (1892) considered it to be mainly a winter visitor to the county, although a few pairs had become established in Cumberland. Edenhall was considered the breeding stronghold of the species but it had also begun to nest at Brampton, Woodside, Corby Castle and Warwick Bridge. Interestingly keepers were blamed for the species' scarcity. Birds continued to increase through the 20th century and, by the 1960s, Stokoe (1962) remarked that it was widespread and frequently met with in suitable habitat. A comparison between the *Old* and *New Atlases* shows that, although birds were lost from two 10km squares in the Solway Basin, there was little evidence of any major changes in distribution and that birds were most abundant in the south of the county. The results of a Cumbria Bird Club survey during 1994–95 confirmed this view and suggested an increase in abundance in both the west of the county and south Lakeland (Atkins & Callion 1997).

Analysis of line transect data from *this Atlas* gives a population band of 3,000–13,000, suggesting a mean population of 6,000 birds. Note, however, the rather wide band limits. The highest densities of 3.6 birds/km² occurred in intricate lowland landscapes with many natural woodland features such as are to be found in the south and west fringes of Lakeland.

The distribution of the county's semi-natural broad-leaved woodland greatly influences the range of the Great Spotted Woodpecker. Away from the well-wooded lowland areas in the south, much of Cumbria is an upland treeless landscape, and broad-leaved woodland is limited to the steep valley sides of meandering river systems or to isolated stands in intensively farmed areas. Such habitat is found around the periphery of Lakeland, along the entire length of the Eden Valley and in areas of the Border Uplands and Cumbria Dales. Recent increases in the county mean that populations in optimum woodland habitat are approaching saturation level, leading to birds moving out into the marginal habitat found along the Coastal Plain. Here the varied lowland landscape includes many sparsely wooded riparian valleys and small fields surrounded by copses and hedges. Birds remain relatively scarce in parts of the Solway Basin and

Sponsored by C.C. Flindall

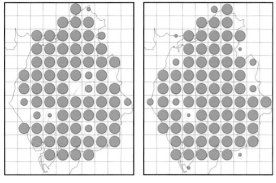

**1968-1972**      **1997-2001**

(For explanation of maps, see page 45)

**Conservation status**

| | |
|---|---|
| European: | Non-SPEC |
| UK: | **GREEN** |

**Populations**

| | |
|---|---|
| European status: | 3,700,000 |
| Britain – pairs: | 27,500 |
| Cumbria – pairs: | 3,000 |

**30-year distribution change**

| | Old Atlas | This Atlas | % |
|---|---|---|---|
| No. of 10km squares: | 73 | 78 | **+6.8** |

| **Survey data** | **Tetrads** | **%** |
|---|---|---|
| Confirmed breeding: | 280 | 15.2 |
| Probable breeding: | 288 | 15.6 |
| Possible breeding: | 162 | 8.8 |
| Total: | 730 | 39.6 |

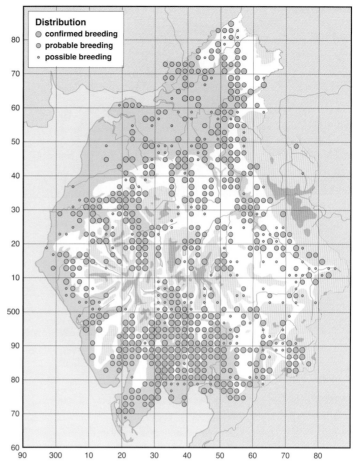

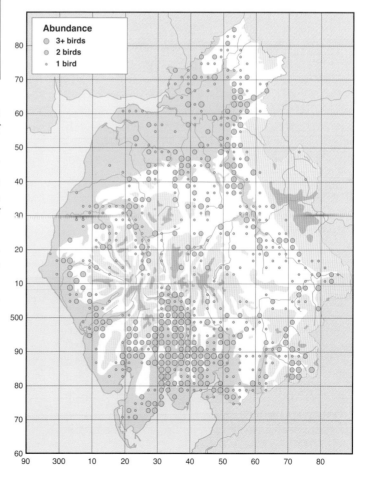

Coastal Plain, due to the presence of large tracts of farmland and mosses which lack areas of suitable woodland.

The future for the Great Spotted Woodpecker in Cumbria looks assured, especially as a less intensively managed landscape in the wake of the foot-and-mouth disease epidemic looks likely. If these sub-optimum habitats are left to regenerate, then the characteristic sound of drumming in spring could increase further throughout the county.

Roy Atkins

# Lesser Spotted Woodpecker *Dendrocopos minor*

WHEN observed for the first time it can be quite a shock to see just how small Lesser Spotted Woodpeckers really are; these delightful little birds are in fact woodpeckers in miniature. Unlike the similar-sized Nuthatch, which draws attention to itself with loud calls and constant activity, the Lesser Spotted Woodpecker goes quietly about its business and is easily overlooked. Although its soft drumming and Kestrel-like *'pee-pee-pee'* calls may attract attention in the spring, it is a fortunate observer who catches more than a glimpse of its attractive pied plumage, let alone witnesses its butterfly-like display flight.

A Palearctic species, its distribution extends eastwards from Europe, through central and southern Siberia to Kamchatka and Japan. Although occurring considerably further north in Norway and Sweden, in Britain, the Lesser Spotted Woodpecker is right at the northwestern limit of its range and is largely restricted to Wales and southern England. It does not breed in Scotland or Ireland.

Preferring open broad-leaved woodland, woodland edges, spinneys, orchards, parkland and avenues of trees, it often feeds high up in the canopy, gleaning insects from the thinner outer branches and foliage, and may even be seen flycatching on occasions. It is thought that the availability of easily worked, decayed wood may be of more importance than tree height for this species, which has a rather shorter, weaker bill than other woodpeckers. It prefers decaying wood in which to search for wood-boring beetles and their larvae and to excavate its nest. This can be up to 25m above the ground, usually in the underside of a branch or limb, and is generally higher than other British woodpeckers.

Nationally, the species increased in numbers and distribution with the outbreak of Dutch Elm disease and the resultant additional food supply. This trend was reversed as the disease waned, and as the population returned to former, or even lower, levels it became clear that elms were also one of their most favoured nesting sites. More recently, the *New Atlas* indicated an 11% decline in distribution and the latest available CBC data reveals a 64% drop in population since 1970, with the species now elevated to the BoCC Red List. Alarmingly, the Lesser Spotted Woodpecker is now also considered too rare to be monitored reliably by BBS; in 1999 it was recorded in just 30 plots in the whole of Britain. The decline of such a woodland specialist is thought to suggest a deterioration in the quality of some woodland habitats.

Cumbria is at the northern limit of the Lesser Spotted Woodpecker's range in Britain. Indeed, although there are 19th century records of pairs nesting in Cumberland at Dalemain in 1847 and Edenhall in 1882, Macpherson (1892) states that Lakeland lies outside the usual breeding range for this species with no records from Westmorland or Furness. Stokoe (1962) considered it to be a scarce resident in the county and remarks that it may have bred at Levens Park in 1961, with further sightings from Hesket Newmarket, Keswick, Newby Bridge, Carlisle and Broughton-in-Furness. Hutcheson (1986) also found breeding records to be sparse, only forthcoming from a few sites around Ullswater, Grasmere, Windermere and Coniston Water. The *Old Atlas* found birds in 17 10km squares, and although a few birds occurred in central Lakeland, the preponderance of records came from the south of the county. By the time of the *New Atlas,* this range had contracted with only four 10km squares occupied, all in the south of the county. However, a Cumbria Bird Club survey in 1994–95 located birds in seven tetrads, spread around the edge of Lakeland, with confirmed breeding at Isel Bridge (Atkins & Callion 1997). This perhaps suggests a degree of under-recording in the *New Atlas* but also the possibility arises that the decline had halted with numbers stabilizing.

These findings are supported by *this Atlas*. Although remaining a rare sight in a Cumbria, birds were again located in eight tetrads spread around the periphery of Lakeland, implying that numbers, though still very low, remain constant. Breeding was confirmed at two sites with pairs feeding young at Wythop Hall and Brigsteer; all other records referred to single birds.

Line transect data is not particularly helpful with rare or scarce species and evidence on population levels has to be gathered from other sources. Combining the data from *this Atlas* with the 1994–95 Cumbria Bird Club survey indicates the presence of Lesser Spotted

Sponsored by Calluna Books

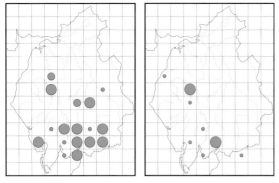

**1968-1972**          **1997-2001**
(For explanation of maps, see page 45)

*Conservation status*
European:                  Non-SPEC
UK:                        **RED: BD**

*Populations*
European status:           210,000
Britain – pairs:           4,500
Cumbria – pairs:           10–15

*30-year distribution change*
|  | Old Atlas | This Atlas | % |
|---|---|---|---|
| No. of 10km squares: | 17 | 8 | −52.9 |

| Survey data | Tetrads | % |
|---|---|---|
| Confirmed breeding: | 2 | 0.1 |
| Probable breeding: | 0 | |
| Possible breeding: | 6 | 0.3 |
| Total: | 8 | 0.4 |

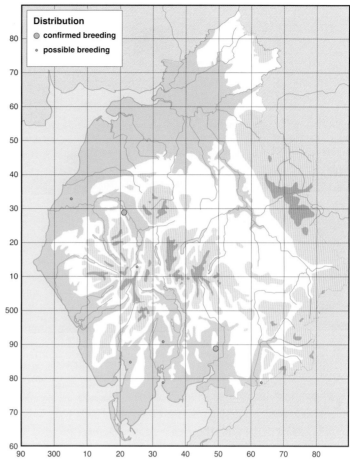

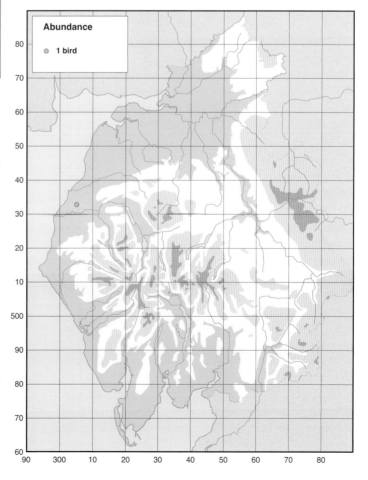

Woodpeckers in around 15 10km squares. Given the largely sedentary and secretive nature of the species, it is reasonable to assume that the county currently holds a population of 10–15 breeding pairs.

It would appear that the Lesser Spotted Woodpecker population in Cumbria has always been small and *this Atlas* shows that, although scarce, numbers remain relatively constant. It has been suggested that this bird could benefit from global warming, and if it does there is certainly plenty of suitable habitat into which it could expand. However, recent CBC and BBS data give little cause for optimism and we can only hope that the species continues to keep at least a toe-hold in the county until its fortunes improve.

Roy Atkins

C.M. Isherwood

WORDSWORTH pronounced the Skylark an ethereal minstrel, a pilgrim of the sky; Shelley's judgement was that of a blithe spirit, showering the earth with a rain of melody. An inspiration to poets and composers through the ages, the Skylark has long been one of Britain's best-loved birds. A calm, spring morning on saltmarsh or moorland, when the air is heavy with the Skylark's sustained and full-throated song, is an unforgettable experience.

Quintessentially a bird of open countryside, the Skylark occurs over much of the Palearctic. Recent changes in agricultural practices in continental Europe have resulted in drastic decreases in many areas. In Britain and Ireland, numbers have suffered catastrophic declines in the last 30 years. Its greatest densities now occur in the areas of eastern Britain where mixed or arable farming still predominates, and it is least common in the Scottish Highlands.

Originally a bird of steppe habitat, the Skylark has benefited greatly from deforestation and has long been associated with cultivation. It nests in a variety of grassland habitats, from coastal sand-dunes to elevated moorland, where the female alone builds the cup-shaped nest of grass, usually beside a tussock. Two or three broods are usual and both parents feed the young on a variety of small seeds and invertebrates.

According to Macpherson (1892), "If the numbers of individuals sacrificed to the exigencies of the kitchen table can be trusted to supply a criterion, the Sky Lark has long been a very abundant bird in Lakeland." Stokoe (1962) regarded the Skylark as "numerous" throughout low open country from the coast to the vicinity of fells and on upland pastures and high tops, up to 793m asl, but remarked on its absence from the river valleys.

In Cumbria, at the beginning of the 20th century, Skylarks were commonest on the farmed lowlands where tillage and grassland provided an ideal mix of habitats. Today's agriculture, however, has evolved into a technologically-based industry, and modern farming practices have had disastrous consequences for the Skylark; the latest available CBC index shows a 52% decline in the national population since 1970.

*This Atlas* shows little change in distribution from that in the *Old Atlas,* with strongholds along the Coastal Plain and in upland areas such as the North Pennines and central Lakeland. Studies at Ravenglass in the 1960s found 18 breeding pairs/km$^2$ with evidence of site fidelity and a strong territorial bond (Delius 1965). Today, although similar densities still occur at a few coastal sites, where mixed farming continues, it is mainly in upland areas, like the MoD Ranges at Warcop, where comparable populations exist (pers obs).

That agricultural change has had the greatest impact on populations is borne out by the fact that the intensively worked farmland and heavily managed grasslands of the Solway Basin, lower Eden Valley and south Lakeland now support less than 1% of the county population. In contrast, although many upland areas, especially heather moorland, have also suffered from agricultural intensification and overgrazing, stemming from an increase in the numbers of livestock, this habitat now contains 30% of the Cumbrian population. Although such pressures are not normally associated with conservation benefits, the deleterious effect of reducing heather and increasing the proportion of grasses has introduced a more open and diverse vegetation structure that has created new breeding opportunities for Skylarks. Birds along the Coastal Plain, principally those nesting in sand-dunes, maritime grassland and smaller, hedged fields make up around 11% of the population, but even here a decline can be detected where arable elements are absent.

Analysis of line transect data from *this Atlas* gives a population band of 19,000–41,000, suggesting a current county population of 28,000 males. The highest densities of 17.5 males/km$^2$ occurred on the narrow coastal zone.

Three million Skylarks have been lost from the British countryside since 1972; between 1968 and 1996, the area of spring-sown cereals grown in Britain dropped from 73% to just 16% of the total cereal area. This decrease, resulting from the EU's Common Agricultural Policy, has contributed significantly to a 75% decline in Skylark numbers on British farmland over the same period.

Spring-sown cereals allow the stubble remains of the previous crop to be left unploughed, providing food

Sponsored in memory of Reginald & Marjorie Scholefield

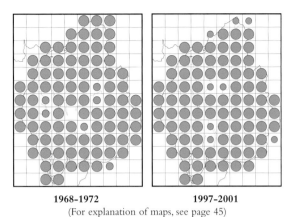

**1968–1972**      **1997–2001**
(For explanation of maps, see page 45)

*Conservation status*
European:                    SPEC Cat 3
UK:                          **RED: BD**

*Populations*
European status:             30,000,000
Britain – pairs:             1,046,000
Cumbria – pairs:             28,000

*30-year distribution change*
|  | Old Atlas | This Atlas | % |
|---|---|---|---|
| No. of 10km squares: | 91 | 91 | n/c |

| **Survey data** | **Tetrads** | **%** |
|---|---|---|
| Confirmed breeding: | 648 | 35.1 |
| Probable breeding: | 541 | 29.3 |
| Possible breeding: | 63 | 3.4 |
| Total: | 1,252 | 67.8 |

and cover for Skylarks over the succeeding winter months. Spring sowing also provides safer nesting sites and allow Skylarks to make more breeding attempts, as the growing crop remains relatively short and more open throughout the breeding season. Further benefits to Skylarks arise from the use of spring cereals in farming systems involving both arable and livestock production. These systems provide a patchwork of grass pasture and arable crops. Extending environmental schemes, such as Countryside Stewardship, could be a feasible solution to the challenges of Skylark conservation: such schemes should support the arable sector by encouraging farmers to grow spring-sown cereal and leave winter stubbles.

Malcolm Stott

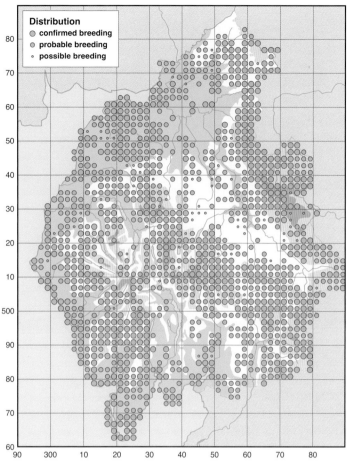

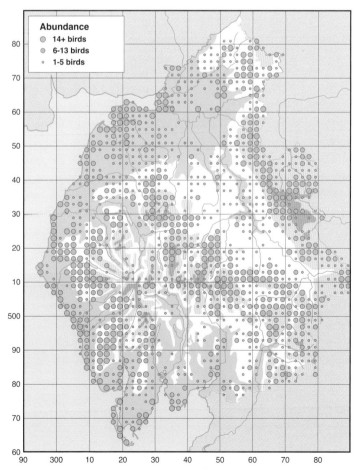

# Sand Martin *Riparia riparia*

ONE of the earliest signs of the approach of summer is small flocks of Sand Martins twisting and turning as they feed late into the evening over lakes, reservoirs or rivers. These early-returning birds fleetingly visit colonies occupied the previous year, but the relatively short early spring days, when food is sparse, force them to feed during most of the daylight hours.

The Sand Martin is a summer visitor to a vast area of the northern hemisphere, from North America through Europe and the central band of Asia to the Far East. In Britain and Ireland, it has a widespread but patchy distribution, with the species absent in parts of southern England and northwestern Scotland.

A tunnel nesting species, Sand Martin populations are entirely dependent on the availability of suitable nest sites. Distribution is in part dictated by geology since their preferred habitat is stable but soft vertical banks in the vicinity of water. Sandy cliffs are most often used, but even sandy soil exposed by rabbit burrows may be used. In some parts of Britain, man-made sites now far outnumber natural ones, and the creation of sand and gravel pits, railway and road cuttings and drainage holes have all provided the birds with potential nest sites. They are opportunist nesters since many sites, whether natural or man-made, change dramatically from one year to another, and the birds are forced to move as old sites deteriorate and new ones become exposed. Unusual Cumbrian nest sites include drainage holes in walls in a number of urban locations and spoil heaps (Stokoe 1962).

During the 19th and early 20th centuries, the national population appeared to change little, but

thereafter came a slow but steady decline particularly in Scotland and northern England until 1968/69 when a population 'crash' occurred. Prior to that time, the population in Britain and Ireland was estimated to be between 250,000 and 500,000 breeding pairs, but subsequently numbers fell in some areas by as much as 84%. This was a direct consequence of drought conditions, which seriously affected the birds' wintering grounds in the Sahel region of Africa. The population had little time to recover before a second similar tragedy hit the species in 1983/84.

In Cumbria, at the end of the 19th century, large numbers of birds reportedly perished in 1886 as a result of severe weather, and many colonies in the Rockcliffe area were deserted. However, this must have been a local cataclysm as Macpherson (1892) considered the species to be well distributed in Lakeland, away from the wilder dales of Westmorland, and commented that a "nice colony" existed in the sandstone cliffs near Maryport. By the mid-20th century, although Stokoe (1962) still regarded the Sand Martin as "widespread and locally common", he also commented on some decrease in numbers and cited an 11.25km stretch of the River Eden, above Appleby, where six colonies each holding 50–70 nests had declined to around 50 nests in total by 1960.

Cumbrian populations continued to decline into the mid-1980s. Thriving, pre-drought colonies such as at Faugh Quarry, with upwards of 300 nests, were reduced to a mere handful of pairs and some smaller colonies such as one at Midgeholme which had held 65 nests in 1983 was completely deserted the following summer. A countywide Cumbria Bird Club survey in 1991 showed something of a recovery, and established that 88% of colonies, accounting for 71% of the population, were located in riverbanks. Sand quarries provided the other main habitat, and, although only holding 8.6% of colonies, these were generally larger and held 27.5% of the population. The largest riverbank colonies were found on the rivers Esk, Lyne, Eden and Lune. Sample counts at randomly-selected colonies produced a nest hole occupancy rate of 69% giving a county population estimate of 3,468 breeding pairs in a total of 185 colonies (Underhill-Day *et al* 1993).

During *this Atlas,* substantial populations were still to be found in the Solway Basin, Eden Valley and Lune Valley with smaller numbers on the Coastal Plain, north of Ravenglass, and in northern Lakeland. The generally unsuitable riverine habitats of southern Lakeland hold few birds, although several small colonies occupy coastal sand-cliffs in Furness. Applying the 69% occupancy rate found in the 1991 survey to the 4,834 nest holes reported during *this Atlas* produces a minimum figure of 3,335 breeding pairs, lower than the suggested current county

 Sponsored by Alcan Packaging Lawson Mardon

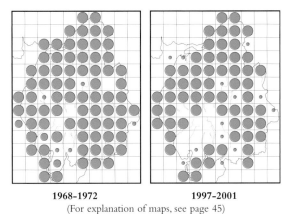

**1968-1972**     **1997-2001**

(For explanation of maps, see page 45)

***Conservation status***

| | |
|---|---|
| European: | SPEC Cat 3 |
| UK: | **AMBER** |

***Populations***

| | |
|---|---|
| European status: | 2,400,000 |
| Britain – pairs: | 160,000 |
| Cumbria – pairs: | 3,500–5,000 |

***30-year distribution change***

| | Old Atlas | This Atlas | % |
|---|---|---|---|
| No. of 10km squares: | 82 | 74 | **−9.7** |

| **Survey data** | **Tetrads** | **%** |
|---|---|---|
| Confirmed breeding: | 168 | 9.1 |
| Probable breeding: | 0 | |
| Possible breeding: | 168 | 9.1 |
| Total: | 336 | 18.2 |

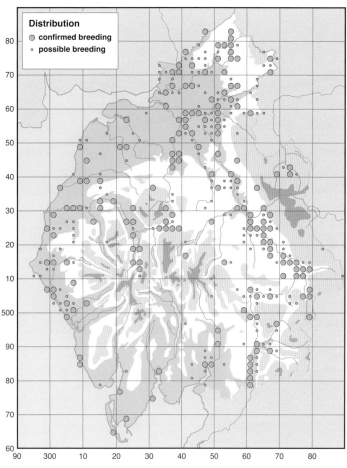

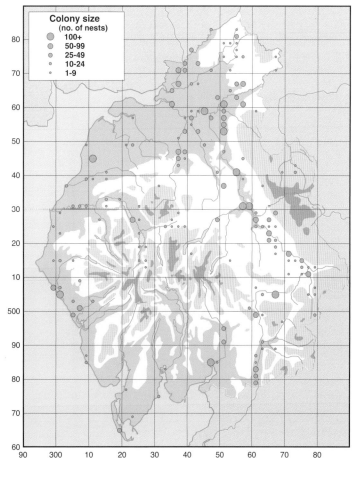

population of 3,500–5,000 breeding pairs, from counts at 168 occupied colonies.

The species' future remains unpredictable. Global warming may cause more frequent and more prolonged extremes in climate with as yet unknown impacts on trans-Saharan migrants. Colonies also face a number of threats including predation from Stoats, Weasels and perhaps surprisingly, Hedgehogs. However, artificial Sand Martin 'banks' using pipes set into concrete walls have been introduced at various places, including the River Kent in Kendal, with great success, and could provide a realistic alternative to sites affected by the predicted spring flooding and consequent bank erosion that climate change may bring to Cumbria.

Mike Carrier

THIS mercurial harbinger seldom fails to deceive that summer's lease awaits, and seldom does snow fail to fall after it has first arrived. Nevertheless, the Swallow represents summer in folklore, and remains with us to raise several broods, until the first signs of autumn signal the start of its journey south.

Being truly cosmopolitan, it ranks alongside that other bird of barns, the Barn Owl, as one of the most widespread species in the world. Its range covers most of Europe and Asia as far east as Kamchatka, and as far south as south China, and in the New World it breeds throughout North America. Within its European range, it is absent as a breeder only from the arctic and subarctic regions. In Britain and Ireland its range extends throughout, Swallows being scarce or absent only from the Western and Northern Isles, and from much of the high ground of the Scottish Highlands.

The Swallow normally builds its mud cup nest on a small ledge against a vertical surface, for instance a beam or window ledge in a building to which it can gain regular access. Only quite exceptionally will it nest in a cave or tree; Stokoe (1962) mentions birds nesting under bridges on the Solway saltmarshes and alludes to a nest on a rock face but does not give any further details. Given its preference for farm buildings, especially where these are close to meadows with an abundance of flying insects, the Swallow naturally attains high densities in rural locations. Although potential nest sites are plentiful in urban areas these are seldom occupied; presumably the lack of suitable feeding is a determining factor.

In Cumbria, the Swallow has been regarded as widespread and common since at least the 19th century with birds nesting in rural communities up to 305m asl (Macpherson 1892, Stokoe 1962). Brown (1974) reported a breeding density of 7.5–16.5 birds/km² and noted that on a 150 acre farm as many as eight or nine pairs might breed in some years, with as few as three or four in others, the annual variations thought to be due to losses on migration. The *New Atlas* concurs with this, noting in addition that feeding conditions in their winter quarters and on the long journey north also

have an effect on the breeding success, with birds arriving in poor body condition in some springs, and then raising smaller broods.

Both the *Old* and *New Atlases* found evidence of breeding in all but three 10km squares in Cumbria, and this is also the case for *this Atlas*. However, this 'coarse' grid masks much variation at a tetrad level: some 10km squares, particularly those with much high ground, have few tetrads occupied. Comparison of available tetrad information suggests, however, that there has been no significant change in distribution since the *New Atlas*. Swallows are absent only from the higher ground of the Cumbria Dales, North Pennines and Lakeland, where neither nest sites nor feeding opportunities are readily available.

Nationally, although the latest CBC index indicates a 23% rise since 1970, a decline in Swallow populations has been detected in some southern counties. This is perhaps due to changes in farming practices, with a greater reliance on chemicals over the last 50 years, and the renovation of redundant farm buildings into rural dwellings, with the loss of nest sites. Such local fluctuations in populations are also apparent in certain areas of Cumbria, mainly where traditional mixed arable and livestock farming has changed in favour of intensive cultivation. Swallow densities in these areas can be less than half that found on marginal farmland in the upper Eden Valley and peripheral areas of Lakeland, where small scale cultivation and pastoral farming are still a predominant feature of the landscape.

Analysis of line transect data from *this Atlas* gives a population band of 126,000–232,000, suggesting a mean population of 170,000 birds. The highest densities of 82.4 birds/km² occurred on marginal upland farmland and areas transitional to enclosed pasture, predominantly in the Lakeland valleys and upper Eden Valley catchments. In comparison the intensively managed farmland found on the lower Eden Valley and eastern parts of the Solway Basin held just 6 birds/km².

These findings support the earlier speculation that Swallows reach their highest densities in rural areas

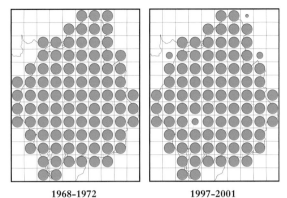

**1968-1972**          **1997-2001**
(For explanation of maps, see page 45)

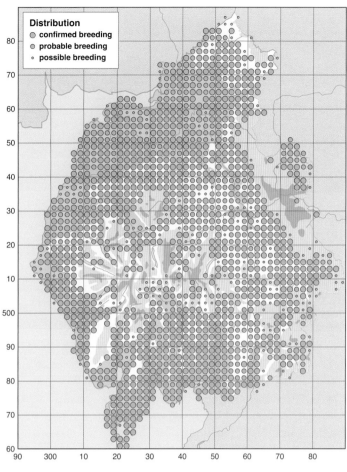

*Conservation status*
European:                    SPEC Cat 3
UK:                              AMBER

*Populations*
European status:           15,000,000
Britain – pairs:                570,000
Cumbria – pairs:                85,000

*30-year distribution change*
                          Old Atlas  This Atlas   %
No. of 10km squares:   91        91      n/c

| Survey data | Tetrads | % |
|---|---|---|
| Confirmed breeding: | 1,039 | 56.3 |
| Probable breeding: | 275 | 14.9 |
| Possible breeding: | 154 | 8.4 |
| Total: | 1,468 | 79.6 |

where traditional mixed farming, especially cattle grazing, is still practised. With continued intensification and specialization of farming in the county, reduced numbers of cattle especially in upland areas following BSE and foot-and-mouth disease, and continued piecemeal urbanization, the outlook for this species is less than rosy. However, where sufficient food supplies still exist, the imaginative provision of new nesting sites, for instance on existing or new rural housing and in modern agricultural buildings, may help to prevent this eagerly-awaited summer visitor suffering the same decline that we have witnessed in populations of many other farmland birds.

Jake Manson

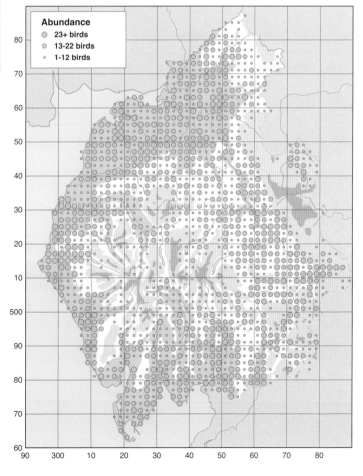

# House Martin *Delichon urbica*

THE crack of leather on willow, warm beer, and the scent of freshly-mown grass; these quintessential summer sensations would not be complete without the hearty chirruping of House Martins, wheeling overhead. Their blue-black upperparts, clean white underparts and striking pure white rump, coupled with a close association with man, make them an easily recognized species.

The House Martin is a summer visitor; wintering widely over Africa south of the Sahara, it returns in April to breed throughout most of the temperate areas of the Palearctic. Within Europe, the species is absent only from northern Scandinavia. It is absent too, or at best scarce, in exposed parts of the Scottish Highlands, and the far north and west of both Britain and Ireland. In Cumbria, given the similarity of habitat and nest site requirements to Swallow, it shares a similar range, but with a much sparser population.

House Martins build their closed cup nest from mud pellets, and nest mostly on the outer walls of buildings, under eaves or other overhangs, and also under bridges, culverts and in old quarry workings. Natural sites on cliffs and outcrops, coastal and inland, are occasionally used with Carrock Fell, Whitbarrow Scar and St Bees Head utilized historically (Brown 1974, Hutcheson 1986). They are semi-colonial, and occasionally many nests may be stuck together. Both sexes build the nest, although males are more active at the start. Pellets of wet mud are collected close by, and the lining of vegetable fibres and feathers is collected in the air, or stolen from other nests. Factors which limit both numbers and distribution are the lack of suitable sites for nest construction, and possibly also

the availability of liquid mud with which to build or repair the nest. Despite its reputation for rain, the early Cumbrian summer, when House Martins are nest-building, can be quite dry, restricting colonies to sites near to where liquid mud is available.

Although there have been total losses from some areas of the Home Counties (Mead 2000), the British population is thought to be stable, with the latest available CBC data actually showing a 19% increase since 1970. Comparison of the *Old* and *New Atlases* however does not substantiate this, with a slight decline indicated in the Scottish Highlands, southwest Scotland, throughout Ireland, and to a lesser extent northeast England.

Macpherson (1892) was not definitive on the House Martin's status in Cumbria, but did note that "many colonies are established in the farms and country houses". Stokoe (1962) reported it to be widespread and fairly common, but noted some decline, in particular citing colonies in fell-side villages in north Westmorland which had halved in ten years. Brown (1974) also refers to a great fluctuation in the numbers nesting from year to year at any one site, while Hutcheson (1986) comments on some local declines but with no drastic reduction in the county's population overall.

A comparison between *this Atlas* and the *Old Atlas* also indicates a stable county population. With the species present in 84 10km squares and little change in distribution recorded, it is fair to assume that their habitat in Cumbria is not changing rapidly, and hence the population remains relatively steady. However the situation is very different when viewed at the tetrad level: although in *this Atlas* there are occupied tetrads in every 10km square, none has every tetrad occupied. While still well represented in lowland areas supporting high levels of human occupation, such as the Eden Valley, Solway Basin and Coastal Plain, as its wider distribution within Britain suggests, the species avoids the uplands of the Cumbria Dales, North Pennines, Border Uplands and central Lakeland.

Analysis of line transect data from *this Atlas* gives a population band of 52,000–133,000, suggesting a mean population of 83,000 birds. The highest densities of 45 birds/km² occurred on the transitional zone between the urbanized Coastal Plain and Lakeland.

As with the Swallow, a decline in insect populations generally, and especially those associated with agricultural land, bodes ill for this species. In addition, it is reliant on nesting near sources of wet mud, which are becoming scarcer as ponds are drained and generally tidied up. It is however a species which takes readily to nestboxes, and a concerted nestbox scheme could certainly help it. Some householders object to these birds nesting on their property on the grounds of the mess made; however this seems a small price to pay

 Sponsored by Andy & Isabel Senior

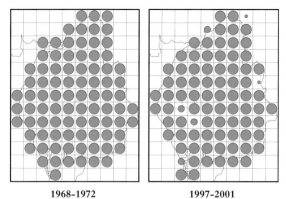

| 1968–1972 | 1997–2001 |
|---|---|

(For explanation of maps, see page 45)

***Conservation status***

| | |
|---|---|
| European: | Non-SPEC |
| UK: | **AMBER: BDM** |

***Populations***

| | |
|---|---|
| European status: | 12,000,000 |
| Britain – pairs: | 375,000 |
| Cumbria – pairs: | 41,500 |

***30-year distribution change***

| | Old Atlas | This Atlas | % |
|---|---|---|---|
| No. of 10km squares: | 87 | 84 | −3.4 |

| **Survey data** | **Tetrads** | **%** |
|---|---|---|
| Confirmed breeding: | 545 | 29.6 |
| Probable breeding: | 169 | 9.2 |
| Possible breeding: | 120 | 6.5 |
| Total: | 834 | 45.2 |

to help such a striking and charismatic species to survive in the increasingly bird-hostile modern environment.

Jake Manson

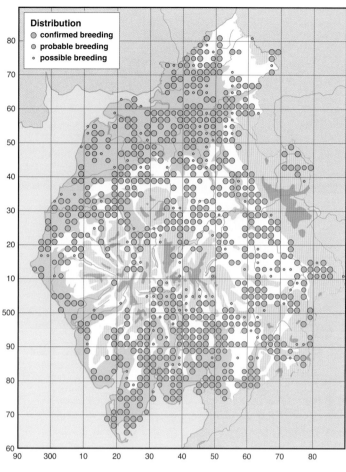

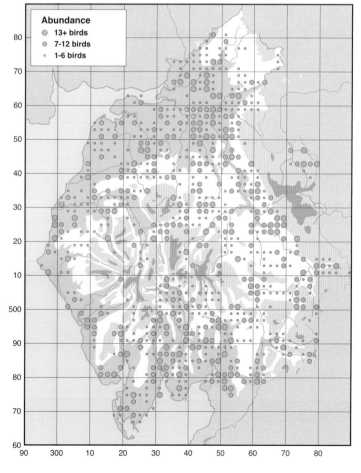

# Tree Pipit *Anthus trivialis*

THE Tree Pipit would pass unnoticed by many were it not for its distinctive and exuberant song and characteristic, parachuting display-flight down to an exposed tree-top. Once learned, the rich golden plumage tones with clean streaking help to distinguish it from the much commoner Meadow Pipit, with which it overlaps in both breeding and feeding habitats.

Within Europe it is almost universal, except for the coastal areas of the Mediterranean and much of Turkey. Beyond Europe the range extends to the far east of the former USSR in a broad swathe, with a southern extension to the western Himalaya. In Britain it is largely absent from the low-lying counties of East Anglia and from eastern Scotland, Orkney, Shetland, and the Outer Hebrides. Its stronghold areas are the wooded upland areas of western England, Wales, the Pennines and Scotland, where it occupies open woodlands and heaths with occasional trees. It is very rare as a breeding bird in Ireland.

The male requires isolated song perches, so Tree Pipits are absent both from areas lacking trees and from woodland areas with a closed canopy. A sparse field and shrub layer, such as is often characteristic of grazed upland woodland, suits this species well, and it also finds a home, albeit a temporary one, in areas of clearfell in coniferous plantations. It nests in low cover, or more or less in the open. A shallow depression holding a cup of dry grass leaves and stems, often with moss foundation, is lined with finer grasses and hair and is built by the female alone.

Nationally, there has been a serious long-term decline in numbers since 1970 with the latest CBC index showing a 77% decline; the species has moved onto the BoCC Amber List. However, Tree Pipits were not affected by the west African droughts to the same degree as some other migrants, possibly because they winter in more wooded areas to the south of the Sahel zone, which was the subject of severe droughts in the mid-1970s. Between the *Old* and *New Atlas* periods, there was a reduction of 15% in the number of occupied 10km squares, more particularly in the eastern parts of Britain. This decline is considered to be primarily due to habitat loss or degradation. In Britain, they are affected by scrub removal, tree felling, loss of lowland heath, and urbanization, all of which to some degree are significant in Cumbrian.

At the end of the 19th century, Cumberland held many favoured haunts with birds even breeding sparsely along the North Pennines north of Appleby; however, the species was not as abundant in Furness and southern Westmorland as could have been expected considering the amount of apparently suitable habitat available (Macpherson 1892). Stokoe (1962) considered it to be locally common and frequently met with in open country with scattered trees, up to 210m asl, although it was decreasing in the Carlisle district. This decline was first noted in 1945, when birds still bred in the country lanes around Carlisle, but the species was absent from here by 1970 (Brown 1974). The *New Atlas* reaffirmed this range contraction with further losses apparent in the Solway Basin.

A comparison between *this Atlas* and the *Old Atlas* emphasizes this decline; currently the species is largely absent from the Solway Basin, North Pennines, Cumbria Dales, Lune Valley and Furness peninsula. Its strongholds are the Border Uplands, lower Eden Valley and Lakeland, where the largest populations are found in the well-wooded valleys in the south of this area. Tree Pipits are highly visible and audible birds during the breeding season, which makes it an easy species to survey with a high degree of confidence. This picture of decline, especially in the east of the county, matches the national trend and could suggest a climatic factor is at work in addition to habitat changes.

Analysis of line transect data from *this Atlas* gives a population band of 10,000–22,000, suggesting a mean population of 14,000 males. The highest densities of 5.4 males/km$^2$ occurred, perhaps surprisingly, in areas predominantly of rough grazing and scattered woodland or afforestation, such as the foothills of the North Pennines and south Lakeland.

The reasons for the decline of this species indicate that habitat preservation is the main hope of halting the trend. In large areas of the county, suitable habitat is probably not under significant threat, and is already protected in the National Park. In other areas however, where it was previously common, the decline looks set

 Sponsored by Gordon Clarke

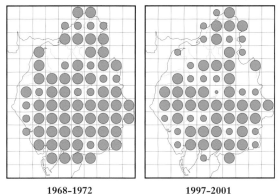

**1968–1972**      **1997–2001**
(For explanation of maps, see page 45)

*Conservation status*
European:              Non-SPEC
UK:                 **AMBER: BDM**

*Populations*
European status:       17,000,000
Britain – pairs:         120,000
Cumbria – pairs:        14,000

*30-year distribution change*

|  | Old Atlas | This Atlas | % |
|---|---|---|---|
| No. of 10km squares: | 71 | 64 | **−8.4** |

| **Survey data** | **Tetrads** | **%** |
|---|---|---|
| Confirmed breeding: | 128 | 6.9 |
| Probable breeding: | 308 | 16.7 |
| Possible breeding: | 46 | 2.5 |
| Total: | 482 | 26.1 |

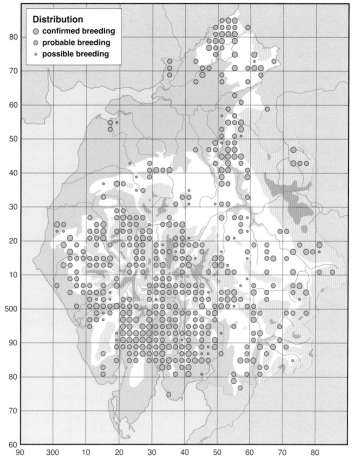

to continue. Sensitive management of woodland and heathland would help, and the recent trend towards broad-leaved planting might be of benefit in future years. Meanwhile its return to the lanes around Carlisle seems unlikely.

Jake Manson

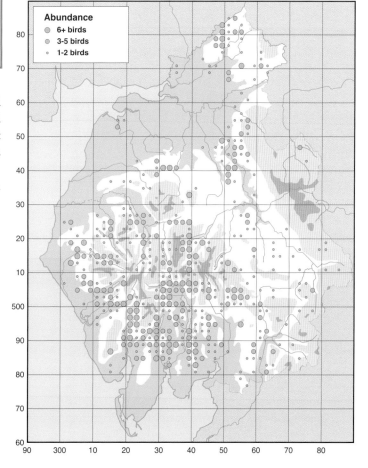

# Meadow Pipit *Anthus pratensis*

EITHER parachuting down in its display flight or flicking up from amongst bracken and heather, with a characteristic *'seep, seep'* alarm call, the Meadow Pipit is so much a part of the upland scene that it is often ignored by human observers. It is, however, an integral component of several habitats, not least moorland. Despite its familiarity, much remains to be learned about this dainty little bird.

A Western Palearctic species, its range extends from Iceland and Scandinavia through central and northern Europe, including Britain and Ireland, eastwards to western Siberia. It nests from sea-level to over 1,000m asl, occupying various habitats including saltmarshes, flood meadows, rough grassland, lowland heaths, grazed fens, bogs, and moorland. Indeed, over 500m asl it is often the commonest nesting passerine. The Meadow Pipit prefers breeding habitats which are open but not too dry, with relatively thick vegetation of a varied composition and structure, providing nest sites and insect food. The well-hidden nest of dried grass is built on the ground with finer grass and hair lining the small neat cup. The laying period is from April to June, with most pairs attempting a second brood.

The Meadow Pipit has long been a widely distributed species, breeding throughout Britain and Ireland. However, there are major regional variations in densities. It has always been thinly distributed in the English lowlands, except on lowland heath, coastal dunes and saltmarsh, and is suspected to have declined in the 20th century as a result of changes in farming, such as conversion from grassland to arable. Elsewhere, despite CBC and BBS data showing recent declines, it

is still very common in northern England, Wales, Scotland and Ireland with densities of 25–50 breeding pairs/km² occurring on saltmarsh, sheepwalk and moorland habitats.

Long term CBC monitoring provides useful trend data and shows a 35% decline since 1970, but unfortunately this under-represents the upland habitats where the bulk of the population breeds. This index recorded an initial increase in the early 1960s, followed by fluctuating levels through the 1970s and then a decline during the early 1980s. The *New Atlas* reflects this decline with range contractions most evident in the south of England and the Midlands.

In Cumbria, at the end of the 19th century, Macpherson (1892) described the Meadow Pipit as the commonest bird on the hills in the summer and also mentions it as breeding on lowland mosses, recently reclaimed rough meadows and in coastal areas as far as the high-water mark. The species will have suffered local declines in areas of post-war forestry plantings, although these would be initially beneficial, and more widespread declines are likely to have occurred as a result of intensification of land use in the uplands, including the loss of hay meadows, 'improvement' of pastures, and over-grazing of moorland. Despite this a countywide distribution was maintained through the 20th century, with populations remaining relatively stable. Indeed, Stokoe (1962) considered it to be numerous, with birds breeding in rough open country from the coast to 885m asl.

During the period between the *Old* and *New Atlases,* the Meadow Pipit's Cumbrian breeding distribution remained unchanged. The results of *this Atlas* confirm the widespread occurrence of the species within the county, but also emphasize its preference for moorland and fellside habitats. Although birds are still to be found along the Coastal Plain it is most abundant in the North Pennines, Cumbria Dales and higher ground of Lakeland, while birds are noticeably absent from the Eden Valley and much of the Solway Basin.

Analysis of line transect data from *this Atlas* gives a population band of 360,000–460,000, suggesting a mean population of 410,000 birds. The highest densities of 150 birds/km² were found, perhaps not surprisingly, in the uplands.

A partial migrant, ringing and observational evidence suggests that many birds leave the county in autumn to overwinter in southern Europe and North Africa. It has been suggested that climate change may have a major influence on Meadow Pipit populations, the decrease during the 1980s possibly being a result of harsher winters in southern Europe, combined with colder, wetter summers in Britain. Despite the widespread distribution in the county, increased grazing pressure on moorland and intensification of grassland production are also likely to have

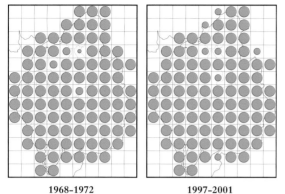

**1968–1972**          **1997–2001**
(For explanation of maps, see page 45)

| Conservation status | |
|---|---|
| European: | Non-SPEC |
| UK: | AMBER: BDM |

*Populations*

| | |
|---|---|
| European status: | 9,000,000 |
| Britain – pairs: | 1,900,000 |
| Cumbria – pairs: | 205,000 |

*30-year distribution change*

| | Old Atlas | This Atlas | % |
|---|---|---|---|
| No. of 10km squares: | 94 | 94 | n/c |

| Survey data | Tetrads | % |
|---|---|---|
| Confirmed breeding: | 975 | 52.9 |
| Probable breeding: | 308 | 16.7 |
| Possible breeding: | 77 | 4.2 |
| Total: | 1360 | 73.8 |

contributed to the decline in Meadow Pipit populations. Now that such habitat changes have slowed, and show indications of reversing under conservation schemes, climate change aside, the future within the county for this adaptable species seems reasonably secure.

Sean Reed

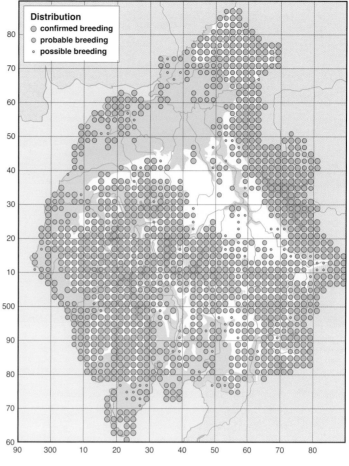

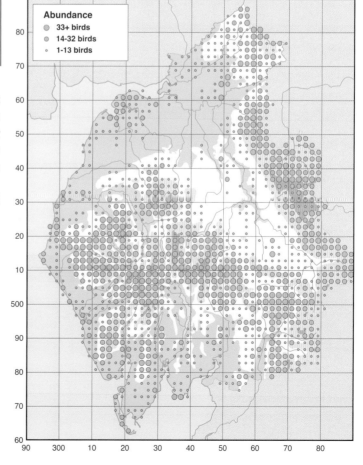

# Rock Pipit *Anthus petrosus*

THIS stout-hearted denizen of the coast is completely at home in amongst the rocks and boulders that form the most conspicuous feature of its rather limited habitat in Cumbria, and at some times of the year it can be the only passerine present. Its rather grey tones and thinner more metallic voice pick it out from the Meadow Pipit, a species which often occurs along shores outside the breeding season, and may also nest close by.

The range of this species extends from Britain and Ireland to western France, and the coastal fringes of Fennoscandia and the northwest of the former USSR. The Rock Pipit is well-represented in Britain, although absent from the 'soft' eastern coastline south of Flamborough Head, and sparsely distributed along the south coast of England. Given its absence from much of the predominantly estuarine shores of northwestern England, the isolated Cumbrian population has regional significance.

This species is very selective in its choice of nesting habitat, showing a strong preference for rocky coastlines; it is unknown in Cumbria's many rocky habitats away from the coast, and is found in other coastal habitats only outside the breeding season. It nests in a hole or hollow in a cliff or bank, or may use thick vegetation to conceal the nest cup, which is made of grasses, stems and leaves. The female alone builds the nest, and as befits this shorebird, may include seaweed in its construction. A suitable nest site may be used for many years.

Between the *Old* and *New Atlas* periods an 11% decline in the number of occupied 10km squares in Britain was recorded, with the main losses reported from the coasts of southwest England, Wales and eastern Scotland. Mead (2000) notes that these losses were mainly from low-lying, sandy coastlines, including those of northwest England. Similar declines were also recorded in Ireland at this time. However, the species remains largely under-surveyed and the limited information available is insufficient to predict any trends at a local or national level.

In Cumbria, at the end of the 19th century, Macpherson (1892) reported that "there is only one bit of marsh in the English Solway district that holds a pair of Rock Pipits in breeding time" but unfortunately he did not give the location. He also noted that "it is not plentiful in the summer time on Walney Island", where the sole breeding record occurred in 1864 (Dean 1990), and reported the main breeding location as St Bees Head. This was reaffirmed by Stokoe (1962), who gave a population estimate of 28 pairs, and this locality was to remain the breeding stronghold for the species in the county into the 1990s. However, the *Old Atlas* showed that the Rock Pipit's distribution was beginning to expand northwards from St Bees Head and this was confirmed by the *New Atlas* which also found evidence of breeding once again on the saltmarshes of the inner Solway.

While the red sandstone cliffs of St Bees Head are a well-known nesting area, this survey also found concentrations northwards along the coast to Whitehaven, Workington and Maryport. The absence of nesting from the Solway area and from Walney Island would appear to be consistent with the observations of Mead (2000), and this seems to be a genuine contraction in range in Cumbria.

For such a scarce breeding species with a restricted range, it is possible to gauge its numbers based on count data from *this Atlas* and local knowledge, although this will only hint at a current county population of 20–40 breeding pairs, since inaccessible areas along the base of the cliffs at St Bees Head may hold hitherto unknown nest sites.

The closest significant populations to Cumbria are on the Scottish Solway and the Isle of Man, and, given the isolation of the Cumbrian population from these, the few pockets of suitable habitat which lie empty around the coast are likely to remain unoccupied, although they may be sporadically used, as historical data would suggest.

This is likely to remain a local species in the county. Potential threats faced include the extension of agriculture right up to cliff and shore edges, reducing foraging areas, disturbance from recreational use of the coast, and marine pollution. There is no strong evidence to date that any of these has had a detrimental effect on the local population; rather it is the isolation from the main British populations, and

 Sponsored by a CBC Member

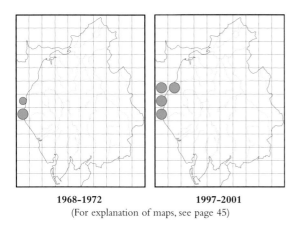

**1968-1972**          **1997-2001**
(For explanation of maps, see page 45)

*Conservation status*

| | |
|---|---|
| European: | Non-SPEC |
| UK: | **GREEN** |

*Populations*

| | |
|---|---|
| European status: | 400,000 |
| Britain – pairs: | 34,000 |
| Cumbria – pairs: | 20–40 |

*30-year distribution change*

| | Old Atlas | This Atlas | % |
|---|---|---|---|
| No. of 10km squares: | 2 | 4 | +100 |

| Survey data | Tetrads | % |
|---|---|---|
| Confirmed breeding: | 8 | 0.4 |
| Probable breeding: | 1 | 0.05 |
| Possible breeding: | 1 | 0.05 |
| Total: | 10 | 0.5 |

the limited availability of suitable habitat, which may be the principal factors affecting the Rock Pipit in Cumbria.

Jake Manson

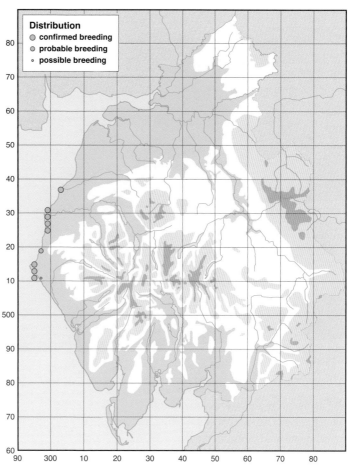

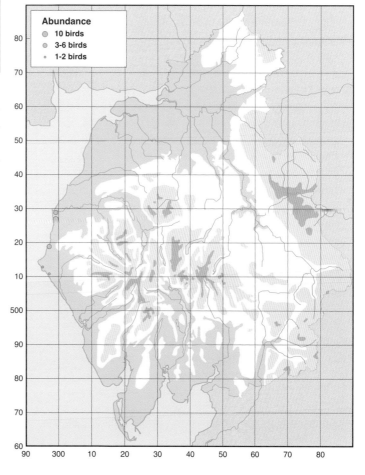

# Yellow Wagtail *Motacilla flava*

FOR those still fortunate enough to witness it, the sight of this, the most graceful and fairylike of our wagtails, as it dances in the air over marshy fields or darts to and fro after insects disturbed by grazing cattle, is one of the delights of spring. In the breeding season, this ground nesting bird is largely associated with marshy fields, particularly those in the lower reaches of river valleys.

The Yellow Wagtail is a member of a complex represented throughout its Western Palearctic range by several races – or perhaps species – with quite different head patterns. The race *M.f. flavissima* has a very restricted breeding range, with its principal base in southeast England, though it also nests locally in coastal districts of the adjacent continent from northern France to southwest Norway. Cumbria is currently situated close to the northern limit of its range in Britain, with the bird having retreated as a breeding species from southern Scotland, west Wales, southwest England and Ireland between the 1930s and 1950s (Simms 1992).

The status of the Yellow Wagtail in Cumbria has undergone some dramatic changes over the last 150 years. Macpherson (1892) described it as "a decidedly scarce summer visitant to Lakeland." It increased and extended its range from the 1920s onwards, reaching a peak in the late 1940s and 1950s, when it was described as a "common summer visitor", nesting in the alluvial meadows and delta land around many of the lakes and some of the tarns of Lakeland, on meadows and rough pastures in the Eden Valley, in the

fell-foot country of the North Pennines and the valley bottoms of the Lune Valley and Cumbria Dales, up to an altitude of 305m asl and, more locally, within the Solway Basin (Blezard *et al* 1943, Cleasby 1999, Stokoe 1962). A substantial and widespread decline has taken place since then, however, with birds disappearing from the Border Uplands and much of the North Pennines and Coastal Plain. Where it does still breed, densities have fallen significantly. The decline in Cumbria is mirrored in other parts of Britain; analysis of the latest available CBC data reveals a 31% decline since 1970.

As with many long-distance migrants, the causes of the Yellow Wagtail's decline are likely to involve a complex combination of factors. Losses of important floodplain habitats have taken place in the winter quarters in West Africa since the 1960s, while a series of cold, wet springs in northern Britain from the early 1960s to the late 1980s are likely to have adversely affected breeding success. A significant reduction in hay meadows and rushy moorland pastures as a result of drainage operations, increased commercial afforestation and changes in grassland management regimes is a further contributory factor particularly relevant to northern Britain. Animals and machinery are now often brought onto the land several weeks earlier in the year than was the case a few decades ago, resulting in increased trampling by cattle, destruction of nests and eggs by farm machinery and a reduction in the opportunities for repeat nesting. Increases in natural predators, such as the Red Fox and Carrion Crow, to which ground-nesting birds are particularly vulnerable, may be a further factor.

Results of *this Atlas* reveal a very patchy distribution in the county, with a current population of 30–50 breeding pairs, derived from count data enhanced by supplementary records. Most nesting birds are to be found in the valleys of the Lune, Kent and Leven in the south; in the Eden Valley, particularly its upper reaches, in the east; and in the Solway Basin in the north. Just a handful remain in Lakeland, around Windermere and Derwent Water.

Predictions that the range of the Yellow Wagtail could begin to extend northwards again as a consequence of global warming must be regarded as highly speculative. Whilst there may be a slight increase in average temperatures over the next few decades, there is a strong probability that this will be associated with an increased incidence of wetter, stormier weather in spring and early summer and increased drought conditions in the birds' winter quarters. This, together with a continuation of some of the factors outlined above, does not bode well for the future of the Yellow Wagtail in Cumbria.

Sponsored by Kath Atkinson

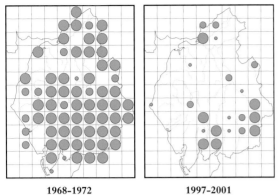

**1968-1972**          **1997-2001**
(For explanation of maps, see page 45)

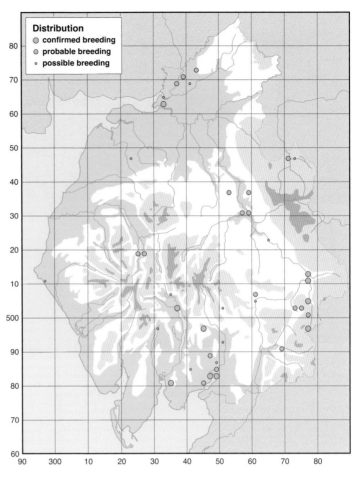

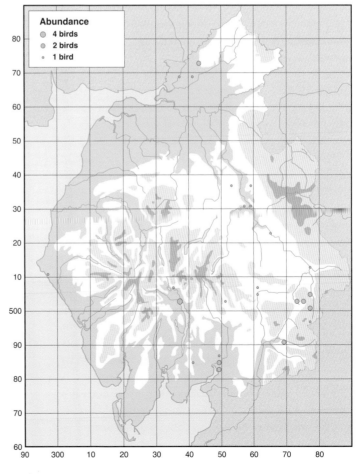

**Conservation status**

| | |
|---|---|
| European: | Non-SPEC |
| UK: | AMBER: BDM |

**Populations**

| | |
|---|---|
| European status: | 4,500,000 |
| Britain – pairs: | 50,000 |
| Cumbria – pairs: | 30–50 |

**30-year distribution change**

| | Old Atlas | This Atlas | % |
|---|---|---|---|
| No. of 10km squares: | 66 | 22 | −66.6 |

| **Survey data** | **Tetrads** | **%** |
|---|---|---|
| Confirmed breeding: | 10 | 0.5 |
| Probable breeding: | 18 | 1.0 |
| Possible breeding: | 13 | 0.7 |
| Total: | 41 | 2.2 |

**Blue-headed Wagtail** *Motacilla flava flava*
This attractive race of the Yellow Wagtail occurs almost annually in the county, mostly on spring passage. Birds with characters suggestive of this race have nested on a few occasions. It is not known if any of these birds do in fact originate within the range of Blue-headed Wagtail, or are locally-bred mutants resembling this race. Such mutants are known to arise at times in isolated populations. Pairs nested at Alston in 1928 (Blezard *et al* 1943) and in the foothills of the Northern Pennines in 1983 (Hutcheson 1986). In 1991, a pair nested successfully in fields alongside the Kent Estuary and a male was paired with a female of unspecified race at Bassenthwaite Lake. During the period of *this Atlas,* a male and female were at South Walney on 1st May 1998 and single males were at Meathop on 13th June 1998 and Milnthorpe sewage works on 21st April 2000, but there was no evidence of breeding.

Clive Hartley

# Grey Wagtail *Motacilla cinerea*

THE contrasting slate grey back and brilliant buttercup yellow underparts of the Grey Wagtail are a familiar sight of fast-flowing, upland watercourses, as it darts through the air, twisting and turning in search of insects, before swooping down to a stone in mid-stream.

The Grey Wagtail's breeding range stretches across Eurasia, embracing the temperate and warm temperate zones in the west and the temperate and boreal zones in the east. It is widely distributed in Britain and Ireland, though scarce or absent from much of lowland, eastern England and scarce too in the Outer Hebrides, Orkney and Shetland.

The bird's basic requirements for breeding include the presence of rocks, boulders or shingle, with riffles of disturbed water passing over them; the shelter and food resources from overhanging trees and shrubs; and the availability of holes and ledges for nests. These conditions are most widely met with in the upland areas of the north and west of Britain and in Ireland, where the bird is at its most numerous, although it also breeds by the faster-running sections of lowland rivers and lakes, down to sea level, and alongside man-made features, such as weirs, locks and mill-races.

The population of the Grey Wagtail in Britain increased during the first half of the 20th century, with this increase being most marked in the more marginal areas of the east and south of England. This period of expansion came to an end with the hard winter of 1962/63, which resulted in severe losses, especially in southeast England (Parslow 1973). Numbers have fluctuated since then, with a period of gradual recovery in the 1970s being followed by further losses during hard winters. Analysis of the latest available WBS data reveals a 48% decline in the population since 1974, though the high proportion of WBS plots in sub-optimal lowland habitat may serve to exaggerate the scale of this decline. The species is double-brooded and it is claimed that it can normally recover quite quickly from natural depletions in its population, though WBS data would seem to contradict that view.

In Cumbria, Macpherson (1892) described the Grey Wagtail as common, with the bird to be found nesting on most rivers. Stokoe (1962) regarded it as "frequent on streams and swifter rivers, breeding up to 1,500 feet [457m]." In contrast to the national picture, a review of the literature since that date, including the results of previous atlases, provides no evidence of any substantial long-term decline in the status and distribution of the Grey Wagtail in the county. Whilst there have been short-term fluctuations, particularly in response to severe winter weather, over the long term, the population appears to have remained relatively stable.

During *this Atlas,* 70% of records came from the relatively swift-flowing rivers and streams that drain the fells of the North Pennines and parts of Lakeland. Here, where deciduous trees bound the watercourses, densities reached 4 birds/km², almost double those found on slower flowing rivers in the transition zone between Lakeland and the Coastal Plain. Densities fell further, to less than 1 bird/km², where slow-moving waters meander across flat alluvial plains such as the Solway Basin.

The largely linear distribution of this species does not lend itself to easy analysis; the species would make a good subject for a dedicated survey. On a small sample, line transect data gives a population band of 4,000–23,000, and suggests a mean population of 10,000 birds, noting, however, the wide band limits. A subjective view based on count data and supplementary records would suggest a lower figure.

Studies of the ecology of the Grey Wagtail, in both upland and lowland situations, indicate that, unlike the Dipper, its breeding abundance is little affected by the acidification of watercourses, probably because a significant proportion of its insect prey is of non-aquatic origin (Ormerod & Tyler 1987). This is particularly so where streams are lined with broad-leaved trees, with adult flies being numerically the most important prey and spiders and caterpillars of value in the diet of nestlings. Notwithstanding this, the pollution of watercourses, particularly as a result of the

 Sponsored by Keswick Natural History Society

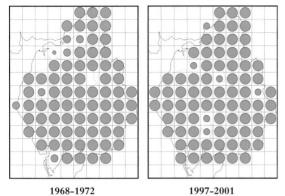

**1968-1972**   **1997-2001**

(For explanation of maps, see page 45)

**Conservation status**

| | |
|---|---|
| European: | Non-SPEC |
| UK: | **AMBER: BDM** |

**Populations**

| | |
|---|---|
| European status: | 720,000 |
| Britain – pairs: | 34,000 |
| Cumbria – pairs: | 5,000 |

**30-year distribution change**

| | Old Atlas | This Atlas | % |
|---|---|---|---|
| No. of 10km squares: | 77 | 80 | +3.9 |

| **Survey data** | **Tetrads** | **%** |
|---|---|---|
| Confirmed breeding: | 303 | 16.4 |
| Probable breeding: | 206 | 11.2 |
| Possible breeding: | 136 | 7.4 |
| Total: | 645 | 35.0 |

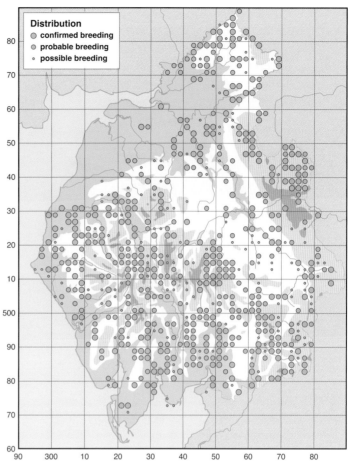

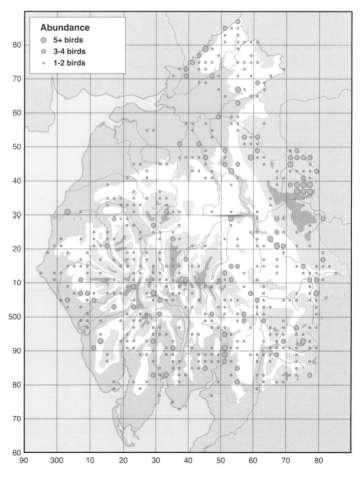

careless use or improper disposal of synthetic pyrethroid sheep dips, poses a potential threat to the Grey Wagtail population. The bird's dependence on shallow runs of water and bankside nest sites means that it is also vulnerable to direct alteration of the course of rivers through straightening and dredging. Fortunately, this is far less likely to occur on Cumbria's game fishing rivers than on watercourses in some other parts of Britain. For these reasons, and taking into account the likelihood of an increased incidence of warmer, wetter winters and springs over the coming decades, the immediate prospects for this most elegant and vivacious bird in Cumbria appear to be reasonably well assured.

Clive Hartley

# Pied Wagtail *Motacilla alba*

C.H.Isherwood

THE distinctive black and white plumage of the Pied Wagtail, with its confiding nature and tendency to breed in close proximity to man, make this the most familiar of our wagtails. It is a busy little bird, often to be seen running swiftly here and there across farm tracks or the roofs of farm buildings, before leaping into the air or taking short flights in pursuit of the gnats and flies on which it feeds.

The Pied Wagtail is one of a number of races of 'alba wagtails' that are widely distributed across Eurasia, breeding in all climatic zones from the warm temperate to the Arctic. The bird occurs throughout all parts of Britain and Ireland and, sparingly, along the west coast of Europe, where its breeding range overlaps with that of the nominate White Wagtail. It reaches its greatest breeding density in the north and west of Britain and in parts of Ireland, where areas of mixed farming still predominate and nest sites are readily available in the form of dry-stone walls. It will nest up to 700m asl, but largely deserts the uplands in favour of lower ground in winter, with many Cumbrian birds moving to southern England, France, southern Spain and Portugal.

Less closely associated with water than other wagtails, Pied Wagtails favour areas of open country under mixed cultivation and are frequently to be found around farms and farm buildings, sheep and cattle pastures, roadways and tracks, airfields and parks and gardens, where the vegetation cover is low and there are open spaces. The bird nests in holes, crevices or ledges in stone walls as well as natural fissures. It feeds on small invertebrates, including midges, adult and larval mayflies and grasshoppers, dragonflies,

damselflies, spiders and small snails. Pairs breeding along roadsides often take insects damaged by vehicles and caterpillars falling from overhanging trees.

Macpherson (1892) considered the Pied Wagtail a common and widespread breeding bird in Cumbria. Whilst there have been short-term fluctuations since, its status and distribution appear to have remained largely unchanged up to the present day. The *New Atlas* indicated that the Pied Wagtail had undergone a significant decline in eastern England since the 1970s, particularly in areas where mixed farmland had been replaced by arable crops, with concomitant high inputs of chemicals, dearth of livestock and disappearance of farm ponds. Fortunately, this experience has not been replicated in the north and west of Britain, with an expansion of range having taken place into the Outer Hebrides, Orkney and Shetland during this period, along with an increase in the number of breeding birds in the west of Ireland. Analysis of the latest available CBC data indicates a 45% increase nationally since 1970.

Fieldwork for *this Atlas* confirms that the Pied Wagtail remains one of the most widely distributed birds in the county, found in all but four 10km squares. In many parts of Cumbria, modern farming methods have robbed the bird of one of its most reliable former food sources, the traditional farmyard. Yet although straw-bedded courts have been almost entirely replaced by supposedly more hygienic slurry systems and more efficient methods of insect control have been introduced, these changes appear to have had little impact on the species' county distribution. The highest breeding densities of 33.4 birds/km² were recorded on the narrow coastal strip, backed by good quality farmland. Further inland, on the Coastal Plain and parts of the Solway Basin, densities fell to 22.8 birds/km², with a further decrease to 17.2 birds/km² at higher altitudes on the edge of Lakeland. In the east, densities declined from 16.2 birds/km² in the Eden Valley to just 4.9 birds/km² in more elevated open moorland habitats. As might be expected, birds were absent from the high tops and the heavily afforested parts of the Border Uplands.

Analysis of the line transect data from *this Atlas* gives a population band of 76,000–126,000, suggesting a current county population of 96,000 birds.

Despite the fact that a substantial proportion of Cumbria's birds moves south for the winter, the Pied Wagtail population is susceptible to severe winter weather conditions (Cawthorne & Marchant 1980), although numbers have been generally quick to recover, particularly after a series of mild winters. Future climate change scenarios suggest an increased incidence of warmer, wetter winters and springs over the next few decades. This, together with the bird's adaptability, means that the Pied Wagtail is likely to

Sponsored by Margaret Roberts

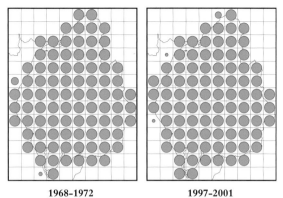

**1968-1972**          **1997-2001**

(For explanation of maps, see page 45)

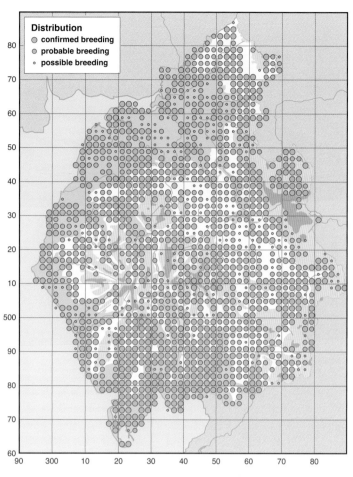

Distribution
- confirmed breeding
- probable breeding
- possible breeding

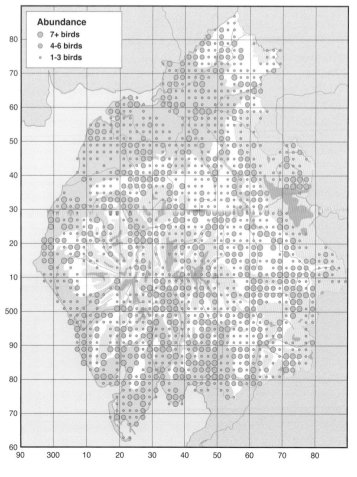

Abundance
- 7+ birds
- 4-6 birds
- 1-3 birds

---

**Conservation status**

| | |
|---|---|
| European: | Non-SPEC |
| UK: | **GREEN** |

**Populations**

| | |
|---|---|
| European status: | 9,000,000 |
| Britain – pairs: | 300,000 |
| Cumbria – pairs: | 48,000 |

**30-year distribution change**

| | Old Atlas | This Atlas | % |
|---|---|---|---|
| No. of 10km squares: | 89 | 90 | +1.1 |

| Survey data | Tetrads | % |
|---|---|---|
| Confirmed breeding: | 790 | 42.8 |
| Probable breeding: | 451 | 24.5 |
| Possible breeding: | 198 | 10.7 |
| Total: | 1,439 | 78.0 |

---

recover from any temporary setback which it may have suffered very recently through the cleansing operations associated with foot-and-mouth disease and that it will remain a familiar sight around Cumbrian farms for the foreseeable future.

**White Wagtail** *Motacilla alba alba*

This race is a common passage migrant through the county, most often recorded on its way north in spring when it is more easily identified. The first and only confirmed breeding attempt occurred in 1917, when a pair was seen feeding young near Grasmere (Blezard *et al* 1943). There have been no instances of summering or attempted breeding in the county since.

Clive Hartley

THE boundless energy and enterprise of this dapper semi-aquatic athlete are a true joy of our rivers all year round, with early spring territorial disputes and courting especially vocal and frenetic.

The Dipper is well distributed in river systems across Europe, North Africa and as far east as western China. In Britain and Ireland, the Dipper is widespread across the uplands and their fringes, being found up to 600m asl in Scotland, down to lowland rivers with suitable fast-flowing, gravelly shallows with abundant invertebrate food. This species' great charisma is heightened by several of its unusual habits. Nesting from mid-February, eggs are protected in a camouflaged domed nest of moss and grass stems tucked under riverbanks or artificial sites (*eg.* bridge overhangs). Food is secured by submerging in watercourses using a combination of walking and wing propulsion whilst shifting pebbles on the streambed to expose large invertebrates.

During the 19th century, numbers declined in Britain and Ireland due to persecution from anglers on northern trout and salmon waters, who regarded the Dipper as a competitor. Expanding industry, particularly mining in the uplands, also affected river water quality, with acidification and heavy metal contamination causing local extinctions.

Historically, the Dipper, also known as the Water Ouzel, Bessy Ducker and Water Pye, was always a common Cumbrian species. Macpherson (1892) records a strange outbreak of tree nesting around the Corby area, causing a flurry of interest in the local press. He also recounts observations in the Eden valley, with one account of a Dipper's thrush-like pasture-foraging during a period of high flow in the River Eden. Stokoe (1962) considered the Dipper "common on rivers and fell becks from coast to at least 1,500 feet [457m], occasionally nesting up to 2,250 feet [686m] and ranging higher still." He goes on to comment on decreases in Low Furness west of Ulverston, where "none is now known to breed" and says that "no nests were found on the River Liza or its tributaries above Ennerdale Water in 1961, though birds were present below the lake and in neighbouring valleys."

Recent localized declines in population densities across Britain and Ireland have been linked to upland afforestation, with resulting acidification of watercourses reducing preferred invertebrate prey, such as mayflies and caddis larvae and perhaps also creating calcium shortages for egg-laying females (Ormerod & Tyler 1987). Recent studies also show organochlorine residues and PCB traces in most Dippers analysed from Scotland, Wales and Ireland. These worrying findings are countered by research suggesting that breeding performance has improved over time as laying dates have become earlier, perhaps because of climate change (Crick & Sparks 1999).

The British population has fluctuated over the last 30 years with no obvious long-term trend, though the latest available WBS data indicate a 16% decline since 1974. This national picture appears to be reflected in Cumbria with no significant change in distribution found between the *Old Atlas* and *this Atlas*. However, small numbers of breeding birds do appear to have been lost from some lower lying stretches of the River Eden and other northern rivers.

During *this Atlas* period, Dippers were found in almost 25% of tetrads in the county. Most records occurred along upland watercourses throughout Lakeland, the North Pennines, the Cumbria Dales and the Border Uplands. Low densities in parts of central Lakeland probably reflect the acidic nature of many of these watercourses, with poor invertebrate loads reducing suitability for breeding (Ormerod & Tyler 1987). The highest abundance was recorded on the South Tyne and upper Lune, with a distinct decline with lowering altitudes onto the slower-moving waters of the Solway Basin and lower Eden Valley.

Analysis of line transect data from *this Atlas* gives a population band of 3,000–14,000, suggesting a current county population of 6,000 birds. Species with a linear distribution such as Dipper do not lend themselves to this type of survey, so these figures should be treated with caution. However, until a dedicated survey is undertaken it remains the best estimate available.

                    Sponsored by Barbara White

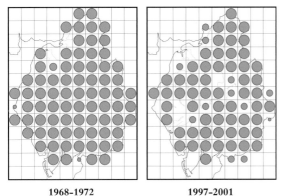

**1968-1972**          **1997-2001**

(For explanation of maps, see page 45)

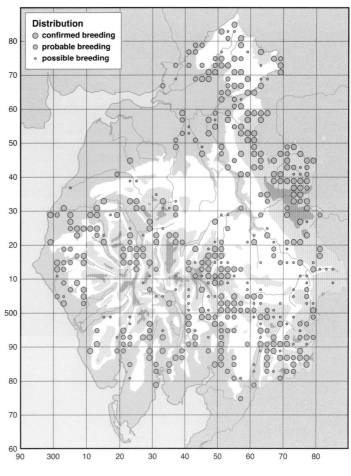

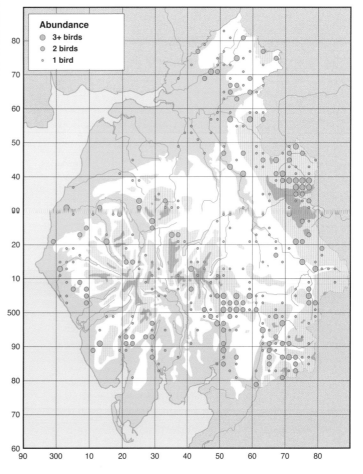

***Conservation status***

| | |
|---|---|
| European: | Non-SPEC |
| UK: | GREEN |

***Populations***

| | |
|---|---|
| European status: | 180,000 |
| Britain – pairs: | 14,000 |
| Cumbria – pairs: | 3,000 |

***30-year distribution change***

| | Old Atlas | This Atlas | % |
|---|---|---|---|
| No. of 10km squares: | 79 | 70 | **−11.4** |

| **Survey data** | **Tetrads** | **%** |
|---|---|---|
| Confirmed breeding: | 213 | 11.6 |
| Probable breeding: | 133 | 7.2 |
| Possible breeding: | 108 | 5.9 |
| Total: | 454 | 24.7 |

For the future, any factor impacting on river water quality or flow rates could have detrimental effects on populations. In the short-term, sympathetic forestry management (*eg.* in the Border Uplands) could be critical in maintaining populations close to softwood plantations. Conservation of riparian habitats, particularly in the uplands, will also be crucial; Cumbria holds nearly half the length of national riverine SSSI (624km), with four rivers warranting designation under EU legislation. Such designations may assist in targeting conservation funding to bring some upland streams and becks into better management. In the long term, the currently predicted global climate change, with a shift to wetter summers and potential for extreme precipitation, frequent flooding and changes in upland hydrology, might have a significant adverse effect on the breeding success of the Dipper.

Nick Mason

DESPITE its diminutive stature and habit of lurking in inaccessible undergrowth, picking off small invertebrates, the Wren is easily located by its unfeasibly loud, explosive song and characteristic 'ticking' alarm call.

A Holarctic and locally Oriental species, the Wren appears to have originated in the Americas, where there are many other species in the family, and it is thought likely to have crossed the North Pacific relatively recently, thereafter colonizing much of the Palearctic. It breeds throughout Britain and Ireland, though most numerous south of a line from the Mersey to the Humber. Compared to other European countries, the species is especially numerous in Britain and Ireland, with a population greater than those of France, Germany, Netherlands, Belgium and Italy combined.

Males set up territory in early spring, usually building several nests; the female, once attracted, may inspect several of these before selecting one in which to lay. The Wren tends to make its domed nest in small cracks, crevices or holes, often on banks, and usually protected by tangled vegetation. Although its preferred habitat is dense undergrowth within broad-leaved woodland and along river and stream banks, it is found in virtually every habitat, absent only from the very centre of large cities and the most uniform of low intensively managed vegetation. Frequently encountered on the slopes of the higher fells where there is tall heather or boulder fields, gaps in distribution usually reflect uplands denuded of dwarf shrub vegetation, either through intensive sheep-grazing or burning management, such as are to be found in parts of the Lune Valley and Lakeland. Moorland densities begin to decline at altitudes above 400m asl and the bird becomes progressively more localised over 600m asl. Its adaptability has meant that the Wren has been one of the most consistently widespread and abundant British birds. Despite major changes in farm practices and in the landscape itself, it retains that status to this day, occurring in 97% of the 10km squares in Britain.

Although the Wren is quite a resilient species, the major factor limiting its distribution appears not to be available habitat, but its own diminutive size and therefore its high surface/volume ratio, which causes rapid heat-loss, and hence fat-loss; its energy balance becomes critical when food supply is restricted in harsh winters. Cold periods – such as the 1962/63 winter when 80% or more of the population perished – produce drastic, but short-term, fluctuations. Temperature is the crucial factor; snow, in itself, is relatively unimportant as the birds can feed, and even roost, beneath it in masses of tangled vegetation or beneath piles of boulders. In favourable conditions, Wrens, being double-brooded, can raise 10 or more young in a season and have the ability to replenish their numbers in a remarkably short time. Analysis of the latest CBC data reveals a 25% increase nationally since 1970, though the species is prone to very large fluctuations from year to year.

In the late 19th century, the Wren was considered abundant in Lakeland (Macpherson 1892), and, 70 years later, Stokoe (1962) regarded it as "ubiquitous and common from shore-line up to 2,000 feet [610m] or more on high moorlands." The results from *this Atlas* show that the situation is much the same today, as the species occurs in every 10km square in Cumbria. It is generally absent only from tetrads covering the highest, most exposed ground of the North Pennines and Lakeland. However, though an almost obsessively vocal species, its presence could have been missed in these regions as territorial song may be reduced in areas of low density. The highest densities occur in coastal areas, where winter temperatures are generally milder, and in mixed farmland which offers the widest choice of suitable nesting and feeding habitats.

Analysis of the line transect data from *this Atlas* gives a population band of 114,000–166,000, suggesting a current county population of 130,000 males. The highest calculated densities of 43 males/km² were on the Coastal Plain.

If predictions about climate change prove accurate, the recent run of mild winters may well continue,

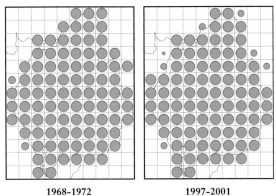

| 1968-1972 | 1997-2001 |
|:---:|:---:|

(For explanation of maps, see page 45)

*Conservation status*

| | |
|---|---|
| European: | Non-SPEC |
| UK: | **GREEN** |

*Populations*

| | |
|---|---|
| European status: | 22,000,000 |
| Britain – pairs: | 7,100,000 |
| Cumbria – pairs: | 130,000 |

*30-year distribution change*

| | Old Atlas | This Atlas | % |
|---|---|---|---|
| No. of 10km squares: | 92 | 93 | +1.1 |

| **Survey data** | **Tetrads** | **%** |
|---|---|---|
| Confirmed breeding: | 1,039 | 56.3 |
| Probable breeding: | 578 | 31.3 |
| Possible breeding: | 43 | 2.3 |
| Total: | 1,660 | 89.9 |

allowing even higher numbers in the future. While so many other species are suffering from the effects of habitat loss and land use change, the Wren's versatility has enabled it to adapt and continue to thrive.

Stephen Garnett

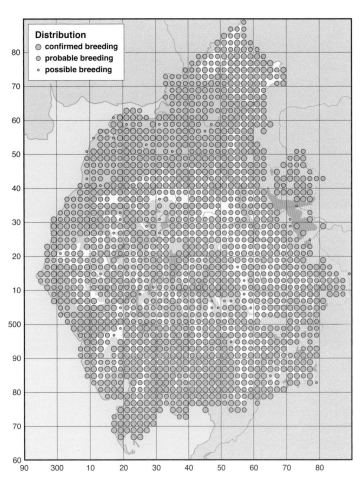

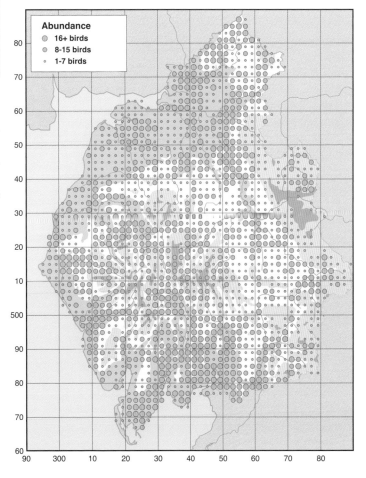

IN 1856, the Reverend F.O. Morris extolled the virtues of this quiet and unobtrusive bird to his parishioners and suggested that the species might form a role model for them. Little did the poor vicar know! For such a common bird, its behaviour was surprisingly unstudied until the early 1980s. Many people dismissed it as a 'little brown job'. What makes the species so interesting is that, unlike many European passerines, the Dunnock exhibits a range of mating systems. The commonest is monogamy, but polygyny, polyandry and even polygynandry are all regularly found. Male breeding success is highest when a male has more than one female, whilst female breeding success increases with the number of males helping to feed the chicks (Davies 1992). A hedge or bush are among the chosen nest sites, with the nest, usually supported by a small platform of twigs, neatly built from finer twigs, grass and moss and lined with hair and wool.

Unlike the other 11 accentor species, which are purely mountain dwellers, the Dunnock has relatively recently extended its range into lowland temperate habitats. It is primarily a species of scrub, but has taken advantage of the urbanization in Britain and Ireland to inhabit hedgerows, parks and gardens. Gregory and Baillie (1998), in an analysis of national populations, showed that the main habitats – scrub, suburban, rural and some farmland types – had over 20 birds/km².

The Dunnock is widely distributed across Europe. In the north and eastern parts of its range, the species is a summer migrant. In Britain and Ireland, it is a resident species with the highest abundance levels occurring in the south and east while northwest Scotland supports only low densities. The *New Atlas* reported that the national distribution was largely unchanged from the *Old Atlas* with just a 2.9% drop in the number of occupied 10km squares. However, there has been a shallow but progressive decline in the population with the latest CBC index showing a 44% fall since 1970. Nest record card analyses showed rising nestling mortality and a reduction in nest habitat diversity through the 1970s and early 1980s, but the driving force behind these changes remains unknown (O'Connor & Pearman 1987).

The Dunnock favours feeding close to cover. Most of its food is taken directly from the ground and consists primarily of small seeds and invertebrates such as beetles, flies, earthworms and spiders. Anecdotal evidence suggests that an increase in predator populations such as Magpies and Sparrowhawks may affect Dunnock numbers. At a study site in Cambridge University Botanical Gardens, neither predator was present through the 1980s. During this time, the colour-ringed population numbered some 70–80 birds. After the arrival of both Magpie and Sparrowhawk in the early 1990s, the population declined over a few years to 30–40 birds. The birds in the study area also appeared to change their behaviour as a result of predators being present. Whilst they had previously foraged in the open on the short cut lawns well away from shelter, they now restricted their feeding to areas of cover (N. Davies pers comm). The effect of this change appears to reduce the amount of feeding habitat available, which might impact on the ability to adequately feed nestlings. However, it should be stressed that the CBC index shows a sharp national decline for Dunnocks around this time and the arrival of Magpies and Sparrowhawks may be coincidental.

In Cumbria, the Dunnock was considered a numerous resident in the 19th century, "breeding up to 1,200 feet [366m] on the eastern fells" where it was known as the 'creepy-dyke' (Macpherson & Duckworth 1886). The population remained relatively stable well into the 20th century: Stokoe (1962) regarded it as "widespread and numerous throughout, reaching exposed situations with a minimum of cover in fell valleys and on the coast."

Compared to the *Old Atlas,* there has been little change in the Cumbrian distribution at the 10km square level although *this Atlas* reflects the species' preference for habitats containing scrub. The North Pennines and higher Lakeland fells have little in the way of trees and shrubs to attract Dunnocks, and as a result the bird is often absent or present only in low numbers. Lowland distribution is patchy, with fewer confirmed breeding records than one might expect. Whether this is attributable to the secretive nature of the species or low breeding densities is not clear.

Analysis of line transect data from *this Atlas* gives a population band of 63,000–109,000, suggesting a mean

          Sponsored by Jean Scott

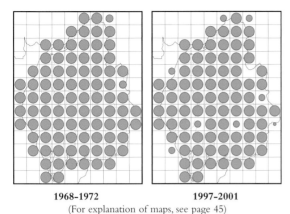

**1968-1972**  **1997-2001**
(For explanation of maps, see page 45)

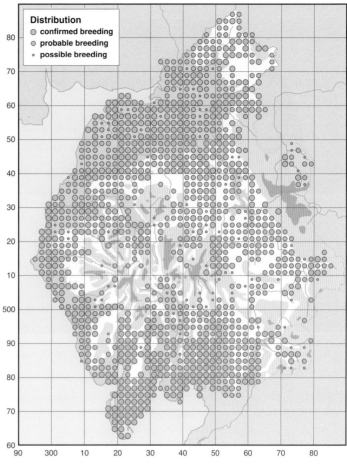

*Distribution*
- confirmed breeding
- probable breeding
- possible breeding

*Conservation status*

| | |
|---|---|
| European: | Non-SPEC |
| UK: | AMBER: BDM |

*Populations*

| | |
|---|---|
| European status: | 11,000,000 |
| Britain – pairs: | 2,000,000 |
| Cumbria – pairs: | 41,500 |

*30-year distribution change*

| | Old Atlas | This Atlas | % |
|---|---|---|---|
| No. of 10km squares: | 89 | 88 | −1.1 |

| **Survey data** | **Tetrads** | **%** |
|---|---|---|
| Confirmed breeding: | 576 | 31.2 |
| Probable breeding: | 530 | 28.7 |
| Possible breeding: | 89 | 4.8 |
| Total: | 1,195 | 63.7 |

population of 83,000 birds. The highest densities of 43.3 birds/km² occurred on varied lowland landscapes with hedged small fields, often close to urbanization, found on the Solway Basin and Coastal Plain.

It is unclear from *this Atlas* whether populations have actually declined in the county as they have across Britain and Ireland. Hopefully, a benchmark has been set against which changes can be monitored. It would appear that the main threats to the species come from habitat loss such as the grubbing out of hedgerows from farmland and the loss of scrub.

Phil Byle

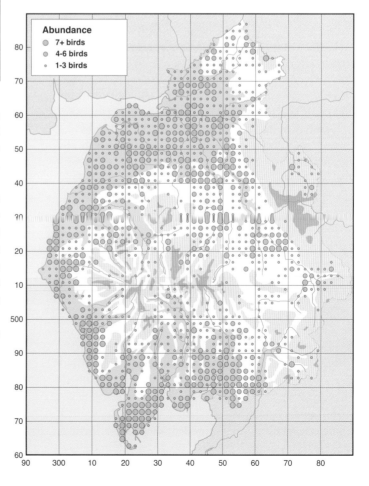

*Abundance*
- 7+ birds
- 4-6 birds
- 1-3 birds

THE Robin is perhaps the best known bird in Britain and its sweet but mellow song can be heard from a wide variety of habitats throughout the year, although it is very much less conspicuous as a breeding bird than it is in winter, when few gardens are without their resident Robin. As the breeding season progresses, adults seem to all but disappear, but soon the first spotty juveniles are afield, and later many a patch of brambles plays host to a 'ticking' bird as summer slips away. Once autumn arrives, it becomes difficult to distinguish resident breeders from incoming migrants.

Breeding across the Western Palearctic, the Robin is absent only from southeast Europe and northern Scandinavia. It is also absent from the Ural Mountains, but east of that, its range extends into central Asia. The species breeds throughout Britain and Ireland, being most abundant in Ireland and south of a line between the Dee and Wash. It is scarce or absent only from areas with few trees such as the fens of East Anglia and the Northern Isles, or from upland areas such as the Scottish Highlands.

The nest is usually built in a natural hollow in a tree stump or bank, among tree roots, in a rock crevice, or in a hollow tree. However, it may use artificial holes in man-made objects, the classic item being an old kettle, while it also takes readily to nestboxes. The nest consists of a base of dead leaves, on which a cup of moss, grass and leaves is built, lined with hair, vegetable fibre, or occasionally feathers, and is built by the female alone. Generally double-brooded, the female usually deserts the young before they are fledged, leaving the male to feed them, while she builds a new nest and lays

a second clutch. When the second brood hatches, the male is ready to help feed them as the first brood are now independent. It is not unknown for pairs to raise three or four broods in a season, the last clutches being sometimes not laid until July (Lack 1965).

Nationally, the distribution shown in the *New Atlas* is very similar to that in the *Old Atlas,* and the latest CBC index shows a 23% increase since 1970. In Cumbria, historical accounts all allude to the species being widespread and numerous in lowland and woodland areas (Macpherson 1892, Stokoe 1962). Given the generally stable national picture, the likelihood is that the Cumbrian population has also remained relatively stable. Certainly, comparison of *this Atlas* with the *Old Atlas* supports this probability, with the distribution unchanged, although local variations in tetrad abundance are not discernible without comparable data.

During *this Atlas* the Robin was found to be almost ubiquitous. With its habitat requirements of woodland, gardens, scrub, or any area with reasonably dense vegetation cover, it is totally absent only from the high ground of the North Pennines, Cumbria Dales and Lakeland. It is somewhat scarcer in the west of the Solway Basin than might be expected, possibly due to the relative lack of woodland and scrub, and, reflecting the national picture, the more intensive agriculture practised in this area.

Analysis of line transect data from *this Atlas* gives a population band of 200,000–270,000, suggesting a mean population of 230,000 birds. The highest calculated densities of 68.4 birds/km$^2$ occurred in the low-lying well-wooded areas of the Coastal Plain and Solway Basin. In comparison, just 2.4 birds/km$^2$ were found among the highest fellside plantations.

The Robin would appear to be not only one of the commonest breeding birds in Cumbria, but also one of the least prone to change. There may have been some losses in arable areas, but new housing with gardens and shrubs elsewhere has probably more than compensated for this. Historically, there have been periods of decline nationally, due to the effects of hard winter weather, although these have never been long-lasting, with the species returning to its former numbers within several years. At the risk of seeming complacent, little if any action seems to be required to support this species, although the possible local impact of intensive agricultural practices will need to be monitored in future.

Jake Manson

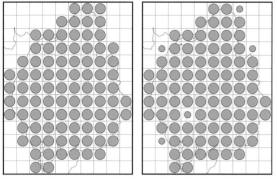

**1968-1972** **1997-2001**

(For explanation of maps, see page 45)

*Conservation status*

European: Non-SPEC

UK: GREEN

*Populations*

European status: 37,000,000

Britain – pairs: 4,200,000

Cumbria – pairs: 115,000

*30-year distribution change*

| | Old Atlas | This Atlas | % |
|---|---|---|---|
| No. of 10km squares: | 90 | 91 | +1.1 |

| Survey data | Tetrads | % |
|---|---|---|
| Confirmed breeding: | 1,026 | 55.6 |
| Probable breeding: | 420 | 22.8 |
| Possible breeding: | 51 | 2.8 |
| Total: | 1,497 | 81.2 |

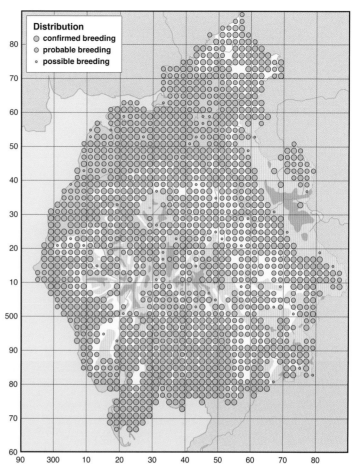

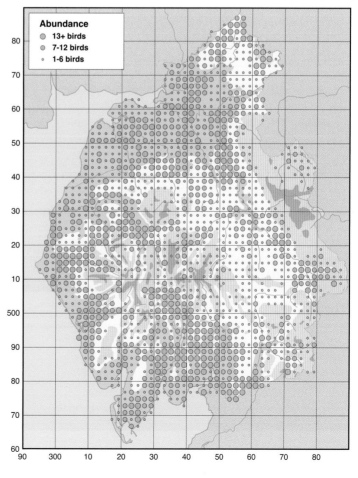

THIS dapper little chat brightens up the Cumbrian woodland scene from late April onwards, when it returns to breed. The male's short, sweet, but undemonstrative song can often be heard from mature trees, especially in open deciduous woodland; catching sight of the songster is a different matter, however, in spite of its bright colours.

The breeding range of the Redstart extends widely through the Western Palearctic, although it becomes patchy in parts of the Iberian Peninsula, the Balkans, and the Middle East. Further east, it breeds in a large area of central and northern Asia as far as Lake Baikal. The entire population winters across the Afrotropics north of the equator. In Britain, this is a typical species of northern and western oak woodlands. It is absent from much of the Inner and Outer Hebrides, Orkney and Shetland, where there is little suitable woodland. Strangely, it is only a very rare breeding bird in Ireland.

The Redstart or 'Firetail' as it is known locally, builds its nest in holes or cavities in trees or walls, amongst rocks, and less often in banks, tree root-balls, or in piles of stones. It makes frequent use of nestboxes and has benefited from such box schemes in many woods in Cumbria. Brown (1974) records a pair which bred under a limestone slab on Whitbarrow Scar, even with suitable sites available in nearby trees, so the species is presumably catholic in its tastes. The nest is a loose cup of grass, moss and other vegetation, lined with wool, hair and feathers, and is built by the female alone.

A severe decline was apparent in the national population in 1969, reaching a low point in 1973, and although a recovery was underway by the time of the *New Atlas* it was still absent from many areas of southern and central England occupied during the *Old Atlas*. This decrease was attributed to drought conditions in the Sahel wintering quarters and – given the apparent increasing disruption of the world's weather systems by global warming – a recurrence cannot be ruled out. However, the latest available CBC data shows a 38% increase since 1970.

Cumbria has long been a stronghold for this species in Britain and Macpherson (1892) states that it "becomes numerous where timber affords it suitable nesting places", but that it was scarce on the Cumberland Plain and in the neighbourhood of the coast. Brown (1974) notes five pairs nesting along a 1,100m stretch of tree-lined dry-stone wall in the Skirwith area. A similar 550m stretch near Elterwater held three breeding pairs and in the Caldew Valley, three pairs were within 320m. Although anecdotal, these records do suggest a very healthy population at least in parts of Cumbria between 1920 and 1970. However, Hutcheson (1986) comments on a decrease from the population levels found in the 1960s, particularly in parts of the southern fells. The *New Atlas* also shows a reduction in distribution on the Solway Basin since the *Old Atlas,* but it is possible that this has been due to habitat changes, such as loss of suitable trees in which to nest, rather than any effects in the wintering grounds.

The distribution found during *this Atlas* reaffirms the decline since the *Old Atlas* and reflects the deciduous hardwood areas of Cumbria. Population strongholds still occur on marginal upland farmland associated with the well-wooded peripheral valleys of Lakeland, the lower Eden Valley, the Border Uplands and the foothills of the North Pennines. Elsewhere, although well-dispersed and scattered in the less wooded districts of the Solway Basin and Coastal Plain, it is completely absent only from higher ground above the modern tree-line, which, due to grazing pressure from sheep, is now mostly well below its natural level.

Analysis of line transect data from *this Atlas* gives a population band of 9,000–23,000, suggesting a mean population of 14,000 males. The highest densities of 6 males/km$^2$ occurred in areas predominantly of rough grazing and scattered open, woodland such as the foothills of the North Pennines and valleys of Lakeland.

The Redstart does seem to be safe in its stronghold areas for the time being, and as long as these woodland habitats are maintained, it should continue to thrive. Past clearance of old hedgerows containing mature trees which provided nest sites has compromised its survival in marginal areas, possibly the reason for the decline in the Solway Basin. The coniferous plantations which now clothe vast areas of the county lack suitable nest sites even at maturity, and so hold little potential. However, new environmentally friendly agricultural

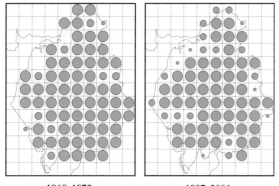

**1968-1972**    **1997-2001**

(For explanation of maps, see page 45)

*Conservation status*

| | |
|---|---|
| European: | Non-SPEC |
| UK: | **AMBER** |

*Populations*

| | |
|---|---|
| European status: | 2,300,000 |
| Britain – pairs: | 90,000 |
| Cumbria – pairs: | 14,000 |

*30-year distribution change*

| | Old Atlas | This Atlas | % |
|---|---|---|---|
| No. of 10km squares: | 73 | 74 | +1.4 |

| Survey data | Tetrads | % |
|---|---|---|
| Confirmed breeding: | 344 | 18.7 |
| Probable breeding: | 302 | 16.4 |
| Possible breeding: | 59 | 3.2 |
| Total: | 705 | 38.3 |

subsidies, targeted at tree planting schemes, may prove effective in reversing some of the recent losses, especially on open farmland habitats. New deciduous planting is to be encouraged, although it will be many years before such new habitat has the diversity to match the number of nesting sites provided by existing mature woods. Whilst the provision of boxes may overcome this particular problem, this is no substitute for the continued maintenance of primary habitats.

Jake Manson

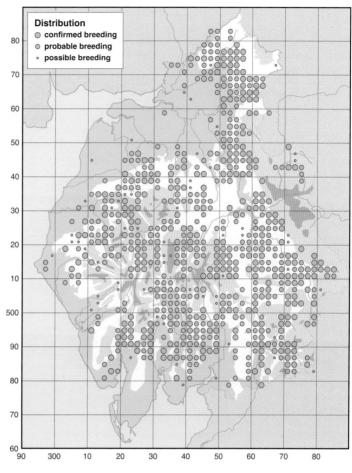

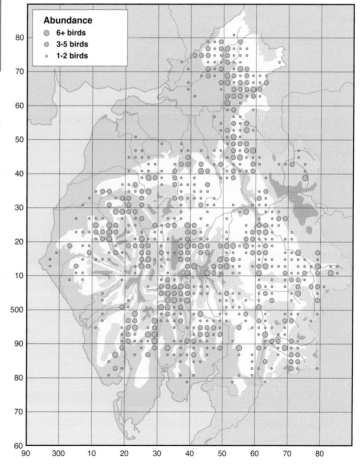

# Whinchat *Saxicola rubetra*

HAVING evolved as long-distance migrants, Whinchats have a slim aerodynamic shape. On arrival on territory in spring, the male's loud liquid song and striking appearance are a delight. With age, the male's plumage colour intensifies (pers obs), whereas the female's colours are softer, as befits incubating birds.

Generally replacing the Stonechat in northern European countries, its range stretches from Ireland to the western edges of Siberia; north up to the very tip of Norway and south to the Spanish/French border. Within Britain and Ireland, it is now principally confined to the uplands of Wales, northwest England and Scotland and has all but disappeared from the lowlands of southeast England.

Frequently nesting in close proximity to Stonechats, interaction between the two species is commonplace, with Stonechats being dominant. Stonechats usually nest in the more elevated drier levels and are regularly on their second clutch of eggs when Whinchats arrive towards the end of April. Whinchat nests are built into the ground in thick cover or sometimes under a tuft of thick grass with the strands hanging down over the nest, curtain-like, shielding the bright blue eggs or incubating female. Usually only one brood is attempted, though – if it is a warm spring and birds are in good condition – two are possible; during the *New Atlas* period, an isolated group of three pairs, occupying a southwest facing Cumbrian fellside of bracken and gorse, all produced two successful broods. In 2000, a nest with three young was found in the first week of August (P. Blinco pers comm).

In Cumbria, it was considered by Macpherson & Duckworth (1886) to be "common, nesting generally in meadow lands and railway cuttings"; presumably in the late 19th century railway cuttings would have been a fairly recent addition to its breeding habitat. However, less than 80 years later, Stokoe (1962) had reported a decline, declaring that it was "formerly more widespread and numerous, now unevenly distributed in small numbers on rough grassland in fell valleys, up to 1,000 or 1,300 feet [305 or 395m]".

In the years between the *Old* and *New Atlases,* a 60% decline in distribution had taken place nationally, with its disappearance from much of lowland England. Most western European countries also reported decreases. At this time, there was no obvious decline in Cumbria, in fact, at least four additional 10km squares had been occupied in the Solway Basin. More recently, analysis of BBS data indicates a 21% decline nationally during the period 1994–2000, albeit based on a relatively small number of plots. Whinchats are obvious birds, drawing attention to themselves at all stages of the breeding cycle, so detection rates should be high, yet *this Atlas* still shows a 8.7% drop in the number of occupied 10km squares since the *Old Atlas,* with the greatest impact again being at lower altitudinal levels. General drainage and 'improvement' for agricultural use are the prime causes in lowland areas, though on the Coastal Plain, open cast coal mining has been responsible for the loss of several key areas of habitat. Loss or deterioration of roadside verges also reduces the supply of suitable habitat and Gray (1974) found that, if verge mowing was delayed from mid-June to early August, breeding success improved from 46% to 64%. Conifer planting provides temporary habitat, often on a large scale, but such areas quickly become unsuitable as the trees mature; a pattern likely to be repeated with the cycle of planting and felling.

Many upland areas still possess good numbers of Whinchats, with several 10km squares having over 30% tetrad occupancy. In these choice places, with mixes of bracken, gorse, heather, bilberry and rank damp grass, breeding densities can be high, with as many as 10 pairs in the best quality tetrads. Away from the uplands, this is now a very local breeding bird, with few present in the Solway Basin, Eden Valley or Coastal Plain. Visually similar in appearance to habitats of high occupancy in Lakeland and the North Pennines, the paucity of records from the Cumbria Dales is a puzzle.

Although a conspicuous bird of open landscapes, it was rather surprising that the line transect survey undertaken for *this Atlas* produced so few contacts; hence the current county population estimate of 1,500 breeding pairs is based on count data, enhanced

Sponsored by Derek Thomas

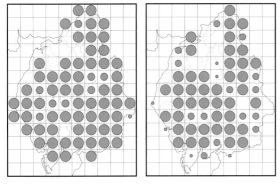

**1968-1972**    **1997-2001**

(For explanation of maps, see page 45)

*Conservation status*

| | |
|---|---|
| European: | Non-SPEC |
| UK: | GREEN |

*Populations*

| | |
|---|---|
| European status: | 2,700,000 |
| Britain – pairs: | 21,000 |
| Cumbria – pairs: | 1,500 |

*30-year distribution change*

| | Old Atlas | This Atlas | % |
|---|---|---|---|
| No. of 10km squares: | 69 | 63 | **-8.71** |

| Survey data | Tetrads | % |
|---|---|---|
| Confirmed breeding: | 135 | 7.3 |
| Probable breeding: | 126 | 6.8 |
| Possible breeding: | 46 | 2.5 |
| Total: | 307 | 16.6 |

by supplementary records, and local knowledge that suggests that 5 males/tetrad is a reasonable density in the better squares.

With the Whinchat's wintering range lying precariously close to the southern Sahara, there is always the threat of winter disaster. On its Cumbrian breeding grounds, only the upland areas seem secure; the likelihood of recolonization of lowland farmland is remote. We may have to accept the permanent loss of this beautiful summer migrant from lowland and coastal areas, except as a passage migrant.

John Callion

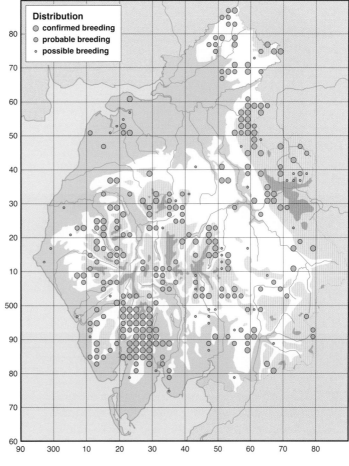

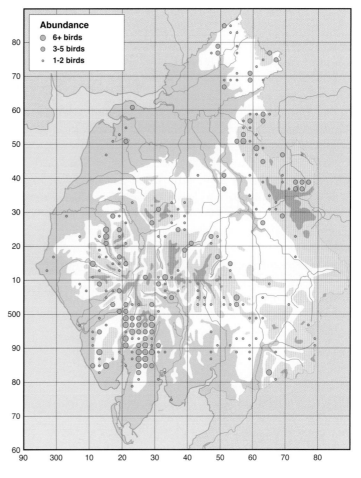

# Stonechat *Saxicola torquata*

THE male Stonechat's bright contrasting plumage, delightful song and sky-dance are a welcome early spring enjoyment, as this is one of our earliest nesting passerines; the female's duller-veiled colour is typical of species requiring camouflage for breeding success. During the breeding season Stonechats are often more audible than visible, scolding any intruder or predator with an incessant *'tac...tac...tac'*. This alarm call is frequently accompanied by a characteristic twitching of the wings, especially when delivered from more exposed perches.

The Stonechat ranges extensively over the Old World in around 20 subspecies, including virtually the whole of Asia and much of subtropical Africa. Many central and southern European countries have particularly strong populations. In Britain and Ireland, it is present as a partial migrant, with a temperate breeding range. Stonechats are generally scarce or absent from both eastern England and eastern Scotland between East Anglia and the Moray Firth. The highest levels of abundance occur in western Ireland and northwestern Scotland.

Stonechats require extremely rough open country for nesting, shunning all woodland and most farmland habitats. Indispensable is the combination of low perches used for scanning for terrestrial invertebrates and a thick ground cover of gorse, heather, bracken or rank grass in which to conceal their nests. The nest itself is substantial, generally placed on or close to the ground, often at right angles to a short entrance-tunnel. In Cumbrian coastal habitats, heather is rare and, consequently, most nests are in gorse or grass. In the uplands, heather, gorse and bracken predominate, though in damper areas rushes are sometimes utilized. Generally, three broods are attempted (pers obs) and the breeding season can extend from late March to early August. Productive pairs can rear as many as 18 chicks in a season, indicative of the Stonechat's ability to recover quickly from harsh winters. In suitable habitats, Stonechats can appear to be colonial though males will fiercely defend their own territories.

Although there is little comprehensive historical information on distribution or breeding biology in the county, Macpherson (1892) commented that the Stonechat "occurs all along our coast-line from Drumburgh to Skinburness, and westward to Maryport, Whitehaven and Walney Island." Stokoe (1962) regarded it as "common on open coast from Grune Point to Walney Island, almost invariably near gorse; scarce on estuaries; sparse and local inland, where less reliant on gorse, nesting up to 1,600 feet [488m]," and went on to say that "inland breeding populations are now building up from an extremely low level reached in 1941".

There were 40 occupied 10km squares in Cumbria at the time of the *Old Atlas,* when it was stated that Stonechat population levels were high. Nationally, the change map in the *New Atlas* showed some fairly serious declines, notably in Ireland, eastern Scotland, southwest Wales, Devon and Cornwall, thought to have been the result of a run of cold winters in the mid- and late 1980s. In Cumbria, the overall loss had been of five 10km squares, reflecting an increase in the centre of the county, but a decline on the periphery. By contrast, *this Atlas* documents the current occupation of 56 10km squares, demonstrating how successful Stonechats can be if winters are benign, allowing the species to increase both in distribution and density. Stonechats are adaptable, both in summer and winter, moving to other areas and habitats if conditions deteriorate. The distribution map shows their preference for milder western areas, with nesting from just above the shingle line on coasts to habitats as high as 500m asl. Breeding was recorded as far inland as the North Pennines, though there were few records from the Border Uplands, away from the coast on the Solway Basin or in the Eden Valley. Most breeding territories are occupied in winter, probably by non-migrating adults, while there is evidence from colour ringing that inland bred juveniles have moved to the coast by September (pers obs).

Results from fieldwork during *this Atlas,* coupled with known densities of up to 4 males/tetrad, suggest a current county population of 1,000 breeding pairs.

Although individual pairs or even some fellside populations can be affected by burning of heather and gorse, it seems that the habitat in the main Cumbrian

 Sponsored by Dr Mike Hall

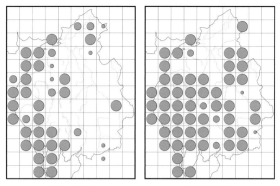

**1968-1972**   **1997-2001**
(For explanation of maps, see page 45)

***Conservation status***
European:                          Non-SPEC
UK:                                     AMBER

***Populations***
European status:               1,500,000
Britain – pairs:                    15,000
Cumbria – pairs:                  1,000

***30-year distribution change***

|  | Old Atlas | This Atlas | % |
|---|---|---|---|
| No. of 10km squares: | 40 | 56 | +40 |

| Survey data | Tetrads | % |
|---|---|---|
| Confirmed breeding: | 168 | 9.1 |
| Probable breeding: | 52 | 2.8 |
| Possible breeding: | 18 | 1.0 |
| Total: | 238 | 12.9 |

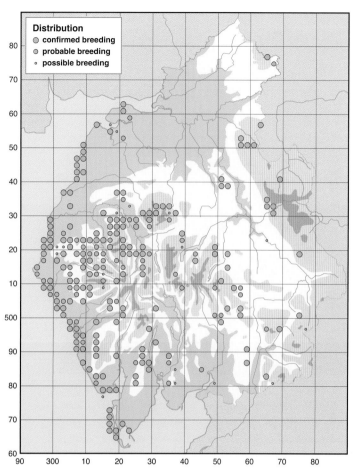

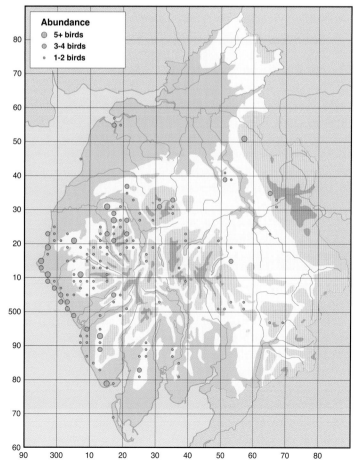

range remains stable. Having evolved as a partial migrant to guarantee the survival of at least a proportion of the population in case of either migratory or wintertime disasters, the most serious threat to the Stonechat is still the potential of a run of severe winters. However, the continuing amelioration of British and Irish winters bodes well for the foreseeable future. Despite some national declines in southern and eastern England where fragmentation of habitat has occurred (Mead 2000) the position here seems positive. The inevitable increase in range as the population rises should see further colonization of the eastern uplands of Cumbria, presently little occupied.

John Callion

caterpillars are readily taken when feeding young, Conder (1989) found that the bulk of prey items consisted of ants. In addition to short grass, there must also be readily available holes in rocks, boulders or dry-stone walls for nesting in, with Rabbit burrows sometimes utilized at lower altitudes.

On a national level, the *New Atlas* noted that the Wheatear population was declining, especially in the southern half of England, with the British and Irish distribution showing a 9.8% drop in the number of occupied 10km squares since the *Old Atlas*. This decline is thought to have resulted from habitat loss to agriculture and afforestation. Much of the short-grass sward favoured in southern England has been ploughed up, rendering it unsuitable. Other influences which affect the maintenance of close-grazed grassland, such as the reduction of Rabbit populations through myxomatosis, may also have reduced available habitat. Overseas factors, such as the droughts in its wintering areas, may also affect Wheatear populations, although the latest BBS data do not show any clear trends since 1994.

In Cumbria, though absent from the Solway saltmarshes, the 'White-rump' as it was known locally was considered to "breed numerously" on the fells and in the sand-hills around Walney Island, Ravenglass and Silloth at the end of the 19th century (Macpherson 1892). This distribution was to remain relatively unchanged into the mid-20th century when Stokoe (1962) regarded the Wheatear as "common in open country, breeding from the coast up to 3,000 feet [915m]", a situation that was confirmed by the *Old Atlas*.

The distribution maps for *this Atlas* reveal no significant change in the number of occupied 10km squares within the county since the *Old Atlas*. At the tetrad level, it can be seen that the main population is concentrated on the Lakeland Fells, Lune Valley, Cumbria Dales and North Pennines. The scarcity of records from some areas such as the Eden Valley, Solway Basin and southern Lakeland is undoubtedly due to lack of suitable habitat. Some of these areas are heavily wooded, while others are dominated by intensive lowland agriculture.

Analysis of line transect data from *this Atlas* gives a population band of 21,000–46,000, suggesting a mean population of 30,000 males. The highest densities of 14 males/km² occurred predominantly on the steep rough grazing of open uplands, with some areas bordering enclosed land especially on the western fringe of Lakeland.

The *New Atlas* gives a conservative figure of 55,000 breeding pairs in Britain, based on a density of 40 pairs per 10km square with evidence of breeding. *This Atlas* shows that Cumbria has a much higher density in favoured areas, suggesting that the *New Atlas* national

THE bobbing action of an agitated Wheatear atop a vantage point is a familiar sight to many birdwatchers on the Cumbrian coast and scree slopes in spring. It is usually followed by the sound of its harsh scolding alarm call and a view of the characteristic white rump and black tail feathers as the bird flies off when the observer gets too close.

A widespread northern hemisphere species, its vast breeding range extends from eastern Canada and Greenland eastwards through Europe to the former USSR and Alaska. Virtually the entire world population winters in a broad belt south of the Sahara, from the coast of West Africa to the Indian Ocean. The majority of the Britain and Ireland population breeds above 300m asl and consequently displays a clear northwesterly bias in distribution with strongholds in western Ireland, northwest England, Wales and much of Scotland.

In Cumbria, the first returning birds make landfall at coastal sites, such as Walney Island, during early March before quickly moving inland to the fells. Males arrive earlier than females to set up territories. Individuals tend to return to the same breeding area each year, although they may not hold exactly the same territory (Brooke 1979). Upland habitats including limestone pavement and associated grassland, scree slopes and sheep-cropped grassy fell-sides hold the majority of the population, although lowland areas such as sand-dunes and coastal grassland are also used.

Large open areas of short-cropped grass or insect-rich rocky patches mark the preferred habitats. Prey densities are related to vegetation structure – the highest being found on short turf. Although

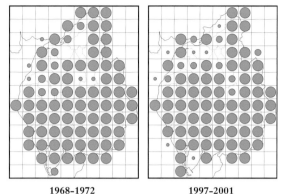

**1968-1972**          **1997-2001**

(For explanation of maps, see page 45)

*Conservation status*

| | |
|---|---|
| European: | Non-SPEC |
| UK: | **GREEN** |

*Populations*

| | |
|---|---|
| European status: | 3,000,000 |
| Britain – pairs: | 55,000 |
| Cumbria – pairs: | 30,000 |

*30-year distribution change*

| | Old Atlas | This Atlas | % |
|---|---|---|---|
| No. of 10km squares: | 83 | 84 | +1.2 |

| Survey data | Tetrads | % |
|---|---|---|
| Confirmed breeding: | 493 | 26.7 |
| Probable breeding: | 216 | 11.7 |
| Possible breeding: | 101 | 5.5 |
| Total: | 810 | 43.9 |

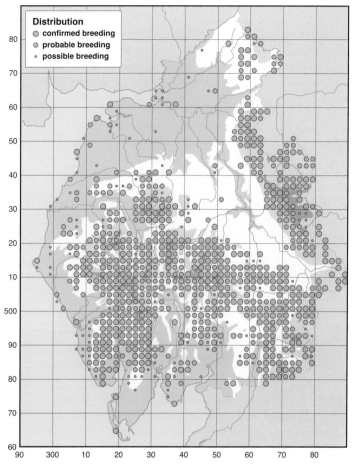

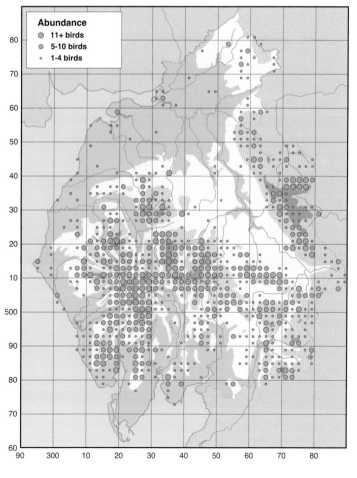

figure may be an underestimate. Nevertheless, the county is evidently home to a significant proportion of the British population.

Climatic influences, along with grazing pressures, are important in the maintenance of short turf at higher altitudes where the majority of the Cumbrian population breeds. What impact global warming will have on this is not clear. In addition, the current crisis in upland farming and the resultant de-stocking of sheep on higher pastures may have a negative effect.

Phil Byle

# Ring Ouzel *Turdus torquatus*

WITH local names of 'Fell Throstle', 'Crag Starling' and 'Mountain Blackbird', the Ring Ouzel is perhaps one of our most popular but least understood upland birds, its territories amongst remote and inaccessible crags. Besides its white breast-crescent, this summer visitor to our hills looks much like a Blackbird, though the two are different in character: Blackbirds are often bold and tame, but Ring Ouzels are shy and difficult to approach. The harsh *'tac-tat-tac'* call, in early spring, is usually the first evidence of the birds' arrival.

The species is confined to the Palearctic, almost wholly within the western part. Its range extends from northwest Europe to northeast Iran. Recognizably different from that in central and southern Europe, the nominate race ranges from Scandinavia to the mountainous regions of Ireland, Scotland, Wales and north and northwest England.

On passage, the Ring Ouzel can occur in a variety of habitats, but its breeding grounds are the uplands, above the 250m contour line, with a mixture of crags, gullies and areas of grazed grassland with a mosaic of dwarf shrubs, bracken, and small trees such as rowan. The nest is usually at ground level, hidden away beneath overhanging heather; occasionally trees will be used and there are records of old buildings associated with mining activities being utilized (Graham 1937).

The main influx is usually in March and early April. The male birds are often obvious in the early part of the season, singing from rocky outcrops and the tops of small trees, but become progressively harder to find as breeding commences. Two broods are often reared, and on occasion the same nest may be used twice.

Macpherson & Duckworth (1886) noted that until the late 1800s several pairs of Ring Ouzels nested on the cliffs south of Whitehaven but no indication is given as to when breeding ceased. Wilson (1933) stated that the Ring Ouzel had shown signs of increase at the time of his writing, but Blezard *et al* (1943) suggested a decline. Stokoe (1962) regarded it as "locally frequent in fell country, especially the Pennines, nesting up to 2,500 feet [762m]," adding "in Ennerdale, except on Bowness Knott, nests are mainly above 1,750 feet [534m], at which level there is a chain of territories around the valley."

Comparing surveys, there has been a reduction in the number of occupied 10km squares from 48 in the *Old Atlas* to 35 in *this Atlas,* suggesting a contraction in the range of the Ring Ouzel in Cumbria. The distribution map shows the population to be centred on the North Pennines, Lakeland and the Cumbria Dales, with apparent 'hot-spots' such as the Coniston Old Man area and the Geltsdale Fells. It is interesting to speculate as to whether there are genuine reasons for this or whether it is a reflection of observer fitness and enthusiasm levels! The most westerly record to appear in *this Atlas,* inland from Whitehaven, for which there is no dot in the *New Atlas,* also appears in the *Old Atlas.* This perhaps illustrates the difficulty in surveying this species consistently. The fieldwork for *this Atlas* coincided with the first national survey of Ring Ouzels. Although a different methodology was adopted it has indicated a population figure for northern England of 1,516–1,638 breeding pairs, with no breakdown for Cumbria.

Although there are possible signs of a continuing decline it is clear that Cumbria remains an important population stronghold for the Ring Ouzel in Britain. Analysis of line transect data from *this Atlas* gives a population band of 200–5,000, suggesting a mean population of 1,000 males. Given the wide band limits, it is clear that discretion must be exercised with this estimate; a subjective view is that the true figure will be lower than this. The highest densities of 0.82 males/km$^2$ occurred, perhaps surprisingly, in the North Pennines, rather than the Lakeland fells, with their vastly more diverse topography.

The causes of the decline of the Ring Ouzel are as yet unknown; research sponsored by the RSPB is still being analysed. Both habitat changes in Britain through agricultural intensification and problems on the wintering grounds in southern Spain and North Africa might be implicated. Being essentially a ground-nesting bird the young and brooding adult are vulnerable to mammalian predators, but there is no evidence to suggest that an increase in mortality at this stage of the breeding cycle has occurred. Gordon (1912) noted the proximity of breeding Ring Ouzels

Sponsored by United Utilities plc

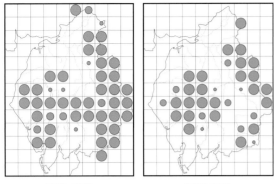

| 1968-1972 | 1997-2001 |

(For explanation of maps, see page 45)

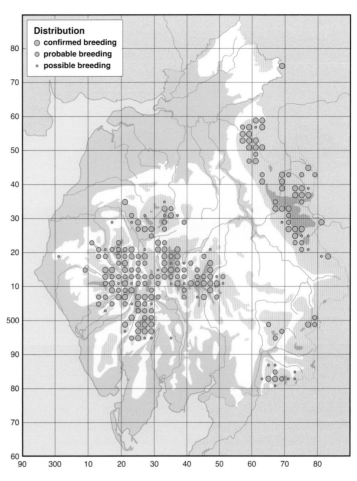

**Distribution**
- confirmed breeding
- probable breeding
- possible breeding

| **Conservation status** | | | |
|---|---|---|---|
| European: | Non-SPEC | | |
| UK: | **RED: BDM** | | |

**Populations**

| | | |
|---|---|---|
| European status: | 280,000 | |
| Britain – pairs: | 8,000 | |
| Cumbria – pairs: | 1,000 | |

**30-year distribution change**

| | Old Atlas | This Atlas | % |
|---|---|---|---|
| No. of 10km squares: | 48 | 35 | −27 |

| **Survey data** | **Tetrads** | **%** |
|---|---|---|
| Confirmed breeding: | 89 | 4.8 |
| Probable breeding: | 91 | 4.9 |
| Possible breeding: | 41 | 2.2 |
| Total: | 221 | 11.9 |

to Golden Eagle nests in Scotland, indicating a possible positive correlation. However, our own Haweswater eagles have been seen to predate a Ring Ouzel nest on at least one occasion (D. Shackleton pers comm), suggesting the relationship is not without a price. Other references infer competition from Blackbirds; however, the most recent work has found no evidence to support this and Brown and Grice (in prep) also regard this as unlikely.

Whilst the future is uncertain, one gleam of hope is that there is now a national Ring Ouzel Study Group of enthusiasts from across Britain, including Cumbria, whose aim is to raise the awareness of the plight of the Ring Ouzel and secure its future. Largely through the efforts of this group, the Ring Ouzel has been included as a Red List species in the review of BoCC.

Alistair Crowle

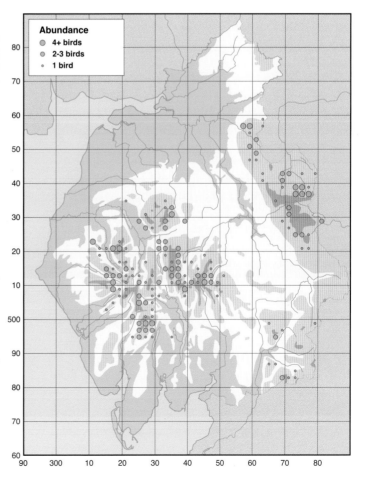

**Abundance**
- 4+ birds
- 2-3 birds
- 1 bird

C.H.Isherwood

INSTANTLY recognizable, the Blackbird is a common sight in gardens at all times of the year. The male's mellow, fluted song is one of the most beautiful ingredients of the dawn chorus, enriching many an early spring morning.

Widely spread throughout the Western Palearctic, the Blackbird is resident over much of its range. However, the northern and eastern populations tend to migrate south or west to their wintering grounds in southern or western Europe. Breeding throughout Britain and Ireland, it is most abundant in lowland areas in the south and east of its range, becoming significantly scarcer in upland areas and in the north and west of Scotland.

The species is found in many different habitats including dense woodland, rural and suburban areas, farmland and heath. In Britain and Ireland, the highest densities of 115 birds/km² are found in suburban areas, with urban and rural areas holding 95 birds/km². Most other habitats hold densities of less than 20 birds/km² (Gregory & Baillie 1998).

In more marginal habitats such as farmland, factors such as hedge quality and management have been found to have a significant effect on breeding densities. Male Blackbirds hold significantly smaller linear territories in tall hedgerows compared to those with trimmed hedges (Williamson 1971).

Trees, bushes and hedges or, occasionally, a ledge or a hole in a wall provide sites for the nest which is usually built several feet off the ground. It is a fairly large but neat structure of interwoven grass, twigs and rootlets, cemented inside with mud which forms a smooth cup and is covered with a lining of dry grass.

Unsurprisingly for such a common bird, the breeding biology of the Blackbird has been studied in some detail. In a recent study, the primary cause of nest failure in its key urban and rural habitats was predation, with failure rates of 80% or more (Hatchwell *et al* 1996). In one urban study area, fewer than 5% of broods produced fledged young. Many nests failed for unknown reasons, but where the cause was known, the majority of failures resulted from predation by Magpies (Groom 1993). However, it is worth pointing out that, even in the face of such apparently high levels of predation, Blackbird populations overall are successfully maintained, since there is always a movement of 'surplus' birds from areas of higher productivity to lower.

Predation is not the only problem facing young Blackbirds. Weather effects are important in determining starvation rates and nestling survival. The diet of nestlings is dominated by caterpillars and earthworms, and since the availability of earthworms is strongly influenced by soil moisture, dry periods are associated with lower earthworm availability. As a result, the breeding success increases in wetter periods. Failure rates due to starvation were found to be around 12% in garden and parkland habitats and 1.2% for woodland areas (Chamberlain *et al* 1999).

Nationally, the Blackbird population increased through the 19th and 20th centuries, peaking in the early 1970s. Since then, there has been a slight downward trend, thought to be related to the colder winters of the mid-1970s to mid-1980s. The latest available CBC index, backed up by CES data, indicates a 26% decline since 1970; however, BBS data suggests that the population may have recently stabilized.

In Cumbria, there is historically little information on how Blackbird populations have changed. However, Macpherson & Duckworth (1886) considered it to be a "common and increasing resident" at the end of the 19th century and by the mid-20th century Stokoe (1962) regarded it as "widespread and abundant, breeding up to 1,000 feet [305m], where it overlaps with the Ring Ouzel" and comments that "a barely fledged juvenile was found at 2,930 feet [893m] on Cross Fell". The *Old Atlas* confirmed the opinion of historical authors, with birds found in almost every 10km square in the county.

*This Atlas* reiterates the widespread distribution of the Blackbird in Cumbria. The maps show that birds are totally absent only from the barren high ground of the North Pennines, Cumbria Dales and Lakeland while the areas of high abundance in the Eden Valley, Solway Basin and Coastal Plain, reflect the species' habitat preference for the urban and more populated rural lowland areas of the county.

Analysis of line transect data from *this Atlas* gives a population band of 140,000–200,000, suggesting a

Sponsored by Katie Weir

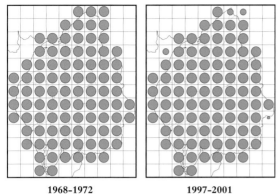

**1968-1972**          **1997-2001**

(For explanation of maps, see page 45)

***Conservation status***

| | |
|---|---|
| European: | Non–SPEC |
| UK: | **GREEN** |

***Populations***

| | |
|---|---|
| European status: | 43,000,000 |
| Britain – pairs: | 4,400,000 |
| Cumbria – pairs: | 170,000 |

***30-year distribution change***

| | Old Atlas | This Atlas | % |
|---|---|---|---|
| No. of 10km squares: | 90 | 91 | **+1.1** |

| **Survey data** | **Tetrads** | **%** |
|---|---|---|
| Confirmed breeding: | 1,055 | 57.2 |
| Probable breeding: | 363 | 19.7 |
| Possible breeding: | 44 | 2.4 |
| Total: | 1,462 | 79.3 |

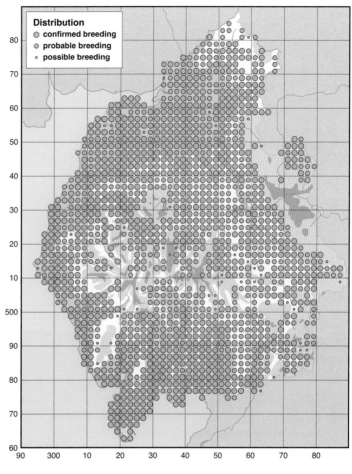

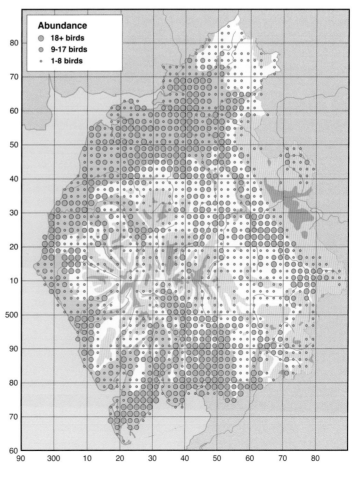

mean population of 170,000 males. The highest densities of 72 males/km² appeared on the seaward fringe of the Coastal Plain. In contrast, upland areas held just 6.5 males/km² on marginal farmland along the edge of the North Pennines, increasing to 11.6 males/km² in the upper Eden Valley and Lakeland.

Overall, the prospects for the Blackbird in Cumbria look favourable. One might conclude that the main threats to the population are posed by factors not directly related to human activities, such as predation and the weather effects from global warming.

Phil Byle

# Fieldfare *Turdus pilaris*

THIS handsome thrush, with its dove-grey head, chestnut back and bold, arrowhead breast streaks is primarily a winter visitor to Britain. It breeds from central Europe, north of the southern Alps and the Balkans, east beyond Lake Baikal into Mongolia. In the western part of this range, nesting takes place right up to the arctic shores of Norway and Russia.

Unlike other European thrushes, the Fieldfare is, in the main, a colonial breeder although this strategy is less pronounced in some parts of the range, southern Sweden for example. Some colonies are very dense and may have four or five nests in a single tree, but the norm is for pairs to be spaced about 30m apart. An interesting feature of Fieldfare colonies is the presence of other nesting species such as finches, shrikes and even Merlin (Norman 1994). It is probable that these interlopers benefit from the Fieldfare's sustained and vigorous attacks on potential nest predators, attacks that include well-aimed defecation!

Throughout the last 150 years, the breeding range has expanded westwards in central Europe, reaching western Germany in the latter half of the 19th century, Switzerland in the 1920s and France in the 1950s. A further burst of expansion in the 1960s and 1970s brought breeding Fieldfares to Denmark, the Low Countries, Italy and the Balkans (Simms 1978). It was during this period that the first confirmed breeding took place in Britain, when a nest was found in Orkney in 1967. From 1968 to 1974, breeding was almost an annual event in Shetland, after which it became sporadic. Fieldfares first bred in mainland Scotland at Inverness in 1970 and thereafter breeding was recorded in several Scottish counties north of the

Clyde/Forth line, though nowhere with any consistency. In England, breeding has been recorded in six counties (Norman 1994). Between 1989 and 1992, there were 11–13 records of probable or confirmed breeding each year in Britain but numbers fell to five in 1993 and have remained at this low level since (Ogilvie *et al* 2000).

In Cumbria, neither Macpherson (1892) nor Stokoe (1962) mention Fieldfares as anything other than winter visitors, and it was not until 1977 that the first confirmed breeding occurred, when birds were seen taking food into a patch of hawthorn scrub near Newby Bridge. In more modern times, birds have regularly lingered in the county into May and have sometimes been heard in song. Birds at Whitbarrow on 2nd June 1974 were probably very late migrants, but records such as a bird on Coniston Old Man on 3rd July 1975 are harder to classify. More intriguing records came from Kirkbride on 13th August 1971, Loughrigg Fell on 5th August 1978, Kendal from 27th to 29th July 1982 and from Grange-over-Sands, where a bird summered in 1988. Further records such as at Cockermouth on 31st August 1983 and Bassenthwaite on 29th August 1996 fall into the grey area of possible early migrants. In 1988, the same year that a bird summered in Grange-over-Sands, breeding was confirmed in the county for the second time, on this occasion near Geltsdale.

During *this Atlas,* there were seven relevant records, including three in the North Pennines and one in the Lamplugh area. At the last of these sites, breeding was confirmed for only the third time in the county. A female was seen carrying nest material on 10th May 2000, whilst a male was singing and displaying nearby. From late May through to early July, the birds were seen regularly, usually arriving from the northwest and feeding in the same damp, cattle grazed pasture. On two occasions in June, they were seen to carry food away to the northwest, to a small river valley with stands of conifer. The last sighting was of an adult calling from the top of a chestnut tree on 12th July. It is interesting to note that, in the *New Atlas,* a similar number of records emerged in Cumbria and that they were roughly in the same area, an arc running from northeast of Carlisle, through northern central Lakeland into west Cumbria.

The small and irregular British breeding population has, in the past, been biased toward Scotland. This has encouraged the belief that Britain's breeding birds are recruited from the Scandinavian rather than central European populations. Fieldfares are now regularly breeding as close to Britain as northeastern France and the Low Countries and, as the central European population has made great strides westwards in the 20th century, it is possible that a major colonization may come from this direction (Norman 1994). It has

Sponsored by a CBC Member

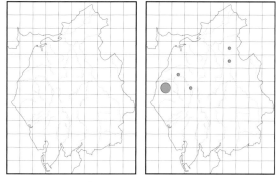

**1968-1972**        **1997-2001**
(For explanation of maps, see page 45)

*Conservation status*

European:                          Non-SPEC

UK:                          **AMBER: BDM & BR**

*Populations*

European status:                     6,000,000

Britain – pairs:                             4

Cumbria – pairs:                          0–1

*30-year distribution change*

|  | Old Atlas | This Atlas | % |
|---|---|---|---|
| No. of 10km squares: | 0 | 5 | n/a |

| **Survey data** | **Tetrads** | **%** |
|---|---|---|
| Confirmed breeding: | 1 | 0.05 |
| Probable breeding: | 0 | |
| Possible breeding: | 6 | 0.3 |
| Total: | 7 | 0.35 |

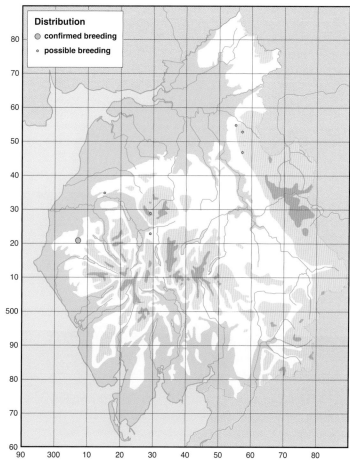

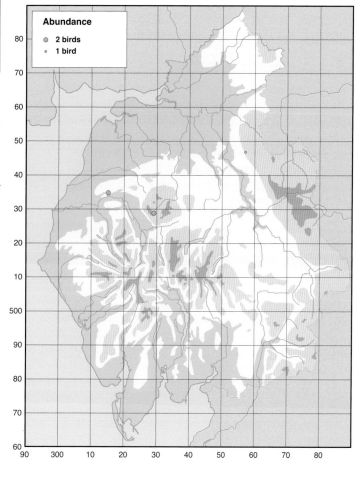

to be said, however, that up until now, the English Channel has proved a somewhat surprising barrier to these birds. Habitat would certainly not be a problem as the species is quite catholic in its taste, nesting in situations ranging from treeless tundra to parks and gardens. The colonization of Britain has been both slow and erratic and it may be that the sparse summering population, which gives little opportunity for more successful colonial nesting, is an inhibiting factor.

Derek McAlone

# Song Thrush *Turdus philomelos*

STILL a common sight in many gardens, the Song Thrush, with its speckled breast and fluid song, is often seen out on open lawns searching for food. It is well known for the habit of regularly using stones as anvils to crack open the shells of snails to get at the flesh inside. Interestingly, this species has been earmarked as one of the key indicator species by politicians for measuring the 'quality of life'. This has brought the recent population decline very much to the attention of the general public.

The Song Thrush is found in the upper and middle latitudes of the Palearctic. It is mostly resident, but northern European populations, such as those in Scandinavia and Russia, are partially or entirely migratory. Breeding across the majority of Britain and Ireland up to 1,000m asl, the highest densities are found in southeast England and East Anglia. Nest sites are generally within two metres of the ground, in the fork of a tree or stout bush, a hedge, the shelter of an evergreen, a ledge or crevice in a wall or building. Twigs, roots, stems, grass, leaves, wool and moss go into the building of the nest which has a smooth mud lining.

Predominantly a bird of lowland woodlands and valleys, the conversion of the lowlands to agricultural production and urban uses appears to have stimulated a habitat switch towards small woodlands, parks, and gardens. Analysis of national BBS data show that the highest densities, of 15 birds/km², occur in rural areas with around 10 birds/km² in woodland and urban or suburban areas. Other habitats have densities of 5 birds/km² or less.

Nationally, the population seems to have markedly declined through the 20th century. In the early 1900s Song Thrushes outnumbered Blackbirds but, since the 1940s, this position appears to have reversed. The British and Irish population suffered a marked decline between 1975 and 1993. Over this period, the CBC index for farmland populations fell by 65% – equivalent to an annual fall of 5.7%. Recent BBS trends suggest that this decline may have levelled off.

In Cumbria, the Song Thrush was considered an abundant resident at the end of the 19th century, although many districts were devoid of birds during the winter months (Macpherson & Duckworth 1886). Stokoe (1962) also suggested that many birds departed during the autumn but regarded the species as "widespread and numerous in the breeding season, though rarely remote from cultivation" and commented that it "nests commonly throughout the spruce plantations of Ennerdale and Blengdale". The *Old Atlas* found a countywide distribution which was reiterated by the *New Atlas*.

The results of *this Atlas* show that the species has a very similar distribution in the county to the Blackbird, although it is slightly less widespread. The maps reveal a preference for urban and rural lowlands such as those found in the Eden Valley, Solway Basin and Coastal Plain, with few records from the higher ground of the North Pennines, Cumbria Dales and Lakeland, although birds use river valleys to encroach well into the heart of Lakeland.

Analysis of line transect data from *this Atlas* gives a population band of 45,000–82,000, suggesting a mean population of 61,000 birds. The highest densities of 32.2 birds/km² occurred mainly on lowland mixed, farmed country with many hedgerows and small woods. In comparison upland areas such as the North Pennines held less than 1 bird/km².

The national decline appears to be related to the annual survival rates of first-year Song Thrushes – these were found to be significantly lower over the period of decline than in earlier years (Thomson *et al* 1997). This reduced rate of recruitment may be sufficient to explain the decrease in the breeding population. However, why the survival rates should have fallen is not clear. Increasing Magpie and Sparrowhawk populations cannot be conclusively linked to the declines (Gooch *et al* 1991, Newton *et al* 1997). Although weather does impact on survival rates, which are lower in years with cold or dry winters, why Song Thrushes should be more susceptible than Blackbirds is not obvious.

Feeding ecology may give some clues to the decline. Contrary to popular belief, molluscs such as slugs and snails are not the preferred prey. Invertebrates such as earthworms, caterpillars, beetles and their larvae are

Sponsored by Jill Damment

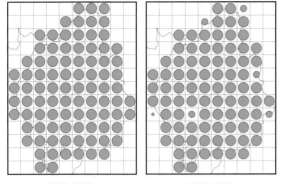

**1968-1972**     **1997-2001**
(For explanation of maps, see page 45)

*Conservation status*

| | |
|---|---|
| European: | Non-SPEC |
| UK: | **RED: BD** |

*Populations*

| | |
|---|---|
| European status: | 16,000,000 |
| Britain – pairs: | 990,000 |
| Cumbria – pairs: | 30,500 |

*30-year distribution change*

| | Old Atlas | This Atlas | % |
|---|---|---|---|
| No. of 10km squares: | 90 | 90 | n/c |

| **Survey data** | **Tetrads** | **%** |
|---|---|---|
| Confirmed breeding: | 741 | 40.2 |
| Probable breeding: | 497 | 27.0 |
| Possible breeding: | 61 | 3.3 |
| Total: | 1,299 | 70.5 |

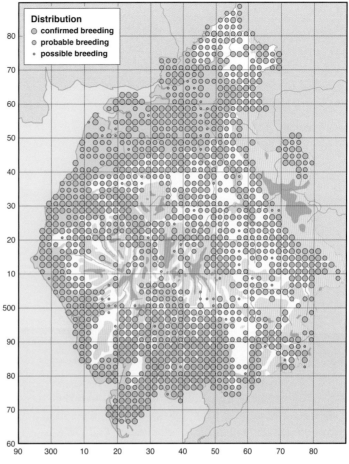

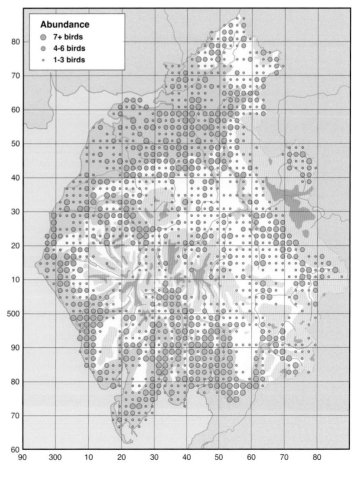

important in their diet. Slugs and snails are taken with a marked seasonality that corresponds to periods of hardship (Marchant *et al* 1990). It has been suggested that there may have been reductions in mollusc numbers due to the increased use of molluscicides. If this is true, it might significantly reduce an important food source at a time when the bird most needs it.

It is to be hoped that the reasons for the decline in the Song Thrush population can be identified and appropriate measures put in place to assist the species. There is no reason to suppose that the national declines have not been mirrored in Cumbria and it would be a great shame if its distinctive song disappeared from our gardens.

Phil Byle

# Mistle Thrush *Turdus viscivorus*

THE first sign that a Mistle Thrush is around is the loud dry rattling *'rrrrr'* call as the bird flies off across the hillside with its familiar bounding flight. It is by far the largest of our resident thrushes and probably the most aggressive. Its defence of trees bearing berries against other species during the winter has been regularly described.

Present over most of the Western Palearctic, the species is migratory in the east and north of its European range. In Britain and Ireland, it is largely resident with a widespread but patchy distribution, and although it is most abundant in southeast England, pockets of high density are found as far north as the Moray Firth. Its habitat requirements are hard to define, seemingly a combination of open grassland mixed with stands of tall trees and a ready access to trees and shrubs bearing seasonal berries. Dense forest and treeless areas are avoided. Close human contact is shunned. They eat a wide range of invertebrates as well as berries such as juniper, yew, mistletoe, holly, hawthorn and rowan. Territories and home ranges are large by thrush standards and can cover several hectares.

It is an early nesting species, and in Cumbria the season generally begins in late March although a pair at Ulverston successfully fledged three young in January 1985 (Hutcheson 1986). The nest site is usually in the fork or on the branch of a tall tree, but is often quite low in a tree or bush, or on the ledge of a wall or quarry, and occasionally on the ground. Two and sometimes three broods are raised in a season with nestlings fed on flies and caterpillars collected from the tree canopy.

The species appears to have spread markedly through Britain and Ireland during the 19th century; it advanced northwards through mainland Scotland, into the Inner Hebrides, and through Ireland. By contrast, there was little change in distribution through the 20th century (Mead 2000). However, whilst it remains widely distributed, there have been significant population declines since the mid-1970s, with the latest available CBC index showing a 42% fall since 1970. Recent BBS data suggests that this decline may now have eased.

Farmland feeding sites form important foraging areas for both woodland and farmland breeding pairs (O'Connor & Shrubb 1986). As a result, populations could well be affected by changes in farming practice. The switch from hay to silage could be seen as beneficial, since the more frequent mowing regime of silage fields maintains the grass at a shorter level, making foraging easier. In addition, mowing produces a sudden flush of invertebrates previously out of reach in long grass. Both clutch size and fledgling productivity have been found to rise steeply with increases in the extent of mown grass available for feeding sites. Factors such as berry availability in cold winters are also likely to be important.

In Cumbria, the species' spread has followed national trends. Although considered to be scarce in Cumberland at the end of the 18th century, Macpherson (1892) regarded the Mistle Thrush as "fairly well distributed". Later Stokoe (1962) considered it to be widespread and frequent, nesting up to 460m asl, and states that birds were found to "nest commonly on the edge of spruce plantations at Ennerdale". The *Old Atlas* showed that the species was present throughout the county, a distribution confirmed by the *New Atlas*.

*This Atlas* reveals that, although widespread, the Cumbrian distribution is patchy with a surprising number of empty tetrads compared to Blackbird and Song Thrush. The strongholds are in southern and northwestern Lakeland with the population becoming sparser in the Border Uplands, Eden Valley and much of the Coastal Plain. As could be expected, the barren upland areas of the North Pennines, Cumbria Dales and Lakeland have very few records. Why the species should be unrecorded from so many lowland tetrads in the Solway Basin is not clear. It may be because Mistle Thrushes are not as obvious as other thrush species and can be overlooked where densities are low. Being an early nesting species, song is only intermittent from April onwards, and birds often sit quietly in the tree canopy. Alternatively the intensively farmed habitat may not be suitable.

Analysis of line transect data from *this Atlas* gives a population band of 16,000–45,000, suggesting a mean

 Sponsored by C.C. Flindall

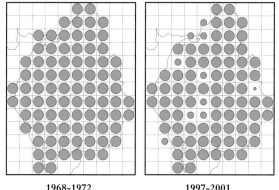

**1968–1972**          **1997–2001**
(For explanation of maps, see page 45)

*Conservation status*
European:                              Non-SPEC
UK:                              **AMBER: BDM**

*Populations*
European status:                      2,500,000
Britain – pairs:                       230,000
Cumbria – pairs:                        13,500

*30-year distribution change*
|  | Old Atlas | This Atlas | % |
|---|---|---|---|
| No. of 10km squares: | 85 | 84 | **–1.2** |

| **Survey data** | **Tetrads** | **%** |
|---|---|---|
| Confirmed breeding: | 443 | 24.0 |
| Probable breeding: | 382 | 20.7 |
| Possible breeding: | 158 | 8.6 |
| Total: | 983 | 53.3 |

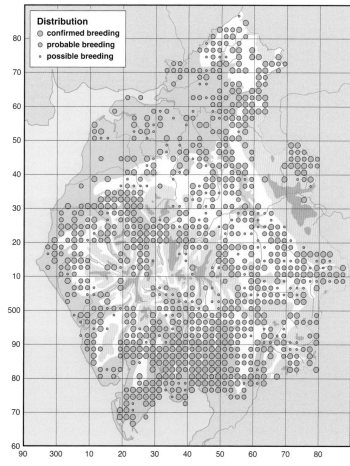

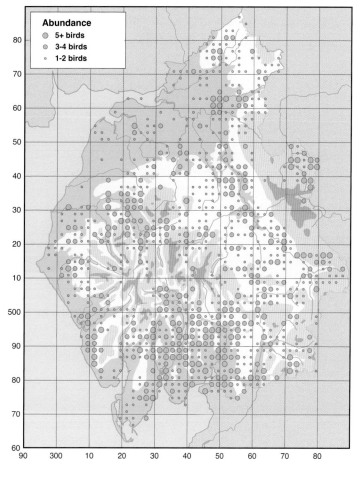

population of 27,000 birds. The highest densities of 11.8 birds/km² were calculated for the narrow coastal zone, while 7.2 birds/km² were found in the south Lakeland valleys.

Because of its more secretive nature and lower densities, the Mistle Thrush has been less studied than most other thrush species. Little is known on the population dynamics and breeding biology and this is a species where much more detailed work is needed. Until this research is done, it is likely to remain an enigmatic bird. However, there is evidence of some local declines from the periphery of its range within Cumbria, with the species recently becoming extinct as a breeding bird on Walney Island.

Phil Byle

# Grasshopper Warbler *Locustella naevia*   Common Grasshopper Warbler

a.m.Isherwood

SELDOM seen before it is heard, the Grasshopper Warbler has a distinctive 'reeling' song delivered from a low perch. Once seen, the singer may often be approached closely, but the song is surprisingly ventriloquial and difficult to pinpoint – a trick resulting from the bird's constant head-movements whilst singing. The streaky brown plumage and ability to move 'mouse-like' through cover mean that Grasshopper Warblers are rarely seen during the incubation period. Once feeding young, they can be extremely approachable, though still difficult to observe as they bring food into the thick base vegetation that serves as the nest site.

Due to its secretive habit of nesting low in rank vegetation and unknown migratory strategy (very few ringed birds having been recovered), the Grasshopper Warbler remains very much an enigma. The nominate race breeds throughout central Europe, and east to Russia where it intergrades with the Siberian race. Despite a 38% reduction in 10km squares between the *Old* and *New Atlases,* Grasshopper Warblers remain reasonably well distributed in Britain and Ireland with all but the Hebrides, Orkney and Shetland holding breeding pairs. However, they are largely absent from higher altitudes. There is little knowledge of the wintering area, though two birds ringed in Senegal during the winter of 1992/93 were recovered in the following breeding season, one at Allonby and the other just across the Solway Firth close to Castle Douglas.

With its unique song and behaviour, it always attracts attention. Macpherson & Duckworth (1886) commented, "The Grasshopper Warbler is a local summer visitor rare in the Lake District, not reported from south Cumberland, but well established in several localities in the east of Cumberland, tolerably plentiful near Carlisle and numerous on the Solway littoral." Stokoe (1962) described it as "local and variable in numbers, frequenting coastal mosses, rough ground inland and near lakes in central region, breeding up to 500 feet [152m]." Both these statements hold true today.

The *New Atlas,* in showing changes over the period since the *Old Atlas,* reveals a disturbing 38% decline in distribution affecting all of the species' British and Irish range. A combination of factors was implicated, including habitat destruction on, and deterioration of, farmland due to increased mechanization, and the maturation of conifer forests, the planting of which was believed to be partly responsible for the Grasshopper Warbler's distribution increase in the late 1950s and early 1960s, especially in Ireland and northwestern counties of England and Scotland. Over this same period, the Cumbrian distribution suffered an overall loss of ten 10km squares, predominantly in Lakeland and the Eden Valley.

*This Atlas* indicates an almost identical distribution in the county as the *New Atlas.* However, while some of the most favoured 10km squares have up to 40% tetrad occupancy, almost half have two or fewer tetrads occupied. In west Cumbria, some of the best habitats have been destroyed by opencast coal mining.

With breeding confirmed in hardly 20% of cases, fieldworkers' difficulty in proving breeding is obvious. Nevertheless, the high count of probable breeding indicates the presence of singing males throughout the season. Grasshopper Warblers are known to be double and occasionally triple-brooded, with males singing between broods (Callion *et al* 1990). The distribution map reveals a northwesterly bias with most records being close to the coastline. However, the scattering of dots in the Border Uplands is encouraging, as are the number around Bassenthwaite Lake and Derwent Water, surprisingly the only waters in Lakeland to support Grasshopper Warblers. Whilst there is little penetration of the Lakeland fells, there was a record of probable breeding at 350m asl at the head of the River Caldew, in the area known as 'Back o' Skiddaw', 50m higher than the national altitude limit given in the *New Atlas.*

This is a bird with crepuscular habits and a fragmented distribution. With timed visits producing only just over half of the records, it is obvious that most Grasshopper Warbler contacts were made in the early mornings or late evenings. Consequently both distribution and population are likely to be significantly greater than the maps suggest, and the current county population is estimated at 300 breeding pairs.

Though, as stated earlier, little is known of the Grasshopper Warbler's winter quarters and its migration routes remain uncharted, it has been speculated that

Sponsored by a CBC Member

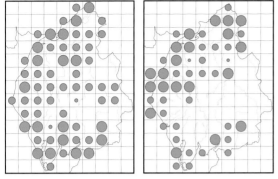

**1968-1972**       **1997-2001**
(For explanation of maps, see page 45)

*Conservation status*
European:                    Non-SPEC
UK:                          **RED: BDM**

*Populations*
European status:             330,000
Britain – pairs:             10,500
Cumbria – pairs:             300

*30-year distribution change*
|  | Old Atlas | This Atlas | % |
|---|---|---|---|
| No. of 10km squares: | 61 | 49 | −19.7 |

| **Survey data** | **Tetrads** | **%** |
|---|---|---|
| Confirmed breeding: | 31 | 1.7 |
| Probable breeding: | 105 | 5.7 |
| Possible breeding: | 18 | 1.0 |
| Total: | 154 | 8.4 |

wintering in apparent close proximity to the Sahel zone may be affecting survival rates, as has been the case with the Whitethroat. The present range within Cumbria appears to be similar to the levels of over 100 years ago. The information gained in *this Atlas* will give a more accurate and definitive picture for the future.

John Callion

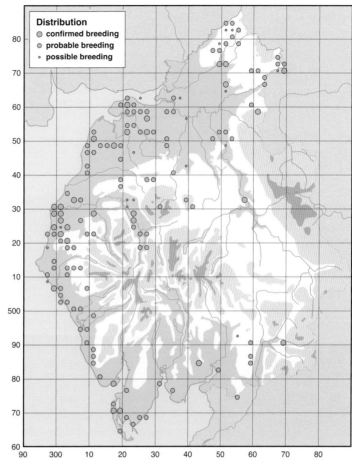

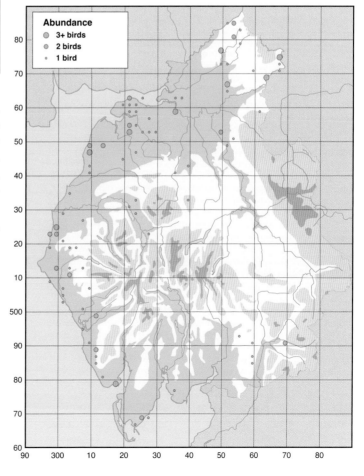

# Sedge Warbler *Acrocephalus schoenobaenus*

A LOUD outburst of rapid, scolding notes announces the presence of this small streaked bird as it clings to a swaying reed stem, gape wide open and conspicuous white eyebrow a prominent feature. The Sedge Warbler has a far-carrying chattering song, often delivered in a bouncy song flight as it flits between song-posts, although more commonly the bird is hidden in thick luxuriant vegetation. From late April onwards, when spring migrants begin to arrive in Cumbria, males can be heard singing at most times of day – and very often at night, when their eruptive song is frequently mistaken by non-birdwatchers for that of the Nightingale.

The Sedge Warbler is a widely distributed species, found throughout most of northern Europe and as far east as central Siberia. In the last 100 years, it has been extending its range northwards and can now be found breeding well into the Arctic region. In more recent times, however, due to habitat loss and adverse climatic conditions in its winter quarters, the west European population has suffered a considerable decline. In Britain and Ireland, the highest breeding densities are found in the eastern counties of England and the species is scarce or absent over 350m asl. Orkney was colonized in the mid-19th century, the Outer Hebrides in the first half of the 20th century, and breeding was confirmed from Shetland in 1996.

Unlike the Reed Warbler, which almost exclusively breeds in wetland habitats, the Sedge Warbler will nest in a variety of locations, often in dry situations some distance from water with vegetation such as willowherb, nettles, thick bramble or dense hedgerow

being utilized. Because of this, the Sedge Warbler is less vulnerable to habitat destruction through drainage and development than warblers with more specialized breeding requirements.

The males are first to return to establish breeding territories; the females arrive a week later. Males busily proclaim and defend territories while the female alone builds the nest. Sedge Warblers are normally single-brooded although in Cumbria double-brooding would appear to be more common than at first thought, judging by observations from a long-term study at Siddick Pond (J. Callion pers comm). Although no detailed research has been published of the Sedge Warbler's breeding ecology in Cumbria, studies elsewhere show five eggs as the most common clutch size. Incubation is by the female alone, and takes around two weeks, with fledging 14 days later.

Historical references show that the Sedge Warbler population in Cumbria has increased markedly over the last 200 years. Although considered rare in the late 18th century, it was described as "widely distributed" at the end of the 19th century (Macpherson & Duckworth 1886). Stokoe (1962) regarded the Sedge Warbler as "frequent in thickets and rank vegetation on damp ground or near water; often nesting some distance from water and occasionally in wholly non-aquatic habitats." Although this remains an adequate description of its haunts, *this Atlas* found more evidence of birds choosing to nest in drier habitats such as farmland hedgerows. This may partially explain the recent increase in the county population, although it is difficult to disentangle habitat usage from productivity and winter survival rates. On Walney Island for instance, numbers have risen from 12 pairs in 1990 to 107 pairs by 1997, a significant 87% increase (Raven & Sanderson 1997).

During *this Atlas,* the principal strongholds were found along the Coastal Plain, especially north of St Bees Head, with a significant population around the Furness peninsula. Riparian valleys that radiate out from central Lakeland act as linear habitats attracting increasing numbers of breeding pairs. Elsewhere, especially in upland country, birds remain very localized in small numbers or are absent altogether.

It is perhaps perplexing why a bird with such a strident song can be so difficult to census using the broad continuum of NLCs. Although the sample size is unquestionably small, and thus the data are not statistically robust, the calculated figure suggests a current county population of 4,000 breeding pairs; this appears plausible, based on current knowledge of densities at a variety of sites. It must be emphasised that a degree of scepticism may be necessary until better data is available. Clearly this is a species that calls for a re-survey in the near future.

Sponsored by a CBC Member

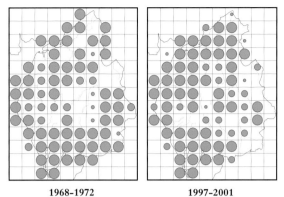

**1968-1972**          **1997-2001**
(For explanation of maps, see page 45)

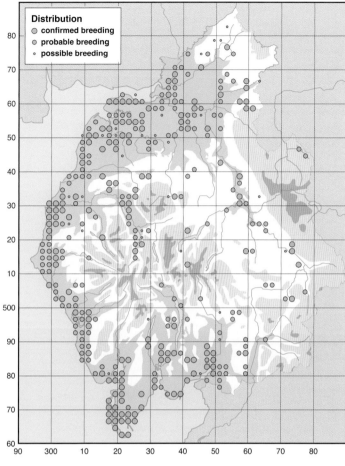

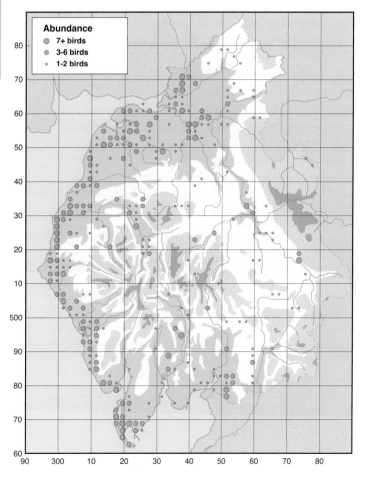

*Conservation status*
European:                Non-SPEC
UK:                      GREEN

*Populations*
European status:         2,300,000
Britain – pairs:         250,000
Cumbria – pairs:         4,000

*30-year distribution change*

|  | Old Atlas | This Atlas | % |
|---|---|---|---|
| No. of 10km squares: | 72 | 74 | +2.8 |

| Survey data | Tetrads | % |
|---|---|---|
| Confirmed breeding: | 156 | 8.5 |
| Probable breeding: | 158 | 8.6 |
| Possible breeding: | 31 | 1.7 |
| Total: | 345 | 18.8 |

The Sedge Warbler is a trans-Saharan migrant like the Whitethroat, although it did not suffer the same catastrophic decline following the 1968/69 Sahel drought. Comparison of the distribution in Cumbria between *this Atlas* and the *Old* and *New Atlases* shows little change. The apparent stability in the county distribution screens the birds' dependency on favourable conditions in its African wintering quarters. In 1983 for example, it was estimated that fewer than 5% of adult Sedge Warblers successfully completed their return migration to breed in Britain and Ireland.

The amount of available habitat in Cumbria would appear capable of supporting a larger breeding population than that at present. The main factor affecting the future of the Sedge Warbler in the county is, therefore, likely to be climatic change in the main African wintering quarters, which could result in greatly diminished numbers of birds returning each spring.

Allan Mackenzie

THE loud, chatty song and lavish mimic compositions of the Reed Warbler can be heard both day and night as males sit towards the tops of phragmites stalks proclaiming their territory. Without song, they would seldom be noticed, as their sober rufous-brown plumage is not eye-catching amidst the mass of dense reed that they inhabit.

Reed Warblers are Old World warblers with a summer distribution that includes all European countries, except Iceland, with some recent colonization into southern Scotland and the merest toehold in Ireland, and extending east to the Caspian Sea. In England, the distribution shows a southeastern bias, with the highest densities in East Anglia and Kent. Its winter range is south of the Sahara, stretching across the breadth of Africa as far south as Zambia.

Although there are occasional historical records, up to the last three decades the Reed Warbler was considered to be a rare breeding bird in Cumbria. Macpherson & Duckworth (1886) published details of a nest with four eggs taken on the River Eden and an undated record of a summer adult shot at Bassenthwaite Lake. Almost 80 years later, Stokoe (1962) still considered them to be "a scarce breeding visitor", though he did comment that the species "has nested in at least nine localities, mainly in the centre and south of the area, at one time or another; annually at one Westmorland tarn and for several years at a former Cumberland haunt". In 1959, a nest containing four eggs was discovered at Siddick Pond. In 1978, nesting was re-established at this, the premier site in Cumbria, but on a larger scale, when four different females with brood-patches were mist-netted. This

increase is noted by Mead (2000), who states that after the *Old Atlas,* "extra sites in northern England were colonized". Nationally, the latest available CBC data indicate a massive 114% increase since 1970.

With a protracted breeding season, chicks have been found in the nest into the second week of September (pers obs) and the constancy of singing males, both after arrival and between the two broods, offers every opportunity for an accurate survey. On the other hand, actual proof of breeding is difficult to obtain, given the inaccessibility of the breeding habitat, the ingeniously crafted structure of the nest being woven onto reed stems in thick impenetrable cover over oozing mud and water.

Almost at the northern limit of their British breeding range in Cumbria, Reed Warblers are now well established at several specific reedbed sites in the county, consolidating their position in the years between the *Old Atlas* and the *New Atlas.* There was not one record of confirmed breeding during the period of the *Old Atlas;* however, by the close of the *New Atlas,* a remarkable change had occurred, with nesting confirmed in no less than ten 10km squares and probable breeding in two more: not only had they pioneered their way into Cumbria, they had become abundant, at least at sites with extensive areas of phragmites reed. Ringing activities at Siddick Pond revealed that the site held in excess of 30 pairs in most years, with good site fidelity. Populations at Bassenthwaite Lake, Cavendish Dock and Helton Tarn have also flourished.

During the period of *this Atlas,* the Reed Warbler has reaffirmed its position at stronghold sites, with further limited expansion into tarns and ponds in southern parts of the Coastal Plain, where phragmites beds have developed. Additionally, probable breeding at Windermere, Rydal Water and Grasmere could doubtless have been upgraded to confirmed if ringing took place there. All the larger central lakes that possess reedbeds now hold Reed Warblers, the western and eastern lakes having, as yet, no suitable habitat.

The paucity of birds in the county reflects the very limited amount of suitable habitat. Line transect surveys do not produce reliable results for species with specific habitat requirements such as this but the findings of *this Atlas* suggest a current county population of 200 breeding pairs.

The predicted onset of warmer springs and summers will benefit late-arriving migrants, such as Reed Warblers; phragmites beds will expand, giving further opportunities for increased densities. This has already been evident at Siddick Pond, where the area of the reedbeds has increased by around 30% over the last three decades. Due to the dense nature of reedbed habitats and the communal nesting behaviour of this species, territories are small and, consequently,

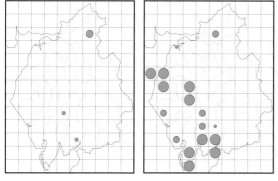

**1968-1972**     **1997-2001**
(For explanation of maps, see page 45)

*Conservation status*

| | |
|---|---|
| European: | Non-SPEC |
| UK: | **GREEN** |

*Populations*

| | |
|---|---|
| European status: | 3,100,000 |
| Britain – pairs: | 60,000 |
| Cumbria – pairs: | 200 |

*30-year distribution change*

| | Old Atlas | This Atlas | % |
|---|---|---|---|
| No. of 10km squares: | 3 | 16 | +433.3 |

| **Survey data** | **Tetrads** | **%** |
|---|---|---|
| Confirmed breeding: | 14 | 0.8 |
| Probable breeding: | 11 | 0.6 |
| Possible breeding: | 2 | 0.1 |
| Total: | 27 | 1.5 |

densities can be high. In other parts of England, Reed Warblers also nest in willowherb and arable crops; as yet only phragmites supports them in Cumbria and, without a change in habitat selection, this is likely to be the factor limiting any further expansion.

John Callion

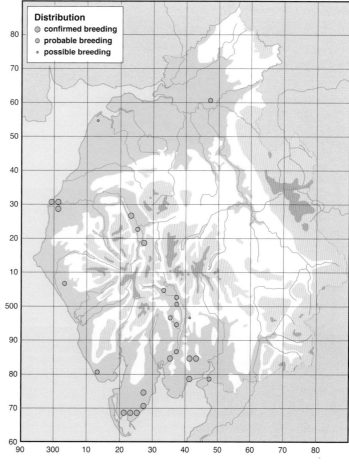

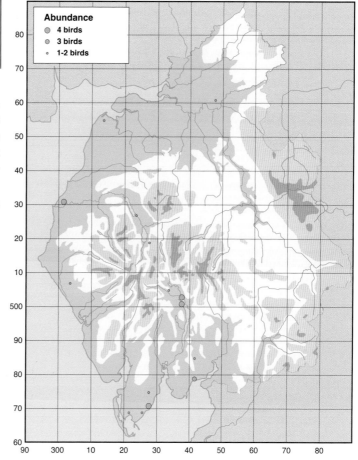

# Lesser Whitethroat *Sylvia curruca*

THE broad black face mask, and clean grey head and back give a jaunty, dapper appearance that overstates the Lesser Whitethroat's vocal qualities; unlike similar species it is not known for melodious warbling notes. The far-carrying song is more reminiscent of that of a bunting, except at close quarters when a soft burble can be heard to precede the loud rattle.

The Lesser Whitethroat is one of the most widely distributed of the Old World warblers, spreading eastwards from Britain and Ireland to central Siberia, Mongolia and northern China and bounded by the arctic regions to the north and the deserts of the Middle East and the Himalaya to the south. It is, however, noticeably absent from the Iberian Peninsula, and most of France and Italy. Lesser Whitethroats in Cumbria are toward the extreme western edge of their range, although in recent years there has been some expansion into western Scotland and Ireland, with further increases recorded in Wales.

In parts of its continental range, the Lesser Whitethroat can be found breeding from sea level up to altitudes of 2,000m asl and occupying a wide range of habitats that include closed canopy forest and open country. It has a preference in Britain for thick hedgerows or patches of scrub, usually of thorny bushes such as bramble, hawthorn and blackthorn and is normally only present below 200m asl. A tangle of luxuriant vegetation, usually about 0.5m to 1.5m above ground, is the favoured nest site and a single clutch of four to six eggs is normal.

A study of distribution and site-fidelity in a population of Lesser Whitethroats in Cleveland, which, like Cumbria, is on the limit of the breeding range, suggested that young birds showed little fidelity to their natal areas, and that the population was governed by the numbers of adults returning each spring, augmented by first-time nesters from outside the immediate vicinity (Norman 1992). In Cumbria, data obtained from ringing birds at Eskmeals tend to support these suggestions: of 40 adults ringed between 1989 and 1999, 25% were retrapped at the site in subsequent years, while, from the same population, less than 3% of 141 juveniles returned to their natal site.

The Lesser Whitethroat is more numerous and widespread in Cumbria today than ever before. Macpherson and Duckworth (1886) knew the bird only as a very scarce summer migrant, "tolerably established in the Lake District and breeding irregularly in the north of the county." Stokoe (1962) described the species as "sparse and local". It is still the scarcest of the four *Sylvia* warblers that breed in Cumbria and its scattered distribution in the county reflects its specialist habitat requirements. McAlone (1994) analysed all the county breeding records from 1977 to 1992 and found that, although birds were recorded in a total of 33 10km squares during the period, 17 of these squares held birds in only one or two years. He concluded that the Lesser Whitethroat was not well established in as wide and expanding an area of the county as was generally believed and commented that, of the eight or nine strongholds, just two nesting areas, Hodbarrow and Eskmeals, contained significant numbers of birds each year. The former site is a disused industrial complex, the type of habitat which it has been suggested aided the species' expansion in other parts of Britain. The latter is a military range, dominated by sea buckthorn, that until the mid-1980s had severe restrictions on access, so breeding birds might have gone unrecorded previously.

Comparison between the *Old* and *New Atlases* reveals a doubling in the number of confirmed or probable breeding records and the results of *this Atlas* reveal a further significant increase to 37 occupied 10km squares. The rise in the county population would appear to stem from immigration augmenting numbers of local breeding birds. Despite the quite dramatic range expansion since the *Old Atlas,* the species is still more or less confined to the low-lying Coastal Plain, Solway Basin and lower Eden Valley. Perhaps not surprisingly, there are no records from the uplands of the North Pennines or the high fells of Lakeland.

This is another species whose precise habitat

Sponsored by Nicholson Multimedia

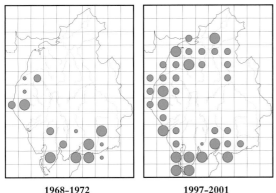

**1968-1972**  **1997-2001**
(For explanation of maps, see page 45)

| Conservation status | | | |
| --- | --- | --- | --- |
| European: | Non-SPEC | | |
| UK: | **GREEN** | | |

*Populations*

| | | |
| --- | --- | --- |
| European status: | 2,200,000 | |
| Britain – pairs: | 80,000 | |
| Cumbria – pairs: | 400 | |

*30-year distribution change*

| | Old Atlas | This Atlas | % |
| --- | --- | --- | --- |
| No. of 10km squares: | 15 | 37 | +146.6 |

| Survey data | Tetrads | % |
| --- | --- | --- |
| Confirmed breeding: | 25 | 1.4 |
| Probable breeding: | 60 | 3.3 |
| Possible breeding: | 14 | 0.8 |
| Total: | 99 | 5.5 |

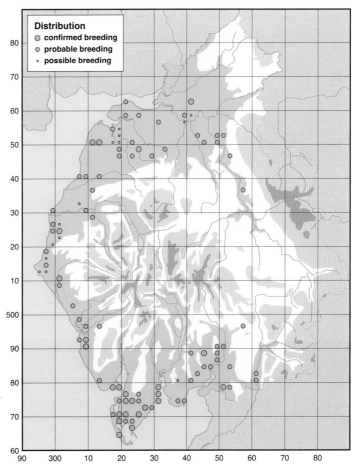

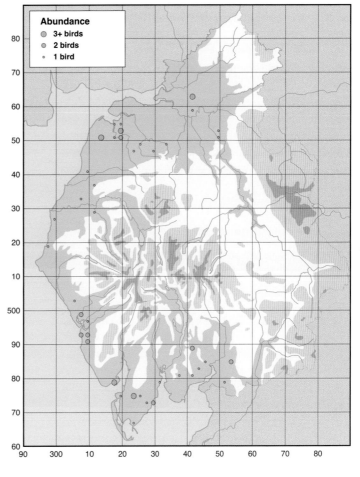

requirements are well-fragmented in Cumbria, and overly emphasised by the use of NLCs, thus generating an exaggerated population figure. The current county population of 400 breeding pairs, based on knowledge at local study sites, probably offers a more realistic population estimate.

The population is still increasing in the main breeding areas. There seems to be no immediate threat to the birds' breeding habitat and many apparently suitable areas within the county still remain to be colonized: factors which suggest that the new millennium holds a promising future for this attractive little bird in Cumbria.

Allan Mackenzie

WITH its scratchy warble as distinct as its rusty-brown wings, slate-grey crown and conspicuous white throat patch the Whitethroat is one of the more easily observed of British warblers. The male habitually delivers his song from a prominent perch or during a bouncy song-flight and territorial birds make their presence known as they chatter and scold at any intruder.

Cumbrian Whitethroats are of the nominate race which breeds throughout western and central Europe, northwest Africa and as far east as Poland and Hungary. Other races breed through to the Middle East and central Siberia. In Britain and Ireland, the species is widely distributed, apart from on the highest ground, across England, Wales and southern and eastern Scotland. Breeding is more patchy in northern Scotland and Ireland and Whitethroats are scarce or absent throughout the Western and Northern Isles.

Spring migration into Cumbria begins in mid-April, with most territories established in May. The chosen habitat is low scrub or hedgerows with plentiful song perches and room for the male's aerial display flight. The nest is usually concealed in thick cover such as bramble, nettles or long grasses, where a single clutch of four or five eggs is laid. Although normally single-brooded, two broods are not uncommon. Incubation takes around 11 days and involves both sexes. Although the young birds fledge after 10–12 days, they do not become fully independent for a further 14–20 days.

Macpherson (1892) had little to say on the status of the Whitethroat in Cumbria, restricting his comments

to the behaviour of birds on their return in spring. Stokoe (1962) regarded the species as "numerous in fairly open country with rough hedgerows, wood borders, clearings with tangled vegetation and gorse commons: nests in fell districts up to 1,300 feet [396m]."

The diminished numbers of British and Irish Whitethroats returning in the spring of 1969 alerted conservationists to the disastrous events in the Sahel region of Africa. The severe droughts of the 1968/69 winter caused a massive population crash of many western European birds and an estimated 75% of the Whitethroat population perished on their wintering quarters in West Africa that winter. In subsequent years, the species suffered further sharp declines and, by 1974, its numbers had reduced to around 16% of pre-drought levels. Since that catastrophic decline, the story has been one of a steady recovery, though interrupted by setbacks during the winters of 1983/84 and 1990/91.

Although the Cumbrian population has not been immune to these events, Hutcheson (1986) believed the decreases were not as severe in the county as in some other areas. However, numbers must certainly have fallen significantly in the period after a long-term study of breeding warblers in Lakeland (Brown 1954), which had concluded that in some years the Whitethroat vied with the Willow Warbler as the most numerous breeding warbler in the area. The population estimates for *this Atlas* show that, although the Whitethroat is now vying with Blackcap and Garden Warbler for the title of second most numerous breeding warbler in the county, the present numbers would need to increase considerably before they would approach those of the Willow Warbler.

The distribution map shows that Whitethroats are currently widespread throughout all of the low-lying areas of the county, with particular strongholds on the Furness peninsula, Coastal Plain and the Solway Basin. The population now appears to be spreading inland using river corridors and has reached central Lakeland. Although the species is almost totally absent from land higher than 300m asl, presumably due to a lack of suitable habitat at these altitudes, newly established plantations, especially broad-leaved woodland, can be utilized in the early years and abandoned as the canopy closes. This may account for some losses from the county's upland 10km squares between the *Old* and *New Atlases,* which occurred against a national trend of a continuing population recovery.

Analysis of the line transect data from *this Atlas* gives a population band of 11,000–30,000 singing males, suggesting a mean population of 18,000 males. The highest densities of 13 males/km$^2$ occurred along the Coastal Plain.

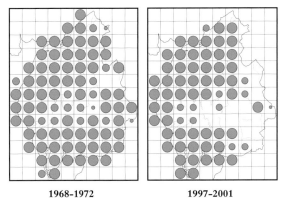

**1968-1972**     **1997-2001**
(For explanation of maps, see page 45)

*Conservation status*
European:                    Non–SPEC
UK:                          **GREEN**

*Populations*
European status:             7,300,000
Britain – pairs:             660,000
Cumbria – pairs:             18,000

*30-year distribution change*
                    Old Atlas  This Atlas   %
No. of 10km squares:    85        67    **–21.2**

| Survey data | Tetrads | % |
|---|---|---|
| Confirmed breeding: | 312 | 16.9 |
| Probable breeding: | 303 | 16.4 |
| Possible breeding: | 36 | 2.0 |
| Total: | 651 | 35.3 |

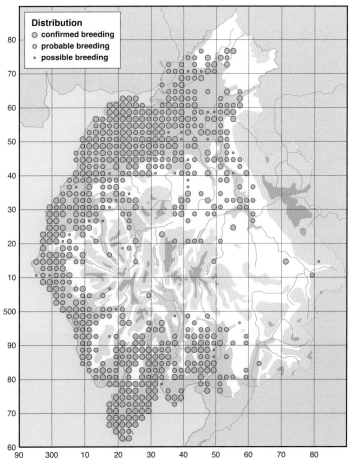

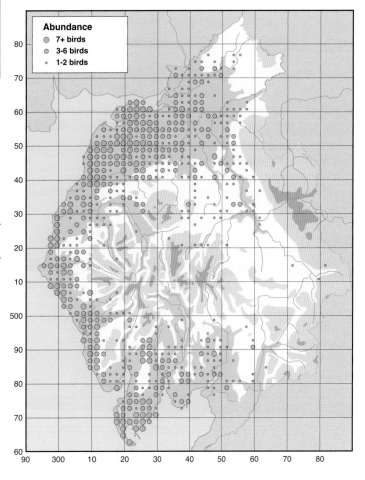

There is little doubt that capacity exists for the Whitethroat population to return to the level that was maintained before the 1969 crash. On Walney Island, the population increased from 20 pairs in 1990 to 92 pairs by the start of survey work for *this Atlas,* demonstrating the continuing upward population trend (Raven & Sanderson 1997). There remains, of course, the serious problem of unpredictable rainfall patterns on the wintering grounds and, unless these stabilize, any hope of the Whitethroat's cheerful scratchy song being heard as often as the descending lilt of the Willow Warbler will remain merely wishful thinking.

Allan Mackenzie

# Garden Warbler *Sylvia borin*

THE vigorous and sustained notes of this fine songster announce its intentions of proceeding with the breeding season without delay. Often nesting in brambles, building a structure that seems barely able to survive the rigours of a full brood, the Garden Warbler prefers fairly open woodland with some dense undergrowth but will also breed in scrub, young conifer plantations and rhododendron thickets. Its breeding range includes most of Europe, extending eastwards in a narrowing band as far as central Siberia. Although widely distributed throughout most of Britain, it is absent from much of northern Scotland and is very sparsely distributed in Ireland.

Historical information on Garden Warbler population fluctuations in Cumbria is very limited. Macpherson (1892) stated that they were fairly widely distributed though hardly as abundant as Blackcaps, whereas both Blezard *et al* (1943) and Stokoe (1962) felt they were the more numerous of the two species, with the latter commenting that they were "common in woods, gardens and waste ground with tangled bushy undergrowth". Wilson (1933) described them as "somewhat local" in the Eden Valley in the 1930s, whereas they are now well distributed throughout the length of the valley. Nationally, at the time of the *Old Atlas,* Garden Warbler numbers, though still relatively high, were starting to show signs of a decline. Subsequently, and coinciding with the Sahel droughts, the population declined to a low point in 1975–76, though this was apparently less pronounced in northern England. Wintering further south than the drought region, the Garden Warbler's decline occurred

later and the recovery sooner than for those migrants wintering in the Sahel region. They had recovered in woodlands by the time of the *New Atlas* and were still recovering in the less favoured farmland habitats, as well as expanding in Scotland. The recovery has been sustained with the latest available CBC data indicating a 24% increase since 1970.

The findings of *this Atlas* confirm that the few areas still not reoccupied at the time of the *New Atlas* have been recolonized and that a slight range extension has occurred since the *Old Atlas*. Six new 10km squares have been colonized, new coastal sites have been occupied and pairs are now prepared to nest further into the higher reaches of some valleys in the Border Uplands and North Pennines. The current distribution map indicates that they are present in most of their preferred habitat as well as in some less suitable farmland areas of the Solway Basin north and east of Carlisle. They are particularly widespread in south Lakeland, even more so than Blackcaps, despite the fact that most of the tetrads would appear to contain suitable woodland and that Blackcaps are presumed to be the dominant species, with the added advantage of being the first to arrive. Although almost ubiquitous, Garden Warblers have an aversion to upland areas, decreasing in abundance from well-wooded shores of lakes such as Buttermere, Derwent Water and Ullswater as altitude and grazing intensity increases. The classic grazed upland oakwoods of Lakeland do not generally have the undergrowth required for nesting; nor do the wooded upland gills frequented by Willow Warblers. Though the highest breeding record in Britain noted by Mason (1976) was at 250m asl, *this Atlas* recorded birds breeding up to 450m asl. Presumably the move into sub-optimal habitats is a result of more favourable areas reaching an upper carrying capacity.

Analysis of the line transect data from *this Atlas* gives a population band of 10,000–25,000, suggesting a mean population of 16,000 males. The highest densities of 5.22 males/km² occurred, perhaps surprisingly, on the better-farmed land around the periphery of Lakeland, in the lower Eden Valley and in the Border Uplands.

Despite the changes wrought by modern agriculture and the decline of some woodlands, Garden Warblers are thriving in Cumbria and are probably as widespread and as numerous as at any time over the last century or so. We can, however, no doubt expect as wide population fluctuations in the future as in the past. These are most likely to be driven by factors that affect them on migration and on their wintering grounds, though any habitat degradation and climate change in Cumbria could well play a part.

Dave Piercy

Sponsored by Jill Damment

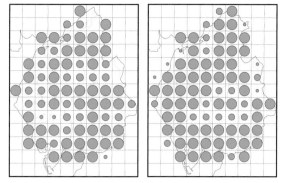

**1968-1972**       **1997-2001**

(For explanation of maps, see page 45)

*Conservation status*

European:                    Non-SPEC
UK:                          GREEN

*Populations*

European status:             11,000,000
Britain – pairs:             200,000
Cumbria – pairs:             16,000

*30-year distribution change*

|                      | Old Atlas | This Atlas | % |
|----------------------|-----------|------------|------|
| No. of 10km squares: | 77        | 83         | +7.8 |

| Survey data         | Tetrads | %    |
|---------------------|---------|------|
| Confirmed breeding: | 216     | 11.7 |
| Probable breeding:  | 527     | 28.6 |
| Possible breeding:  | 58      | 3.1  |
| Total:              | 801     | 43.4 |

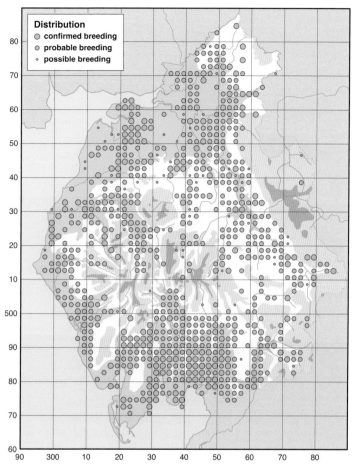

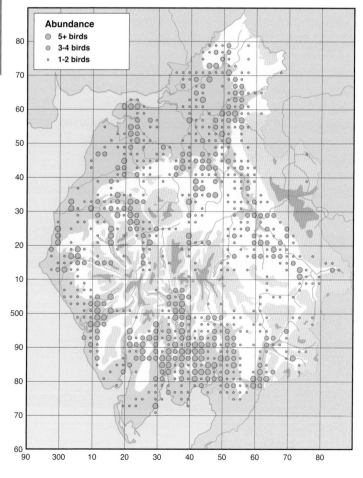

# Blackcap *Sylvia atricapilla*

THE Blackcap's concentrated bursts of pure music delivered from bushes and trees above tangled undergrowth are one of the joys of early spring. With the recent increase in wintering birds of central European origin, views of this attractive bird may now be enjoyed all year round.

Their breeding range covers most of Europe and the tip of North Africa, with a narrow finger of distribution extending as far east as the Urals. They are widely distributed throughout Britain, except for much of northern Scotland, and widely but locally distributed in Ireland. Often nesting in brambles and other rank undergrowth, Blackcaps prefer deciduous woodland with shrubby understorey but will nest in overgrown thickets, hedgerows and rhododendrons, especially where some taller trees provide song-posts.

In Cumbria, Macpherson (1892) commented that "nowhere in Lakeland can the Blackcap be accurately termed a very numerous bird," while Stokoe (1962) regarded it as "widespread but local and less numerous than Garden Warbler, though habitat similar."

Over the last few decades, the Blackcap has been one of Britain's most successful warblers, with its population increasing from as early as the 1950s. By the time of the *New Atlas,* in northern Britain generally, Blackcaps had become more numerous than Garden Warblers. Analysis of the latest available CBC data reveals a 104% increase since 1970. The fact that many winter well to the north of the drought-affected Sahel region may explain why they have not declined in parallel with some other migrants. There is, however, no full explanation of why their numbers have increased so dramatically. It may be that increasing numbers are wintering north of the Sahara, resulting in improved breeding numbers due to a higher winter survival rate. There is also a theory argued by Mason (1995) that a decrease in the number of Blackcaps killed annually by hunters in the Mediterranean over the last four decades may have increased the survival rate of many that winter in this region.

The results of *this Atlas* confirm their continuing success. Compared to the *Old Atlas,* Blackcaps have extended their range, with an additional six 10km squares occupied. Birds have now extended their range further along the higher reaches of the valleys on Cumbria's eastern boundary, and new sites on the Coastal Plain are now occupied. The remaining five are all coastal. Although earlier research (Mason 1976) found evidence of breeding in Britain only up to an altitude of 250m asl, it would now appear that pairs in Cumbria are prepared to attempt to nest up to 400m asl – a further sign of their range extension in the county.

Blackcaps occupy a similar county range in *this Atlas* to Garden Warblers. They are certainly now more numerous but are marginally less widespread, with four fewer tetrads occupied. Blackcaps are more widespread and abundant in the north of the county, particularly in the lower reaches of the Eden Valley and in the Solway Basin. Comparing the densities for the two species highlights the differences even more strikingly. In the intricate lowland areas of south Lakeland, Garden Warblers occur in far greater densities than Blackcaps, while the converse is true for intensively farmed areas such as the Eden Valley.

Analysis of the line transect data from *this Atlas* gives a population band of 15,000–36,000 singing males, with a mean population of 24,000 males. The highest calculated densities of 10.44 males/km² were in areas of optimum scrubland habitat along the narrow coastal strip.

Inland of the coastal strip, where the highest densities were recorded, the Coastal Plain, although dominated by a varied lowland landscape, with hedged small fields, a mix of arable and good grassland with some urbanization, still supports densities of 7.3 males/km². On the other hand, perhaps surprisingly, the well-wooded, undulating farmland of south Lakeland, considered more typical Blackcap habitat, recorded just 6.4 males/km². Densities in the intensively farmed areas to the northeast and south of Carlisle reached 5.9 males/km² but fell sharply to 1 male/km² in upland areas, dominated by permanent pasture and discontinuous woodland.

Blackcaps are probably as widespread and as numerous in Cumbria as they have been for at least 100 years. With both Blackcap and Garden Warblers in the ascendance, there may come a point when

 Sponsored by Mike Porter

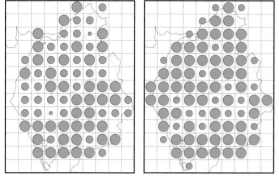

**1968–1972**  **1997–2001**
(For explanation of maps, see page 45)

*Conservation status*
European:                Non-SPEC
UK:                      GREEN

*Populations*
European status:         21,000,000
Britain – pairs:            580,000
Cumbria – pairs:             24,000

*30-year distribution change*
|  | Old Atlas | This Atlas | % |
|---|---|---|---|
| No. of 10km squares: | 76 | 82 | +7.9 |

| Survey data | Tetrads | % |
|---|---|---|
| Confirmed breeding: | 237 | 12.9 |
| Probable breeding: | 514 | 27.9 |
| Possible breeding: | 46 | 2.5 |
| Total: | 797 | 43.3 |

competition in their overlapping habitats will be seen to have an effect on their respective populations. At present, as the national population is still increasing, they may be expected to carry on expanding in Cumbria, particularly in areas where there are schemes for replanting, rejuvenating or regenerating woodland.

Dave Piercy

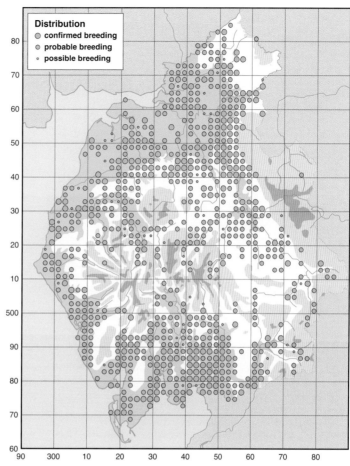

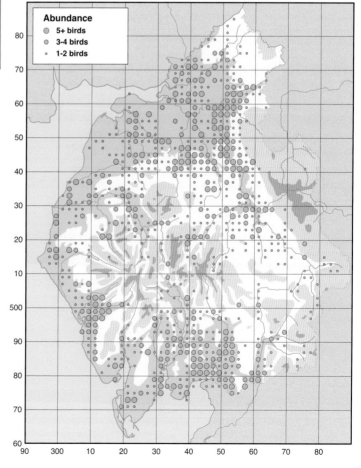

# Wood Warbler *Phylloscopus sibilatrix*

A BIRD of the closed canopy, the Wood Warbler has one of the most distinctive and unmistakable songs of any of our summer woodland visitors. The male's energetic courtship, with quivering body and vibrant wings, is reminiscent of light shimmering on water, though the attractive combination of green, yellow and white plumage can be surprisingly inconspicuous amid sun-dappled foliage. Wood Warblers have a dual song, the first phase a resonating, accelerating trill; the second, a soft *'pew'*, which is also the alarm call of both adults during the nesting season.

The largest *Phylloscopus* warbler in the Western Palearctic, its breeding range extends across much of northern, central and eastern Europe. In Britain, it occurs throughout much of the west and south, favouring upland oakwoods, and is absent from the Northern Isles. In Ireland, it remains relatively scarce though apparently expanding its range. In winter, its distribution straddles the equator, where it inhabits forest edge and clearings (Serle 1965).

Wood Warblers are true ancient forest birds, favouring sparse secondary growth with ample ground cover for their well-concealed nest and dependent on mature broad-leaved woodland, especially oak, beech and birch. The domed nest is built into the previous year's debris on the woodland floor, with only the entrance hole visible to the 'knowing eye'.

They inhabit a niche that has little changed for centuries: in Cumbria, Macpherson & Duckworth (1886) commented that "the Wood Wren is a local numerous summer visitant, delighting in well-sheltered valleys clothed with old timber". Stokoe (1962) regarded the species as "locally common in fairly open woods with sparse undergrowth, breeding up to 1,250 feet [381m]" though he stated that it was "now absent from some traditional haunts and reduced elsewhere" and then remarked on its disappearance from former haunts near Brampton and Loweswater and declines at Keswick and elsewhere. These declines were considered "partly due to disturbance and loss of habitat".

Singing Wood Warblers are easy to detect, so atlas distribution maps should accurately reflect their occurrence − particularly important as the species is poorly represented on CBC plots. Comparison of data between the *Old Atlas* and *this Atlas* shows that the essentially unaltered habitat it favours has allowed the distribution to remain little changed in the intervening 30 years. Unfortunately, we are unable to compare abundance within the 10km squares.

The least common of the three *Phylloscopus* warblers breeding in Britain, the Wood Warbler has a northwestern bias, which is mirrored in Cumbria, where *this Atlas* reveals that the widest distribution and greatest densities occur in Lakeland and the higher wooded valleys of the lower Eden Valley; outside these areas, distribution is patchy and densities inferior. Wood Warblers are almost absent from the North Pennines and Solway Basin. Highest densities occur in the relatively undisturbed mature woodlands around Loweswater, Nether Wasdale, Torver and Elterwater. The distribution map clearly demonstrates that, in Cumbria, Wood Warblers are absent from most coastal and lowland farmland habitats. Even at their most abundant in Lakeland, they are generally found at lower altitudes in the valley bottoms, where they can be extremely concentrated, though nesting up to 300m asl is not uncommon in favoured habitat. Although reasonably well distributed throughout the county, the Wood Warbler's restricted habitat selection gives an imbalance when comparing distribution to abundance. In the best habitat, the number of singing males can be so high as to give the misleading impression that Wood Warblers are common and widespread.

This is another species for which line transect methodology or NLCs proved unsuitable to measure densities. The current county population of 2,500 breeding pairs was derived from count data, enhanced by supplementary records, as being a more reliable population estimate.

Wood Warblers appear to be one of our migrants that have not been affected by the drought conditions in sub-Saharan Africa; if that situation continues, it seems that threats to their stability, at least from that source, remain minimal. However, they now occur on too few CBC plots for effective monitoring, and analysis of BBS data reveals a worrying 43% decline during the period 1994–2000. Their woodland

Sponsored by United Utilities plc

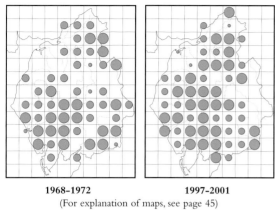

**1968–1972**          **1997–2001**
(For explanation of maps, see page 45)

**Conservation status**
European:                           Non-SPEC
UK:                        **AMBER: BDM**

**Populations**
European status:                   6,500,000
Britain – pairs:                      17,200
Cumbria – pairs:                       2,500

**30-year distribution change**

|  | Old Atlas | This Atlas | % |
|---|---|---|---|
| No. of 10km squares: | 53 | 58 | **+9.41** |

| Survey data | Tetrads | % |
|---|---|---|
| Confirmed breeding: | 67 | 3.6 |
| Probable breeding: | 169 | 9.2 |
| Possible breeding: | 33 | 1.8 |
| Total: | 269 | 14.6 |

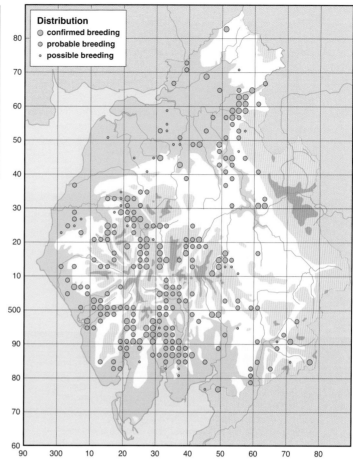

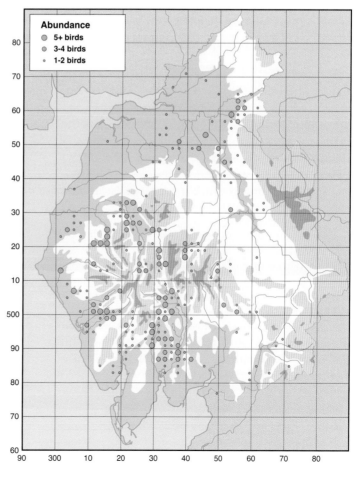

strongholds in Cumbria lie mostly within the boundaries of the Lake District National Park, thus, hopefully, ensuring their security. On the other hand, the recent policy of either reducing or removing sheep from Park woodlands will allow understorey to develop, especially in more open areas; this is likely to bring in *Sylvia* warblers, such as Blackcap and Garden Warbler, perhaps to the exclusion of the Wood Warbler, one of our most delightful site-specific species.

John Callion

# Chiffchaff *Phylloscopus collybita*

Common Chiffchaff

THE hardy Chiffchaff's cheerful refrain gives us hope that the last dark days of winter are almost over. The few that decide to spend the winter here can even bring a feeling of impending spring to a mellow mid-winter day. Unlike Blackcaps, there is some evidence that these wintering birds may well stay to breed with us and presumably have an advantage in choice of territory over the majority arriving in March and April.

The range of the Chiffchaff complex covers most of Europe and stretches as far east as the vast forests of eastern Siberia, with outposts in the Canaries and northwest Africa – although a number of the peripheral forms have recently been promoted to full species. Chiffchaffs breed throughout Britain and Ireland, becoming less common north of the Midlands and sparse in Scotland. Much more particular in their choice of habitat than Willow Warblers, they require the presence of mature deciduous trees as well as some thick undergrowth to conceal their dome-shaped nests.

Observations on the population of Chiffchaffs in Cumbria broadly reflect national trends. There is evidence of an expansion during the 19th century, with Chiffchaffs spreading through Britain as far north as the lowlands of Scotland. This was noted in Cumbria, with their first appearance in districts near Carlisle dating from 1884, coinciding with a general increase in north Cumberland (Macpherson & Duckworth 1886). Wilson (1933) found them "practically to be met in any place where hedgerows and bushes are sufficiently plentiful" yet, nearly 50 years later, they were recorded as "mainly passage

migrants in the Eden Valley" (Hutcheson 1986). These extreme variations generally mirror national trends as shown by analysis of CBC data, which reveals a peak in the 1960s, then a trough in 1976, followed by a series of increases since 1984. The decline coincided with droughts in the Sahel area, but for this species the population crash was not as dramatic as for some other migrants. This would be explicable if a proportion of our Chiffchaffs winter north of the Sahara region, thereby remaining unaffected; recent ringing results, however, tend to contradict this, indicating that a higher proportion of birds overwinter in sub-Saharan areas than previously thought.

In Cumbria, a significant increase in range has occurred since the *Old Atlas*, with 11 new 10km squares occupied. Birds have moved into the higher reaches of river valleys and, in particular, they have colonized, albeit sparsely, land above 150m asl in the Eden Valley and sites on the Coastal Plain. An almost complete absence from the upland areas in Lakeland, the Cumbria Dales and the North Pennines is in marked contrast to the distribution of Willow Warblers. They do manage to penetrate into Lakeland where there are well-wooded valleys such as Borrowdale or around Ullswater but, even here, they can be few and far between due to the lack of undergrowth in many grazed woodlands. They are also generally scarce in upland coniferous plantations, as can be seen from the paucity of records in the Border Uplands and around Ennerdale. However, the location of two of the newly occupied squares reveals that birds are moving into this habitat in the Border Uplands. There are also, surprisingly, no records in the forestry around Thirlmere, which does have the broad-leaved trees that Chiffchaffs seem to require in order to breed in coniferous woodland. Altitude is presumably also a limiting factor in this and other habitats in Cumbria. The vast majority of birds in the county were found to breed below 200m asl, although there are breeding records as high as 350–400m asl in coniferous woodland.

Analysis of the line transect data from *this Atlas* gives a population band of 5,000–22,000 singing males, suggesting a mean population of 10,000 males. Note, however, the wide band limits. The highest calculated densities of 11.8 males/km$^2$ appeared in some premium areas along the narrow coastal strip.

Despite concerns about the declining quality of woodland in Cumbria, Chiffchaffs have obviously recovered in recent years to their highest level for some time. At present, their success seems to depend on factors during migration and in the wintering areas, rather than conditions on the breeding grounds. Climate change will also have an effect and there is already a trend towards earlier egg laying (Baillie *et al* 2001). There is still scope for further expansion in

278

Sponsored by Alan Wills

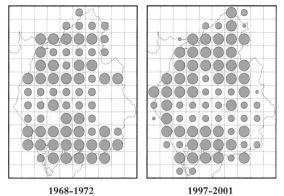

**1968-1972**          **1997-2001**

(For explanation of maps, see page 45)

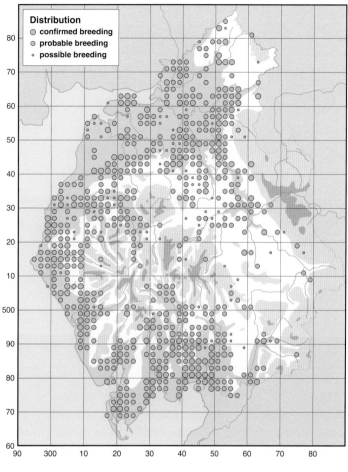

*Conservation status*

| | |
|---|---|
| European: | Non-SPEC |
| UK: | GREEN |

*Populations*

| | |
|---|---|
| European status: | 16,500,000 |
| Britain – pairs: | 640,000 |
| Cumbria – pairs: | 10,000 |

*30-year distribution change*

| | Old Atlas | This Atlas | % |
|---|---|---|---|
| No. of 10km squares: | 69 | 80 | +15.9 |

| Survey data | Tetrads | % |
|---|---|---|
| Confirmed breeding: | 166 | 9.0 |
| Probable breeding: | 416 | 22.6 |
| Possible breeding: | 73 | 4.0 |
| Total: | 655 | 35.6 |

Cumbria, especially in the upland oakwoods where there are schemes to exclude sheep to help regeneration, in sensitively managed coniferous woodland where more broad-leaved trees are allowed to flourish, and in the many small-scale replanting and rejuvenation schemes in the Lake District National Park.

Dave Piercy

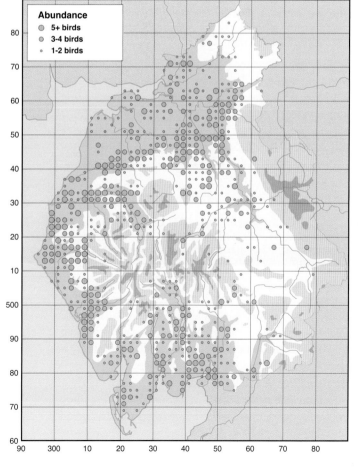

# Willow Warbler *Phylloscopus trochilus*

Ray Harvey

**D**URING late March or early April the eagerly anticipated song of the Willow Warbler heralds the first wave of returning males. Within days it seems that every bush and tree has a male competing passionately for a territory. The female returns later and is soon seen carrying strands of material to its ground nest hidden in whatever undergrowth is available, from sparse grass cover to wild tangles of bramble. More adaptable than most other warblers, the Willow Warbler breeds in a wide range of habitats, occupying young woodland, woodland edge, scrub, young conifers and hedgerow with trees. The breeding range extends from western Europe eastwards in a narrow band through Siberia, and from the European shores of the Mediterranean as far as the North Cape. In Britain and Ireland, it is absent from only the treeless uplands and islands.

During most of the 20th century, the population and distribution in Britain and Ireland seems to have remained more or less stable. As long-distance migrants wintering to the south of the Sahel, they seem to have been unaffected by the droughts affecting that region and, until the late 1980s, they were one of the most stable species monitored by the CBC. Then, in the early 1990s, there was a sudden and unprecedented decline in southern Britain that has been linked to an unexplained increase in mortality amongst adult birds (Peach *et al* 1995). One intriguing possibility is that if the decline was due to problems met on their wintering grounds, then more northerly breeding birds may winter in a different area to those that breed in southern Britain. In Cumbria, there were dramatic declines noted at several monitored sites in 1992 but

most had recovered by the following year, though numbers did remain low at Fingland Rigg Wood until 1995. Analysis of the latest available CBC data reveals a decline of 37% since 1970 and this obviously gives cause for concern, though BBS data for the period 1994–2000 show an encouraging 13% increase. Climate change is also having some effect with a trend towards earlier egg laying dates and increasing brood size (Baillie *et al* 2001).

The Willow Warbler is the most abundant summer migrant in Cumbria and has probably been so since at least the end of the 19th century. Macpherson (1892) described the 'Willow Wren' as "numerously diffuse throughout our woods as a breeding bird", while Stokoe (1962) regarded it as "the commonest warbler. Numerous in a wide variety of habitats with trees and bushes, breeding up to 1,000 feet [305m] in fell regions." With no discernible change in distribution between the *Old Atlas* and *this Atlas,* this remains an extremely widespread and numerous species in the county, with all but two 10km squares occupied. Their adaptability allows them to breed in a wide variety of locations, as long as the habitat provides cover for nesting. They are particularly abundant in the Eden Valley and in the transitional zone between the Solway Basin and the Border Uplands. They penetrate quite far into upland areas and can be found over 500m asl, though they are absent or very scarce on the more open landscapes of sheepwalks and heather moorland. They can occur however where even a few straggly hawthorns and rowans line a ravine, or where bushes grow on scree below lines of cliffs.

High densities of 121.3 males/km$^2$ were found on parts of the narrow coastal strip of scrub backed by good farmland, though the presence of migrants could have inflated this figure. Inland, on intensively farmed lowlands with hedged boundaries such as are found in south Lakeland, the lower Eden Valley and parts of the Solway Basin, densities fell to 53.8 males/km$^2$. Densities declined further to 33 males/km$^2$ at higher altitudes, where permanent pastures and discontinuous tree cover characterize the marginal farmland of Lakeland and the upper reaches of the Eden Valley. In the North Pennines, where lightly wooded ghylls, scattered shrub or even isolated bushes are present, similar densities of 31.9 males/km$^2$ were recorded. In contrast, the more mountainous landscapes of Lakeland held densities of just 4 males/km$^2$.

Analysis of the line transect data from *this Atlas* gives a population band of 200,000–280,000 singing males, suggesting a mean population of 240,000 males.

The Willow Warbler is one of the most widespread and abundant breeding birds in Cumbria. They are adaptable and occupy a much wider range of habitats than other migrants, allowing them to occur in tetrads as diverse as the city centre of Carlisle through a range

 Sponsored by Iggesund Paperboard (Workington) Ltd

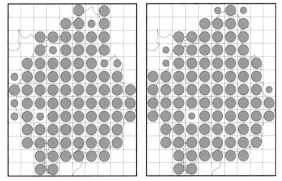

**1968–1972**          **1997–2001**

(For explanation of maps, see page 45)

***Conservation status***

| | |
|---|---|
| European: | Non-SPEC |
| UK: | **AMBER: BDM** |

***Populations***

| | |
|---|---|
| European status: | 39,000,000 |
| Britain – pairs: | 2,300,000 |
| Cumbria – pairs: | 240,000 |

***30-year distribution change***

| | *Old Atlas* | *This Atlas* | % |
|---|---|---|---|
| No. of 10km squares: | 89 | 91 | +2.2 |

| **Survey data** | **Tetrads** | **%** |
|---|---|---|
| Confirmed breeding: | 978 | 53.0 |
| Probable breeding: | 530 | 28.8 |
| Possible breeding: | 31 | 1.7 |
| Total: | 1,539 | 83.5 |

of lowland habitats to remote fellsides. National declines demonstrate that their continued success cannot be taken for granted and we should be alert to any signs of further decline here in Cumbria.

Dave Piercy

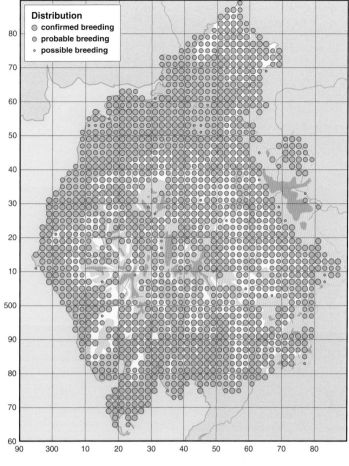

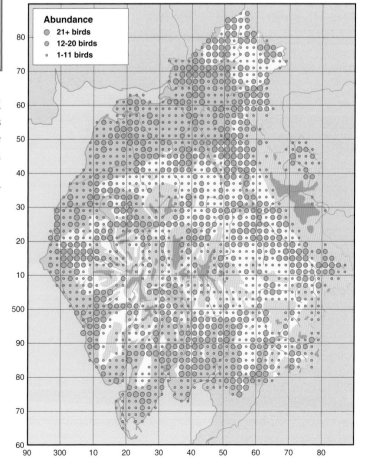

281

# Goldcrest *Regulus regulus*

THE smallest passerine in Cumbria, this industrious and agile bird is usually located by its distinctive, high-pitched call and song, but rarely stays still long enough for close scrutiny as it flits from branch to branch in search of small invertebrates.

The Goldcrest breeds across northern and central Europe into Asia where its greatest abundance tends to coincide with the distribution of major spruce and fir forests. It breeds throughout Britain and Ireland, except in predominantly treeless areas such as the fenlands of Cambridgeshire and the extensive, intensively farmed, arable areas in the Midlands. However increased afforestation in regions such as the Outer Hebrides and Orkney has led to an increase in its breeding range over the last 30 years. Resident populations, especially in the south and east of England, are boosted by Continental birds in the autumn. During the winter Goldcrests can be found in a broader spectrum of habitats such as mixed woodland, scrub and gardens, often accompanying flocks of tits.

Nests are usually found high up in conifer trees hanging below the end of a branch, and hidden by foliage. The most important limiting factors in the breeding range appear to be the existence of suitable woodland combined with a breeding season mean air temperature of above 10°C. Populations can be severely affected by hard winters and show very large fluctuations from year to year. However, the ability to raise two broods of up to 10 young in a good season means that numbers recover quickly following such a crash, given a succession of mild winters.

The highest densities are found in areas of conifer plantation with consistently mild winters, such as Ireland and the west coast of Scotland, where winters are ameliorated by warmer sea temperatures as a result of the Gulf Stream. Populations in such plantations can reach densities of up to 600 breeding pairs/km$^2$, but Goldcrests also occur in mixed and to a lesser extent broad-leaved woodland where significantly lower densities of 160–180 breeding pairs/km$^2$ were found in sessile oak woodland in Ireland (Batten 1976). However these figures may be due to a small census plot as a study in similar woodland in western Scotland produced 26 breeding pairs/km$^2$ (Williamson 1974).

In Britain and Ireland, there was a significant expansion in range during the 19th century as the first large scale conifer planting took place and exotic conifers were introduced for the first time. The *Historical Atlas* records breeding in 102 counties and this had increased to 108 counties by the *Old Atlas*. Densities probably also increased during this period as large areas of conifer forest planted after the First World War began to mature. However, although numbers quickly increased ten-fold following the hard winter of 1961–62, this peak has never been regained and the CBC index has been falling steadily over the last 20 years (Mead 2000). Indeed, the latest available data continues this trend, showing a 30% fall since 1970.

In Cumbria, although numbers in the ancient pine forests that once covered the landscape cannot be known, it is likely that the county held substantial populations before these vast forests were cleared. Macpherson (1892) recounts that Goldcrests were not uncommon in coniferous plantations during the 19th century. Stokoe (1962) considered it common in coniferous and mixed woodland, and alluded to birds nesting even in gorse. The *Old Atlas* found Goldcrests to be widespread in the county and by the time of the *New Atlas* an additional four 10km squares had been colonized around the periphery of the county.

During *this Atlas* there has been little change in distribution; not surprisingly, birds were found to be conspicuously absent from the higher, largely barren, treeless landscape of the North Pennines and Lakeland. The low-lying areas of the Coastal Plain and Solway Basin, where intensive agricultural practices abound and conifer plantations are sparse, also hold few birds. The strongholds for the species are the large conifer plantations of the Border Uplands, while the mixed forest found in the heavily-wooded valleys of Lakeland supports isolated clusters of high abundance which reflect the presence of suitable plantations – often just a few coniferous trees are sufficient to support a pair or two.

Analysis of line transect data from *this Atlas* gives a

Sponsored by Roger Ridley

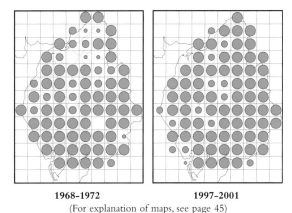

**1968-1972**     **1997-2001**

(For explanation of maps, see page 45)

---

*Conservation status*

| | |
|---|---|
| European: | SPEC Cat 4 |
| UK: | **AMBER** |

*Populations*

| | |
|---|---|
| European status: | 10,500,000 |
| Britain – pairs: | 560,000 |
| Cumbria – pairs: | 16,000 |

*30-year distribution change*

| | Old Atlas | This Atlas | % |
|---|---|---|---|
| No. of 10km squares: | 76 | 80 | +5.3 |

| **Survey data** | **Tetrads** | **%** |
|---|---|---|
| Confirmed breeding: | 323 | 17.6 |
| Probable breeding: | 409 | 22.2 |
| Possible breeding: | 82 | 4.4 |
| Total: | 814 | 44.2 |

---

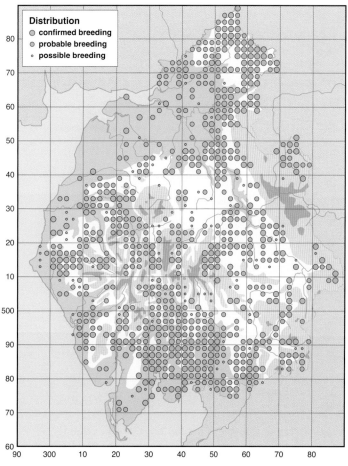

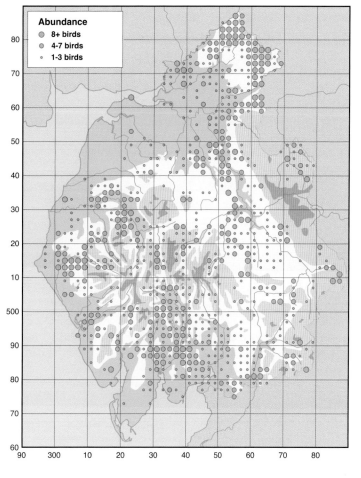

population band of 19,000–54,000, suggesting a mean population of 32,000 birds. The highest calculated densities of 31 birds/km$^2$ were for suitable plantations on the coastal strip.

Although still widespread, densities found during *this Atlas* were significantly lower than earlier surveys elsewhere in Britain and Ireland and the latest CBC data is not encouraging, despite a series of mild winters. The afforestation of uplands through the planting of conifers is becoming less fashionable, resulting in a reduction of habitat, and the complexities of global warming are difficult to forecast. It may well be that a retreat from mixed woodland to optimum coniferous woodland occurs.

Stephen Garnett

# Spotted Flycatcher *Muscicapa striata*

A STYLISH aerial hunter and dynamic long-distance migrant, the Spotted Flycatcher is the last to arrive of our trans-Saharan migrants. Though its dull appearance and weak squeaky song do little to advertise its presence, it charms observers with acrobatic aerial forays after food, seizing flying insects with a clearly audible snap of its bill, before returning to sit bolt upright on its original perch.

Spotted Flycatchers have a long association with man and breed in every European country except Iceland, eastward to Transbaikal, and south to the Mediterranean coasts of North Africa. They are widespread throughout Britain and Ireland, breeding on all the outlying northern islands except Shetland, and as abundant in some northern parts of Scotland as lowland England.

Whilst traditional woodland, both deciduous and, to a lesser extent, coniferous, remains important to the Spotted Flycatcher's fortunes, its use of domestic properties, especially those with mature climbers, has firmly established this aesthetic avian as a familiar favourite among our summer visitors. Its confiding nature and tolerance of indirect disturbance together with its ability to penetrate relatively modern man-made facilities such as large and small gardens, parks, churchyards and orchards, have enabled the Spotted Flycatcher to establish a widespread distribution.

Spotted Flycatchers select a variety of nest sites usually 1–3 metres above the ground. Data from the BTO's nest record scheme show that 60% of nests were in cover against a wall and 32% were in trees, either in shallow cavities or on ledges formed from broken limbs. As well as these conventional sites, *this Atlas* collected details of breeding in nestboxes, old nests of Blackbird and Swallow and an urban coal merchant's yard. They also frequently use interior sites such as open barns, garages, garden sheds and outhouses, wherever there is open access. The nest itself is a shallow structure, which allows a good viewing prospect for the incubating birds. Often the same precise site can be used year after year (pers obs). Two clutches are often attempted, especially if the summer is warm, ensuring a continuous supply of insects. Chicks in the nest have been recorded as late as 12th August (Brown 1974).

In Cumbria, Macpherson (1892) regarded the Spotted Flycatcher as "rather a scarce bird on our western coastline, owing to the paucity of timber," and continued, "Elsewhere in Lakeland it is generally common, most abundant in sheltered gardens and low bushy hollows." Stokoe (1962) commented that it was "widespread and common, following trees up fell valleys to 750 feet [229m], where it occurs with the Pied Flycatcher."

There has been little change in distribution at a 10km square level between the *Old Atlas* and *this Atlas,* but, unless Cumbria is bucking the national trend, breeding densities must have been reduced. The distribution map for *this Atlas* shows that Spotted Flycatchers remain widely and fairly evenly spread across the county, though with few records from higher altitudes in Lakeland and the North Pennines, due to the lack of trees and habitations. The absences from the agricultural Solway Basin are also likely to be attributable to the dearth of woodland there. More strongly represented in eastern parts of the county, Spotted Flycatchers are particularly numerous in the Eden Valley, Cumbria Dales and lower Lakeland, with good abundance along the South Tyne near Garrigill at 600m asl.

Nationally, analysis of the latest CBC data reveals a disturbing 78% decline since 1970, with the species appearing on the BoCC Red List. The reasons for the decline remain a matter of speculation. The *New Atlas* indicated a withdrawal from Ireland, especially the west; this is typical for a species at the limit of its range. In Ireland, there was a reduction of 18% in 10km square occupancy, whereas, in Britain, it was 2%, though, similarly, most of the losses occurred in western or coastal regions. These habitats in Cumbria are the areas where Spotted Flycatchers are scarcest. Perhaps the acknowledged wilder and wetter summers now occurring are reducing the availability of flying insects, as the relevant breeding habitats within the county seem little changed; indeed, many new woodlands are now being planted with the help of government grants.

 Sponsored by Chris Abbot

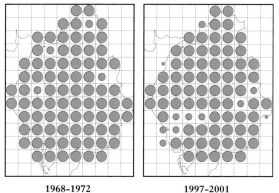

**1968–1972**　　　　**1997–2001**
(For explanation of maps, see page 45)

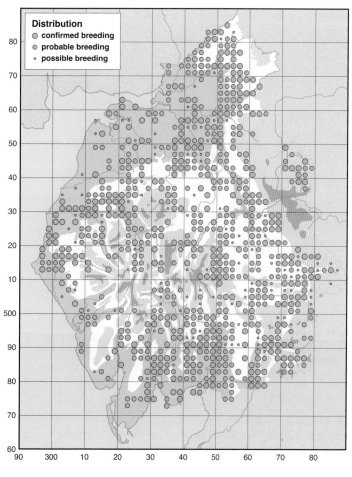

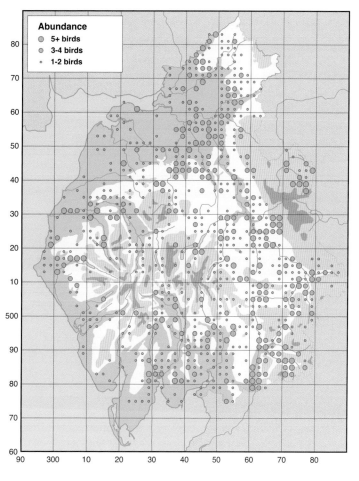

**Conservation status**

| | |
|---|---|
| European: | SPEC Cat 3 |
| UK: | **RED: BD** |

**Populations**

| | |
|---|---|
| European status: | 7,800,000 |
| Britain – pairs: | 120,000 |
| Cumbria – pairs: | 12,000 |

**30-year distribution change**

| | Old Atlas | This Atlas | % |
|---|---|---|---|
| No. of 10km squares: | 83 | 81 | **−2.4** |

| **Survey data** | **Tetrads** | **%** |
|---|---|---|
| Confirmed breeding: | 411 | 22.3 |
| Probable breeding: | 320 | 17.4 |
| Possible breeding: | 100 | 5.4 |
| Total: | 831 | 45.1 |

Analysis of the line transect data from *this Atlas* gives a population band of 15,000–38,000, suggesting a mean population of 24,000 birds. However, given the relatively small sample size, a degree of discretion must be exercised with this estimate.

As is typical of most of our summer visitors, we know little of the Spotted Flycatcher's migration strategy or of the threats it faces in sub-equatorial Africa, except that, apart from the Swallow, it travels further than any other passerine. Assuming food availability and habitat remain secure in Britain and Ireland, further decline is likely to be caused by either poor survival during migration or a change of circumstances in its winter quarters; only time will tell if we are in danger of finding continued population reductions in this superb aerobatic insectivore.

John Callion

# Pied Flycatcher *Ficedula hypoleuca*

A HIGHLIGHT of any spring must surely be the return, into its favoured breeding territory, of the first male Pied Flycatcher of the year. Whilst the song is distinctive, often patience is required before the bird can be seen and the striking black and white plumage admired in all its splendour.

Long-distance migrants, wintering in the vastness of West Africa, Pied Flycatchers breed from Britain and northern France, through Scandinavia to western Siberia. In Britain and Ireland, it breeds regularly through western England, Wales and Scotland, as far north as the Great Glen, with sporadic records from elsewhere, including Ireland.

Although Pied Flycatchers breed in most types of woodland, an important and essential requirement is a supply of suitable holes for nest sites. In Britain, the preferred habitat is the oak-dominated deciduous woodland found in upland valleys and, to a lesser extent, in birch and alder alongside streams and rivers. Any shortage of holes must surely be a limiting factor in population levels, particularly for such a long-distance migrant which arrives well after the resident hole-nesting species, such as tits, have established their territories. Indeed there is evidence that the population would have stagnated or even declined had it not been for the large scale provision of nestboxes. In some studies, the whole Pied Flycatcher population has been attracted to nestboxes while in others densities can be 50% lower in areas of the same wood where no boxes are provided.

In common with other migratory species the males generally arrive a week or so before the females, allowing them time to establish a breeding territory and prospective nest site. Quickly after pairing the male will stop singing unless he wishes to attract another mate. Indeed Pied Flycatchers are often polygamous and may have two or even three females in widely separated territories. Most Pied Flycatcher nests lacking a full-time male belong to a female with a polygamous mate; in Cumbria the proportion of 'single parents' can be as high as 17% of the local population. As the male gives priority to helping his first female raise her brood, secondary females tend to have a lower productivity rate.

Prior to the clearing of the great forests, Pied Flycatchers probably bred over much of Britain, but by the early 19th century it had become a fairly scarce species, apart from a few favoured areas in North Wales and northern England. A slight range expansion saw birds become established in Northumberland and southern Scotland by the turn of the 20th century. From this point, numbers increased slowly in Wales and the Borders, until the 1940s saw the start of a more widespread expansion outwards from their favourite haunts. Although some, mainly local, fluctuations occurred this rise was to continue until the 1990s. More recently, a downward trend has been detected with a succession of poor breeding seasons giving some cause for concern.

In Cumbria the first documented records come from the end of the 18th century when the species could be found around Lowther and was considered abundant in Levens Park. At the end of the 19th century, the county was one of its few strongholds in Britain and, although scarce in Westmorland, Pied Flycatchers were considered plentiful in Cumberland, and were colonizing new areas around Carlisle (Macpherson 1892). Subsequently, the population continued to expand and by the 1940s the species bred commonly in suitable habitat throughout the county (Witherby *et al* 1938–41). By the 1960s, it was regarded as locally common in the valleys of central Lakeland and in the adjacent North Pennines, with nesting recorded up to 230m asl (Stokoe 1962). This distribution was confirmed by the *Old Atlas,* yet the *New Atlas* showed further gains had taken place, birds having spread out from their Lakeland strongholds to colonize peripheral areas in the Coastal Plain, Solway Basin and Cumbria Dales. Fieldwork for *this Atlas* reaffirms this range expansion.

Analysis of line transect data from *this Atlas* gives a population band of 2,000–10,000, suggesting a mean population of 4,000 males. However, given the wide band limits, it is obvious that this estimate may be wide of the true figure. The highest densities of 2.3 males/km² occurred in the mature, deciduous woodlands clothing the steep-sided upland river valleys that cover much of Lakeland. Conversely, much lower densities of 0.6 birds/km² were found in the

Pages sponsored by Neil Henderson

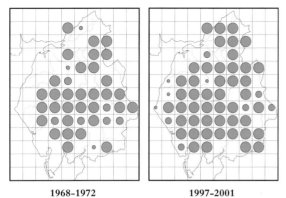

**1968–1972**        **1997–2001**
(For explanation of maps, see page 45)

**Conservation status**

| | |
|---|---|
| European: | SPEC Cat 4 |
| UK: | **GREEN** |

**Populations**

| | |
|---|---|
| European status: | 5,000,000 |
| Britain – pairs: | 37,500 |
| Cumbria – pairs: | 4,000 |

**30-year distribution change**

| | Old Atlas | This Atlas | % |
|---|---|---|---|
| No. of 10km squares: | 41 | 57 | **+39** |

| **Survey data** | **Tetrads** | **%** |
|---|---|---|
| Confirmed breeding: | 161 | 8.7 |
| Probable breeding: | 89 | 4.8 |
| Possible breeding: | 35 | 1.9 |
| Total: | 285 | 15.4 |

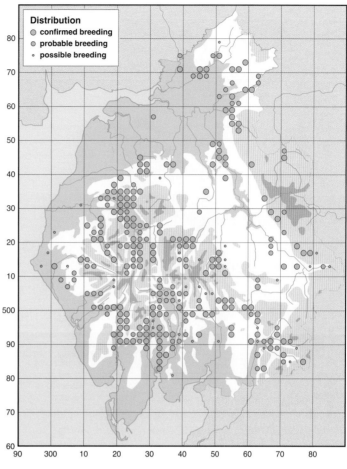

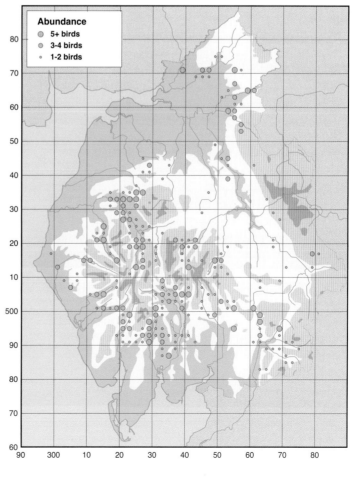

more marginal woodland habitats in the Solway Basin, Coastal Plain and Cumbria Dales.

Nestbox schemes provide a useful guide to population dynamics and are beginning to show a decline in Cumbria which mirrors the national trend. This fall has been particularly noticeable in Dodd Wood where there has been a 66% drop in nestbox occupation in recent years. This decline has not yet been explained, but it may be related to climate change, not least a succession of cold and often wet springs which limit the food supply for what is an almost entirely insectivorous species, leading to poor productivity. However, Cumbria has upland valleys aplenty, supporting old deciduous woodland, and hopefully these will continue to hold Pied Flycatchers for a very long time to come.

Mike Carrier

# Long-tailed Tit *Aegithalos caudatus*

THE diminutive Long-tailed Tit, with its distinctive churring call and confiding, but restless, nature is one of our most engaging birds. Usually encountered in small, roving, family flocks outside the breeding season, as spring approaches birds pair off and become more elusive as they settle down to breed.

A widespread Palearctic species, the Long-tailed Tit is found across Europe, and eastwards to Japan. Although essentially resident, during periods of high population levels massive irruptive movements can occur within the central and northern parts of its range. In Britain and Ireland, although largely absent from the more developed urban areas, the main centres of population are around deciduous woodland, well-developed hedgerows, and gardens on the urban fringe in the south and east, with the distribution gradually petering out towards the north and west.

Although called 'tits' they actually belong to a separate family, albeit with similar characteristics to the true tits. The main food items are insects and their eggs, with relatively little plant matter being taken, and then only in winter when bird tables and peanut feeders are also occasionally visited. The demands of the diet, with a high dependency on invertebrates throughout the year, explain the constant roaming of Long-tailed Tit flocks as they search the tree canopy for food. Interestingly, unlike true tits, they do not hammer or dig for food but pick items off the bark, and even, on occasion, hawk insects from the air.

The Long-tailed Tit is renowned for its elaborate domed nest – so different from that of the true tits – built from small feathers and spiders' webs, and camouflaged with lichen; this method of nest construction is unique amongst Britain's birds. The nest site tends to fall into one of two categories; it is either placed low down in thorny bushes or brambles, or high up in the fork of a tree or against a trunk. Only one brood is attempted in a season. Laying usually takes place from late April into June with a clutch size of 8–12 eggs and an average brood size of 8.47 birds (Brown 1974). Once hatched, it is not uncommon to find one or more extra adults helping to feed the young. Research has shown that these 'helpers' are invariably related to the male, and that where it occurs, there is a significantly increased chance of the nest being successful (Glen & Perrins 1988). Such an event was documented in Cumbria as long ago as 1936, when a nest at Coniston was attended by four adults (Blezard *et al* 1943).

Unfortunately, the Victorian mania for collecting curios resulted in the nests being widely sought out, with an inevitable impact upon the population. In many areas, particularly those close to large urban centres, the bird was almost exterminated for a time. Eventually the craze died out, and numbers recovered quickly. Comparisons between the *Old Atlas* and the *New Atlas* show very little change in distribution. Although populations show very large fluctuations year on year in response to harsh weather conditions, the latest available CBC index reveals a 31% increase since 1970, a trend supported by BBS data, and probably reflecting a series of relatively mild winters.

It is interesting to note that the *Historical Atlas* lists the Long-tailed Tit as being significantly more abundant in Northumberland than Cumbria. This was probably not the case. Although, Macpherson (1892) had little to say about the Long-tailed Tit, other than that it was relatively common outside "exposed areas", he did acknowledge that the bird was particularly common around Morecambe Bay – a situation reflected today. In the mid-20th century, Stokoe (1962) regarded the bird as "frequent in hedgerows, thickets and small woods, nesting up onto lower fell slopes." The *Old Atlas* found a widespread distribution with birds only absent from sections of the Border Uplands and North Pennines.

*This Atlas* shows that the Long-tailed Tit, although still widely distributed, is generally a lowland species with the majority of the population being found around the periphery of the county, although it does encroach into the heart of Lakeland along the river valleys. The population strongholds are on the Solway Basin, Eden Valley and southern Lakeland. This predilection for low-lying areas with good tree cover explains the species' absence from the barren moors of the North Pennines and Lakeland, while birds are also noticeably absent from the vast conifer plantations found in the Border Uplands.

Sponsored by John & Hilary Peatfield

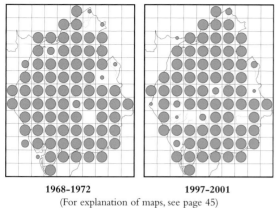

**1968-1972**      **1997-2001**

(For explanation of maps, see page 45)

*Conservation status*

| | |
|---|---|
| European: | Non-SPEC |
| UK: | **GREEN** |

*Populations*

| | |
|---|---|
| European status: | 3,100,000 |
| Britain – pairs: | 210,000 |
| Cumbria – pairs: | 5,500 |

*30-year distribution change*

| | Old Atlas | This Atlas | % |
|---|---|---|---|
| No. of 10km squares: | 81 | 78 | **−3.7** |

| **Survey data** | **Tetrads** | **%** |
|---|---|---|
| Confirmed breeding: | 339 | 18.4 |
| Probable breeding: | 193 | 10.5 |
| Possible breeding: | 81 | 4.4 |
| Total: | 613 | 33.3 |

Analysis of line transect data from *this Atlas* gives a population band of 5,000–22,000, suggesting a mean population of 11,000 birds. Note, however, the wide band limits. The highest densities of 11 birds/km² occurred in areas such as the lower Eden Valley where well-farmed lowlands are intermixed with numerous hedgerows and small woods.

The main threats to the Long-tailed Tit are prolonged cold spells that reduce foraging efficiency. When this happens, increased mortality is the inevitable result. However, like many other small birds, the Long-tailed Tit has shown on many occasions that it is fully capable of recovering from the effects of hard winters and provided Cumbria retains its current diversity of habitats, there is no immediate cause for concern.

Alistair Crowle

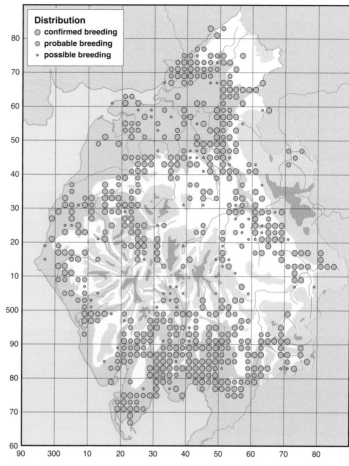

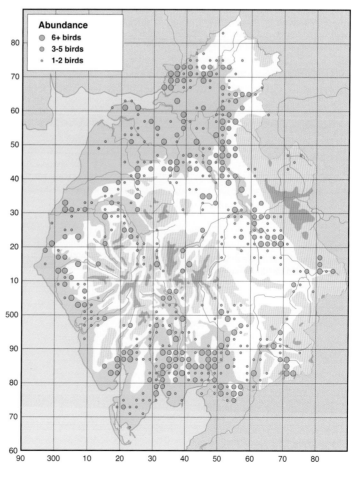

# Marsh Tit *Parus palustris*

C.H.Isherwood

THE Marsh Tit, with its explosive and distinctive *'pitchuu'* call note, separating it from the similar-plumaged Willow Tit, is found in broad-leaf woodland within the temperate and warmer boreal zones of large areas of the Palearctic. In Britain, the greatest densities are found in southern England and it is only thinly distributed over northern England, northwest Wales and west Cornwall. It is absent from Ireland and the Isle of Man. Cumbria is at the northern edge of its British range, with breeding in Scotland confined to a few small pockets in Lothian and the Borders.

The species is extremely territorial throughout the year and has a preference for relatively large stands of open-canopy broad-leaved woodland with a rich shrub understorey within which it can forage. Although it can be found in damp woodlands in similar habitats to the Willow Tit, despite its name it is more common in dry, open, deciduous and mixed woods and hedgerows, and even visits gardens where it will take nuts from bird-feeders.

Owing to the similarity in plumage between the Marsh and Willow Tit and a degree of overlap in their habitat and distribution, it was not realized that the Willow Tit existed as a separate species in Britain until 1900. Thus the early history of the two species, both in Britain and Cumbria, is uncertain. Nevertheless, the assertions by Macpherson (1892) that "the Marsh Titmouse is much the most local of the family in Lakeland; not that it can be termed rare, but rather that it does not enjoy the ubiquity of hardier species" and that "a fair sprinkling of pairs appear to breed every year in Lakeland" still ring true, bearing in mind he was unaware of the existence of the Willow Tit.

The Marsh Tit has been recognized as relatively common in the Furness and Morecambe Bay areas of south Cumbria since the 1920s, particularly within the mixed oak woods of southern Lakeland, the limestone ash woods around Whitbarrow and Arnside and some of the valley woodlands of the Cumbria Dales (Blezard 1943, Cleasby 1999). There is evidence of a range extension into northern Cumbria during the second half of the 20th century (Blezard 1954, Stokoe 1962), which appears to have taken place in parallel with an expansion in the adjoining Borders Region of Scotland. The first such records were from mixed oak and alder woodland during the 1950s, initially from the Gilsland district and the upper valley of the River Petteril and, more recently, from a number of woodlands along the lower and middle reaches of the Rivers Eden and Esk and their tributaries. There are also a limited number of records from some of the valleys that drain the western edge of Lakeland, particularly in the vicinity of Loweswater. A comparison of the *Old* and *New Atlases* provides little evidence of any significant reduction in range in Cumbria during the 1970s and 1980s, a time when a decline was underway in many parts of England and Wales. During this period, some losses occurred in parts of the Border Uplands and Cumbria Dales, but this was counterbalanced by small gains elsewhere.

Survey work during *this Atlas* confirmed that the bird's main stronghold remains the mixed broad-leaved woodlands to be found in south Lakeland and around Morecambe Bay. However, although this area accounts for a significant proportion of the total Cumbrian population, there is evidence of a slight range contraction, with birds now absent from several peripheral 10km squares. There is also a separate and well-established cluster along a number of valleys in the transitional zone between the Solway Basin, North Pennines and Border Uplands, along with a small, isolated pocket around Bassenthwaite Lake.

The *New Atlas* suggests a mean density of 50 birds/100km². However, given that populations in the north of county are sparser than those in the south, a mean density of 25 birds/100km² seems a more realistic figure, from which to derive a current county population of 800 breeding pairs.

The Marsh Tit has recently been elevated to the BoCC Red List, having suffered a decline of 62% since 1970, according to the latest available CBC data. This decline has been steepest on smaller woodland plots; recent research finds that the Marsh Tit requires deciduous woods of at least 0.5ha in which to breed successfully (Siriwardena 2001). Whilst the reasons for the decline are not yet fully understood, they are likely to involve habitat loss,

 Sponsored by Harold Dean

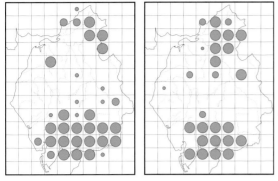

**1968-1972**          **1997-2001**

(For explanation of maps, see page 45)

*Conservation status*

| | |
|---|---|
| European: | Non-SPEC |
| UK: | **RED: BD** |

*Populations*

| | |
|---|---|
| European status: | 3,300,000 |
| Britain – pairs: | 60,000 |
| Cumbria – pairs: | 800 |

*30-year distribution change*

| | Old Atlas | This Atlas | % |
|---|---|---|---|
| No. of 10km squares: | 35 | 27 | **−22.8** |

| **Survey data** | **Tetrads** | **%** |
|---|---|---|
| Confirmed breeding: | 75 | 4.1 |
| Probable breeding: | 49 | 2.7 |
| Possible breeding: | 16 | 0.9 |
| Total: | 140 | 7.7 |

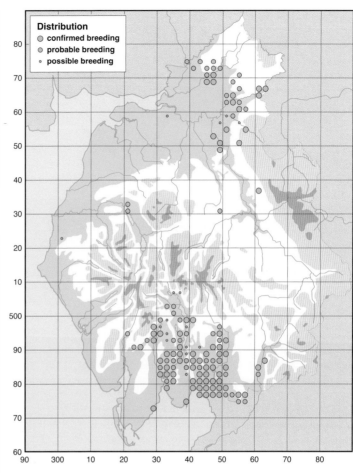

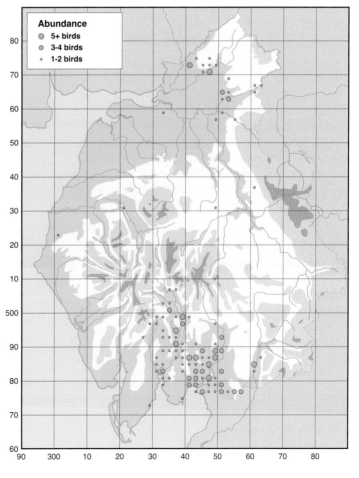

particularly as a result of clear-felling, the replacement of large stands of deciduous trees with conifers and increased recreational use of the remaining areas of deciduous woodland. Although Cumbria is not immune from these changes, it is in the fortunate position of possessing a range of deciduous woodlands that appear to be suitable for the Marsh Tit, with some potential for further colonization, particularly into the base-rich valley woodlands on the northern fringe of Lakeland around Sebergham and Caldbeck. It is important that these woodlands are conserved and their regeneration encouraged through enlightened management measures if the Marsh Tit is to continue to hold its own within the county.

Clive Hartley

# Willow Tit *Parus montanus*

ALTHOUGH the Willow Tit is extremely similar in appearance to the Marsh Tit, with subtle differences in plumage only apparent at close quarters and in favourable viewing conditions, the two species have very distinctive call notes, with the buzzing *'zee, zee, zee'* and harsh nasal *'tchay'* of the Willow Tit being very different from any calls of the Marsh Tit.

Found throughout the cooler temperate and subarctic zones of the Palearctic, from a latitude approximately 45°N to land well beyond the Arctic Circle, the Willow Tit's range stretches to the north of that of the Marsh Tit. It occurs in mixed woods, pure conifer and the northernmost birch forests, whilst the Marsh Tit is largely confined to the deciduous woods found further south. The species is widely but thinly distributed throughout much of England, Wales and the southwest and central Scottish lowlands, but absent from Ireland.

Willow Tits are resident and sedentary, defending their territories throughout the year. The favoured habitat consists of damp deciduous woodlands, with a predominance of alder, birch and willow and a well-developed secondary shrub layer, in which lichens, mosses and decayed wood mix with a tangle of bramble and other low plants. They also occur in pine plantations in certain parts of the country, including Dumfries and Galloway. Their attachment to damp woodlands is probably related to the need for dead trees of a rather small diameter in which they can excavate a new nest hole each year, having first made several trial borings.

Since it was not realized until 1900 that the Willow Tit existed as a separate species in Britain, historical information is obviously limited. In Cumbria, the Willow Tit has traditionally bred in the north and northwest, particularly amongst the damp birch woodlands of the Solway Basin, where it was first recorded nesting in 1903 (Johnston 1936). Stokoe (1962) commented that it "occurs over most of Cumberland, except south and east, in small numbers" and also that it "penetrates into central fells from the west as far as Derwent Water. Only isolated records elsewhere." Since the 1950s, it has extended its range to include some of the streamside oak and alder woods of the North Pennines and Border Uplands, where its range overlaps with that of the Marsh Tit. Areas of damp woodland and willow carr in the northern valleys of Lakeland around Loweswater, Derwent Water, Bassenthwaite Lake and Over Water, were also colonized, along with parts of the Coastal Plain.

The Willow Tit was found in 30 10km squares during the *Old Atlas* (though it was admitted that errors due to incorrect identification had probably not been entirely eliminated at that time), compared to 21 during *this Atlas*. The species has disappeared from the Cumbria Dales and from a number of other previously occupied sites in the south of the Coastal Plain and south Lakeland since the 1960s and this corresponds to the experience in many other parts of Britain. The northern half of the county, especially the Solway Basin and Border Uplands, remains the principal stronghold, though pockets survive around Bassenthwaite Lake and Derwent Water and, to a lesser extent, in the north of the Coastal Plain and the border of the Eden Valley and North Pennines.

The species has a highly localized distribution and a population density too low to allow statistical analysis. The current county population estimate of around 100 breeding pairs is subjective, and is based upon count data enhanced by supplementary records, indicating 2 pairs in some occupied tetrads.

Analysis of the latest CBC data shows a 72% decline since 1970, with major losses in northwest England, while BBS data for the period 1994–2000 reveal an alarming 54% decrease. The Willow Tit has had the dubious distinction of being elevated to the Red List at the 2002–07 revision. The population has remained relatively stable on damp woodland habitats, with the decline concentrated on secondary habitats where optimum conditions no longer apply (Siriwardena 2001). This suggests the decline is linked to habitat loss through the drying out or drainage of damp woodlands for agriculture or commercial forestry, with a consequent loss of rotten wood in which to excavate nest chambers. In this respect, an experiment in Lanarkshire has shown that specifically designed sawdust-filled nestboxes can assist in the conservation of the species; Willow Tits will use them for breeding and also to excavate trial borings before discarding

 Sponsored by Richard Wimpress

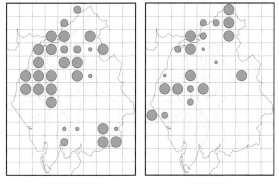

**1968–1972**  **1997–2001**
(For explanation of maps, see page 45)

***Conservation status***

| | |
|---|---|
| European: | Non-SPEC |
| UK: | **RED: BD** |

***Populations***

| | |
|---|---|
| European status: | 5,000,000 |
| Britain – pairs: | 25,000 |
| Cumbria – pairs: | 100 |

***30-year distribution change***

| | Old Atlas | This Atlas | % |
|---|---|---|---|
| No. of 10km squares: | 30 | 21 | –30 |

| **Survey data** | **Tetrads** | **%** |
|---|---|---|
| Confirmed breeding: | 16 | 0.9 |
| Probable breeding: | 19 | 1.0 |
| Possible breeding: | 8 | 0.4 |
| Total: | 43 | 2.3 |

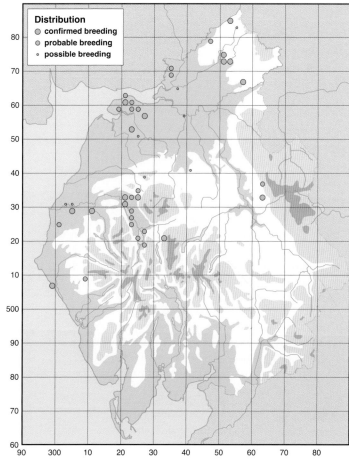

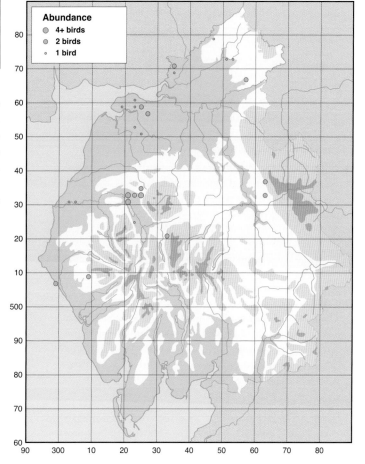

them for natural sites (Maxwell 1999). The extension of this scheme to selected areas of damp woodland in Cumbria would be a positive move in helping to maintain and possibly restore the population of the Willow Tit in the county in the face of both a local and a national decline.

Clive Hartley

# Coal Tit *Parus ater*

c.M. Isherwood

WHETHER perched atop a lone conifer, uttering its distinctive and strident *'seetoo-seetoo-seetoo . . .'* song, or adeptly flitting amongst the pine needles high up in the dense canopy, minutely searching for food, the Coal Tit is a distinctive bird. Its black head, white cheeks, striking white nape patch and double white wing bar set it apart from all other tits.

Found across much of the Palearctic, its range extends in a broad band eastwards from Britain and Ireland, through Europe and the former USSR to the Pacific Coast. Although occurring in a variety of woodland habitats, this species has a preference for conifers, particularly spruce, throughout much of its range. In the absence of blocks of conifers, it will readily use isolated pockets and even single trees amongst deciduous stands. As a result of this versatility, the Coal Tit is found throughout Britain and Ireland, from the coast to the uppermost treeline, although its association with coniferous plantations means that the species is particularly abundant in much of Wales, Scotland and Ireland. In contrast, England holds only isolated pockets of high abundance, and birds are understandably absent from treeless areas such as the Fens and some of the Northern Isles.

The Coal Tit will readily utilize a wider range of nest sites than either the Great Tit or Blue Tit. It makes use of holes low down, often in the ground, under rocks or in a root bole, as well as in trees. This has meant that the species has taken relatively easily to conifer plantations, which tend to hold fewer natural tree holes, as well as to gardens, parks and any other area that contains conifers. The nest itself is built largely of moss with the cup lined with fur or hair. Although a single clutch is usually laid, double-brooding does occasionally take place and in rare cases a third brood is produced. Cumbrian nests monitored by Brown (1974) produced an average brood size of 5.15 birds. The main food items are invertebrates in the summer and seeds in the winter, although any insects found at this time will be readily taken.

The *Historical Atlas* paints a picture of a bird that was common in fir, oak and birch woods over much of Britain and Ireland during the 19th century, with numbers increasing markedly as coniferous plantations were extended. After the First World War, following the establishment of the Forestry Commission, further afforestation took place with the area of land planted with conifers increasing dramatically, and these in turn were readily colonized by Coal Tits. At the time of the *Old Atlas,* the species was considered to be still increasing, with further expansion into areas of new plantation, developed after the Second World War. However, by the time of the *New Atlas,* a slow-down was detected, with little change in distribution since the *Old Atlas,* a situation reaffirmed by the latest CBC index which shows just a 15% population increase since 1970.

In Cumbria, although new plantations over the Penrith Beacon were colonized in the 19th century, neither Macpherson (1892) nor Stokoe (1962) passed much comment on this species other than to record that it was relatively abundant. However, Blezard *et al* (1943) did make the observation that prior to the hard winter of 1916/17, the Coal Tit was more abundant in the Windermere area than the Marsh Tit. At the time of the *Old Atlas,* although widespread, the species was probably still increasing in line with national trends, but the distribution showed little further change up to the *New Atlas.*

The maps for *this Atlas* show that the species remains widely distributed, with a noticeable absence from the treeless areas of the Solway Basin, North Pennines and central Lakeland. Definite centres of population were found in the Border Uplands, around Ennerdale and Bassenthwaite Lake, and in south Lakeland – all areas with substantial blocks of conifer plantation.

Analysis of line transect data from *this Atlas* gives a population band of 21,000–44,000, suggesting a mean population of 30,000 birds; meaningful densities per land class were not generated.

Possibly as a result of its habitat preferences and a predilection for storing food, the Coal Tit appears to withstand periods of cold weather better than most other members of the tit family and as such is not subject to the same population fluctuations during hard winters. Consequently, it is likely that the Coal Tit will continue to thrive within the county for the foreseeable future.

Alistair Crowle

 Sponsored by Shirley Williams & Keith Fawcett

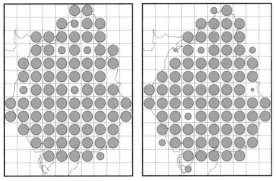

**1968-1972**          **1997-2001**
(For explanation of maps, see page 45)

***Conservation status***
European:                    Non-SPEC
UK:                              GREEN

***Populations***
European status:             14,000,000
Britain – pairs:                 610,000
Cumbria – pairs:                  15,000

***30-year distribution change***
|  | Old Atlas | This Atlas | % |
|---|---|---|---|
| No. of 10km squares: | 82 | 83 | +1.2 |

| **Survey data** | **Tetrads** | **%** |
|---|---|---|
| Confirmed breeding: | 437 | 23.7 |
| Probable breeding: | 381 | 20.7 |
| Possible breeding: | 101 | 5.5 |
| Total: | 919 | 49.9 |

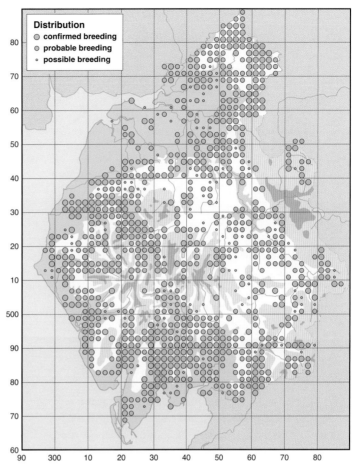

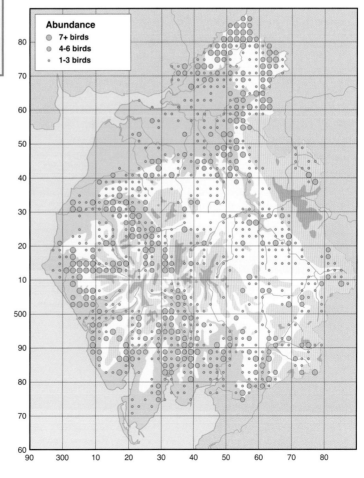

# Blue Tit *Parus caeruleus*

ALONG with the Robin, the Blue Tit must be one of our best known and most loved birds. The increasingly popular practice of feeding birds in the garden has resulted in Blue Tits being drawn into urban areas, where the acrobatic antics of the birds, as they visit feeders, are a delight to millions of people. Despite this use of feeding stations, the Blue Tit remains primarily a species of deciduous woodland, and is particularly associated with the oak.

A Western Palearctic species, the Blue Tit breeds across most of Europe and into western Asia. In Britain and Ireland it is the commonest and most widely distributed member of the tit family with the main areas of abundance being central and southern England. It is absent only from Orkney, Shetland and many of the Hebridean islands.

The nest site is usually a hole in a tree or a crack in a wall, though sites near the ground are avoided. This choice of site mirrors that of the Great Tit, and like that species, the Blue Tit will readily use nestboxes. Macpherson (1892) mentions the appropriation of open nests of Greenfinch and Dunnock. Although the exact timing is dependent very much on the weather, nesting usually takes place from April to May, with the nest a foundation of moss, interwoven with twigs and almost always lined with feathers. The clutch, which is one of the largest of any passerine, can range from 6–16 eggs, but the average is 10–12 eggs, with the hatching timed to coincide with maximum caterpillar abundance (Flegg 1987). It is rare for Blue Tits to be double-brooded. Where nest sites are scarce and the competition greatest, the Great Tit dominates, but the Blue Tit tends to have greater nesting success as it

employs a more efficient feeding strategy, through being more agile and quicker when searching for food amongst the canopy. The diet of the Blue Tit is similar to several other tits in that it takes mainly invertebrates in the summer and a mixture of seeds and insects in the winter.

The *Historical Atlas* presents the Blue Tit as being common across most of Britain and Ireland, absent only from the Isles of Scilly, the northwestern tip of Scotland and the Northern and Western Isles. Since that time, although the Isles of Scilly were colonized in the 1940s, and severe winters have caused short-term fluctuations, the distribution has changed very little and population levels have remained relatively stable. Indeed, the latest available CBC index shows a 28% increase since 1970.

In Cumbria, Macpherson (1892) and Stokoe (1962) had little to say on the distribution and numbers of the Blue Tit, other than to record it was numerous up to the tree line. The *Old Atlas* reaffirmed this widespread distribution, with the *New Atlas* detecting areas of high abundance in the Eden Valley, south Lakeland and parts of the Coastal Plain.

*This Atlas* confirms these earlier findings; the Blue Tit continues to be almost ubiquitous throughout the county with no discernible change in distribution. The strongholds remain in the Eden Valley, south Lakeland and parts of the Coastal Plain, with birds totally absent only from the treeless mountains and moors of Lakeland and the North Pennines.

Analysis of line transect data from *this Atlas* gives a population band of 210,000–280,000, suggesting a mean population of 240,000 birds. The highest densities of 73 birds/km² occurred in areas along the Eden Valley and southern Lakeland, where suitable stands of deciduous woodland back onto intensively farmed lowlands. In contrast, the conifer plantations of the Border Uplands held just 4.3 birds/km².

Although Blue Tits tend to be associated with nestboxes in gardens, urban pairs suffer from lower productivity than their woodland relatives. This has been attributed to the abundance and quality of suitable prey, which is lower in gardens (Cowie & Hinsley 1987). It is likely that productivity in Cumbria is quite good as the majority of nesting sites will be close to native deciduous woodland with its higher quality foraging areas.

The development of BAP targets to increase the amount of native woodland across the county is likely to bring benefits to many members of the tit family, through the provision of additional nesting and feeding areas. Perhaps the one dark cloud on the horizon for the Blue Tit is climate change. The availability of insects, particularly caterpillars, for feeding the young is crucial to successful breeding and the predicted warmer winters and wetter summers are

 Sponsored by Hannah Piercy

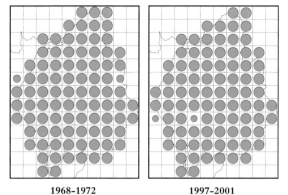

| 1968–1972 | 1997–2001 |

(For explanation of maps, see page 45)

*Conservation status*

| European: | SPEC Cat 4 |
| UK: | **GREEN** |

*Populations*

| European status: | 18,000,000 |
| Britain – pairs: | 3,300,000 |
| Cumbria – pairs: | 120,000 |

*30-year distribution change*

| | Old Atlas | This Atlas | % |
|---|---|---|---|
| No. of 10km squares: | 90 | 88 | −2.2 |

| **Survey data** | **Tetrads** | **%** |
|---|---|---|
| Confirmed breeding: | 1,054 | 57.2 |
| Probable breeding: | 293 | 15.9 |
| Possible breeding: | 65 | 3.6 |
| Total: | 1,412 | 76.7 |

likely to change the timing of prey availability. It will be interesting to see if Blue Tit productivity is adversely affected, or whether the species will adapt to any changes that do occur.

Alistair Crowle

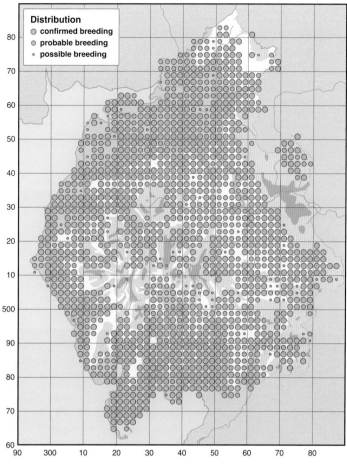

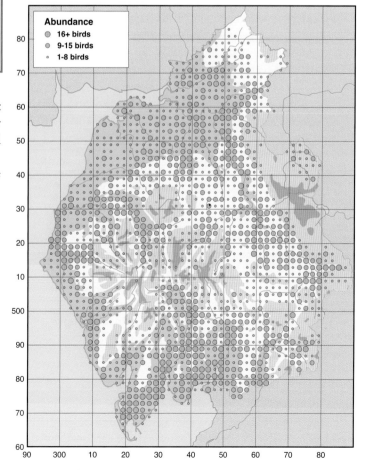

# Great Tit *Parus major*

WITH its glossy black head, white cheeks and broad black band extending down the front of a bright yellow body, the Great Tit is one of our most well-known garden birds. Away from the garden, a springtime walk through an area of broad-leaved woodland will usually be rewarded with the familiar *'teacher-teacher- . . .'* song ringing out through the trees.

An Old World species with a range that extends from Britain and Ireland eastwards through Europe and Asia to the Pacific coast and southwards to India and Thailand, the Great Tit is capable of utilizing a variety of habitats from deciduous or coniferous woodland, through to hedgerows, parks and gardens. In Britain and Ireland, the population is biased towards the south and east with the highest densities found south of a line between the Dee and Humber estuaries. The Fens area, with its open treeless landscape, has significantly lower concentrations than most other areas in southern England, while breeding birds are generally absent from the Northern and Western Isles.

Essentially resident, the Great Tit is primarily insectivorous in the breeding season with its diet supplemented by large numbers of seeds in the winter. It seems that the size of seed crops plays an important role in reducing winter mortality and determining population levels the following spring. The beech crop appears especially important: ringing recoveries show that in poor 'mast' years, Great Tits move over five kilometres further afield than they do in years when there is a good crop.

The Great Tit has a preference for nesting in tree-holes and will readily use nestboxes if provided. Failing these,

a hole or crack in a wall can be used, or even a cavity in an artificial structure such as machinery. Although weather dependent, nesting usually begins in April with the nest itself made mainly of moss and lined with hair or fur; only rarely are feathers used. The clutch varies in size from 3–18 eggs, and this wide variation is the result of a combination of factors such as timing of laying, habitat in which the nest is built (in general larger clutches are produced in oak woodlands than conifer plantations), age of the female and overall population density. Many of these factors also determine whether a second clutch is produced.

At the end of the 19th century, it appears that although the Great Tit was common across most of Britain and Ireland, it was generally absent north of the Great Glen. However, in the early 20th century, the Great Tit underwent a slight increase in range, with the afforestation of moors, particularly after the First World War, providing birds with access corridors into previously isolated broad-leaved woodland. More recently, a comparison of the *Old* and *New Atlases* shows little change in distribution. Although populations fluctuate due to severe winter weather, Brown & Grice (in prep) have concluded that numbers have remained steady since the *Old Atlas*. However the latest CBC index suggests an increase, with a 40% rise since 1970 detected.

In Cumbria, historical authors are of little help in assessing the status of the Great Tit; clearly the bird was very common and as a result attracted little attention. Macpherson (1892) commented that "this species and the Blue Tit frequent the trees of our older parks, such as Holker or the fine avenue of oaks at Levens" and also intriguingly stated that "public opinion appears to be divided as to whether the Great Tit really inflicts much injury on hive-bees". Stokoe (1962) regarded the species as "common in woods, gardens and hedgerows up to the lower fell valleys", a distribution that was confirmed by the *Old Atlas*.

*This Atlas* shows that the Great Tit is still found throughout Cumbria, and its relationship with broad-leaved woodland is readily apparent. Only low densities were found in areas of conifer plantation such as the Border Uplands while the barren uplands of Lakeland and the North Pennines are devoid of birds. Interestingly, on the continent the Great Tit is found up to 1,900m asl, so from a Cumbrian perspective, the limiting factor would appear to be tree cover rather than altitude.

Analysis of line transect data from *this Atlas* gives a population band of 85,000–133,000, suggesting a mean population of 106,000 birds. The highest densities of 37 birds/km² occurred, like the Blue Tit, in areas along the Eden Valley and in southern Lakeland, where suitable stands of deciduous woodland back onto intensively farmed lowlands.

Sponsored by Elaine, Pam, Peter & Geoff of Kirksanton

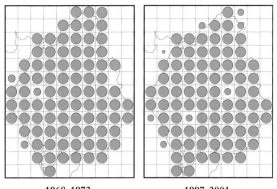

**1968-1972**          **1997-2001**

(For explanation of maps, see page 45)

***Conservation status***

| | |
|---|---|
| European: | Non-SPEC |
| UK: | **GREEN** |

***Populations***

| | |
|---|---|
| European status: | 42,000,000 |
| Britain – pairs: | 1,600,000 |
| Cumbria – pairs: | 53,000 |

***30-year distribution change***

| | Old Atlas | This Atlas | % |
|---|---|---|---|
| No. of 10km squares: | 87 | 88 | **+1.1** |

| **Survey data** | **Tetrads** | **%** |
|---|---|---|
| Confirmed breeding: | 786 | 42.6 |
| Probable breeding: | 395 | 21.4 |
| Possible breeding: | 90 | 4.9 |
| Total: | 1,271 | 68.9 |

It is interesting to note that many of the bird populations of Cumbria in general seem to be showing the same pattern as national populations. In keeping with the wider picture, farmland birds are showing worrying signs of decreases, but, on the other hand this does not yet appear to be the case with woodland species. With the recent proposals for increasing native woodland across the country it seems likely that the biggest threat to the Great Tit in the future is climate change and the possible negative impact upon food availability during the breeding season.

Alistair Crowle

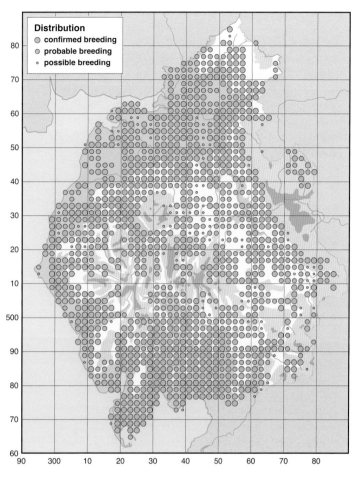

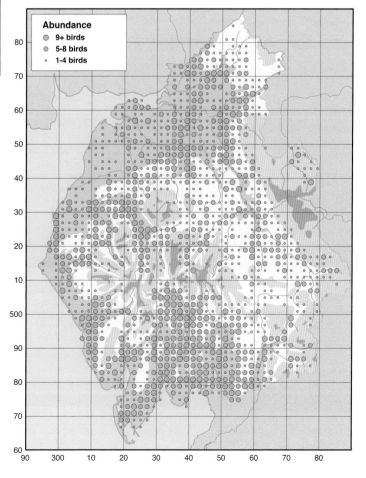

C.M. Isherwood

NOISY and energetic birds, Nuthatches are often easy to locate, their calls ringing loudly through the woods during the spring. They are a species typically of mature deciduous woodland though also to be found in parks and gardens, as long as large trees are present, and they are frequent visitors to bird tables. Nests are made in pre-existing cavities, often in tall deciduous trees. Mud is brought in by the birds, and over-large entrance holes reduced to size by liberal plastering.

Nuthatches are found throughout Europe, south into Morocco and north into southern Norway and Sweden, thence right across Eurasia into China, Japan and the Indian subcontinent. They are common in Britain south of Lancashire, and are particularly so in the south and west of this range. Cumbria is on the northern edge of the species' range, though birds do breed slightly further north in Northumberland, and there are a few sites in southeast Scotland. The species is absent from Ireland.

The story of the Nuthatch in Cumbria is intriguing. First documented at Armathwaite in 1782, it was apparently locally common in the county in the early part of the 19th century, being recorded at Lowther and along the River Eamont (Macpherson 1892); yet it had disappeared from all of northern England before the century's end, with the last report in 1886. Published records for the county were very sparse in the first half of the 20th century, although it was certainly present in Westmorland during 1916 and several subsequent years (Stokoe 1962). There was then a long gap with no acceptable records until 1948 when one was seen at Watermillock, Ullswater. Sightings became increasingly regular, and the *Old Atlas* confirmed its presence in eight 10km squares widely scattered across the county.

A partial survey in 1983–85 (Dean 1987) revealed that the species had undergone a dramatic increase. Breeding was confirmed in 13 10km squares with a total of 80 breeding records for that period. During fieldwork for the *New Atlas* birds were found in 33 10km squares with a disappearance from the more

eastern sites and the first records of breeding in the north of the county. Field data from a further survey in 1994–95 (Atkins & Callion 1997), even given the encouraging results of previous surveys, were astonishing: birds were present in 168 tetrads in 39 10km squares! They had increased in those areas of Lakeland already occupied, and spread into new areas to the north and east. Strongholds included a large area of southern Lakeland spreading southwards from Ambleside in a triangle including Grizedale and the area around Witherslack down to Arnside on the Coastal Plain. An increase was also noted in the valley woods of central Lakeland around Thirlmere, Bassenthwaite Lake, Borrowdale and near Glenridding.

The results of *this Atlas* indicate that the rapid range expansion is continuing apace. Records were received from an astounding 349 tetrads, with confirmed breeding in 146, in 63 10km squares. In comparison to the *Old Atlas,* it appears that wherever there are Nuthatches they are expanding their range into areas nearby. This is particularly true for the southern part of the county, where local densities were already quite high, but in addition new areas are being colonized north and east of Carlisle, and along the River Lune in the southeast.

Analysis of the line transect data from *this Atlas* gives a population band of 1,000–10,000, suggesting a mean population of 4,000 birds. Wide band limits confirm that discretion must be exercised in the use of this estimate, which a subjective assessment suggests is on the high side. The highest densities of 4.7 birds/km$^2$ occurred in the alluvial valleys, particularly in south Lakeland, but also in the upper Eden Valley.

Nuthatches are territorial all year round and their habit of storing food enables them to be sedentary. Once settled in a territory they will tend to remain there; juveniles are the most likely to move, although even then usually only a short distance. In this way, a pair becomes the nucleus for a gradually expanding population. It therefore seems likely that the numerous outlying breeding records could well be the forerunners of future infilling in their continuing

                        Sponsored by Brian Bottomley & Tim Dean

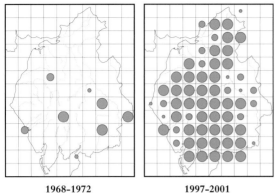

**1968-1972**    **1997-2001**
(For explanation of maps, see page 45)

**Conservation status**

| European: | Non-SPEC |
|---|---|
| UK: | GREEN |

**Populations**

| European status: | 7,000,000 |
|---|---|
| Britain – pairs: | 130,000 |
| Cumbria – pairs: | 2,000 |

**30-year distribution change**

| | Old Atlas | This Atlas | % |
|---|---|---|---|
| No. of 10km squares: | 8 | 63 | +687.5 |

| Survey data | Tetrads | % |
|---|---|---|
| Confirmed breeding: | 146 | 7.9 |
| Probable breeding: | 157 | 8.5 |
| Possible breeding: | 46 | 2.5 |
| Total: | 349 | 18.9 |

spread. In some areas, Nuthatches have taken advantage of nestboxes, and productivity from such sites can be extremely high. This can generate high densities locally, which perhaps encourages juvenile dispersal. A recent run of years with less severe winter weather can be expected to have encouraged better survival, with the birds then normally breeding within their winter territories.

The Nuthatch appears to have made full use of the numerous riparian valleys as a means of extending its frontiers and if these trends continue the future certainly looks good for this species in Cumbria: a distribution similar to that occupied at present by the Great Spotted Woodpecker, another species of mature woodland and parkland, may eventually be reached. With so many species currently in decline, it is a nice change to able to report a bird that is on the up, and when the species is as charismatic as the Nuthatch, then it is even more of a pleasure.

Roy Atkins

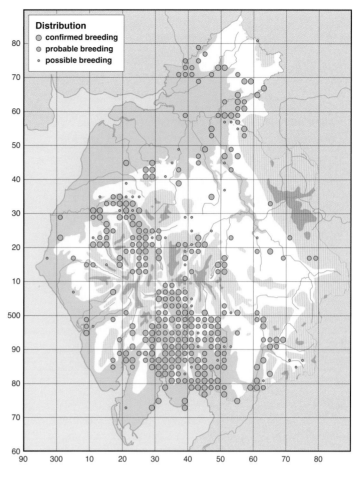

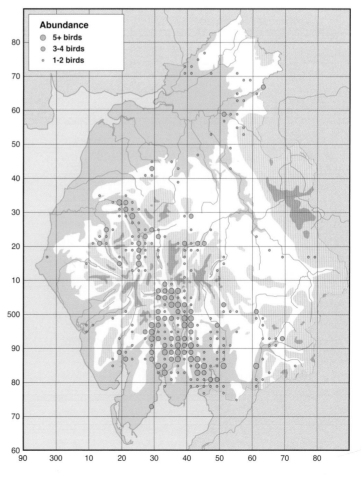

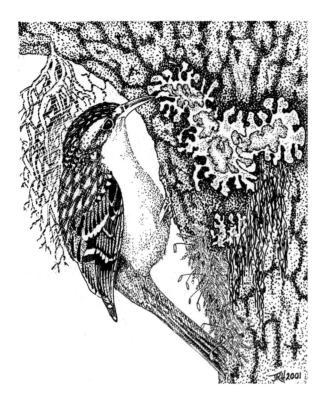

WITH their cryptically speckled brown upperparts, Treecreepers can be rather inconspicuous as they live up to their name, creeping mouse-like up a tree trunk or side branch. However, once the rather insistent high pitched call note, and pretty little song, are learned, it soon becomes evident that Treecreepers are quite common.

A Palearctic species, the Treecreeper is found throughout Europe, eastwards through southern Siberia and north-central Asia to Japan; it is however replaced by the Short-toed Treecreeper over large areas of central and southern Europe. Where the ranges of the two species overlap, Short-toed tends to dominate in broad-leaved forest, our bird being largely restricted to coniferous woodland. It is postulated that after the last glaciation the Treecreeper moved into Britain with the rapid northwards expansion of Scots pine. The sea then severed the land-bridge with the continent before the arrival of Short-toed Treecreepers, which were moving north at a slower rate linked to the spread of broad-leaved trees. In the absence here of the latter species, the former has occupied all available woodland habitats. In Britain and Ireland, Treecreepers are absent only from areas where there are few trees such as large tracts of moorland and mountainous regions, becoming generally more numerous in southern England and South Wales.

Treecreepers occur wherever there is deciduous woodland, including parkland, orchards or large gardens with plenty of trees. They are also found in coniferous woodland though at lower densities, particularly in younger plantations, where there is a

shortage of nest sites. The nests are usually placed behind loose pieces of bark or within a crevice in a tree trunk, although sometimes cavities, especially behind ivy or creeper, and occasionally nestboxes, are used. Interestingly, Macpherson (1892) records a nest found in a dry stone wall on a moorland area in the east of Cumbria.

It seems likely that the species' historical distribution within Cumbria did not change greatly for some considerable time. Macpherson (1892) considered it fairly common in the woodlands of Lakeland at the end of the 19th century and Stokoe (1962) regarded the Treecreeper as "common in well-grown timber, including conifers". Although the *Old Atlas* confirmed this widespread distribution throughout the county, by the time of the *New Atlas* a slight range contraction was apparent in parts of the Solway Basin.

Although still found to be widespread in Cumbria, with some areas of the Solway Basin recently reoccupied, *this Atlas* reveals some puzzling gaps in distribution, particularly in areas of south Lakeland where extensive areas of apparently suitable woodland habitat exist. However, there are very healthy populations along the river corridors in and around the periphery of Lakeland and in the north of the county, especially to the north and east of Carlisle. Not surprisingly altitude also affects the distribution of the species with few records from the barren, treeless high ground of the North Pennines, Cumbria Dales and Lakeland. The acidic pastures of Lakeland and the upper Eden Valley with fringe, albeit discontinuous, woodlands held nearly 30% of all contacts. Although Treecreepers share habitat in the county in common with species such as Nuthatch and Great Spotted Woodpeckers, their distribution differs in that they have a stronghold in the northeast and that they become less abundant in some of the well-wooded areas in the south.

Analysis of the line transect data from *this Atlas* gives a population band of 4,000–14,000, suggesting a mean population of 8,000 birds. However, given the relatively small sample size, discretion should be exercised with this estimate.

The Treecreeper is known to be one of the most sedentary of birds and fluctuations have occurred depending on the severity of the winter, but numbers generally recover quickly. Until recently the national trend was thought to be one of gradual increase (Marchant *et al* 1990) but the *New Atlas* indicated a 10% decline in distribution, with a particularly large fall in Ireland, and the latest available CBC data shows a 16% fall since 1970.

These declines cause some concern for the future of the county's Treecreeper population, though solace may be taken from the fact that Cumbria is influenced

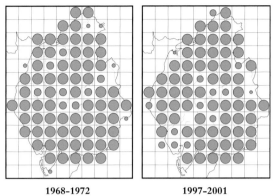

**1968-1972**     **1997-2001**
(For explanation of maps, see page 45)

*Conservation status*
European:                    Non-SPEC
UK:                          GREEN

*Populations*
European status:            3,000,000
Britain – pairs:              200,000
Cumbria – pairs:                4,000

*30-year distribution change*
                  Old Atlas  This Atlas   %
No. of 10km squares:   81        77     −4.9

| **Survey data** | **Tetrads** | **%** |
|---|---|---|
| Confirmed breeding: | 190 | 10.3 |
| Probable breeding: | 284 | 15.4 |
| Possible breeding: | 131 | 7.1 |
| Total: | 605 | 32.8 |

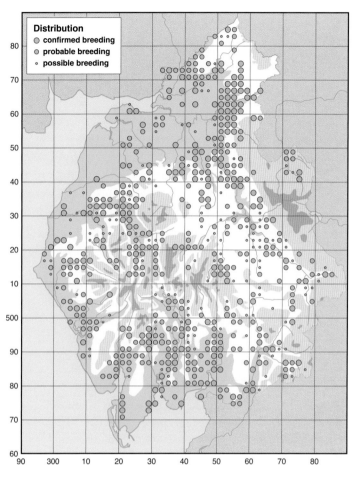

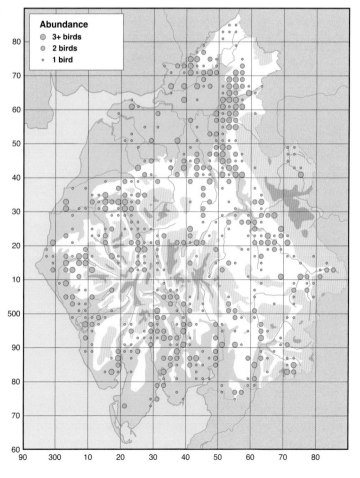

by the Gulf Stream, and that the effects of global warming may result in milder winters. It is possible, as a consequence, that survival rates amongst young birds will increase from one season to the next. Also, if the current trends for integrated mixed woodland are continued in forestry management and farm woodland initiatives, encouraging deciduous tree planting, remain then Cumbria may well see an expansion in the Treecreeper population.

Roy Atkins

OF all Britain's crows, the Jay is the most brightly coloured and yet the most secretive. In woodland, its raucous call is usually the first indication of its presence and often all that one is able to observe is a striking white rump as it flies away. A well-watched bird is a rarity but occasionally, persistent searching in woodland during the breeding season may result in the finding of a male uttering its subdued courtship song made up of a collection of bubbling, chirruping, chattering and clicking notes.

It is found through much of Europe and reaches across Siberia and central Asia to southeast Asia and Japan. Essentially a sedentary species its distribution is influenced by three factors: cover, food and persecution. The Jay is the most arboreal of the corvids and nests in a wide variety of wooded habitats. Oak woods seem to be preferred, but its catholic tastes are reflected in an ability to utilize all types of woodland, from coniferous spruce and Scots pine plantations and deciduous beech and chestnut stands to suburban parks, gardens and farm hedgerows. Recent increases in Scotland are most likely the result of afforestation.

Sustenance is chiefly provided by invertebrates, especially beetles and caterpillars, plus fruits and seeds, particularly acorns. Its proclivity for storing thousands of acorns underground has aided the propagation of oak trees. However, other foods include garden soft-fruits, and birds' eggs and young, amongst which are those of game species – an aspect of the Jay's ecology which has resulted in long-standing human persecution. Up until the First World War, game-keeping and to a lesser extent the trades of millinery

and fly-tying were considered to be the main reason for its widespread decline in Britain. However, increased human tolerance in subsequent years has benefited this adaptable species.

In Cumbria, Macpherson (1892) suggests persecution when stating that the Jay was "less numerous than formerly". Mitchell (1892) describing the bird as "every year decreasing in numbers; its propensity for emptying Pheasants' eggs causing it to be mercilessly destroyed by the game-keeping fraternity. It is very shy and wary, and seldom falls to the gun; poison being the chief element in its extermination." Subsequent authors paint a slightly different picture. Oakes (1953) while acknowledging "incessant persecution" indicates that the Jay "is not only holding its own but actually increasing in a few localities." Spencer (1973) describes the species as "locally numerous north of the Kent."

The *Old Atlas* indicated confirmed breeding in 45 of the county's 10km squares with probable and possible breeding in a further 29. Records are sparse for the upland areas, especially the North Pennines and higher parts of central Lakeland. It was also thinly distributed on the Coastal Plain in the Whitehaven and Workington areas. A similar state of affairs is gleaned from the *New Atlas:* although a loss of breeding birds is evident from the Solway Basin, the abundance map highlights the Border Uplands, lower Eden Valley, and particularly south Lakeland and southern areas of the Coastal Plain as strongholds.

During *this Atlas,* Jays were recorded in 387 tetrads; yet due to their secretive nature making breeding status difficult to ascertain, breeding was confirmed from just 70 tetrads. However, the maps reinforce the results of the *Old* and *New Atlases* by confirming that the Jay's chief centre of population lies within the mainly deciduous woodlands of south Lakeland. Other healthy clusters occur in the lower Eden Valley, along the western edge of the Border Uplands and in the vicinity of Derwent Water and Bassenthwaite Lake, while the northern section of the Coastal Plain and much of the Solway Basin are again highlighted as supporting few, if any, birds.

In comparison with the previous national atlases, there are some striking differences. *This Atlas* reveals confirmed breeding in just 25 10km squares, a drop of 20 since the *Old Atlas,* and the presence of Jays in much of central and eastern Cumbria is now almost negligible. Birds are totally absent from the North Pennines and much of eastern Lakeland and the Lune Valley, areas that were occupied at the time of the *Old Atlas.* While many of these regions contain upland areas and are possibly marginal habitats with few nest sites, more surprising are the absences from the upper Eden Valley and Cumbria Dales, areas where woodland is not in short supply.

                          Sponsored by C. C. Flindall

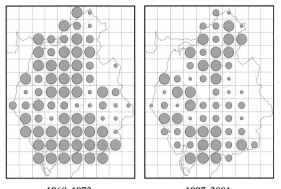

**1968–1972**   **1997–2001**

(For explanation of maps, see page 45)

*Conservation status*

| | |
|---|---|
| European: | Non-SPEC |
| UK: | GREEN |

*Populations*

| | |
|---|---|
| European status: | 6,500,000 |
| Britain – pairs: | 160,000 |
| Cumbria – pairs: | 1,500 |

*30-year distribution change*

| | Old Atlas | This Atlas | % |
|---|---|---|---|
| No. of 10km squares: | 74 | 63 | −14.9 |

| Survey data | Tetrads | % |
|---|---|---|
| Confirmed breeding: | 70 | 3.8 |
| Probable breeding: | 183 | 9.9 |
| Possible breeding: | 134 | 7.3 |
| Total: | 387 | 21.0 |

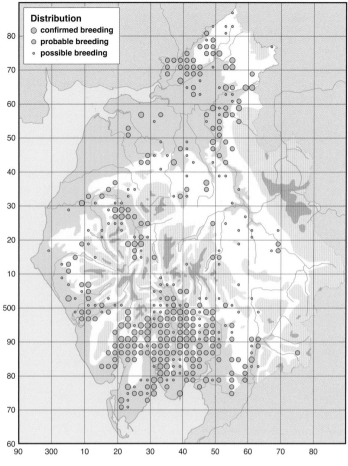

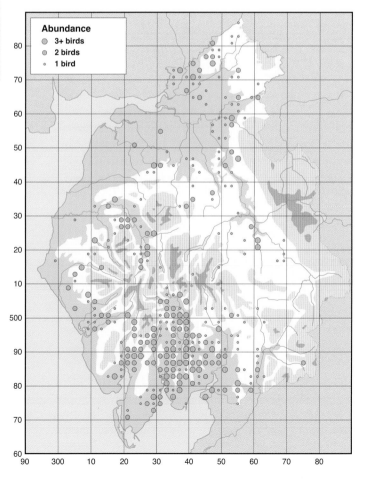

For such a colourful and often noisy bird, the Jay can be very elusive and difficult to survey. Although the line transect data is not statistically robust for this species, given the few contacts, it does produce a figure consistent with the data generated by the timed count visits. However, for a county with so much good habitat, this is considered to be very low, and a more subjective assessment of the current county population would suggest 1,500 breeding pairs.

The latest available CBC index indicates a 11% fall in the population since 1970, with the decline most noticeable in farmland populations. The results of *this Atlas* also give cause for concern; it may well be that farming intensification on marginal habitats within the county has led to the range contraction, with the species retreating to its preferred woodland haunts.

Tim Dean

# Magpie *Pica pica*

**B**OLD and confiding, raucous and gregarious, the distinctively plumaged Magpie is one of the most familiar of all our native birds. It is found in much of the northern hemisphere, with a range which is continuous throughout Europe and Asia, extending into the western parts of North America. It is common throughout England, Wales and Ireland, although the distribution is more fragmented in Scotland.

The Magpie has enjoyed substantial increases in its national population during the 20th century – the latest available CBC data reveal a huge 102% increase since 1970, the species benefiting from reduced levels both of control by gamekeepers and of indiscriminate use of poisons. A bird of woodland and farmland, it has also flourished in new and expanding habitats such as suburban parks and gardens, in conifer plantations, and also in coastal dune areas.

Magpies are opportunistic feeders with an unspecialized diet including plant materials, small invertebrates, carrion and household scraps. In the breeding season, conspicuous raids on the eggs and nestlings of songbirds and gamebirds have led to public dislike and human persecution. However, research has shown no evidence of a link between Magpie predation and changes in songbird breeding populations (Gooch *et al* 1991). An omnivore with catholic tastes, the Magpie survives in a variety of landscapes with suitable trees, shrubs, thickets, thorn hedges or plantations for nesting. The nest is a sturdy domed structure of twigs lined with mud, as low as one metre from the ground in a holly or hawthorn bush and up to 30m in mature trees. Protection is afforded by difficulty of access rather than concealment and nests are often easy to locate, helping confirmation of breeding.

Towards the end of the 19th century, the Magpie was described as a "generally abundant resident" in Cumbria "more strongly established in inland districts than in the vicinity of the seaboard" (Macpherson 1892). Fifty years later, it was thought to be most numerous "on such low-lying grounds as the Solway region and the Foulshaw and Grange districts" (Blezard *et al* 1943). Stokoe (1962) regarded it as "frequent on low ground with thick hedges and scrub, also in coniferous woods up to 1,500 feet [457m]" and commented that it was "generally rather local and least common in fell country". Subsequent records emphasized a continuous increase in the population, with large numbers breeding, particularly in the south of the county.

Magpies are bold and noisy throughout the breeding season, characteristics that make them an easy species to map accurately. *This Atlas* reveals a 7.6% increase in the number of occupied 10km squares since the *Old Atlas* and confirms the widespread distribution of the species throughout Cumbria, apart from its absence on the treeless plateaux of the North Pennines and Lakeland over 400m asl. Population densities are markedly higher in the south and along the Coastal Plain. In these districts, expanding residential areas, the patchwork of open and wooded landscapes, and the milder winters may all be beneficial to Magpie survival. In contrast, much of the Eden Valley remains sparsely populated, although parts of the upper valley have been colonized since the *Old Atlas,* particularly as birds have moved into maturing forestry plantations. Limitations on population densities are not entirely clear. Locally, persecution may still depress numbers, especially where the remarkably efficient Larsen trap is deployed. In addition, Magpies are very sedentary and the process of expanding into new territories may be prolonged.

Analysis of the line transect data from *this Atlas* gives a population band of 12,000–29,000, suggesting a mean population of 19,000 birds. This figure is much less than suggested by the estimated recent national population average, based on an average of 10 pairs/km$^2$ in woodland and suburban habitats and half this figure on more open farmland (Gooch *et al* 1991).

The fortunes of Magpies are closely tied to human activities and attitudes. Environmental and tree-planting schemes in urban and rural areas, suburban housing developments and maturing conifer plantations all promise further niches for this most adaptable bird. The stability of future populations will also depend upon the intensity of measures reacting to the perception of the species as a pest.

Malcolm Priestley

 Sponsored by Julian & Maxine Gould

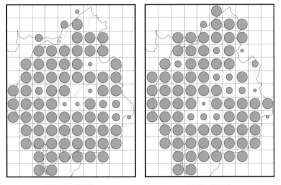

**1968–1972**      **1997–2001**

(For explanation of maps, see page 45)

*Conservation status*

| | |
|---|---|
| European: | Non-SPEC |
| UK: | GREEN |

*Populations*

| | |
|---|---|
| European status: | 9,000,000 |
| Britain – pairs: | 590,000 |
| Cumbria – pairs: | 9,500 |

*30-year distribution change*

| | Old Atlas | This Atlas | % |
|---|---|---|---|
| No. of 10km squares: | 79 | 85 | +7.6 |

| Survey data | Tetrads | % |
|---|---|---|
| Confirmed breeding: | 409 | 22.2 |
| Probable breeding: | 321 | 17.4 |
| Possible breeding: | 244 | 13.2 |
| Total: | 974 | 52.8 |

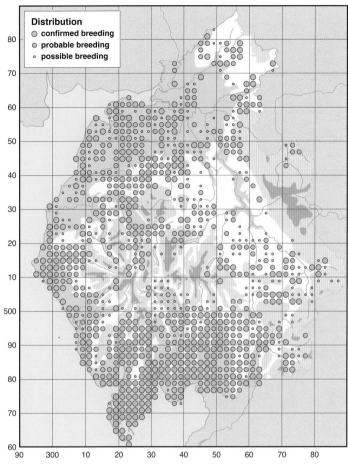

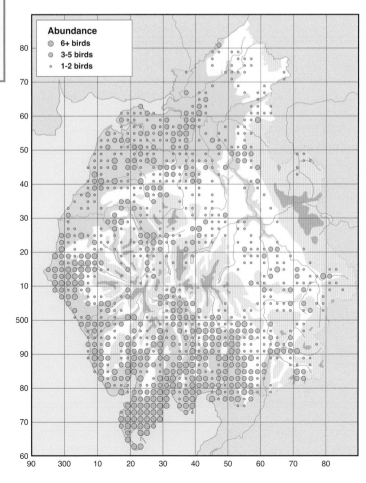

THE Jackdaw, renowned for its 'thieving' habits, is the smallest of Britain's crows and, like its close relative the Rook, probably spread from central Europe and Russia. Inquisitive, noisy and communal, it is a feature of older and smaller towns and villages. The characterful facial expressions created by the adults' white eyes, the obvious affection between the members of a pair, illustrated by the frequent sessions of mutual grooming during rest periods, and the endlessly cheerful chacking calls of flocks around ruins and old buildings – all help to give the Jackdaw a certain charm, lacking in some of its relatives.

A Palearctic species, its range extends eastwards from Europe through the former USSR to Kashmir and Mongolia. It is found throughout most of Britain and Ireland but is extremely local in the far northwest of Scotland and tends to shun moorland and high altitudes. Its absence in these areas may simply be linked to the equal absence of human habitation – and therefore of nest sites – coupled with little good grazing pasture.

It breeds in a wide variety of habitats including the centres of towns and villages, sea cliffs, ruins, inland quarries and crags, hedgerow trees, parkland and woods. Nest sites are most typically holes, cracks and crevices in old buildings, cliffs and trees with rabbit burrows utilized in many coastal locations. Sites normally chosen are close to adjacent grassland where it feeds on surface invertebrates. It will also feed on fruits, seeds, carrion and scraps but seemingly the pre-eminent requirement during the breeding season is an abundance of insects. The Jackdaw occurs in its greatest numbers where nest sites are plentiful and the grazing

of sheep and cattle is commonplace. It needs areas of mixed farmland where short grassland provides food for nestlings and access to livestock feeds when adverse weather conditions, early in the breeding season, may mean other foods are difficult to obtain.

Historical authors are in agreement regarding the species' abundance in Cumbria. At the end of the 19th century, Macpherson (1892) states, "Daws we have in plenty, rearing their young in cliffs, hollow trees, Rabbit holes and church belfries" while Mitchell (1892) describes the bird as "resident and distributed in small numbers over the whole of the county." In the mid-20th century the species was regarded as a common resident, especially in Furness, while its extreme abundance in many Lakeland towns was also stressed (Oakes 1953). Twenty years later, Spencer (1973) referring to Lancashire North of the Sands, asserts that the Jackdaw is "particularly abundant in the limestone districts of the north". Hutcheson (1986) was of the opinion that the population had increased dramatically in the 20th century, being most common in towns and villages where it nested in old buildings and chimneys. They could also be found up to 305m asl nesting in old quarries and cliff faces.

The *Old Atlas* reported confirmed breeding in almost all the county's 10km squares. The *New Atlas* depicted a similar occupancy, only one square being without confirmed breeding. However, the *New Atlas* does show a low level of abundance in areas of central Lakeland and the western section of the Solway Basin.

*This Atlas* shows the species to be still widely distributed within the county. The areas that hold the most abundant populations are the lowland farmland landscapes found in the valleys of southern Lakeland, the southern Coastal Plain and along the Eden Valley, regions also supporting human habitations, which provide nesting opportunities. Slightly less densely populated, although still supporting significant breeding populations, are the Solway Basin, Lune Valley, Cumbria Dales and the western sections of the Coastal Plain. Typically the species is noticeably absent only from the highest areas of the North Pennines, Border Uplands and central Lakeland.

Analysis of line transect data from *this Atlas* gives a population band of 112,000–206,000, suggesting a mean population of 150,000 birds. The highest densities of 60 birds/km² occurred on the intensively farmed lowlands of mixed cereal and good grasslands with a plentiful choice of nest sites. Areas of enclosed rough upland pasture held 39 birds/km², a habitat typical of many sheep-grazed fell-sides of Lakeland and the North Pennines.

The latest CBC index reveals that the national population continues to rise steadily with an 80% increase since 1970. This trend is supported by the recently instigated BBS, which shows a 21% rise, and

Sponsored by D. Stuart Halder

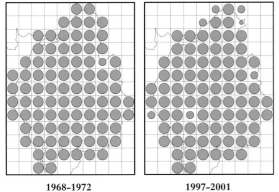

|  | 1968–1972 | 1997–2001 |
|---|---|---|

(For explanation of maps, see page 45)

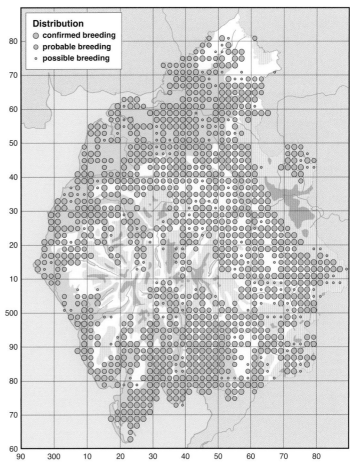

**Distribution**
- confirmed breeding
- probable breeding
- possible breeding

**Conservation status**

| European: | SPEC Cat 4 |
|---|---|
| UK: | GREEN |

**Populations**

| European status: | 5,300,000 |
|---|---|
| Britain – pairs: | 390,000 |
| Cumbria – pairs: | 75,000 |

**30-year distribution change**

|  | Old Atlas | This Atlas | % |
|---|---|---|---|
| No. of 10km squares: | 88 | 88 | n/c |

| Survey data | Tetrads | % |
|---|---|---|
| Confirmed breeding: | 736 | 39.9 |
| Probable breeding: | 326 | 17.7 |
| Possible breeding: | 143 | 7.8 |
| Total: | 1,205 | 65.4 |

when taken in conjunction with the results of *this Atlas,* suggests the prospects for this bird in Cumbria, at least for the immediate future, are bright.

Tim Dean

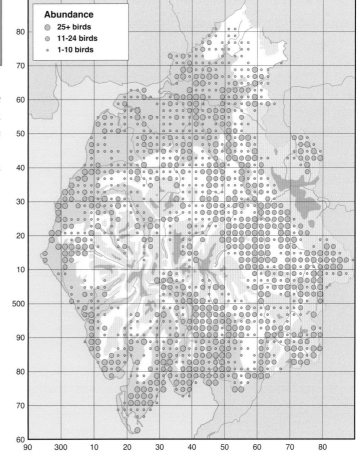

**Abundance**
- 25+ birds
- 11-24 birds
- 1-10 birds

# Rook *Corvus frugilegus*

THE harsh cawing emanating from rookeries close to human habitation make this highly gregarious bird one of the best known of our crows. Its breeding range extends across most temperate and boreal zones of the Western Palearctic. It is abundant and widely distributed throughout most of Britain and Ireland, but of only local occurrence in the extreme northwest mainland and islands of Scotland.

During the breeding season, it depends on the presence of groups of trees for colonial nesting and also on farmland, particularly grassland, in order to forage for soil invertebrates, such as earthworms, wireworms and cranefly larvae. National surveys have shown that a general increase in the Rook population took place in Britain between the early 1930s and the mid-1950s (Parslow 1973), followed by a substantial decline of over 40% in breeding numbers during the next 20 years (Brenchley 1986, Sage & Whittington 1985). This decline was most marked in drier, eastern counties and was probably related to agricultural intensification, including the loss of land from grass to cereals, the persistent effects of pesticides and a widespread shift from spring to autumn sown cereals, with a consequent adverse effect on the availability of soil invertebrates during the breeding season. The decline came to a halt in the late 1970s, and a National Survey indicated an increase of almost 40% between 1975 and 1996.

Historical accounts confirm the abundance and widespread distribution of the Rook throughout much of Cumbria, with Macpherson (1892), in common with most of his contemporaries, regarding the bird as "far too numerous in every part of Lakeland" due to the perceived damage inflicted on arable crops and its serious interference with "the interests of sportsmen". Cumbria, in common with other parts of Britain, has experienced the break-up of established rookeries over the years, including losses to urban development and roadworks, but this appears to have been more than compensated for by the establishment of new colonies and the expansion of some existing ones. There is no evidence of a decline during the middle of the 20th century of the same magnitude that occurred in eastern Britain. The county did, however, share in the substantial increase in breeding population that took place nationally between 1975 and 1996. A Cumbria Bird Club Survey in 1996 estimated a county population of 44,738 nests in 1,325 rookeries. In comparison with comparable data from a national BTO survey in 1975, these figures represent a 48% increase in the number of rookeries and a 37% increase in occupied nests over this period (McAlone *et al* 1997).

The Rook's stronghold in the county is in the lowland farming areas of the Solway Basin, Eden Valley and Lune Valley, where optimum breeding conditions are to be found. It also nests along parts of the Coastal Plain and within the fell-foot country, up to a height of 430m asl. In fact, the only places without rookeries are the high, unenclosed fells of the North Pennines, Cumbria Dales and central Lakeland; the heavily afforested parts of the Border Uplands; and the centres of some of the larger towns. Rookeries within the county are commonly sited in roadside trees and small woods around large country houses, farmhouses and churchyards, with a preference for fairly tall, well-established groups of trees. At least 14 tree species were used, both coniferous and deciduous, the majority nesting in oak, sycamore, beech or pine.

Rookeries are best counted in early April, before most fieldwork for *this Atlas* began. However, a sample study in the north of the county showed that the overall number of nests remained virtually unchanged between 1996 and 1999 (pers obs). Mild winters and favourable breeding conditions since the 1996 CBC survey suggests the likelihood of a further small increase since 1996. The county population is, therefore, estimated to be about 45,000 breeding pairs.

The prospect for the Rook in Cumbria remains one of guarded optimism. Climate change, including global warming, is likely to benefit the Rook population in the county over the next few decades: a reduction in frozen ground conditions with an increased incidence of warmer, wetter weather during the winter and spring might assist the birds' foraging activities at this critical time of year, and contribute to overall breeding success. Although this could be partly offset by the effects of further agricultural intensification, such an outcome is probably less of a threat in Cumbria than

 Sponsored by Paul & Eng Li Green

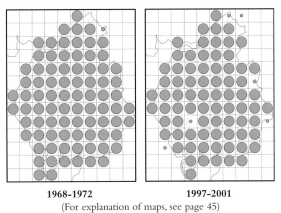

**1968–1972**          **1997–2001**

(For explanation of maps, see page 45)

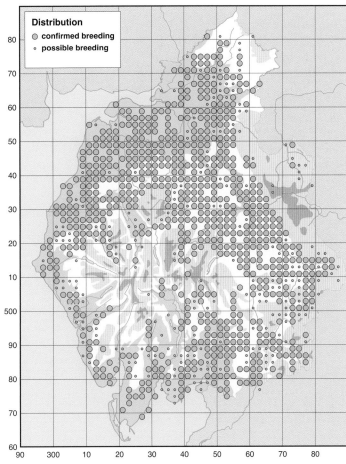

***Conservation status***

| | |
|---|---|
| European: | Non–SPEC |
| UK: | **GREEN** |

***Populations***

| | |
|---|---|
| European status: | 3,500,000 |
| Britain – pairs: | 855,000 |
| Cumbria – pairs: | 45,000 |

***30-year distribution change***

| | Old Atlas | This Atlas | % |
|---|---|---|---|
| No. of 10km squares: | 84 | 82 | **–2.3** |

| **Survey data** | **Tetrads** | **%** |
|---|---|---|
| Confirmed breeding: | 766 | 41.5 |
| Probable breeding: | 0 | |
| Possible breeding: | 204 | 11.1 |
| Total: | 980 | 52.6 |

in the drier southern and eastern parts of England. Whilst there is a possibility that available nest sites could be reduced as a result of felling and increased fragmentation of woodland, most well-managed estates fell on a rotational basis, with replanting an integral part of the process. There are also a significant number of suitable sites available that are not currently used, including unoccupied trees at existing rookeries.

Clive Hartley

(Note that the distribution map also includes confirmed breeding from the 1996 CBC Rookery Survey. The abundance map is based upon counts obtained from the 1996 survey; in tetrads where rookeries were found in 1997–2001 fieldwork, but not found in the 1996 survey, a dot appears in the smallest size-band.)

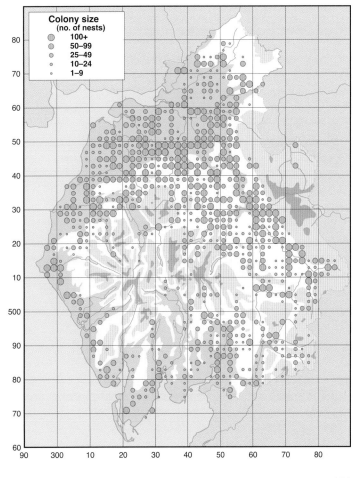

# Carrion Crow *Corvus corone*

THE Carrion Crow is not the most popular of birds; its habits can bring it into conflict with farmers, gamekeepers and birdwatchers alike. While its diet does include a high proportion of carrion – be it sheep in the hills or a road casualty Rabbit – and much grain and invertebrates, the crow is also a major predator. On moorland and wetland edges, its presence may be marked at a convenient fence post by the broken shells of wader and gamebird eggs. In sheep country, the Carrion Crow is known to peck out the eyes of weak lambs and even kill those undergoing a difficult birth; at such times they will even take out the eyes of the prostrate and defenceless ewe (pers obs).

This is a common species; it is found throughout Britain and Ireland, continental Europe and Asia roughly between the tundra and the Himalaya. Its range just extends into North Africa, and it is represented by related species in North America.

The Carrion Crow is usually a solitary breeder and its nests are easily found in large field and hedgerow trees. In mature woodland, it often selects one of the tallest trees in which to build its nest, whereas elsewhere it may use low bushes, crag ledges and even build on the ground. In upland areas, the nest is often to be found in whatever tree is available along gill courses. Wherever it is situated, the nest site will have a nearby vantage point from which the off-duty bird will look for danger and potential threats.

There is little historical data, anecdotal or otherwise, on the status of the Carrion Crow in Cumbria. It appears to have largely been ignored by the county's naturalists, unless recounting the effects upon other species of its activities. Its distribution in the county probably changed little during the 19th century and there is no evidence of any change between the *Old Atlas* and the *New Atlas*. Although it is generally assumed that Carrion Crow numbers increased during the last 50 years – with a decline in gamekeeper numbers and activities – RSPB data from a recent upland bird survey (2000) in the North Pennines show a 26% decline since a previous survey.

During the survey period of *this Atlas*, the Carrion Crow's abundance was shown to vary between geographical areas, being least frequent as a breeder in the North Pennines, where large areas are intensively managed by gamekeepers. Although the main concentration of breeding birds was recorded in the lower, more fertile, areas of the Eden Valley, the Solway Basin and the Coastal Plain, where mature hedgerow trees presumably provide plenty of suitable nest sites and the pickings are richest, they were also common in areas of rough grazing, pasture and forestry. As the distribution map suggests, they occurred in any habitat and any location, with no obvious pattern.

Analysis of the line transect data from *this Atlas* gives a population band of 52,000–83,000, suggesting a mean population of 66,000 birds.

The widespread cessation in the use of poisons as a means of controlling crow numbers has removed an indiscriminate and lethal tool from the countryside. Although poison baits are still used by some unscrupulous game-managers, these are now in the minority and most use shooting or trapping as the main control method. In the first year of *this Atlas*, one tetrad held 21 breeding pairs, 10 of which bred in a single kilometre square. After just three years of implementing legal control methods, the number of nesting attempts had been reduced to seven, of which only four proved successful. Although more time-consuming and labour-intensive, these methods prove an extremely effective means of limiting local populations, without resorting to the outdated and illegal measures that cannot distinguish an opportunist crow from a hungry Buzzard.

**Hooded Crow** *Corvus corone cornix*

This race dominates in eastern and northern Europe, in north and west Scotland, in Ireland and in the Isle of Man. It is mostly a passage migrant and winter visitor to England and, in Cumbria, is thought mainly to originate from the Isle of Man rather than Scotland. Pairs are known to have bred in Cumbria in the past, such as at Gowbarrow in 1925 and Anthorn in 1940 (Blezard *et al* 1943), but it is mostly recorded in mixed pairs with Carrion Crows. During *this Atlas* period, such mixed pairs produced hybrid young at Harrington, Whitehaven and Otter Bank near Kendal.

David Walker

 Sponsored by Matthew Mackenzie

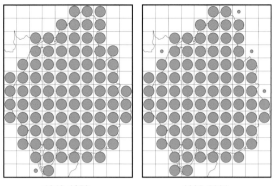

**1968-1972** **1997-2001**
(For explanation of maps, see page 45)

*Conservation status*
European:                    Non-SPEC
UK:                          GREEN

*Populations*
European status:             6,200,000
Britain – pairs:               970,000
Cumbria – pairs:                33,000

*30-year distribution change*
               Old Atlas  This Atlas   %
No. of 10km squares:  91       92    +1.1

| Survey data | Tetrads | % |
|---|---|---|
| Confirmed breeding: | 948 | 51.4 |
| Probable breeding: | 450 | 24.4 |
| Possible breeding: | 251 | 13.6 |
| Total: | 1,649 | 89.4 |

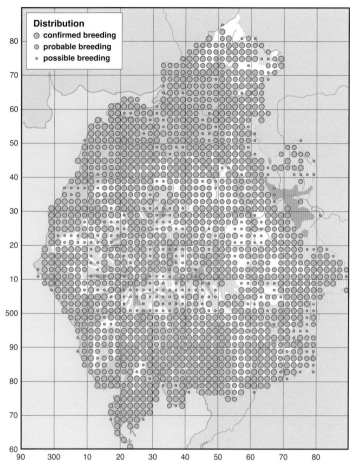

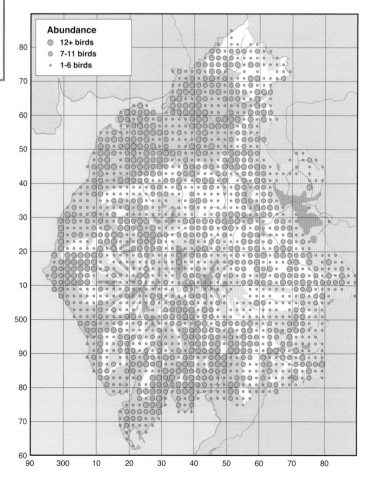

RAUCOUS *'cronk cronk'* call notes temporarily fill the almost eerie silence of an upland valley as a Raven returns to its nest with a stick. Its jet-black plumage contrasts sharply against a dazzle of brilliance as it flies across a late snowfield. These are the first signs that winter is loosening its grip and spring once more returns to the high frozen crags of Lakeland.

The Raven's enormous breeding range covers most of North America and North Africa, much of Asia and virtually all of Europe. In Britain, it is largely restricted to the north and west but is more evenly distributed in Ireland. Although usually found on precipitous crags, where it often occurs alongside the Peregrine, the Raven also nests in trees, quarries, on viaducts and disused buildings, and even occasionally on the ground.

It has long suffered from persecution by man, due to its habit of feeding on sheep carrion and the perceived damage it does to gamebird stocks; even its collective noun 'an unkindness of Ravens' does the bird no favours. Though carrion does form a large part of the diet, Ravens are omnivorous and consume much vegetable matter. Nevertheless, man's prejudices have influenced its numbers and distribution over many centuries. At one time, it accompanied kites as a city scavenger and was widespread as an inland breeder over much of England. Numbers were probably at their lowest before the First World War when persecution was at its height; since then there has been a gradual increase (Coombs 1978).

Macpherson (1892) remarked upon instances of persecution in Cumbria as early as 1636; in some areas this has persisted to this day. Stokoe (1962) regarded it as "widespread; nesting in all mountain areas." He knew of only one coastal haunt – St Bees Head – and considered the breeding population to be relatively stable. Nowadays, population trends are showing a steady increase, perhaps influenced by a tendency to nest more frequently in trees. Scots pines are most frequently used, although it will also nest in deciduous trees. This habit could be paying dividends, giving the Raven a wider choice of nest sites in more productive habitat, where prey items are more abundant or easier to come by. Although this is not a new phenomenon – Macpherson and Duckworth (1886) believed it to be fairly widespread during the 18th century and Stokoe (1962) mentioned several tree nests – it could be an old strategy that works well in a modern environment.

Current population levels are perhaps the highest in recorded history. Ratcliffe (1997) stated that there were 81 known territories in Cumbria during 1900–1970, with a mean of 69 regularly occupied sites. This had risen to 82–92 pairs during 1980–1995, with a mean of 87 pairs; an increase of around 26% on the earlier period. Between the *Old* and *New Atlases* there was little difference in numbers, although fewer birds were found on the grouse moors of the North Pennines. Some moorland sites have, however, fared better than others with some traditional nest sites being reoccupied while others remain vacant. A typical site in the north of the county was recorded as occupied during the *Old Atlas,* empty during the *New Atlas,* and occupied again during *this Atlas.*

Although *this Atlas* reveals that Lakeland remains the stronghold, there has been an obvious increase in numbers breeding on the coast between St Bees Head and Workington since the *Old Atlas,* while quarry and tree-nesting has allowed an expansion into new lowland areas south of Kendal. The Border Uplands, Eden Valley and North Pennines still support few birds, while the Solway Basin remains unoccupied, presumably due to a lack of nest sites. The Raven's early breeding season – females can be incubating by the third week in February – should not have biased the survey results, since parents would be busy feeding young well into May. For some unknown reason, in a few 10km squares where nesting has been long established, no confirmed breeding records were received during *this Atlas*. Non-breeders or birds that had failed earlier in the season are likely to explain many of the possible breeding dots on the distribution map.

Unsurprisingly, given the Raven's sporadic breeding distribution, the line transect survey failed to produce

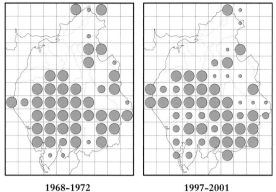

**1968-1972**     **1997-2001**
(For explanation of maps, see page 45)

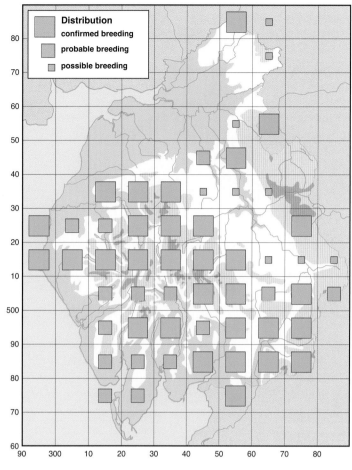

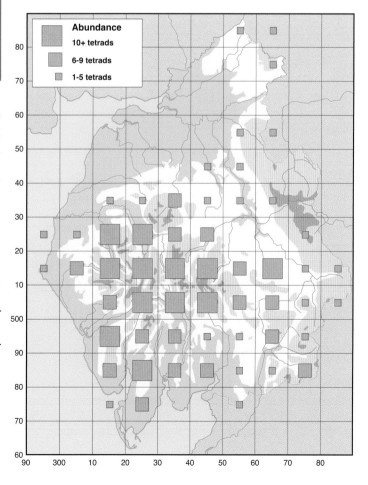

*Conservation status*
European:                 Non-SPEC
UK:                       **GREEN**

*Populations*
European status:          220,000
Britain – pairs:          7,000
Cumbria – pairs:          80–110

*30-year distribution change*

| | Old Atlas | This Atlas | % |
|---|---|---|---|
| No. of 10km squares: | 47 | 55 | +17 |

| **Survey data** | **Tetrads** | **%** |
|---|---|---|
| Confirmed breeding: | 66 | 3.6 |
| Probable breeding: | 83 | 4.5 |
| Possible breeding: | 215 | 11.7 |
| Total: | 364 | 19.8 |

meaningful data for this species. The current county population estimate of 80–110 breeding pairs has been derived from a long-term monitoring scheme under the auspices of CRSG.

Despite persistent persecution in some key areas, there appears to be little threat to the Raven's future in Cumbria at the present time, though any increase in disturbance could pose problems. Dare (1986) considered that future trends in population size and breeding success were likely to be influenced mainly by food availability; more rapid removal of carcases by farmers and lower stocking levels in the wake of foot-and-mouth disease could reduce the amount of sheep carrion available for this most regal of birds.

Derek Hayward

THE often-maligned Starling is denigrated for its superficially dull-coloured plumage, for its 'greedy' behaviour at feeding stations, and causing public nuisance. While its fouling of the streets and polluting of its winter woodland roosts has to be admitted, this star-spangled bird does receive an unjustly bad press. The near-mesmeric sight of wheeling flocks above their roosts is a marvel to behold, and the Starling's exuberant bubbling song, often including mimicry of better-loved species, is a welcome addition to the chorus of bird-song. While others may be more melodious, few birds sound as cheerful as the Starling.

The Starling's abundance cannot be denied; its natural range extends throughout the Western Palearctic and includes summering populations eastwards into Asia. It is also probably the most successful of species introduced on to other continents, most notably in North America and Australia (Feare 1984). The Starling is found throughout Britain and Ireland and is only absent from the more upland treeless regions. Starlings often nest semi-colonially, taking advantage of local conditions, but are also to be found nesting singly and often in some isolation. They are opportunistic nesters using holes in trees, buildings and quarries and elsewhere when circumstances permit. They are territorial only in the sense that they defend the nest site against intruders; otherwise Starlings live a gregarious lifestyle. Although two broods are sometimes raised, only a single clutch is typical in the northern portions of their range.

The Starling has not always been numerous and its British range was in retreat 200 years ago, the species being lost from the north and west in particular (Feare 1984). Macpherson (1892) commented that it was scarce in Cumbria until the second half of the 19th century and linked the subsequent increase to the conversion of moors and wet flows into pasture and rough grazing. The *Old Atlas* includes climatic change as another relevant factor.

Although the *Old Atlas* indicated a continuing increase, the *New Atlas* suggested an apparent decline in numbers and, unlike in these previous surveys, during *this Atlas* breeding was not confirmed in all 10km squares. The proportion of occupied tetrads where breeding was not confirmed was higher than expected – perhaps also reflecting a decreasing population in Cumbria. Such tetrads tend to be in areas fringing the more exposed upland regions but also include areas with apparently suitable habitat. One such example is in a tetrad near Burnbanks: a loose colony of 10–20 pairs occupied a single wood during the 1980s, yet the birds had disappeared by the time of *this Atlas*.

The distribution map shows that the Starling's strongholds are clearly in the more fertile agricultural areas such as the Solway Basin and the Coastal Plain. The Eden Valley also has a comparatively strong population although this becomes fragmented in the central part of the area, in the vicinity of Penrith. The abundance map, in fact, suggests that the Eden Valley is less densely populated overall than the more coastal areas with a similar distribution. These differences may be linked to land use: the Eden Valley, except where it broadens near Carlisle, has much rough grazing, with some pasture and forestry, in comparison to the cultivation and better quality grasslands of the Solway Basin and Coastal Plain, which make for a more attractive habitat. Perhaps not surprisingly, large concentrations of nesting birds were recorded around towns and villages, presumably linked to ample nesting opportunities and easier pickings from garden feeding stations.

Analysis of line transect data from *this Atlas* gives a population band of 160,000–270,000, suggesting a mean population of 200,000 birds. The highest calculated densities of 145 birds/km² were along the coastal zone.

Why the species has been lost from some areas and is declining in others remains a puzzle, especially since habitat changes appear to be minor, and farming practices have altered little. All too often, birds of prey such as Sparrowhawks are mistakenly blamed for declines in songbirds. In the case of the Starling it is less likely that predation would adversely affect the breeding population to any great extent. As a partial

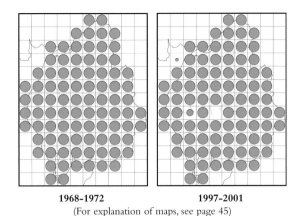

**1968-1972** **1997-2001**

(For explanation of maps, see page 45)

*Conservation status*

| | |
|---|---|
| European: | Non-SPEC |
| UK: | **RED: BD** |

*Populations*

| | |
|---|---|
| European status: | 40,000,000 |
| Britain – pairs: | 1,100,000 |
| Cumbria – pairs: | 100,000 |

*30-year distribution change*

| | Old Atlas | This Atlas | % |
|---|---|---|---|
| No. of 10km squares: | 88 | 88 | n/c |

| **Survey data** | **Tetrads** | **%** |
|---|---|---|
| Confirmed breeding: | 829 | 45.0 |
| Probable breeding: | 216 | 11.7 |
| Possible breeding: | 140 | 7.6 |
| Total: | 1,185 | 64.3 |

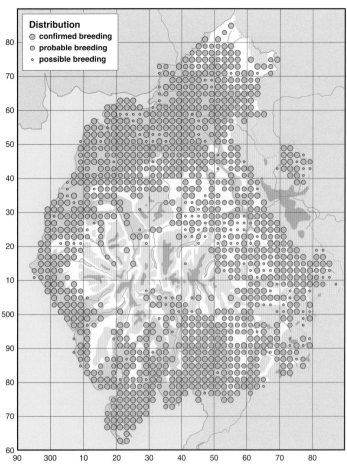

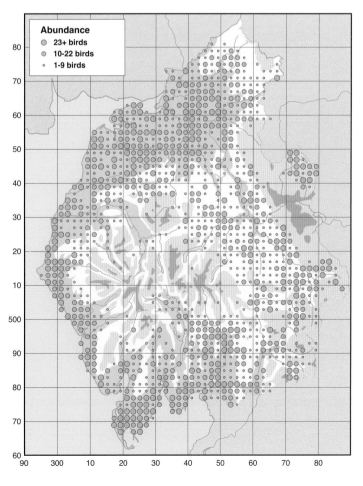

migrant deserting its more exposed upland breeding haunts before the onset of winter, other factors could intervene to reduce the actual numbers of birds returning to these isolated populations. Equally, any factors affecting numbers in the main breeding range may limit recruitment and cause losses from the fringe population.

As with the Song Thrush in the recent past, it is difficult to envisage the Starling as a species in decline. Although its breeding numbers and range do appear to be declining, it is unlikely to be lost from the county as a whole. The species does not appear to be in major decline in urban areas, probably because of a fairly constant food supply and availability of nest sites there, but the modernization of buildings and town expansions on to 'green field' areas may result in further decreases.

David Walker

# House Sparrow *Passer domesticus*

ONE of our least colourful and least inspiring songsters, the House Sparrow was, until recently, often considered to be a pest. Now undergoing an alarming decline, it has become something of a *cause célèbre*, its plight a matter of countrywide concern; its disappearance from inner-cities making headlines in 'heavyweight' newspapers, national television and radio alike.

Although the House Sparrow is present in every continent in its many forms, the nominate race occurs from Britain and Ireland through Eurasia, east to the Sea of Okhotsk and south to Spain and Portugal. Colonization and establishment have often been associated with man's development and settlement providing buildings for nesting and cultivation as a source of food. Many introductions of the species into regions outside its normal range were made to reduce insect infestation on arable crops. It is widespread throughout Britain and Ireland, being absent only from high ground in the Scottish Highlands.

A loose cone-shaped nest is built, usually in a natural or man-made cavity, with a preference for buildings. Nestboxes and old nests of House and Sand Martins are sometimes used; indeed, House Sparrows will often commandeer nests of the former just before the rightful occupants make the entrance too narrow. Additionally, bulky constructions may be built in hedgerows, ivy or thickets.

According to the *Historical Atlas,* it was apparently so abundant nationally in the 19th century and caused so much damage to crops that "Sparrow Clubs were set up with the aim of eradicating it from every parish".

Similarly, Macpherson & Duckworth (1886) stated that "the Sparrow is an only too numerous resident, having increased immensely of late years"; however "in some of the vales about Keswick, where there is little or no grain produced and few inhabitants, it is an extremely scarce bird". Nearly 80 years later, Stokoe (1962) regarded it as "abundant in towns, villages and all but the most isolated farms".

Analysis of the latest CBC data indicates a 43% decline since 1970. Though this is based on a small sample size, at least in the early years, the CBC is not the only survey to reveal declines in House Sparrow numbers. The BTO's Garden Bird Feeding Survey, which began in the winter of 1970/71, shows that average weekly peak counts fell from 15–20 birds in the late 1970s to about six in the late 1990s. The RSPB's Big Garden Birdwatch reveals that average garden counts have more than halved from 10 in 1979 to four in 2000.

In both the *Old* and *New Atlases,* House Sparrows were present and proved to breed in all but six 10km squares in the county. *This Atlas,* with the improved 'resolution' given by tetrad data, shows that several 10km squares in the proximity of higher ground and non-tilled agriculture have very low levels of occupancy and abundance. The Lakeland and Pennine valleys, which until the 1960s were still farmed rotationally, have given way to more sheep and silage with little or no grain grown; this, together with former farmsteads and older habitations being structurally improved, has denied the House Sparrow both food and suitable nesting cavities.

An early indication of this rural decline is the *New Atlas* change map for the period since the *Old Atlas:* over 100 10km squares in Ireland, Wales and Scotland had recently been abandoned by House Sparrows. The post-war agricultural reform polarized farming into high-yielding cereal crops, with a greater reliance on chemicals and 'cleaner' harvesting methods, and higher livestock densities, especially in the sheep industry, with intensively managed grasslands. As a result of these changes, House Sparrows have only a tenuous hold on what were, in any case, marginal habitats in central and eastern Cumbria.

The distribution map for *this Atlas* shows House Sparrows still have a strong presence in all arable lowland areas of Cumbria, but with some 'thinning' or total absence from upland habitats or interior valleys, typical of a species that is in retreat. As House Sparrows are noisy and confiding, the map is likely to be a true reflection of the current situation.

Analysis of the line transect data from *this Atlas* gives a population band of 260,000–420,000, suggesting a mean population of 330,000 birds. The highest calculated density of 152 birds/km$^2$ was on the Coastal Plain.

The future is uncertain. Present speculation cites unleaded petrol as a potential agent for urban decline,

Sponsored by the Carr Family

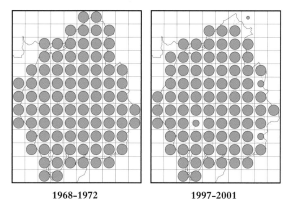

**1968-1972**　　　　**1997-2001**

(For explanation of maps, see page 45)

*Conservation status*

| | |
|---|---|
| European: | Non-SPEC |
| UK: | AMBER: BDM |

*Populations*

| | |
|---|---|
| European status: | 54,000,000 |
| Britain – pairs: | 3,600,000 |
| Cumbria – pairs: | 165,000 |

*30-year distribution change*

| | Old Atlas | This Atlas | % |
|---|---|---|---|
| No. of 10km squares: | 88 | 85 | −3.4 |

| Survey data | Tetrads | % |
|---|---|---|
| Confirmed breeding: | 825 | 44.7 |
| Probable breeding: | 206 | 11.2 |
| Possible breeding: | 40 | 2.2 |
| Total: | 1,071 | 58.1 |

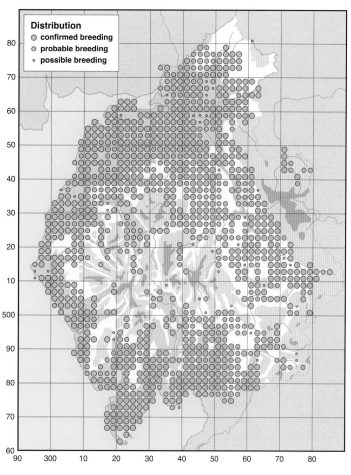

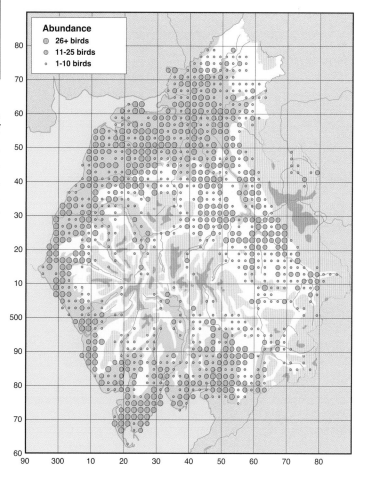

but this is surely not the reason for its rural recession. Some threats are obvious: 'tidying up' of urban and rural buildings has a deleterious effect on the availability of nesting sites; and even though some numbers will survive winters at garden feeding stations during the darkest months, the real villain as far as winter survival is concerned is likely to be present farming practice. Reduced cereal planting, and the more serious advent of winter-sown crops, affect the amount of stubble available for finches, larks, buntings and sparrows alike. Unless there is some reversal, it seems likely the House Sparrow's decline will continue, as will that of many other associated farmland-dependent species.

John Callion

319

# Tree Sparrow *Passer montanus*     Eurasian Tree Sparrow

OFTEN in the company and shadow of the closely related and more forward House Sparrow, the Tree Sparrow is an engaging species that captivates with its homely chirp, alert but confiding nature, chocolate head and dark smudge on white cheek reminiscent of an impressionist's single brushstroke. These features clearly distinguish it from the House Sparrow, as does the fact that the sexes have the same plumage.

Having recently spread into Fennoscandia, the species is now present in all European countries except Iceland. Elsewhere its range extends as far east as Japan and south to Indonesia. Although occurring in the outlying geographical areas of Britain and Ireland, such as Caithness, the Western Isles and the westernmost limits of Kerry and Connemara, Tree Sparrows are concentrated in the lowlands of central and eastern England, with some pockets of abundance in low-lying areas of eastern Scotland. Despite being mainly sedentary, they are prone to irruptive movements, often resulting in colonization of new areas, or re-colonization, as happened in Ireland in the 1950s after a number of years of absence. There is also some evidence of diurnal migration at coastal sites in Britain and Ireland, including South Walney.

Significant influxes into Britain occurred in the second half of the 19th century and between 1957 and 1962; the latter movement coincided with a peak exodus from Falsterbo in Sweden (Summers-Smith 1989). In Cumbria in the 19th century, Macpherson & Duckworth (1886) found them to be "very scarce" with "a few pairs nesting annually in certain isolated localities," though "at all times an exceedingly scarce bird," while Macpherson (1892) considered them "unaccountably scarce in Lakeland". He searched for them in vain in Westmorland and Furness but commented on a permanent colony of a few pairs at Allonby and noted that they nested at Kirkoswald in 1871 and How Hill in 1888, his only records for what he refers to as "interior Lakeland". According to Stokoe (1962), it had "become increasingly widespread, nesting in small colonies near farms, old buildings and in rural areas generally to the fringes of the central fell region". This statement appears to confirm the consequences of the influxes of the 1950s and early 1960s.

Unlike House Sparrows, Tree Sparrows are essentially rural birds, not even penetrating into suburbia. Trees are important to them, but not woodland. They have a preference for mature hedgerow trees and loose stands, and they are very much associated with farms and outbuildings. Being generally cavity-nesters, they readily take to nestboxes, sometimes colonially; several records for *this Atlas* have referred to this habit.

Nationally, Tree Sparrows are now found on too few CBC plots to produce meaningful data, though BBS results for the period 1994–2000 reveal an encouraging 25% increase. Despite this apparently encouraging recent trend, the species has declined by an alarming 95% since 1970 and may have been affected by a reduction in winter seed supplies. The change map between the *Old Atlas* and the *New Atlas* shows that the Tree Sparrow had been in a period of decline, with an 18% reduction in the number of occupied 10km squares in all parts of Britain and Ireland. At this time, Tree Sparrows were lost from 14 10km squares in Cumbria – a 20% decline, occurring primarily outside the stronghold in the Solway Basin. *This Atlas* suggests that the decline may have been arrested locally, in distribution, if not in numbers, except in the southwest, an area that had also incurred the greatest losses in the *New Atlas*. Four 10km squares have also been reoccupied since the *Old Atlas*. In areas where Tree Sparrows are uncommon they can easily be overlooked, especially if they are isolated or singular in large colonies of House Sparrows. Nevertheless, it is puzzling that, despite their disclosing character, breeding was confirmed in only 40% of occupied tetrads. Although the scientific epithet *montanus* is justified in some parts of its wide range, in Britain and Ireland the Tree Sparrow is essentially a lowland farmland bird, avoiding all types of upland. In Cumbria, it is very much restricted to the Solway Basin, the Eden Valley and tributary valleys, the southern Coastal Plain in Furness and around the lower River Kent; elsewhere, there are isolated pockets, though it avoids the narrow angular central valleys.

     Sponsored by Mike Critchley & Neil & Marjorie Hutchin

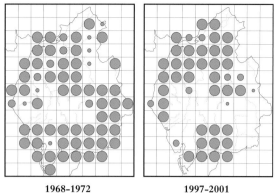

**1968–1972**     **1997–2001**
(For explanation of maps, see page 45)

*Conservation status*

| | |
|---|---|
| European: | Non-SPEC |
| UK: | **RED: BD** |

*Populations*

| | |
|---|---|
| European status: | 15,000,000 |
| Britain – pairs: | 110,000 |
| Cumbria – pairs: | 5,000–10,000 |

*30-year distribution change*

| | Old Atlas | This Atlas | % |
|---|---|---|---|
| No. of 10km squares: | 65 | 45 | **−30.8** |

| **Survey data** | **Tetrads** | **%** |
|---|---|---|
| Confirmed breeding: | 93 | 5.0 |
| Probable breeding: | 92 | 5.0 |
| Possible breeding: | 45 | 2.4 |
| Total: | 230 | 12.4 |

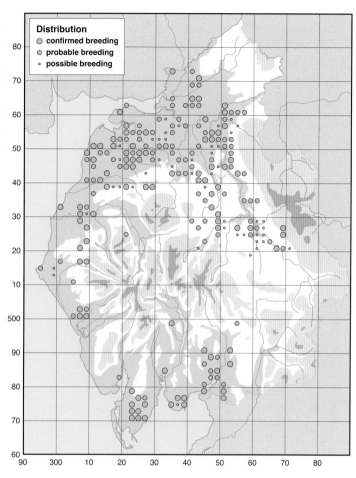

Analysis of line transect data from *this Atlas* gives a population band of 7,000–53,000, suggesting a mean population of 20,000 birds. However, given the wide band limits, it is obvious that this estimate must be treated with caution; a more subjective assessment would be half this figure.

Given the species' reliance on invertebrates in summer and grain in winter, the future for the Tree Sparrow is totally dependent upon the direction of farming; if there is no move away from winter-sown cereals, then the chances of it reverting to its 19th century status seem real, if not immediate. On the other hand, rapid changes in arable farming practices might also, as rapidly, favour the Tree Sparrow.

John Callion

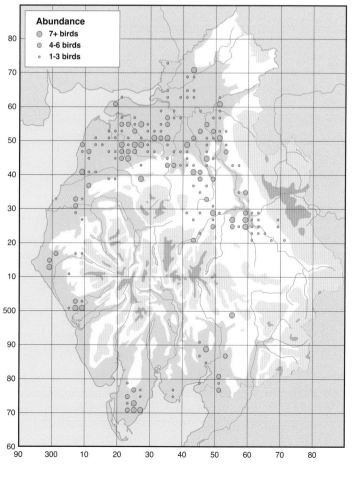

# Chaffinch *Fringilla coelebs*

THE cock Chaffinch in fresh new breeding plumage is a sure sign that spring has arrived. He begins his short, repetitive, yet pleasant song in February and delivers it with vigour from any prominent perch in hedgerow or tree. The Chaffinch once had the distinction of being the most numerous bird in Cumbria and until a few years ago would have been without rival, but recently its numbers have declined.

Very much a bird of the Western Palearctic, it breeds from the tree-line in temperate and boreal regions, south to North Africa and from the Azores east into Siberia. In Britain and Ireland it is almost ubiquitous, penetrating even into the most urbanized of areas and being scarce only in treeless uplands and the outlying isles of Scotland.

In autumn and winter the Chaffinch eats a variety of seeds, but is greatly dependent on cereals and weed seeds uncovered by the disturbance of cultivation. These are gleaned almost exclusively from the ground rather than taken directly from the plant (Newton 1972). This feeding strategy gave the bird its name as it became a familiar sight around farmyards, hayricks and stubble fields in its search for food amongst the chaff. In April and early May breeding begins, with the neat, lichen-decorated nest placed near the centre of a shrub in garden, woodland or hedgerow. By this time the Chaffinch is almost totally insectivorous and the young will be in the nest in May and June to reap the benefits of the surge of insect life at this time. Chaffinches are usually single brooded though capable of producing replacement

clutches for predated or infertile eggs. These later clutches are more successful as food becomes more abundant and growing vegetation hides the nest more effectively.

Both Macpherson (1892) and Stokoe (1962), writing 70 years apart, describe Chaffinches as widespread and common in the county, and it seems hard to imagine them as ever being anything else. Nevertheless, as suggested by Holloway (1996), it does seem likely that the spread and increase of agriculture over the last three centuries has helped establish the current population and distribution by providing hedgerows for cover, crops for seeds and, at least in the past, winter stubble. However, agriculture, as we know only too well, is a double-edged sword and the heavy use of organochlorine seed-dressings was implicated in the fall in Chaffinch numbers in the late 1950s and early 1960s (Newton 1972). Since the control of the worst of these chemicals the species has made a rapid recovery. Several bursts of conifer planting, particularly those following the two World Wars, have allowed encroachment into previously unwelcoming upland areas.

The distribution in Cumbria mirrors the national picture in that there are very few places away from the fell tops where the song of the Chaffinch will not be heard. Again, as with Britain as a whole, conifer plantations have allowed expansion into the foothills and higher valleys of the fells, as evidenced by Stokoe (1962) who stated that, "apart from Titmice, Chaffinches were the commonest nesters in spruce plantations." There appears to be no significant change to the status of the Chaffinch in Cumbria between the *Old Atlas* and *this Atlas*. On each occasion breeding was confirmed in all but four 10km squares in the county, even those containing mainly fells. Indeed, *this Atlas* confirmed breeding in more than half of the county's tetrads.

Male Chaffinches are persistent and obvious territorial performers making them easy to survey, so the estimated number of males is probably as close to the actual population as this type of survey allows. Analysis of line transect data from *this Atlas* gives a population band of 310,000–410,000 singing males, suggesting a mean population of 360,000 males. The highest calculated densities of 129 males/km$^2$ were recorded on the Coastal Plain.

Despite more efficient cropping, a change from spring to autumn sowing and little winter stubble, Chaffinches have managed to adapt to the modern countryside. Since the recovery from the ravages of pesticide pollutants in the late 1950s and early 1960s, the trend in CBC surveys has been a steady, if shallow, climb to today's healthy population (Marchant 1990). It is probable that their ready use of

Sponsored by Jill Damment

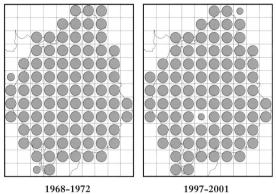

**1968-1972** **1997-2001**

(For explanation of maps, see page 45)

| Conservation status | |
|---|---|
| European: | SPEC Cat 4 |
| UK: | **GREEN** |

| Populations | |
|---|---|
| European status: | 85,000,000 |
| Britain – pairs: | 5,400,000 |
| Cumbria – pairs: | 360,000 |

**30-year distribution change**

| | Old Atlas | This Atlas | % |
|---|---|---|---|
| No. of 10km squares: | 90 | 90 | n/c |

| Survey data | Tetrads | % |
|---|---|---|
| Confirmed breeding: | 1,094 | 59.3 |
| Probable breeding: | 453 | 24.6 |
| Possible breeding: | 51 | 2.8 |
| Total: | 1,598 | 86.7 |

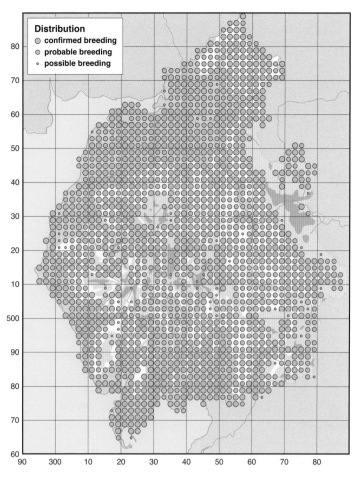

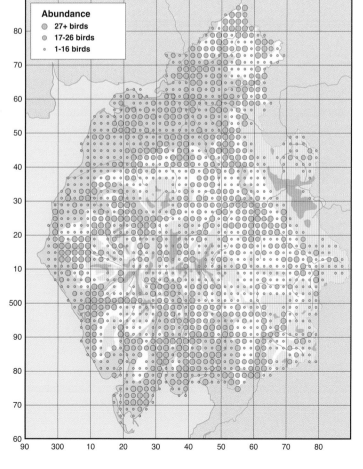

our gardens for both breeding and winter survival has helped cushion the impact of agricultural change.

Derek McAlone

AS the breeding season approaches, abrasion of feather-tips alters the male's somewhat dull winter appearance to a magnificent mixture of canary-yellow and lemon-green, shown to best effect as he advertises his presence from a lofty song perch. In the most intense display, the Greenfinch, sometimes called the 'Green Linnet', also stages a song flight, circling on slowly flapping wings. This is a sociable species, found in large gardens and wherever trees and bushes are common.

The Greenfinch breeds over much of the western half of Eurasia, except for the extreme north and the mountainous spine of Scandinavia, and extends south to the warm shores of the Mediterranean. Another, isolated, population inhabits the highlands of Turkestan. In Britain and Ireland, it is widespread and common except in northern Scotland and the outer islands.

Greenfinches nest in hedgerows, woods and gardens and once the chicks have hatched the adults will forage over a wide area in order to feed them. Two or three broods may be produced and fledglings may leave the nest as late as September. However, nests are heavily predated so numbers of fledged young are not as high as such a prolonged breeding season may suggest. The BTO's Nest Record Scheme has shown an, as yet, unexplained increase in nest failure over the last 15 years (Mead 2000).

The history of the Greenfinch in Britain is similar to that of other seed-eating birds, in that the rise of agriculture in the last three centuries brought expansion in both range and numbers. Macpherson and Duckworth (1886) knew it as a common resident,

plentiful in most parts of the county but scarcer in the southeast, a status that had changed little by the time of Stokoe's (1962) work.

The Greenfinch's diet changes through the seasons, but it always prefers larger seeds. In summer those of dog's mercury and elm are favoured, whilst in autumn yew and hornbeam, and in winter rose and bramble are particularly sought. Farmland weeds such as charlock and chickweed are important, especially in winter. Greenfinches are attracted to cultivated seeds, perhaps because of their large size, and will take them from standing crops as well as from the ground (Newton 1972). Exploitation of oilseed rape is important in summer as it provides food until cereals start to ripen in autumn. Improvements in the efficiency of harvesting and changes in crop regimes have brought problems for this species as they result in less spilled grain and less winter stubble. Happily these problems have, to a large extent, been alleviated by the species' vigorous exploitation of garden feeding stations.

In Cumbria, the Greenfinch is found wherever there are hedgerows, woods, parks or gardens, particularly those with conifers, but is absent from the treeless fellsides. Fieldwork for *this Atlas* found Greenfinches in more than half of Cumbria's tetrads, and confirmed them as breeding in nearly 25%. Their distribution is similar to that of the Chaffinch though they are much sparser in number, especially in Lakeland and the North Pennines, where birds are usually confined to river valleys. This was also the case 100 years ago when it was found to be "especially abundant in Furness" (Macpherson 1892). No significant change in distribution is discernible between the *Old Atlas* and *this Atlas*.

Analysis of line transect data from *this Atlas* gives a population band of 53,000–87,000, suggesting a mean population of 68,000 birds. The highest densities of 25 birds/km$^2$ occurred in the folds and wooded valleys of south Lakeland.

For such a colourful and noisy bird it can be remarkably unobtrusive in the immediate environs of its nest. Coupled with the fact that many pairs breed in private gardens, this makes the Greenfinch something of a problem for the surveyor. That said it is hard not to come to the conclusion that this species' willingness to use gardens for both breeding and winter-feeding will offset some of the problems within the wider environment.

Derek McAlone

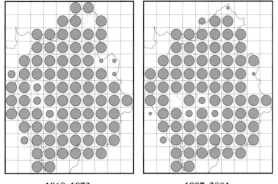

**1968–1972**   **1997–2001**
(For explanation of maps, see page 45)

***Conservation status***

| | |
|---|---|
| European: | SPEC Cat 4 |
| UK: | **GREEN** |

***Populations***

| | |
|---|---|
| European status: | 13,000,000 |
| Britain – pairs: | 530,000 |
| Cumbria – pairs: | 34,000 |

***30-year distribution change***

| | Old Atlas | This Atlas | % |
|---|---|---|---|
| No. of 10km squares: | 86 | 83 | **−3.5** |

| **Survey data** | **Tetrads** | **%** |
|---|---|---|
| Confirmed breeding: | 453 | 24.6 |
| Probable breeding: | 457 | 24.8 |
| Possible breeding: | 103 | 5.6 |
| Total: | 1,013 | 55.0 |

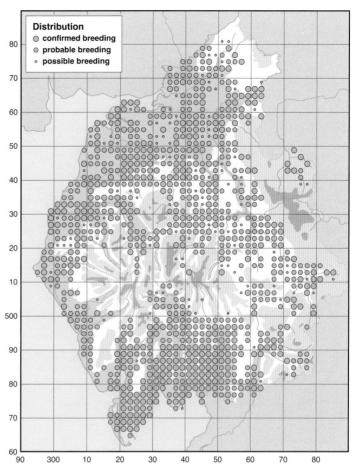

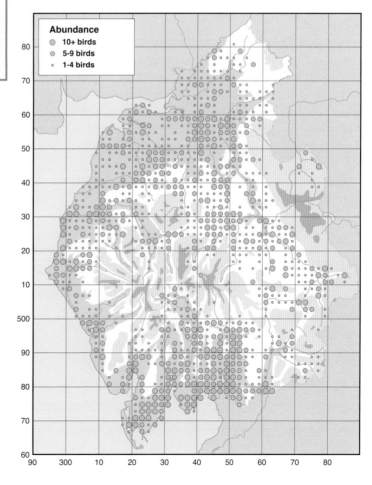

ONE of the most appealing sights and sounds of the British countryside must be the sudden appearance of an aptly named 'charm' of Goldfinches. Black and golden wings, black hood and red facemask contrast with a more sober body plumage, and are a true delight to brighten up even the dullest of spring mornings.

Although widespread in Europe, except for Scandinavia where it has a mere toehold in southern Sweden, the Goldfinch is much more abundant in the southern part of its range, particularly the northern shores of the Mediterranean Sea and the Iberian Peninsula. In Britain and Ireland it is widely distributed, although absent from the Outer Hebrides, Orkney and Shetland.

The preferred food is seeds and especially those belonging to various species of thistle, groundsel, and other members of the compositae family (Newton 1972). This makes the Goldfinch a bird of open, unimproved land, abandoned industrial sites, roadsides and railway embankments. The tiny nest is placed at the outer edge of trees and shrubs, where it survives in the bare branches of winter to taunt the would-be nest finder.

The striking plumage and pleasant twitter of this bird were the causes of its downfall in the latter part of the 19th century when it was widely trapped for the cage-bird trade. The heaviest depredations took place near the larger populations of the southeast, which unfortunately was the departure point for birds migrating to the continent in autumn. In its formative years the RSPB campaigned successfully against the trade and this, combined with a fall in demand, led to a steady recovery. This recovery was spurred on by the post-First World War agricultural depression which left field boundaries and hedgerows full of weeds. In the 1950s a decline took place that was linked to the increased application of herbicides and more efficient weed control. This theory was borne out by the fact that the greatest declines happened to coincide with areas of more intensively farmed land in the southeast (Newton 1972).

In the middle of the 19th century Goldfinches were said to be common in Cumberland and Westmorland. They were especially so in west Cumberland, until the fashion of keeping songbirds made bird-catching a lucrative pastime, and as a result local populations declined in this more populated area. Macpherson (1892) described the Goldfinch as scarce everywhere except in the Eden valley. Although populations were thought to have increased through the 20th century, according to Stokoe (1962) they remained sparse and confined to low ground.

Goldfinches were found in 63% of tetrads and were proved to be breeding in 23%. The distribution is mainly around the lowland fringe of the county, with large areas of Lakeland and the North Pennines still virtually unoccupied. The birds are abundant along our river systems and valley bottoms – this is particularly noticeable in the south of the county where the general distribution is sparser than in the north. This is, of course, less to do with water than with the topography of the ground near rivers and streams, which provides corridors of unimproved land on the banks, even in arable areas. The distribution map depicts an evenly spread cluster of tetrads around the hub of Lakeland in comparison to the abundance map which reveals fewer but a more dense concentration of birds on the Coastal Plain and the hinterland of the Solway Basin. This shows admirably the need for quantitative data in identifying important areas for birds and to validate distribution patterns.

Analysis of line transect data from *this Atlas* gives a population band of 65,000–118,000, suggesting a mean population of 87,000 birds.

Cumbria has abundant suitable habitat for the Goldfinch, from the unimproved coastal fringe to overgrown railway embankments, abandoned industrial sites, rough pasture with thistles and weedy roadside verges. This and the now well-established habit of feeding at bird-tables and seed-feeders can only bode well for the future.

Derek McAlone

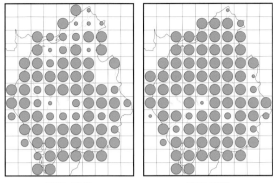

**1968–1972**　　**1997–2001**

(For explanation of maps, see page 45)

*Conservation status*

| | |
|---|---|
| European: | Non-SPEC |
| UK: | **GREEN** |

*Populations*

| | |
|---|---|
| European status: | 8,000,000 |
| Britain – pairs: | 220,000 |
| Cumbria – pairs: | 43,500 |

*30-year distribution change*

| | Old Atlas | This Atlas | % |
|---|---|---|---|
| No. of 10km squares: | 82 | 86 | +4.9 |

| **Survey data** | **Tetrads** | **%** |
|---|---|---|
| Confirmed breeding: | 420 | 22.8 |
| Probable breeding: | 586 | 31.8 |
| Possible breeding: | 148 | 8.0 |
| Total: | 1,154 | 62.6 |

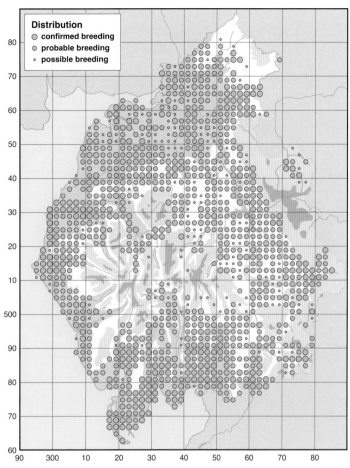

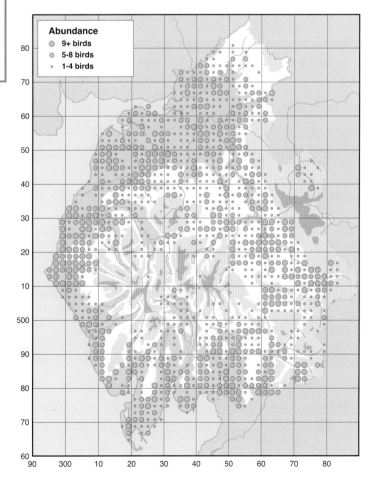

THE stark nakedness of riverside alders in early April can be illuminated with flashes of brilliant yellow and citrus green mixed with black as this, one of our smallest finches, busily feeds on the fruits. The Siskins' conversational twitter and piping call is now a reasonably familiar sound in Cumbria. This would not have been the case 200 years ago when this species was restricted to the northern pine forests.

In the west the breeding range extends from just below the Arctic Circle in Scandinavia and Russia southwards to central Europe and then more sparingly in mountainous regions from the Pyrenees across Asia Minor. In Britain and Ireland, their strongholds have long been in the old pine forests of northeast Scotland, from where they have spread following the upsurge in commercial forestry.

Siskins feed primarily on seeds from spruce and pine cones until these become exhausted from late summer onwards, when they move out of the conifer forests and feed on the seeds of birch and, especially, alder. Like any species that depends on the vagaries of cone production, this species is irruptive. Most birds in northern Britain move south in winter where they are joined by birds from Fennoscandia and the continent. In spring they move back to breed in the northern forests, where the tiny, compact moss nests are placed in the uppermost branches of conifers (Newton 1972).

Nationally, during the 20th century, there has been a steady expansion south in the breeding range of this species. This expansion increased in pace in the 1950s and 1960s when maturing conifer plantations, planted after the First World War, began to bear cones. More

recently, the Forestry Commission's national strategy of planting 12,000 hectares, mainly with coniferous trees, each year between 1977 and 1982 must also have helped (Marchant 1990). In addition, the fashion for planting ornamental conifers in parks and gardens brought the birds into urban and suburban areas and may have been instrumental in introducing the Siskin to our bird-tables and peanut-feeders.

In the middle of the 19th century Siskins were noted as occasional winter visitors to the Kendal area. In the autumn of 1866 huge numbers were seen on the Solway coast near Allonby, and while most of these birds moved on westward, small numbers wintered in the area. About three pairs were said to have bred for several years up to 1885 in plantations near Netherby (Macpherson 1892). In the mid-1940s a few nests were found near Ullswater and near Keswick. Breeding was suspected, but not proven in Lakeland in 1957 and 1961 (Stokoe 1962).

*This Atlas* shows a spectacular 725% increase in distribution since the *Old Atlas*. This is presumably in response to the doubling of the area of conifer plantation in Britain during the period. It is not too difficult to see that there have been some major gains, notably in the Border Uplands and Lakeland, with less significant increases in the Coastal Plain, Solway Basin, Eden Valley and Cumbria Dales. The species' strongholds are at either end of the county in the huge conifer forests of Grizedale in the south and the Border forests in the far northeast.

Analysis of line transect data from *this Atlas* gives a population band of 3,000–19,000, suggesting a mean population of 10,000 birds. The relatively small sample size and wide band limits imply that degree of discretion must be exercised with this estimate. The highest densities of 6 birds/km$^2$ occurred in the vast forests of the Border Uplands.

Although the immediate future looks secure for Siskin, both in Cumbria and nationally, where a long-term increase has been identified in CBC data (Mead 2000), we must remember that cone productivity can be variable so there will be lean, as well as fat, years for this bird. The long-term future is harder to predict and the level of abundance of Siskins may largely depend on government policy towards new and further generations of plantations. In Cumbria we can comfort ourselves with the knowledge that cone production in our forests will continue for many years and the bird's adaptation to garden feeding stations will help it overcome food shortages when cone crops fail.

Derek McAlone

Sponsored by Jill Damment

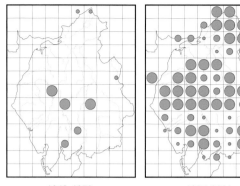

**1968-1972**          **1997-2001**

(For explanation of maps, see page 45)

*Conservation status*

| | |
|---|---|
| European: | SPEC Cat 4 |
| UK: | **GREEN** |

*Populations*

| | |
|---|---|
| European status: | 2,750,000 |
| Britain – pairs: | 300,000 |
| Cumbria – pairs: | 5,000 |

*30-year distribution change*

| | Old Atlas | This Atlas | % |
|---|---|---|---|
| No. of 10km squares: | 8 | 66 | +725 |

| **Survey data** | **Tetrads** | **%** |
|---|---|---|
| Confirmed breeding: | 97 | 5.3 |
| Probable breeding: | 145 | 7.9 |
| Possible breeding: | 95 | 5.2 |
| Total: | 337 | 18.4 |

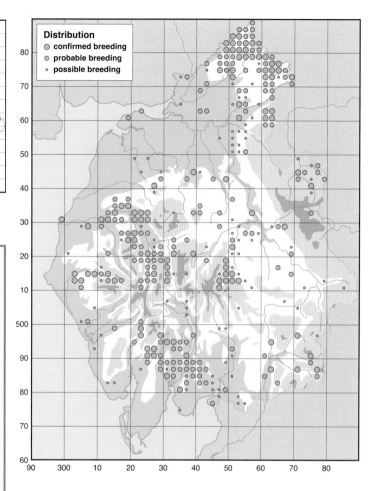

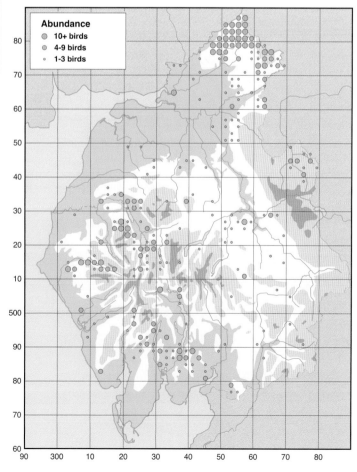

THE cock Linnet is a splendid sight, with his wine-splashed breast and forehead, perched on the top of gorse bushes on a remote fellside or brightening up areas of derelict wasteland with its cheery song. The Linnet has long been a favourite amongst cage-bird enthusiasts and, like other finches, was much prized by the 19th century bird-trappers who cross-bred it with canaries to produce the 'mule-songster'. The female of this small finch is much dowdier with her streaked-brown plumage. The bird is often associated with the edge of agriculture where twittering flocks, sweeping from field to hedge, are much more conspicuous than nesting birds.

Linnets can be found breeding from Ireland and Portugal in the west, east to Iraq and Siberia, and from southern Scandinavia to North Africa. In Britain it is widespread south of the rivers Forth and Clyde, though with an eastern bias. Further north in Scotland it is found mainly in the vicinity of the cultivated east coast from Fife to the Moray Firth. Its distribution in the rest of England, Ireland and Wales is patchy, with denser concentrations around the coasts and in the south Midlands.

Linnets begin to nest early in spring and these early nests are usually hidden in evergreen shrubs such as gorse. Later, the birds can take advantage of burgeoning vegetation to build in a wider variety of deciduous shrubs and small trees. Two or three broods can be produced in a season that can last until August (Newton 1972).

Like so many seed-eaters it benefited from the agricultural recession that followed the First World War and allowed a resurgence of such Linnet staples as fat-hen and various varieties of chickweed. More recently, since the 1970s the Linnet population has experienced a widespread and catastrophic decline, analysis of CBC data revealing a 54% decline on farmland nationally. Although loss of nest sites through hedgerow clearance and afforestation have played a part in this decline, studies have shown that increased efficiency of weed control, leading to the starvation of chicks in the nest, is a major factor. In some areas oilseed rape has provided temporary replacements for both food and nest sites but, beyond staple crops, agriculture is fickle, so it is not known whether this will be a long-term solution.

Both Macpherson (1892) and Stokoe (1962) describe the Linnet as widespread and numerous on lower ground, becoming scarce and localized in hillier districts. In the early 1960s, Barnes and Ratcliffe noted local declines in populations at Arnside and the Carlisle districts respectively (Stokoe 1962). The decline of this species, in distribution at least, is less dramatic than that shown nationally between the *Old* and *New Atlases* where there were significant losses in Scotland and Ireland.

The distribution map from *this Atlas* shows the coastal strip from the Solway Basin down the west coast to the Furness peninsula, to provide a haven for this species, perhaps reflecting the amount of unimproved land. The abundance map highlights this concentrated bias along the Coastal Plain, particularly from Workington south to Furness and, to a lesser extent, around Moricambe Bay. Elsewhere, Linnets are present and breeding in the foothills of Lakeland, the Cumbria Dales, the upper Eden Valley and the northern parts of the North Pennines. It also seems that the different stages of maturity of plantations in the Border Uplands provide habitat that varies from year to year.

Analysis of line transect data from *this Atlas* gives a population band of 55,000–123,000, suggesting a mean population of 93,000 birds. The highest densities of 152 birds/km² occurred along the coastal zone.

In the light of the national concern for this species, it is tempting to say that the picture looks relatively healthy for Linnets in Cumbria, with confirmed breeding from 20% of tetrads. However, we must not become too complacent, especially where local declines have been significant in the recent past. In west Cumbria for example, sterile pastures surrounded by field boundaries shorn of hedges provide little habitat for Linnets, which are slowly exiled to the 'un-improvable' coastal strip. Even here, as also on the rougher moorland edges and the fringes of remaining heathlands, farmers wage endless war on encroaching gorse. With burning, herbicide applications, and then

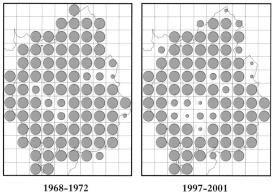

**1968-1972**          **1997-2001**

(For explanation of maps, see page 45)

***Conservation status***

| | |
|---|---|
| European: | SPEC Cat 4 |
| UK: | **RED: BD** |

***Populations***

| | |
|---|---|
| European status: | 8,000,000 |
| Britain – pairs: | 520,000 |
| Cumbria – pairs: | 46,500 |

***30-year distribution change***

| | Old Atlas | This Atlas | % |
|---|---|---|---|
| No. of 10km squares: | 88 | 88 | n/c |

| **Survey data** | **Tetrads** | **%** |
|---|---|---|
| Confirmed breeding: | 361 | 19.6 |
| Probable breeding: | 417 | 22.6 |
| Possible breeding: | 179 | 9.7 |
| Total: | 957 | 51.9 |

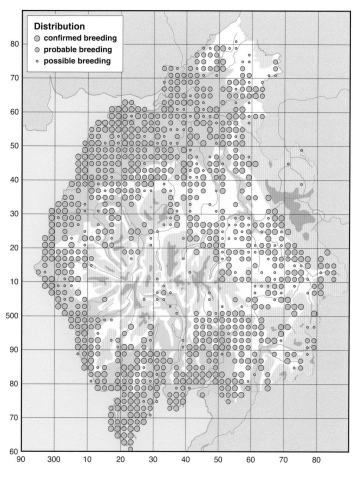

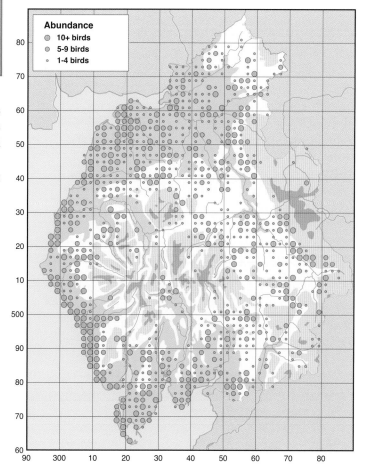

manuring, even long-persistent gorse scrub gives way, and the lurid green grassland which replaces it is inevitably much less diverse for variety and numbers of birds and other wildlife.

Derek McAlone

# Twite *Carduelis flavirostris*

OFTEN overlooked due to its small size and subtle hues, the Twite, once known, is one of the most endearing of upland birds, often approaching humans with apparent curiosity. Although once more widely known – quite aptly – as the 'Mountain Linnet,' to many birdwatchers the Twite is more familiar as a bird of coastal saltmarshes in the winter than on its upland breeding grounds, where it is usually quite localized over large areas.

The Twite has an unusually disjunct world population. As a breeding bird in Europe it is virtually confined to Britain and Ireland and western Norway. These populations are completely isolated from the main range of the species in southwest and central Asia. Even within Britain and Ireland, the main breeding strongholds of the South Pennines, Ireland and Scotland, appear to be separate.

Breeding in open terrain, with most birds found on moorland, Twite are a gregarious species nesting in loose colonies in areas of good habitat. They will nest in a wide variety of vegetation, and occasionally even in rock crevices, but prefer heather, bracken and grass tussocks. The laying period is in May and June, and second broods are sometimes produced. Nests are usually towards the edge of moorland – studies in the South Pennines indicate that the location of nests may be dictated by the close proximity of species-rich hay meadows, which provide the majority of food for nestling and post-fledging Twite (Reed 1995). Rocky exposures, farmsteads and areas of burned grass moor are particularly important pre-nesting feeding habitats, with post-breeding flocks dispersing to weedy unimproved pastures, disturbed ground and roadside verges.

At the end of the 19th century, Twite were widely distributed through Scotland, northern England, the Isle of Man and much of Ireland. However, during the 20th century the species appears to have undergone a steady decline across Britain. By the 1940s, its Scottish range was contracting to the north and west and birds had largely disappeared from the Borders. A similar decline also occurred in England; birds were lost from the Isle of Man, and the Yorkshire and Lancashire Mosses, and breeding became largely restricted to the Peak District and Pennines. The *Old Atlas* reaffirmed the disappearance of Twite from many regions in southern Scotland, though it had increased in numbers in small areas of the South Pennines.

The *New Atlas*, whilst finding that the highest densities occurred in north and west Scotland and on the South Pennine moors, records a 53% decline in distribution in Ireland since the *Old Atlas*.

In Cumbria, at the end of the 19th century, Macpherson (1892) determined that the Twite bred thinly along the Pennine range, on some of the mountains in the centre of Lakeland and also on some of the lowland mosses, including Toddles Moss and Solway Moss. However, there was already some indication of decline, and by the mid-20th century, Stokoe (1962) commented that it was "now a scarce breeding bird" and "quite rare in north Westmorland". Despite this, birds continued to breed locally in the Solway Basin until 1971, at which time the *Old Atlas* confirmed the North Pennines and Cumbria Dales as the last strongholds in Cumbria with an almost complete disappearance of the Lakeland population. The *New Atlas* supports the picture painted by the *Old Atlas* but shows some redistribution with the reappearance of birds in the Solway Basin.

Survey work for *this Atlas* broadly confirms the somewhat sparse and fragmented distribution, with birds found in just 14 tetrads. Although there is, once again, a lack of records in the Solway Basin, there is an isolated dot on the northeast periphery of Lakeland and small populations still exist in the North Pennines and Cumbria Dales.

Analysis of line transect data offers no conclusive evidence on the Cumbrian breeding population – perhaps not surprising given that the Twite is a sparsely distributed bird with a particular habitat niche. The *New Atlas* uses a conservative 100 pairs per occupied 10km square as the basis for an estimate of the national population, equating to a density of 2.0 birds/km². Extrapolating this figure over the number of occupied tetrads derives a current county population estimate of 50 breeding pairs.

If national population trends, which qualify the

 Sponsored in memory of Robert Hartley, who loved his birds

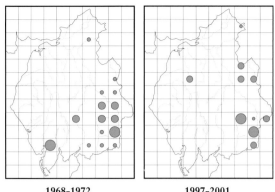

**1968-1972**     **1997-2001**
(For explanation of maps, see page 45)

*Conservation status*
European:                    Non-SPEC
UK:                          **RED: HD**

*Populations*
European status:             300,000
Britain – pairs:             65,000
Cumbria – pairs:             50

*30-year distribution change*
|  | Old Atlas | This Atlas | % |
|---|---|---|---|
| No. of 10km squares: | 15 | 10 | **–33.3** |

| **Survey data** | **Tetrads** | **%** |
|---|---|---|
| Confirmed breeding: | 2 | 0.1 |
| Probable breeding: | 7 | 0.4 |
| Possible breeding: | 5 | 0.3 |
| Total: | 14 | 0.8 |

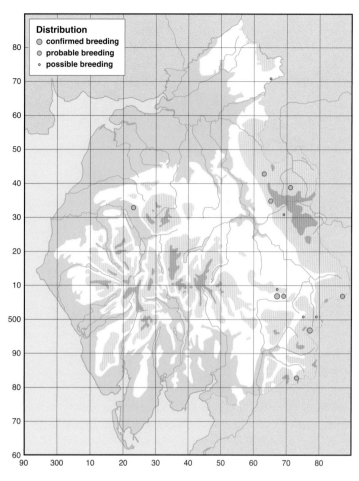

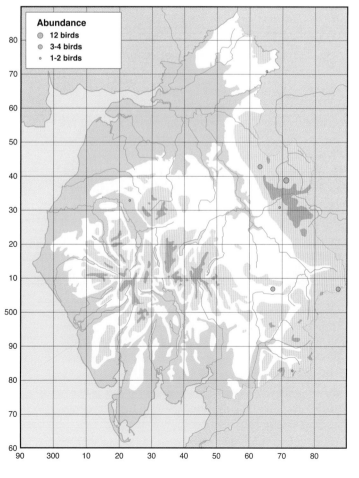

species for inclusion on the BoCC Red List, are reflected in Cumbria, as seems likely, then it would be expected that the population has continued to decline. Although the numbers of Twite found wintering on the Cumbrian coast, particularly through the 1990s, remained buoyant, wintering numbers are not a reliable indicator of breeding numbers, as their origins cannot be guaranteed. Some recent declines at coastal wintering sites, especially Walney Island, where numbers have fallen 88% since 1996, may confirm a decline.

As with so many other species, the decline of the Twite is likely to be related to land use, the main factors being the loss of species-rich hay meadows to heavily fertilized silage, and a continuing 'improvement' of upland pastures.

Sean Reed

# Lesser Redpoll *Carduelis cabaret*

A BLUSH of subtle pink on the breast accentuates a tiny black chin that is overshadowed by a flush of scarlet forehead, but it is, perhaps, the rhythmic twittering and flash of white wing bars, during its undulating flight, which give the best clues to the presence of the Lesser Redpoll. This is an extremely attractive small finch, especially when encountered in the watery sunshine of a spring morning as it performs acrobatic antics on freshly emergent catkins in a bid to extract the tiny seeds.

Breeding patchily in Continental Europe to the Alps and Carpathian Mountains, the Lesser Redpoll has also recently colonized southwest Scandinavia, where it has been recorded breeding alongside the Common Redpoll without interbreeding. In Britain and Ireland it is found over most of the mainland, although much scarcer or even absent in the south Midlands, the Welsh Marches, Somerset, Gloucestershire and Oxfordshire. A map of Britain showing the most abundant populations would coincide well with the large-scale conifer plantations that have emerged through the 20th century.

The Lesser Redpoll is particularly attracted to 'pioneer' trees, so new growth in clear-felled plantations, very often of birch, or alder in wetter areas, will quickly be colonized. It builds a rather large and untidy nest for a delicate and demure bird, usually about two metres above the ground in a small tree or shrub. Egg-laying starts early in late April, and as many as three clutches may be completed by the end of the breeding season (Newton 1972).

The volatile fortunes of this bird have been as complex as its past taxonomic status. The population is irruptive and prone to sudden withdrawals from established breeding areas. Nationally, the CBC index showed a five-fold expansion in both range and numbers in the late 1960s and early 1970s but this favourable situation has dramatically changed: the latest available CBC data reveals an alarming 93% decline since 1970. This collapse does not seem to have been as severe in Cumbria and only the Furness peninsula shows significant change between the *Old* and *New Atlases*. There seems to be little consensus of opinion in the literature as to the explanation of this boom and bust phenomenon, and the era of systematic survey is surely too young to cast new light upon this situation.

At the end of the 19th century, Macpherson (1892) regarded them as sporadic breeders over much of the county, particularly in the south and in central Lakeland, and scarce in the east and on the west coast. Seventy years later Lesser Redpolls were reputedly widespread and common breeders in Cumbria, particularly favouring large forests such as Ennerdale and Blengdale (Stokoe 1962).

From *this Atlas* we see that Lesser Redpolls, whilst appearing to be thinly scattered across the whole county, are much scarcer in the southern part of the Coastal Plain, large areas of the Solway Basin, the Eden Valley and the North Pennines, and are all but absent from the Furness peninsula. The general impression is that of a slight decline over the county as a whole, since the *Old Atlas,* with more noticeable falls in areas such as the Eden Valley, the central Solway Basin and, to a lesser extent, the Border Uplands. It is possible that these declines can be explained with the maturation of conifers developing into a less favourable and sub-optimal habitat for Lesser Redpolls, while the decline in the Solway Basin may be attributable to loss of recruitment from the reduced population in the Border Uplands. An increase since the *New Atlas* was found in west Cumbria in an area that stretches from Whitehaven, northeast to Workington and adjacent inland areas.

Analysis of line transect data from *this Atlas* gives a population band of 3,000–13,000, suggesting a mean population of 7,000 birds. Given the wide band limits, this estimate should be treated with caution.

This is not the easiest of finches to survey, nor is it easy to make a valid prognosis for its future. However, there are some recognized threats to habitat, including drainage of damp woodlands, shading out of trees such as birch and alder by faster growing competitors, and the lack of age variety in the composition of conifer plantations.

Derek McAlone

Sponsored by Miss M. E. Burkett

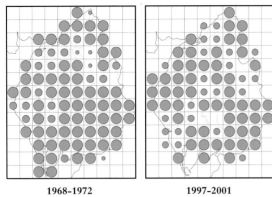

| 1968-1972 | 1997-2001 |
|---|---|

(For explanation of maps, see page 45)

**Conservation status**

| European: | Non–SPEC |
|---|---|
| UK: | AMBER: BDM |

**Populations**

| European status: | 300,000 |
|---|---|
| Britain – pairs: | 160,000 |
| Cumbria – pairs: | 3,500 |

**30-year distribution change**

| | Old Atlas | This Atlas | % |
|---|---|---|---|
| No. of 10km squares: | 85 | 78 | −8.2 |

| **Survey data** | **Tetrads** | **%** |
|---|---|---|
| Confirmed breeding: | 137 | 7.4 |
| Probable breeding: | 301 | 16.3 |
| Possible breeding: | 112 | 6.1 |
| Total: | 550 | 29.8 |

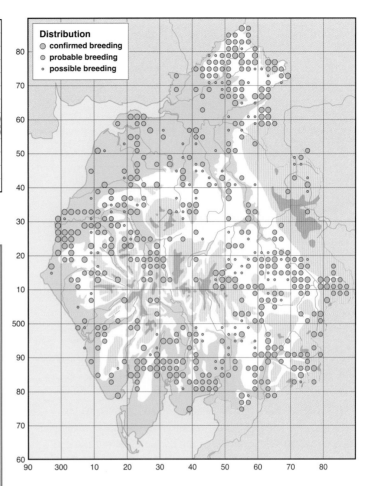

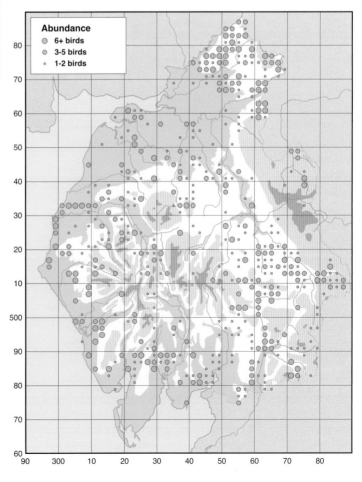

THIS intriguing and much sought after bird is perhaps the best known of irruptive migrants. The confused taxonomic history of the Crossbill does not detract from its splendour, and it is an excellent excuse for a stroll through a mature conifer plantation in the depths of winter. Encounters with this bird anywhere are a delight and will brighten up the dreariest February day. Its tough crossed bill, unique amongst British birds, is adapted to pick the seeds out of conifer cones, its main food.

The strongholds of the Crossbill are, perhaps not surprisingly, the vast coniferous forests that extend to the northern tundras of Scandinavia and northwestern Russia, from where the major irruptions originate. Southwards in Europe, its patchy range follows the conifer forests into the mountains. In Britain and Ireland it can be found wherever there are conifers, particularly Sitka and Norway spruces and therefore Scotland, Wales and northern England have the most abundant populations. Ireland too has now been colonized following its forestry policy of increasing the acreage of conifer plantations (Mead 2000).

The problem of delimiting European Crossbill species is a graphic illustration of niche evolution, wherein the gradation in size of bill meets the specific needs of each member species of the group. The Crossbill's speciality is spruce, and the periodic failure of cone production by this tree sparks the regular invasions that augment our resident birds. Crossbills in Britain also exploit Scots pine, a tree that is more consistent in cone production than the spruce (Marchant 1990). Breeding can take place at any time between August and April but in Britain is usually concentrated in the months of February, March and April, when the bulky nest is built high in the top of a conifer. Winter nests, for obvious reasons, are much bulkier and more thickly lined than those of spring and summer (Newton 1972).

The 19th century was a low point for natural woodlands in Britain due to the extensive logging carried out to meet the increasing requirements of the burgeoning navy and merchant fleets which served the growing Empire (Holloway 1996). This led to the planting of conifer forests, beginning a policy that is still going on today. Conifer plantations have been important in the range expansion of many species and this is certainly true in the case of the Crossbill, as invading populations now have extensive suitable habitat in which to stay and breed.

In the middle of the 19th century there were sporadic breeding records in Cumbria, particularly in the east and northeast of the county. Nests were found at Alston in April 1839; at Cumwhinton in March 1856 and on Penrith Beacon in 1865. The phenomenon of invasion then rapid decline in breeding birds was also noted later in that century when, after the invasion of 1888, birds became scarcer over the next two years until none was found in 1891 (Macpherson 1892). Another invasion in 1956 resulted in breeding over the subsequent years (Stokoe 1962).

Although there are many hectares of conifers in all parts of Cumbria, surveys for *this Atlas* found confirmed breeding in only 12 10km squares. This is, of course, a result of the volatile nature of this species, and a 'snapshot' of even five years duration may miss a major invasion and its subsequent colonization. By far the greatest concentration of breeding records came from the Border Uplands, where 25 tetrads had confirmed nesting. Elsewhere, there were scattered records from Grizedale Forest and the valley of the River Kent in the south and Whinlatter Forest and the shores of Crummock Water in the west. A scattering of probable and possible breeding records can be seen in the lower Eden Valley and the northeastern part of the Solway Basin. These are probably associated with populations in the Border Uplands. Changes since the *Old Atlas* are of questionable significance in this particular species, but it is worth noting a 600% increase in distribution over the 30-year period.

Several factors make the interpretation of survey results for the Crossbill difficult. These include the bird's well known irruptive survival strategy, its unusual breeding season which lies outside the main survey period, and the fact that the birds are quite unobtrusive and live in extensive areas of remote countryside isolated by difficult terrain.

Perhaps the statistical data are misleading for a species which breeds outside the main survey period: hence a cautious decision to use an average abundance

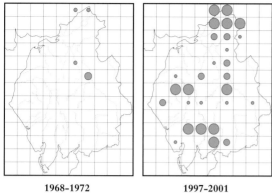

**1968–1972**          **1997–2001**

(For explanation of maps, see page 45)

***Conservation status***

| European: | Non-SPEC |
|---|---|
| UK: | **GREEN** |

***Populations***

| European status: | 1,200,000 |
|---|---|
| Britain – pairs: | 10,000 |
| Cumbria – pairs: | 100–150 |

***30-year distribution change***

|  | Old Atlas | This Atlas | % |
|---|---|---|---|
| No. of 10km squares: | 4 | 28 | **+600** |

| **Survey data** | **Tetrads** | **%** |
|---|---|---|
| Confirmed breeding: | 33 | 1.8 |
| Probable breeding: | 21 | 1.1 |
| Possible breeding: | 38 | 2.1 |
| Total: | 92 | 5.0 |

figure of 4 birds/km² where it does occur, suggesting a current county population of 100–150 breeding pairs.

Cumbria holds extensive areas of rotational forestry, which should mean that lack of suitable breeding habitat is not a limiting factor in the foreseeable future, and that these forests can sustain many more Crossbills following their periodic immigrations.

Derek McAlone

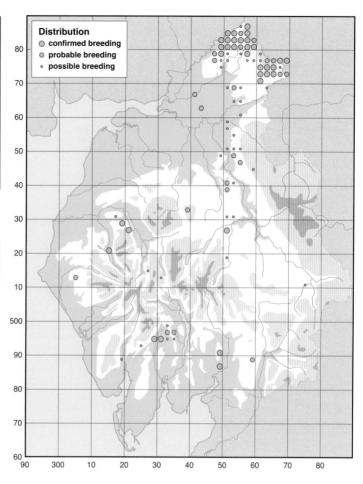

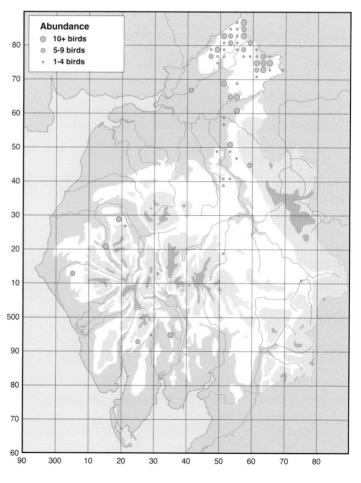

# Common Rosefinch *Carpodacus erythrinus*

THE Common Rosefinch can be elusive and surprisingly difficult to observe, even when uttering its melodic piping song. The striking scarlet plumage on head, breast and rump does not always catch the eye, and is in any case only developed in older males; young males, like females, are dowdy and sparrow-like.

The breeding range extends across much of northern and central Europe east to Kamchatka, Himalaya, and China. In the last 50 years the Common Rosefinch has shown a rate of westward spread and increase in Europe exceeded only by that of the Collared Dove. For example, in Finland the population has increased thirty-fold since the mid-1940s, to about 300,000 pairs, while Sweden, colonized from the 1930s, now has 50,000 pairs. With increasing numbers in all central European countries, spread has also proceeded in a southwesterly direction, reaching France.

Reasons for this striking increase are unclear. Changes in land-use are implicated, with 'broken' forest creating a varied shrub-layer, and abandoned meadows becoming overgrown. Common Rosefinches seem to have changed their habitat preferences towards these human-altered landscapes, and now favour a variety of bushy areas close to watercourses and lakes, including tall hedges, parks and gardens, often bordering fields and rough ground, which provide food. The shift towards warmer springs and autumns may have increased productivity or survival, generating a surplus of birds to act as colonists.

The migration is amongst the longest undertaken by any passerine, and birds do not arrive in their western breeding areas until late May or early June from wintering-grounds in India. Unfortunately for British birdwatchers, the North Sea appears to act as a considerable disincentive to further westward adventure. In spite of small local 'invasions' in springs with favourable winds, breeding attempts remain rare; nesting in Britain may depend upon the chance arrival of a migrating flock, males of which promptly set up territories on arrival. The *Old Atlas* mentions the species in a list of possible colonizers and, whilst there have been several confirmed breeding records since the first in the Scottish Highlands in 1982, the species has failed to establish itself as a regular nester. Prior to 1998, there had been only five Cumbrian sightings; two were of singing, 'red' males in potential breeding habitat, at Lanercost in May and June 1984, and Waterside, Wigton in June and July 1996.

The first, and to date only, breeding record of the Common Rosefinch in the county, indeed in northwest England, occurred during *this Atlas*. On 4th June 1998, a male was located by its distinctive song emanating from a patch of oaks and sycamores by a main road close to Milton, in the northeast of the county. The bird was immature, with no trace of red in the plumage. By 6th June, it was clear that two similarly-plumaged birds were present, and one was seen to carry nest material into the rank grass and newly-planted saplings below the trees. For several days the male sang in the same general area, sometimes flying off with the female to nearby stream banks and an area of semi-derelict industrial workings, where the pair was seen feeding on the buds of flowering shrubs. After long absences, both birds would return to the nesting area, dropping at once out of sight. The male would then often sing briefly, from low hidden perches or from the trees above.

As June progressed, song was heard less often, suggestive of the birds having a nest – unmated males tend to sing more consistently. Eventually, on 7th July, newly-fledged young were seen. The last sightings were on 11th July, when three fledglings were calling separately, two having moved some distance to bushes in nearby gardens. Calculating back from fledging on 6th or 7th July, hatching would have occurred on 24th or 25th June, and incubation started with a full clutch on 11th to 13th June. The first egg might have been laid on 6th to 8th June.

The birds were surprisingly elusive throughout. The parents were observed visiting the area of the nest only very occasionally. Like some other finches, but unlike the majority of passerines, the nestlings are fed by regurgitation from the adult's gullet, and thus large amounts may be supplied in one feed. Adults may therefore be absent for long periods collecting food in quantity, and after a feed fledglings are sufficiently gorged for several more hours.

Given the capricious nature of the Common Rosefinch's appearances in Britain – let alone in

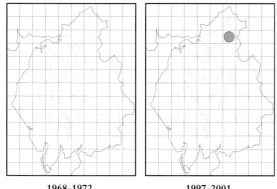

**1968-1972**          **1997-2001**
(For explanation of maps, see page 45)

*Conservation status*
European:                    Non-SPEC
UK:                          AMBER: BR

*Populations*
European status:             560,000
Britain – pairs:             <10
Cumbria – pairs:             0–1

*30-year distribution change*
              Old Atlas  This Atlas   %
No. of 10km squares:   0        1      n/a

| **Survey data** | **Tetrads** | **%** |
|---|---|---|
| Confirmed breeding: | 1 | 0.05 |
| Probable breeding: | 0 | |
| Possible breeding: | 0 | |
| Total: | 1 | 0.05 |

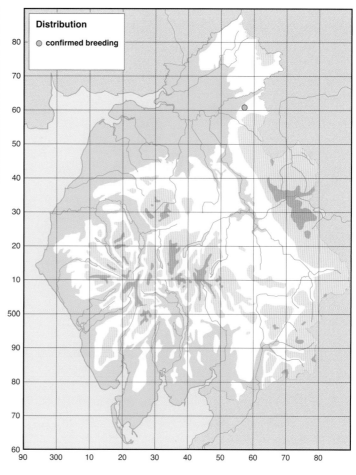

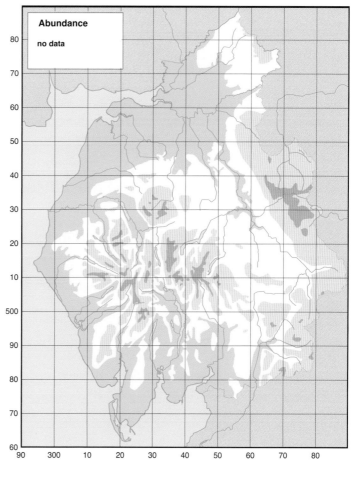

Cumbria – at the very furthest end of its migration, there was little surprise that the birds were not recorded in the following seasons, and there were no further records of the species in the county during *this Atlas* period. Nevertheless, this was an event of national significance and one of the highlights of *this Atlas*. Its importance can be gauged from the fact that there have been just eight other confirmed records of breeding in Britain, five of them in 1992 and the most recent in 1997 (Ogilvie *et al* 2001).

The future of this species as a British breeding bird remains a matter of speculation: if westward expansion continues and nesting becomes a more regular occurrence, then Cumbria may again play host to breeding Common Rosefinches.

Jeremy Roberts

**A** BIRD whose gaudy plumage seems to intensify in colour still more during the starkness of winter was once a much sought-after cage-bird in the 19th century. The Bullfinch can be a controversial species; its powerful build, muscular neck and strong beak are well designed for a species which feeds on a variety of hard seeds, but it is its habit of nibbling newly emergent buds in spring that has struck discord amongst commercial fruit growers.

The Bullfinch has a wide distribution, which extends across Europe, east to China and Japan, and from the Arctic Circle south to the northern shores of the Mediterranean and further south in Italy and the Balkans. In Britain and Ireland it is most abundant in England south of a line drawn between the Wash and the Cheshire Dee, and throughout Ireland. Although widespread Bullfinches are scarce or absent only in parts of the Highlands of Scotland, the Hebrides and the Northern Isles. A peculiarity of the range is that despite being present in Dumfries and Galloway, Cumbria and Northern Ireland, the species is absent from the Isle of Man. British and Irish birds are distinct enough to be regarded as an endemic subspecies (Marchant 1990).

Bullfinches breed in thick hedgerows and woodland understorey, the rather shallow, untidy nest being placed about two or three metres above ground. In spring they feed on the buds of various trees including hawthorn and sallow and in summer they turn to weed seeds such as those of bramble and dock and the insects happened upon during foraging. In winter the seeds of ash and elm are important and of course the bird has a well-documented and troublesome liking for the buds of cultivated fruit trees (Newton 1972).

Like other finches the Bullfinch was a target for the 19th century cage-bird industry. The striking plumage of the male and his ability as a mimic (the birds were taught an increased repertoire with special bird-flutes) more than made up for the simple, monotonous song. An expansion into farmland, less mature hedgerows, and parks and gardens took place in the late 1950s and early 1960s. It has been suggested that this increase may have been more than coincidental with the pesticide-induced decline of that arch hedgerow hunter, the Sparrowhawk. Some weight is lent to this theory by the levelling off and decline of Bullfinch numbers during the 1970s, corresponding well with the recovery and increase in the Sparrowhawk population. However, it has to be said that the decline in Bullfinch numbers has also closely followed extensive agricultural intensification involving the removal of many miles of hedgerow.

At the end of the 18th century and in the first half of the 19th century Bullfinches extended their range in southern Scotland and in Ireland (Holloway 1996). It is not unreasonable to assume that Cumbria too benefited from this northern and western expansion. Macpherson (1892) found the Bullfinch "nesting commonly in all our larger woods and gardens and occasionally in our remoter dales." Stokoe (1962) found a similar situation 70 years later. Although the picture depicted in *this Atlas* is not unlike that previously described, it is unlikely that Cumbria has not been affected by this species' serious national decline.

Although breeding was confirmed in only 7.6% of tetrads and probable breeding recorded in only a further 10%, these records did at least come from all parts of the county. The population is at its densest in the south, particularly in the woodlands of south Lakeland and the valleys of the Rivers Kent and Leven. Elsewhere, the picture is of a widespread but sparse population with notable gaps such as the southwestern parts of the Solway Basin, parts of the Coastal Plain and Inglewood Forest. More understandable gaps occur in the mountainous areas of central Lakeland, the North Pennines and the Cumbria Dales. In the northern part of the Solway Basin, the Border Uplands and the lower Eden Valley Bullfinches have become somewhat more localized.

Should a bird with a striking appearance and habit of singing perched on exposed twigs be so difficult to survey? Yes, if its county range is disjunct and/or the bird is scarce or at a very low density. If either of these two scenarios applied in Cumbria it could explain why so few contacts were made during the line transects. Only by reference to the timed count abundance data can we estimate the current county population at 1,500–2,000 breeding pairs.

Sponsored by Brian White

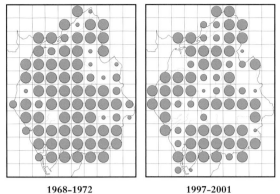

**1968–1972**      **1997–2001**

(For explanation of maps, see page 45)

*Conservation status*

| | |
|---|---|
| European: | Non-SPEC |
| UK: | **RED: BD** |

*Populations*

| | |
|---|---|
| European status: | 3,000,000 |
| Britain – pairs: | 190,000 |
| Cumbria – pairs: | 1,500–2,000 |

*30-year distribution change*

| | Old Atlas | This Atlas | % |
|---|---|---|---|
| No. of 10km squares: | 80 | 73 | **−8.7** |

| **Survey data** | **Tetrads** | **%** |
|---|---|---|
| Confirmed breeding: | 140 | 7.6 |
| Probable breeding: | 184 | 10.0 |
| Possible breeding: | 116 | 6.3 |
| Total: | 440 | 23.9 |

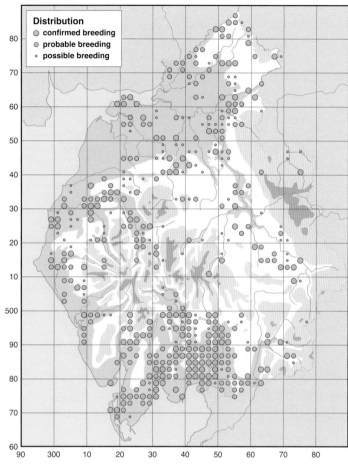

Cumbria, though not an arable county, still suffers from the loss of hedgerows and should this trend continue, Bullfinches will be one species among many birds that will suffer as a consequence. They may well retreat to their former habitat of thick woodland, venturing out only into the most mature of hedges. The national downward spiralling trend of this species is worrying as the latest available CBC data shows a 62% decline since 1970.

Derek McAlone

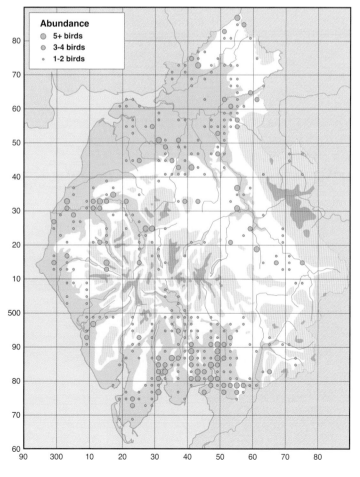

# Hawfinch *Coccothraustes coccothraustes*

Roy Hawley

THE second largest European finch, the Hawfinch's massive head and bill, bull-neck and short tail combine to give a stocky, top-heavy appearance. Hawfinches are, perhaps, the most enigmatic of all finches, and are best known for an ability to crack open the extremely hard stones of cherries, the whole head being enlarged and specialized accordingly.

Hawfinches extend throughout Continental Europe from southern Scandinavia, south to the North African coast and in a distinct band across Asia to Japan. In Britain the finch is widespread but not common southeast of a line from the Wash to Dorset. Elsewhere, there are pockets of denser population amongst the otherwise sparse distribution, with birds breeding as far north as the River Tay. The Hawfinches in Cumbria, along with those in Wales, represent the western edge of its range.

This species depends on broad-leaved woodlands, especially those containing wych elm, hornbeam, beech and sycamore. In more southerly parts of Britain its partiality to cultivated fruits such as cherry, damson and plum is well-known. This led to persecution in the past; for example 87 dead Hawfinches were seen hanging on a line in a Kent cherry orchard (Mountfort 1957). In Cumbria, the lack of large-scale commercial fruit growing combined with the small Hawfinch population ensures that this bird will never be considered a pest species. Hawfinches spend most of their time high in the canopy of deciduous woodland where they are difficult to see and are more often than not located by their subtle, yet far-carrying call.

Nesting begins in early May and, in natural woodland, the flimsy nest is placed rather precariously on horizontal or diagonal branches usually not less than seven metres above the ground.

There is some confusion about the history of the Hawfinch in Britain. Ornithologists in the 17th century regarded it as a winter visitor and, at the end of the 18th century Gilbert White made a similar assertion. The first 40 years of the 19th century saw a rash of breeding records in the southeast and thenceforward this species rapidly spread northwards, reaching Aberdeen by the early 20th century.

Macpherson (1892) quotes a report of a bird in January and February 1833 on the outskirts of Carlisle as possibly the first record of the species in Cumberland. He goes on to say that the Hawfinch was "still not a settled colonist" in the county and that most specimens occurred in winter. This could, of course, be a result of the birds being much more visible in winter compared to their extreme shyness during the breeding season. At the end of the 19th century one or two instances of breeding were noted in the south of the county, for example, at Dallam Tower. It may be a little surprising to modern birdwatchers in Cumbria to find that Stokoe (1962) described the Hawfinch as "increasing and locally common in wooded gardens, especially in the Eden valley". The same account carries a record from 1957 where 40 birds were present in a damson orchard east of Windermere.

In more recent times the Hawfinch has been very much restricted to the heavily wooded areas in the south of Lakeland. Annual records show this area to be the stronghold, though in very recent times records have dwindled to a handful in most years. In most breeding seasons, odd records are received from outside this core area as *this Atlas* reflects. The whole survey period produced only 28 records, 21 of which were in the wooded southern fringe of Lakeland and the Cumbria Dales. Breeding was confirmed in woodland northwest of Coniston Water; on the eastern shore of Windermere; and, to the east, near Sedbergh. Outside the southern stronghold, records where breeding was not confirmed came from the western shore of Derwent Water, Bassenthwaite, Rockcliffe and Brampton. Hawfinches are extremely secretive, especially in the breeding season, so it must be argued that there are many more birds in Cumbria than the few individuals found in *this Atlas*. However, 30 years of data from County Reports suggest that the population is indeed small and possibly declining.

Extrapolation of a meaningful population density is dubious. Therefore the current county population is estimated on known range and abundance, which suggests 30–40 breeding pairs.

Sponsored by Geoff Stansfield

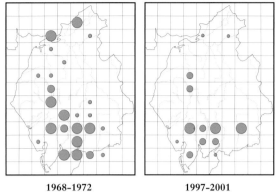

**1968–1972**          **1997–2001**

(For explanation of maps, see page 45)

***Conservation status***

| | |
|---|---|
| European: | Non-SPEC |
| UK: | AMBER: BDM |

***Populations***

| | |
|---|---|
| European status: | 1,300,000 |
| Britain – pairs: | 4,750 |
| Cumbria – pairs: | 30–40 |

***30-year distribution change***

| | Old Atlas | This Atlas | % |
|---|---|---|---|
| No. of 10km squares: | 24 | 13 | **−45.8** |

| **Survey data** | **Tetrads** | **%** |
|---|---|---|
| Confirmed breeding: | 3 | 0.2 |
| Probable breeding: | 14 | 0.8 |
| Possible breeding: | 11 | 0.6 |
| Total: | 28 | 1.6 |

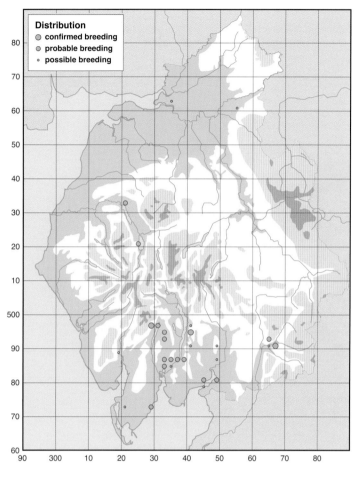

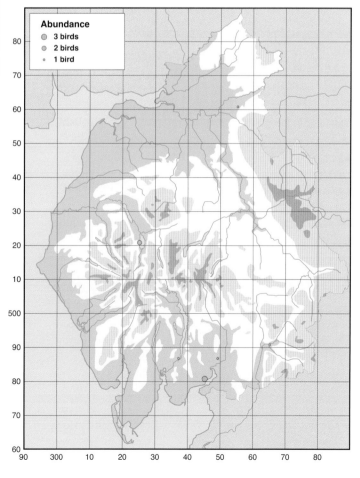

Although it is something of a puzzle as to why many areas of Cumbria with broad-leaved woodland do not hold Hawfinches, it must be said that the bird is on the extreme edge of its range here and the small population may not be enough to expand even into suitable habitat. Nationally this species is apparently in decline (Mead 2000) but the population is so sparse and isolated that this decline is almost impossible to quantify. Likewise it is difficult to assess any threats to its future, either nationally or in Cumbria, but the inexorable spread of the Grey Squirrel into the county may be bad news for a canopy nesting bird such as the Hawfinch.

Derek McAlone

# Yellowhammer *Emberiza citrinella*

THE male Yellowhammer in breeding plumage is one of our most attractive farmland birds. Its song, universally verbalised as 'a-little-bit-of-bread-and-no-cheese', is uttered from the top of a tall bush or roadside hedge from late February until the middle of August. Courtship, when a mate has been attracted, includes a particular energetic chase, in which the cock pursues the hen in twisting flight, at the end of which they may tumble to the ground and mate.

The Yellowhammer breeds commonly across the whole of Central and Northern Europe and into Asia. In Britain and Ireland the species is widespread but absent from some upland areas and islands in the north and west of Scotland. Although mainly associated with open farmland containing a mixture of hedgerows, pasture and arable crops, it also occurs on non-arable land, including the coast, provided there is a variety of appropriate habitats. The key requirements appear to be open areas to feed with a mixture of scrub and taller vegetation to act as song-posts and nesting sites.

Like other buntings the Yellowhammer feeds on the ground with seeds making up the bulk of the diet, but when feeding young more invertebrates are selected. The nest can be on the ground but is typically just above ground level in taller vegetation or bushes. Usually, three to four eggs are laid per clutch and up to three broods may be reared in one season.

Interestingly, both Macpherson (1892) and Blezard *et al* (1943) make very little reference to the Yellowhammer other than to stress its abundance across much of the county. Stokoe (1962) regarded it as "widespread and numerous in open or rough country, breeding up to 1,000 feet [305m]." This general dearth of specific information about distribution gives support to the status put forward by the *Historical Atlas,* which lists the Yellowhammer as one of the most common birds in Britain and Ireland – so much so that it was abundant even in moorland and mountainous regions. This abundance has been ascribed to the growth in cereal production during the course of the 19th century, the population levels appearing to remain stable into the first half of the 20th century.

Analysis of the latest available CBC data shows a 54% decline since 1970, prior to which Yellowhammer numbers remained more or less stable at a time when other farmland bird populations were plummeting. The cause of the time-lag is unknown but the reasons for the decline itself are better understood: changing agricultural practices, amongst which early ploughing of winter stubbles, removing a vital winter food source, is likely to have been a major factor. In addition, destruction of hedges will have considerably reduced the number of available nesting sites. Brown and Grice (in prep) estimated the population of Yellowhammers in England at the time of the *New Atlas* to be 1,141,000 territories, around 95% of the British total. In the ten years since, they consider it probable that the population has declined further.

The results for *this Atlas* suggest a distribution pattern that is generally similar to the *Historical Atlas* with the Yellowhammer still being found across the whole county. Areas holding the largest concentrations remain the Solway Basin and the lower Eden Valley, although the species appears to be relatively common on the Coastal Plain and the western half of Lakeland. The Border Uplands and eastern Lakeland provide the fewest records: it would be interesting to look more closely at the land use of these areas to see if there are any obvious differences from the rest of the county.

Comparisons between *this Atlas* and the *Old Atlas* show a similar pattern of distribution but there are indications of a decline in the southeast of the county. It is possible that much of the population within the county utilizes the more marginal land such as woodland edge, or areas of early successional vegetation, and is therefore less susceptible to some of the changes in agricultural production that have occurred in recent years. This might explain why the Yellowhammer population has remained relatively stable whilst that of the Corn Bunting has declined.

Analysis of line transect data from *this Atlas* gives a population band of 34,000–59,000, suggesting a mean population of 44,000 birds. The highest densities of 22.96 birds/km² occurred on varied farmland of the Coastal Plain where mixed crops and hedged small fields remain. If these numbers can be maintained, they

Sponsored in memory of Joanne Grisedale 1973–1998

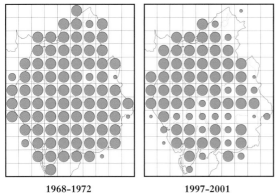

**1968-1972**          **1997-2001**

(For explanation of maps, see page 45)

*Conservation status*
European:                     SPEC Cat 4
UK:                           **RED: BD**

*Populations*
European status:              19,000,000
Britain – pairs:               1,200,000
Cumbria – pairs:                  22,000

*30-year distribution change*
                  Old Atlas  This Atlas    %
No. of 10km squares:   82       78      −4.9

| **Survey data** | **Tetrads** | **%** |
| --- | --- | --- |
| Confirmed breeding: | 170 | 9.2 |
| Probable breeding: | 253 | 13.7 |
| Possible breeding: | 64 | 3.5 |
| Total: | 487 | 26.4 |

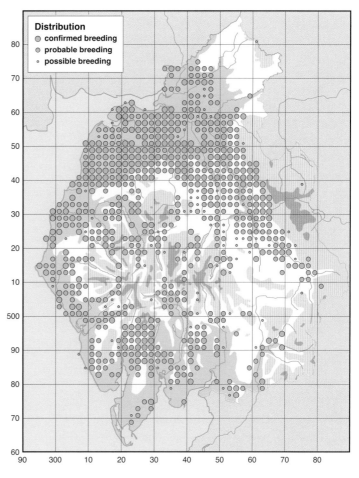

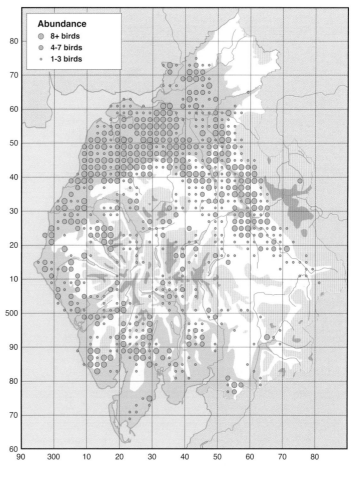

are likely to become an increasingly important component of the national population.

It is difficult to predict the future for the Yellowhammer in Cumbria. The most likely scenario in the short-term is one of declines in the traditionally strong areas of the Solway Basin and the lower Eden Valley, as farming continues to become more specialized in response to subsidies and world markets. In the longer term, if farming subsidies are changed from pure production towards less intensive systems we could see the population increasing. If the more marginal habitats are being used as suggested above, it is probable that the Yellowhammer will remain a widely distributed but only locally common species within Cumbria.

Alistair Crowle

# Reed Bunting *Emberiza schoeniclus*

THE Reed Bunting is a familiar species of wetland areas, where its presence is often advertised by the repetitive song. Surprisingly approachable, the male is a particularly attractive bird in full breeding plumage as it sings from the top of low-lying vegetation. By contrast, the female is less obvious, lacking the striking head pattern of her partner.

Found across the whole of the Western Palearctic, the Reed Bunting is the most widespread of all the buntings. In Britain and Ireland, the species is traditionally associated with wetland fringes, where the favoured habitats usually comprise a mixture of long grasses, herbs and shrubs. In more swampy areas, sedge and grass tussocks provide ideal habitat. However, after the Second World War birds were noted to nest also in drier habitats, such as young conifer plantations and farmland. This move away from traditional wetter habitats appeared to be linked to population increases rather than a particular change in behaviour.

The Reed Bunting usually lays four to five eggs from late April to early May and, although birds are sometimes double brooded, it is likely that this occurs only with females more than one year old. In winter, along with many other passerines, the Reed Bunting feeds almost entirely on seeds, switching to exploit the abundance of insects during the breeding season. The nestlings are fed exclusively on invertebrates.

Although widespread in Britain and Ireland at the end of the 19th century, the Reed Bunting underwent a further range expansion during the middle of the 20th century. However, this was subsequently followed by a decline, and the breeding population has since collapsed. The latest available CBC index reveals a 54%

decline since 1970, and with little encouragement to be found in BBS data which gives a 4% decline for the period 1994–2000, the species is included on the BoCC Red List.

In Cumbria, at the end of the 19th century, Macpherson (1892) considered the Reed Bunting to be "widely distributed" and "not at all uncommon", a situation that was reiterated in the early 20th century (Blezard *et al* 1943). However, Wilson (1933) differs slightly, stating "this bird is well represented in the Eden Valley, but in many districts adjoining the fells it is seldom seen." Stokoe (1962) noted that the species was found at altitudes up to 366m asl, perhaps suggesting that a range expansion, in line with national trends, took place in the 1950s. By the time of the *Old Atlas* birds were found to still be widespread across the county, with *this Atlas* depicting a broadly similar range.

The distribution map for *this Atlas* shows that Reed Buntings still occur widely across the county, with the majority of records coming from lowland areas, centred on the Solway Basin and Coastal Plain. As would be expected, in Lakeland the species is restricted to the valley bottoms where it is found along river systems and around lake margins. The relatively few records along the Eden Valley support the view that although the species does occur on farmland it occurs only at relatively low densities.

The low number of contacts registered during the line transect survey of *this Atlas* makes the scarcity of this bird all too transparent. A more subjective figure of 0.5 birds/km² can only intimate at a credible county population of 1,500–2,000 breeding pairs.

Reed Buntings may specialize in habitat selection, for example by utilizing marshland or the transitional zone from saltwater to freshwater. The decline of Reed Buntings nationally is blamed partially on the loss of foraging areas, following the move away from spring-sown to autumn-sown crops and the associated loss of overwinter stubbles. Winter survival is suspected to be the single most important factor limiting Reed Bunting populations in England (Brown & Grice in prep). Given the largely sedentary nature and ground-feeding habits of the species it is perhaps no surprise that they are susceptible to severe winter weather and, in particular, lying snow.

On the basis of the evidence produced by *this Atlas,* it would seem that the future for the Reed Bunting in Cumbria is less uncertain than it is elsewhere in Britain. Although it is likely that some decline has occurred, the abundance map shows that a large part of the population is based on coastal sites. This raises the possibility that agricultural land use does not play as important a role in Cumbria as it does in other parts of the country. The relatively low levels of arable cultivation perhaps mean that this has not been such

Sponsored by Bill Kenmir

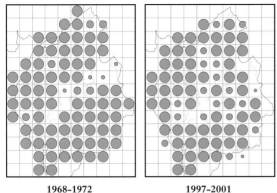

**1968-1972**     **1997-2001**

(For explanation of maps, see page 45)

| *Conservation status* | |
| --- | --- |
| European: | Non-SPEC |
| UK: | **RED: BD** |

| *Populations* | |
| --- | --- |
| European status: | 3,600,000 |
| Britain – pairs: | 220,000 |
| Cumbria – pairs: | 1,500–2,000 |

*30-year distribution change*

| | Old Atlas | This Atlas | % |
| --- | --- | --- | --- |
| No. of 10km squares: | 86 | 76 | **–11.6** |

| **Survey data** | **Tetrads** | **%** |
| --- | --- | --- |
| Confirmed breeding: | 170 | 9.2 |
| Probable breeding: | 253 | 13.7 |
| Possible breeding: | 64 | 3.5 |
| Total: | 487 | 26.4 |

an important source of winter feeding for Reed Buntings in the county. Indeed, if the specific habitats that are being utilized can be confirmed and management guidance developed, it may be that the population will increase.

Alistair Crowle

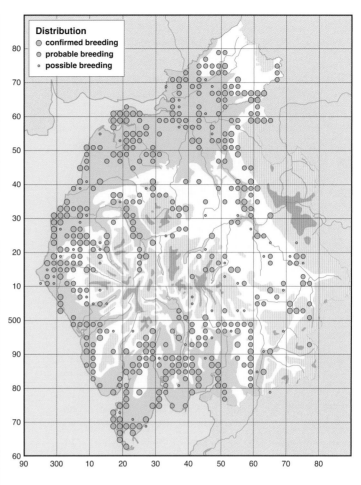

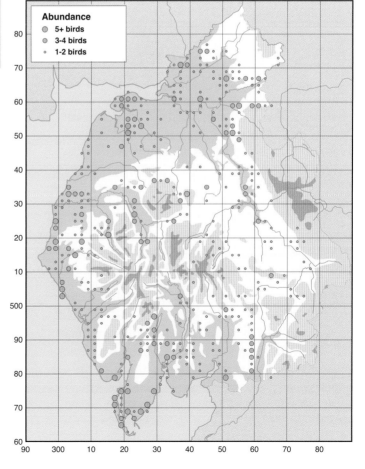

# Corn Bunting *Miliaria calandra*

WHAT is it about the Corn Bunting that makes it so attractive to birdwatchers, rarely failing to bring appreciative murmurings on being sighted? The song is likened to a bunch of keys being shaken and it has no distinctive markings in its plumage. Perhaps it is the often-mentioned but hardly significant way the legs dangle down as it flies up to its song post, or maybe it is to do with the name, harking back to a time when the pace of life was slower, and memories recall longer, hotter summers.

The Western Palearctic holds most of the world population, with major concentrations in central and southern Europe. Its range extends south to the Middle East and North Africa, reaching its highest densities in Spain. In Britain its distribution reflects well-cultivated land, hence its scarcity or absence over much of the north and west, including Wales and southwest England, and most of Ireland.

The favoured habitat appears to be open farmland very often near to the coast, and the nest is found close to or at ground level usually in thick vegetation or tangled grass. Egg laying in southern England begins in late May although further north it can be June or later before the first clutch is complete. The clutch averages three to four eggs and is incubated by the female alone. A small percentage of males are polygynous but this apparently does not have a negative effect on productivity (Hartley *et al* 1994). The species has a tendency to nest at high densities in some areas and yet to be curiously absent from other seemingly similar areas. It also has a propensity to disappear from some traditional nesting sites for no apparent reason.

Brickle (1998) investigated a range of factors affecting the Corn Bunting such as nestling diet, foraging behaviour, breeding success, timing of breeding and habitat use during winter. Not surprisingly, observations found that when feeding young, birds utilized areas with an abundance of available insects, and the timing of breeding was linked to food availability prior to egg laying. Interestingly, this study also found that the length of the breeding season was determined by harvesting times and the availability of uncut nesting habitat. Donald & Evans (1995) identified the importance of winter stubbles to Corn Buntings for feeding and Brickle (1998) demonstrated that feeding behaviour changed over the course of the winter depending on where the best supply of grain could be obtained.

The *Historical Atlas* suggests that the Corn Bunting had a localized distribution in Cumbria, including Lakeland and much of the Pennines, but with its stronghold in the Solway Basin and parts of the Coastal Plain. Macpherson (1892) commented that "this Bunting was formerly common in many districts, but has of late years shown a tendency to disappear from its favourite breeding places, reappearing unexpectedly in unlooked for situations." He regarded it as abundant around Allonby and also cited breeding from a variety of areas, including Walney, St Bees, Tebay and Carlisle. By the time of Blezard (1943), the status of the Corn Bunting had changed so that it had become a "very local resident" although there was an apparent increase in the north of the county. The Allonby and Wigton areas remained a stronghold but the species was largely absent from the southern half of the county although singing birds were recorded in the Orton area in 1942. Stokoe (1962) referred to it as "very local and sometimes variable in numbers" and considered the species "most frequent on the Solway coast, near Wigton and Carlisle, and up the Eden Valley to Kirkby Stephen." He too noticed declines around Carlisle and Appleby.

At the time of the *Old Atlas*, the Corn Bunting could still be found in many areas of the county, with a distribution that encompassed much of the Solway Basin, the Coastal Plain and the Eden Valley and extended into the North Pennines, the Lune Valley and the Cumbria Dales. *This Atlas* paints a depressing picture of the decline of the Corn Bunting within the county; breeding was confirmed in just one 10km square. The number of occupied 10km squares since the *Old Atlas* has declined from 47 to just five in *this Atlas*! The national picture is just as alarming with the latest available analysis of CBC data showing a massive 85% decline since 1970.

The current county population is a meagre 4–6 breeding pairs. If any birds have been overlooked

Sponsored by Jackie Stott

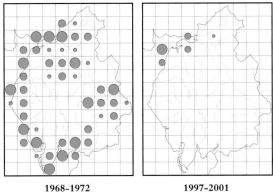

**1968-1972**     **1997-2001**
(For explanation of maps, see page 45)

*Conservation status*
European:                           SPEC Cat 4
UK:                        **RED: BD & HD**

*Populations*
European status:                    4,600,000
Britain – pairs:                       19,800
Cumbria – pairs:                          4–6

*30-year distribution change*
|  | Old Atlas | This Atlas | % |
|---|---|---|---|
| No. of 10km squares: | 47 | 5 | **−89.4** |

| **Survey data** | **Tetrads** | **%** |
|---|---|---|
| Confirmed breeding: | 1 | 0.05 |
| Probable breeding: | 4 | 0.2 |
| Possible breeding: | 1 | 0.05 |
| Total: | 6 | 0.3 |

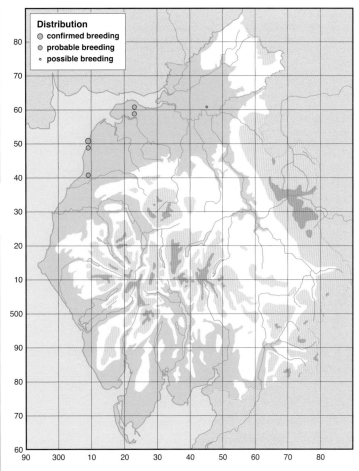

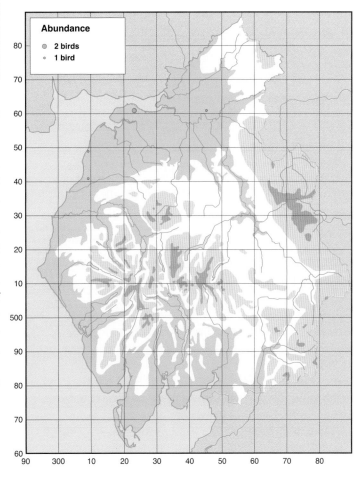

during the course of *this Atlas,* it has certainly not been through lack of interest or effort.

It would seem that we are looking at the extinction of Corn Bunting as a breeding bird in Cumbria and it is difficult to be optimistic about its chances of re-colonization given the overall declines nationally. The only hope for the future lies with reform of agricultural subsidies towards ones which place greater emphasis on preserving farmland wildlife. If more funds become available to promote traditional farmland features such as winter stubbles and sympathetic management of field margins then one day it may be that the jangling song of the Corn Bunting will once more become a familiar sound in the Cumbrian countryside.

Alistair Crowle

In addition to the species covered in the main accounts there are a number of extra breeding species which complement the county list. All historical, occasional and introduced species are covered, and the account also includes potential new breeding birds.

## Historical and occasional breeding species

This section deals with those species that are considered to have bred in a wild state within the county, at least once, prior to the period of *this Atlas.*

**Bittern** *Botaurus stellaris*                    Great Bittern
Macpherson (1892) was in no doubt that odd pairs of Bitterns occasionally spent the breeding season in the county and states that birds were 'procured for the table' at Naworth in July 1618 and 1634. He goes on to quote Richardson that, in the 18th century, the Bittern "sometimes, though rarely, breeds by the side of Eamont" and Dr Heysham who stated "it breeds in bogs and makes its nest upon the ground. In the spring it makes a loud bellowing kind of noise, from which it is called in Cumberland, Miredrum". Even by Macpherson's day, however, the Bittern seems to have become solely a winter visitor, albeit a much commoner one than nowadays.

Despite a modest rise to 19 booming males in 1999 (Gregory 2000), following a steady decline since 1970, the Bittern is currently one of Britain's most threatened species and so may seem unlikely to return to the county as a breeding bird. However, one of the country's prime sites, Leighton Moss, lies just over the county boundary in Lancashire and it is hoped that large-scale restoration and creation of its reedbed habitat throughout the country may encourage a population recovery. If so, Cumbria is well placed to benefit, particularly if any of the proposed habitat creation takes place in the county.

Recent county records have largely involved passage or wintering birds, though, in 1974, one at Whinfell Tarn on 30th May was followed by a report of two birds at the same site on 18th August and there is an intriguing record of a bird flushed from an undisclosed freshwater marsh on 4th July 1977.

**Pintail** *Anas acuta*                    Northern Pintail
Towards the end of the 19th century, the Pintail was considered a scarce wintering bird in the county. Although a pair summered at Bowness Flow in 1890, a nest could not be located despite much endeavour (Macpherson 1892). From 1903, up to 30 birds were reared annually for sporting purposes from pinioned stock kept on the Netherby estate, and by 1908 fully winged birds were nesting within the grounds. A few were still breeding in 1919 and these were supplemented in 1920 by birds hatched from eggs

taken from Loch Leven, Fife. As a result of this breeding programme, which was suspended in 1926, the species became established as a feral breeder in the surrounding area. Consequently, three pairs nesting on the Solway Plain in 1917, a pair at the same location in 1925, several summering birds in Cumberland and Westmorland between 1927 and 1931, and perhaps even a female incubating six eggs on a Westmorland lake in 1932 could conceivably all be connected to the Netherby releases (Blezard *et al* 1943).

Despite a steady increase in the number of wintering birds through the 20th century, no more breeding attempts were noted until a few pairs nested around the Duddon Estuary in the 1960s and on the Leven Estuary in 1965. These birds are likely to be free-flying stock, bred from local pinioned birds on the WAGBI reserve at The Haws, Millom, which were allowed to disperse. It is possible that a pair nesting near Appleby in 1968 was also from this source.

Single pairs, which bred on the Solway Basin in 1973, 1976 and 1982, and also in the Eden Valley the same year, were perhaps the first instances in Cumbria involving wild birds. In 1983, the species bred at three sites and was present at a further two. However, any hint of colonization quickly evaporated, with no further breeding attempts reported in subsequent years (Hutcheson 1986, Fox & Meek 1993). During *this Atlas,* although occasional birds lingered into May, there was again no evidence of breeding.

At present, the small British population is within the range 10–50 breeding pairs per annum, with the bulk of the population in Scotland (Ogilvie *et al* 2000). Considering the very precise habitat requirements of the species, it is likely that the Pintail will remain as just a very occasional breeder in the county in anything other than the long-term.

**Red Kite** *Milvus milvus*
The historical residence of the Red Kite in Cumbria was remarked upon as early as 1709. Ullswater appears to have been the main stronghold, although birds also bred around Derwent Water and Windermere and were considered to nest along the Eden Valley as late as 1796. The last confirmed breeding record comes from Castle Head, Keswick in 1809, whilst a bird shot at nearby Portinscale in 1840, and donated to the Carlisle museum, is considered as perhaps the last indigenous Lakeland bird, although there were occasional further sightings until one was at Workington in June 1921 (Macpherson 1892, Blezard *et al* 1943).

It was then over 50 years before the species reappeared in the county, since when there have been a scattering of records, including a summering bird at Ravenstonedale in 1976–77 and 1977–78 (Hutcheson

1986) and a pair reportedly bred at an undisclosed site in the county in 1981.

The chances of the species returning as a regular addition to the county's breeding list, albeit from introduced stock, continue to increase as a direct result of the English Nature/RSPB reintroduction scheme, which was instigated in 1989. In 1999, 119 pairs of released birds raised around 231 young at various locations and the population is expanding rapidly (Ogilvie *et al* 2001). During *this Atlas* period, single birds were in the Glenderaterra Valley in April 1997 and at Armathwaite in May 2001.

## White-tailed Eagle *Haliaeetus albicilla*

The White-tailed Eagle probably soared over the mountains of Lakeland for many centuries prior to the earliest documented account of breeding in the county, which came from Wallow Crag, Mardale in 1692. Birds were still present there in 1787. Other nesting sites included crags in Borrowdale and Martindale, before breeding English White-tailed Eagles died out in Lakeland during the 1790s. The last occupied eyrie appears to have been at Eskdale, Cumberland in 1791 (Macpherson 1892). The record of a pair at Ullswater, a former breeding site, in 1835 is often quoted as the last nesting record in England; however, there is little evidence to suggest that the pair actually attempted to breed (Holloway 1996). The last sighting in the county to date involves an adult over Coniston Water on 21st March 1934 (Blezard *et al* 1943).

Although a reintroduction scheme is currently underway in Scotland, progress is slow, with the current population considered to be around 20 nesting pairs. It is planned to release more birds in an effort to establish a viable breeding population (Mead 2000) but it may be overly optimistic to assume that this magnificent raptor will ever again soar over Lakeland Fells.

## Marsh Harrier *Circus aeruginosus*  Eurasian Marsh Harrier

The Marsh Harrier, while considered to breed throughout Lakeland during the first part of the 19th century, apparently became extinct soon after, and it is possible that a bird killed at Netherby prior to 1880 and donated to the Carlisle museum was the last of the Marsh Harriers that had frequented the county for many years (Macpherson 1892). Subsequently, for over a century, the species was considered to be only a rare vagrant to the county (Blezard *et al* 1943, Hutcheson 1986).

However, over the last 30 years, Britain has seen a spectacular 20% annual increase in population levels (Mead 2000) and in 1999, 145–164 pairs raised at least 256 young (Ogilvie *et al* 2001). Consequently, an increase in passage migrants became apparent in Cumbria, especially during the final decade of the 20th century when spring records include an immature male displaying and carrying nesting material at Mere Tarn during May 1992.

During *this Atlas* period, a male briefly joined a summering female at Bassenthwaite Lake – which holds the most extensive area of suitable habitat remaining in the county – in May/June 1998. Although fenland habitat is at a premium in the county, smaller reedbeds and even crops are now being utilized in the species' East Anglian stronghold. Given sensitive management, birds may return to breed, especially now that breeding is an annual event just across the county border, at Leighton Moss in Lancashire.

## Montagu's Harrier *Circus pygargus*

The first documented occurrence of Montagu's Harrier in Cumbria concerns a bird killed near Carlisle prior to 1840 (Macpherson 1892). This was followed by four further countywide reports up to 1892 before the first and only breeding attempt to date was made. A pair established in North Cumberland in 1923 might well have nested successfully had the male not been killed in a crow trap baited with eggs; the female remained faithful to the area until August (Blezard *et al* 1943).

There have been just five records since, three involving males, at Maulds Meaburn in October 1961, Claife Heights in April 1978 and South Walney in April 1981 (Hutcheson 1986). While the small British population remains centred on East Anglia and the New Forest, and with no records during the course of *this Atlas,* another breeding attempt in the county would seem unlikely.

## Hobby *Falco subbuteo*  Eurasian Hobby

There is some evidence to support the assertion that the Hobby is likely to have bred at least once in Cumberland in the 1930s (Stokoe 1962). A pair reportedly nested at Hutton, Cumberland, but there is no corroboration of this. However, around that time the species appeared on three separate occasions on an estate in North Cumberland and two adults were killed in September 1930; additionally, two further birds were killed in Cumberland in May 1935. Perhaps the best evidence of a breeding attempt came from the Solway Basin, where a pair regularly frequented a pinewood between 31st May and 15th June 1937, but disappeared before a nesting record could be established (Blezard *et al* 1943).

Records since have been considered to relate to passage birds. However, recent data indicates that the British population has at least doubled in 12 years, with the population recently estimated at 948–1,775 breeding pairs (Chapman 1999), and pairs can now be found in Cheshire, Northumberland and Yorkshire. Although there were no relevant records during *this Atlas,* with further expansion predicted in the range, birds may soon become established in Cumbria.

**Ptarmigan**   *Lagopus mutus*        Rock Ptarmigan
The species was certainly resident historically in the county and there is evidence to suggest breeding continued until the latter half of the 18th century in Cumberland, with Ptarmigan recorded inhabiting the hills around Keswick. A specimen collected on Skiddaw around this time was exhibited in a local museum for some years. However the species must have soon become a rare sight as very few locals could recollect having seen one, and it was probably extinct by the end of that century (Macpherson 1892). Climate amelioration and sheep over-grazing are possible factors contributing to the species' demise in Cumbria; the British population is now restricted to the last remaining remnants of arctic-alpine heath in the Highlands of Scotland.

**Capercaillie**   *Tetrao urogallus*        Western Capercaillie
Macpherson (1892) relates tales told to him of the Capercaillies that once inhabited the "pine forests which clad the naked mountains of Lakeland before so many trees were cut down for ship-building and for charcoal-burning", and predicted that bones of the species "may one day be discovered among the animal remains which lie hidden in the fissures of the limestone rocks of Westmorland".

However there is little evidence of the species in England and whatever its historical range, the indigenous population had died out in Britain by about 1785. Birds were subsequently successfully reintroduced into Scotland in the 1800s, but similar efforts in Cumbria proved less enduring. Macpherson (1892) refers to an undated attempt to introduce Capercaillies to the area around Netherby, with eggs obtained from Scotland. Several young were reared but never became established, although a male, known for his fearlessness, did survive for some years near Longtown.

After two abortive attempts in Grizedale Forest in 1967 and 1968, involving just two clutches of eggs in each case, 52 partly-incubated eggs were brought down from Scotland in May 1970. Some 35 young birds were subsequently released. No breeding activity was observed in 1971, although the following spring lekking calls were reported from an area of 60-year-old larch within the main block of Grizedale Forest. Colonies of Wood Ants were even brought into the forest in an attempt to provide food for the young

Capercaillies, but the birds failed to become established and numbers gradually dwindled away (J. Cubby pers comm). There are no plans to repeat the experiment.

**Spotted Crake**   *Porzana porzana*
Although breeding has never been conclusively proven in the county, the Spotted Crake is believed to have nested occasionally in Cumberland during the 19th century, with birds breeding in marshy ground or along lake shores and riverbanks. There are no records of young being seen, but apparently summering birds were recorded at Biglands Bog, and two birds shot at Wedholme Flow in the early autumn of 1881 were considered to have been bred there (Macpherson 1892). Later, a pair was shot at Rusland Moss in September 1898, with a juvenile taken at the same location a month later (Blezard *et al* 1943).

The species is currently considered a very rare breeding species in Britain and Ireland and there were no records forthcoming in Cumbria during *this Atlas* period.

**Black-tailed Godwit**   *Limosa limosa*
A combination of egg collecting, shooting and land reclamation led to the extinction of the Black-tailed Godwit as a breeding bird in Britain by the early 19th century. However, a slow recolonization began in the 1930s and there are currently 38–50 breeding pairs, mainly in southeast England (Ogilvie *et al* 2000). In Cumbria, an increase in passage birds was noted in the 1950s and 1960s (Stokoe 1962) and this culminated in a nest containing three eggs being found on Rockcliffe Marsh in 1970 (Brown 1974). Subsequent years saw up to four pairs breeding annually until at least 1976, after which there were no further breeding records forthcoming from this site.

Thereafter, the species became just an occasional breeder, with the only evidence of further breeding involving a group of five birds, including two juveniles, on the Irt Estuary in July 1984. A pair and two well-grown young were at an undisclosed location in July 1988; however, as the young were capable of flight it was uncertain whether the birds had actually bred at the site.

Despite the presence of summering birds on the Solway Basin, no further reports have come to light during the course of *this Atlas*, though a few pairs have nested annually on a coastal marsh in Lancashire throughout the 1990s (Ogilvie *et al* 2000). Similar habitat still exists in Cumbria, especially in the north of the county, and given the continued increase in spring passage birds at both inland and coastal sites it is possible that small numbers may in the future breed regularly within the county.

**Green Sandpiper**  *Tringa ochropus*

There have been only two cases of proven breeding for this species in Britain. The first of these was at Levens Park in Westmorland during 1917, when adult birds were seen regularly from June onwards and on 10th August they were observed tending two downy young (Blezard *et al* 1943).

**Roseate Tern**  *Sterna dougallii*

The Roseate Tern was first located breeding in the county in the Common Tern colony on Foulney Island in 1840. However, persecution and disturbance from fishermen appears to have caused the bird's decline. Although three birds were collected during 1864 in the Walney/Foulney area, perhaps unsurprisingly by 1865 only one pair could be located on Walney Island, and the indications are that Roseate Terns ceased to bred in the area after 1876 (Macpherson 1892). The next confirmation of successful breeding came from Ravenglass, where a single pair nested around 1904 (Blezard *et al* 1943).

Later a recolonization occurred on Walney Island; a single pair in 1926 increased to six pairs in 1927, and three pairs were again noted in 1945, with undisclosed numbers breeding in 1949. After another absence, five pairs were present in 1958 and nesting occurred annually at both ends of the island until 1961. Up to 12 pairs continued to breed at the north end until 1967 (Dean 1990). The final breeding record for Cumbria to date occurred back where it had all begun, at Foulney Island, with two pairs present in 1970 (Hutcheson 1986).

Since then, the species has continued to decline as a breeding bird in Britain with just 61–64 pairs located in 1999, although healthier numbers still occur in Ireland (Ogilvie *et al* 2001). As a result, the species is now considered a rare passage migrant in the county. There were just four records during *this Atlas*: singles appeared at Walney in May 1997, Rockcliffe Marsh in June 1997, Walney again in June 1999 and Hodbarrow in June 2000, with no evidence of breeding.

**Black Tern**  *Chlidonias niger*

There are two assertions of the Black Tern breeding in Cumberland during the 19th century. The first of these involves a pair shot at Talkin Tarn in June 1848; upon inspection the female was found to be carrying eggs and the birds could conceivably have been going to breed there. A second, more conclusive record concerns a clutch of eggs, which was taken from a nest on the Solway Plain in 1855 (Macpherson 1892). Since then, there have been no suspicions of breeding, although the species is still regularly seen in the county as a passage migrant, including an unprecedented countywide influx involving about 210 individuals during May 1990.

Although breeding regularly into the 19th century with occasional attempts since, the species is currently extinct as a breeding bird in Britain and Ireland. A long-term decline on the continent does not augur well for the future.

**Turtle Dove**  *Streptopelia turtur*

The Turtle Dove has never been anything more than an occasional breeder in the county. A young bird was killed at Blackwell in September 1832 but it was not until 1885 that the species was proven to breed, when a pair nested at Scotby near Carlisle. There were further breeding records, at Orton in 1889, Floriston in 1912 and Scotby again in 1919, and nearby in several subsequent years (Macpherson 1892, Blezard *et al* 1943). The last attempt was made in Cumberland in 1951 (Stokoe 1962), since when there has been a steady southward contraction of the species' range in Britain, linked to agricultural change. This dramatic decline continues unabated and has been compounded by the large numbers shot during migration through France and Iberia. Consequently, there appears to be little chance of reversing the current trend and all recent Cumbrian records involve occasional passage birds including, during *this Atlas*, single birds at South Walney in May/June 1997, and at Kirkbride on 8th June 2001.

**Wryneck**  *Jynx torquilla*                    Eurasian Wryneck

During the 19th century, the Wryneck bred over most of lowland England, becoming rarer to the north and west but regularly breeding as far as the South Pennine foothills. One of the few exceptions to this southerly distribution involved an isolated population in Cumberland. Here, it was met with annually at the end of the 18th century, and bred, albeit very locally, throughout the first half of the 19th century from Kendal to Carlisle. The last documented nest was at Rickerby in 1863 (Macpherson 1892), and although a female in breeding condition died after hitting wires at Drumburgh in June 1909 (Blezard *et al* 1943) there has been no direct evidence of breeding since. Agricultural change is a most likely cause with the loss of old pasture, and the consequent dearth of ants on which to feed, proving detrimental.

Now effectively extinct as a breeding bird in Britain, although still occasionally nesting in Scotland, a withdrawal from the north of its breeding range throughout Western Europe does not augur well for future recolonization. The Wryneck is now considered a rare passage migrant in Cumbria, primarily in the autumn, although during *this Atlas* a singing male lingered in suitable habitat at Natland between 4th and 8th May 2000.

**Woodlark** *Lullula arborea*                     Wood Lark
During the 19th century, the Woodlark was considered to breed widely, if sparsely, through the county. A small colony existed at Camerton and occasional breeding birds can be traced to Castleheads, St Bees, Ravenglass and Kendal where it was considered rare in 1861, though not uncommon some years earlier (Macpherson 1892, Blezard *et al* 1943). Cumbria was always at the northern periphery of the breeding range and by the turn of the century, the species was probably extinct. As a result, early 20th century records are few, with just singles at Skinburness in September 1933 and Sedbergh in May 1959.

Although susceptible to cold winters, recent data show that numbers in Britain have increased by over 600% since 1986, with a few pairs now breeding in Yorkshire (Mead 2000, Ogilvie *et al* 2001). Perhaps as a direct result, Cumbria has seen a recent rise in passage birds, with singles at Cavendish Dock in November 1990 and again in March 1993, at Bowness-on-Solway in April 1996, and finally Ulverston in October 2000. Currently, the prospects for the species appear good, with a further increase and subsequent range expansion expected. Is it too much to hope that this species may, one day soon, return to breed in the county?

**Golden Oriole** *Oriolus oriolus*   Eurasian Golden Oriole
Despite being recorded in the county only ten times subsequent to a bird in female plumage being shot at Irton, Cumberland in 1857, Golden Orioles bred successfully in 1958 and 1959, when a single pair was present at a site in the Rusland Valley. Birds also appeared at the same locality in 1960 and 1961, although breeding was not proven (Stokoe 1962). Since then, the species has continued to be recorded as a sporadic passage migrant, with most sightings concerning short-staying males in the spring, predominantly in the south of the county. The small British population is currently estimated at 5–24 breeding pairs, with the nucleus of the population in East Anglia (Ogilvie *et al* 2001). However, in Cumbria there have been six records since 1990, two of which were during *this Atlas*. These include long-staying males at Armathwaite during 1990 and Walney Island in 1997. It is, therefore, not inconceivable that Golden Orioles may, one day, again breed in the county.

**Red-backed Shrike** *Larius collurio*
Prior to 1850, the Red-backed Shrike was considered to breed fairly commonly throughout the county. Westmorland and Furness appear to have been the main strongholds. Occasionally pairs reached Cumberland, as far north as the Scottish border. However, the species was already declining rapidly as a breeding bird in Britain, and towards the end of the 19th century it was becoming less common along the northern fringe of its range, including Cumbria. A pair nested at Scotby in 1884 but the last confirmed breeding record comes from Workington around 1922. Birds were however present at Pooley Bridge during the summers of both 1933 and 1934, during which year a pair was reported to have nested at Hebblethwaite Hall, Sedbergh (Macpherson 1892, Blezard *et al* 1943, Cleasby 1999). A single bird was at Lazonby in May 1935, but over 30 years were to pass before the Red-backed Shrike was again recorded in the county (Stokoe 1962, Hutcheson 1986).

Since then, the species has continued to occur as a sporadic passage migrant, primarily in the spring. Britain is now at the extreme edge of the species' range in Europe and although pairs still occasionally breed in Scotland, it is effectively extinct as a breeding bird. Agricultural 'improvement', causing the virtual extirpation of small fields with large hedges and a reduction in lowland heath, along with persecution from egg collectors, are cited as the reasons behind this catastrophic decline. During *this Atlas*, a female was at South Walney on 10th June 2000 but, considering the national trend, it would seem that the species is lost as a breeding bird in the county.

**Chough** *Pyrrhocorax pyrrhocorax*   Red-billed Chough
The Chough has never been anything other than a rare breeder in the county. The earliest reference to the species is from Whitehaven in 1829 and two or three breeding pairs frequented the cliffs at nearby St Bees Head until around 1860. However, the final nesting place for Cumbrian Choughs appears to have been Whitbarrow Scar, where the species remained until about 1865 (Macpherson 1892). Single birds, presumably wandering birds from the Scottish side of the Solway Firth, shot at Longtown and Wigton in about 1870 were the final sightings until several birds were at St Bees Head on numerous occasions between 1955–57 (Stokoe 1962).

Since then, records include long-staying birds at Coniston in 1976–77 and Gutterby in 1978–80 and sightings at St Bees Head in December 1977, May 1978 and June 1981. In Britain and Ireland, the current breeding population remains stable with little sign of any significant increase. Consequently, the species continues to be a rare vagrant to the county with no reports during *this Atlas*, although future recolonization by birds from the Isle of Man, which supported 90 pairs in 1999 (Ogilvie *et al* 2001), is perhaps a possibility.

**Brambling** *Fringilla montifringilla*

Despite first nesting in Sutherland in 1920, the Brambling has yet to establish itself in Britain with confirmed breeding still considered a notable event. Although the song of the Brambling has occasionally been heard in Cumbria during April and May, the only known nesting record for the county occurred near Workington in 1984. On 1st September, a juvenile male in full body moult and an adult male moulting both wing and tail feathers were mist-netted in a suburban garden, while a female was also observed, calling loudly, close by. Bramblings do not migrate until they have undergone a full moult so it was considered that they had nested locally (Spencer *et al* 1986).

The only records in any way suggestive of breeding during *this Atlas* involved a singing male in suitable habitat in Ennerdale on 20th April 1997 and one reported from Kershope Forest on 29th April 1999.

**Cirl Bunting** *Emberiza cirlus*

The Cirl Bunting was first recorded in Cumbria as recently as 1914 when a male appeared at Carlisle. Perhaps surprisingly, the species then went on to breed. Pairs nested at Greystoke in 1930, where a female was seen feeding recently fledged young and at Seascale in 1932, when adults and young were located. A pair was again found to be nesting at Seascale in 1934, a year that also produced one at Grune Point in April and a male nearby at Silloth in October. Another pair was known to have bred on the northwest outskirts of Carlisle in 1955 (Blezard *et al* 1943, Stokoe 1962). There have been no further sightings in the county, primarily due to the dramatic decline in numbers and subsequent contraction of range suffered by the British population.

Although the species now appears safe in its final refuge in Devon, where its numbers are now increasing, the species is unlikely to breed again in Cumbria for the foreseeable future.

## Feral and introduced species

This section attempts to deal with those species that have been introduced by man, either deliberately or accidentally, and which have bred, or potentially could breed, in a wild state within the county. It does not include relatively common introduced species, such as Greylag Goose, Canada Goose and Pheasant, which are dealt with in the main text.

**Chinese Goose** *Anser cygnoides*          Swan Goose

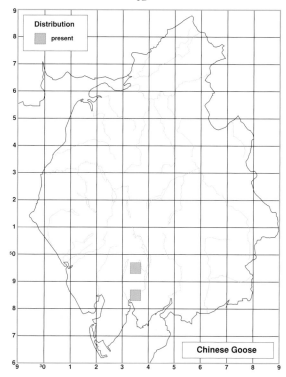

The BOURC concluded that Chinese Geese do not yet occur in sufficient numbers in Britain to warrant any change in categorization or addition to category D4 of the British list – a subgroup of category D for species which would otherwise appear in category C, except that their feral population may or may not be self-supporting (Vinicombe *et al* 1993). In Cumbria, small numbers seem to be in virtually permanent residence at several sites. These include Hodbarrow, where in 1991 a female laid at least one infertile egg, and Esthwaite Water, where four adults and 11 young were recorded on 18th May 1993. During the period of *this Atlas*, up to 13 inhabited Esthwaite Water throughout 1998, and in 2000 a pair with a single gosling were on a small tarn in the Rusland Valley.

**Pink-footed Goose** *Anser brachyrhynchus*

Occasional pairs of Pink-footed Geese have bred in Britain; perhaps, if within the species' wintering range, these involve injured birds, though released birds exist at some sites. (Ogilvie *et al* 1999). Within Cumbria, a number now appear to be resident, though there have

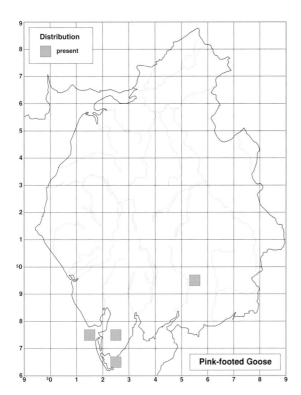

Pink-footed Goose

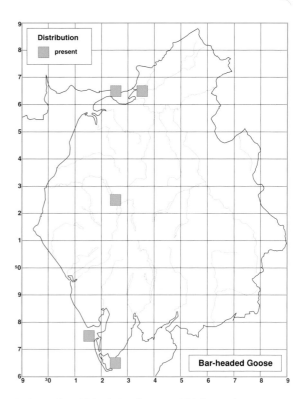

Bar-headed Goose

been no instances of confirmed breeding. It is unclear whether these originate from captive stock or involve injured birds; perhaps both. In the *New Atlas,* birds were recorded, without evidence of breeding, in SD29, NY30 and NY52, while, during *this Atlas,* birds were present during the summer months at Killington Reservoir and several sites in Furness. Atlas workers may have ignored others.

**Bar-headed Goose** *Anser indicus*
This species was placed in category D4 of the British List in 1993 to encourage monitoring (Vinicombe *et al* 1993). Although there could be as many as 100 birds in Britain, very few breeding attempts have been reported: in 1999, no more than eight pairs bred at five localities in five different counties (Ogilvie *et al* 2001).

In Cumbria, during *this Atlas,* a single bird was at Hodbarrow on 15th June 1997 and six on Burgh Marsh on 2nd September the same year may have been a family party, while in 1998, up to nine were on Rockcliffe Marsh in June and one was found dead under power lines at South Walney on 19th June. Finally, in 1999, two birds were seen regularly at Hodbarrow from June to August.

**Snow Goose** *Anser caerulescens*
A flock in Argyll, which moves between Coll and Mull, appears to be self-sustaining and has remained remarkably stable over the last 30 years or more, while at least seven pairs and two hybrid pairs bred in England in 1997 (Ogilvie *et al* 1999). According to Ogilvie *et al* (2001), this species does not seem to breed freely in the wild. In Cumbria, a pair attempted to breed at Haweswater in

1982 and 1983 (Hutcheson 1986) and a pair at Hodbarrow in 1990 was apparently preparing to nest until disturbed. In the *New Atlas,* birds were recorded as present but with no evidence of breeding in SD17, NY41, NY51 and NY52, while, during *this Atlas,* birds were noted in a total of eight 10km squares. Breeding season records came from South Walney; Hodbarrow; Sellafield; Bassenthwaite Lake; Derwent Water; Windermere; Wet Sleddale Reservoir and the Eden Valley.

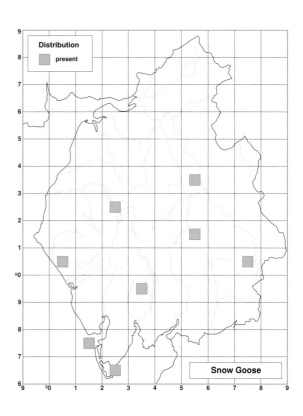

Snow Goose

## Emperor Goose *Anser canagica*

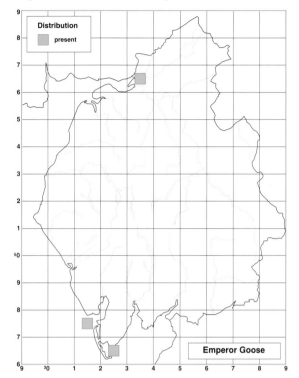

As in the case of Chinese Goose, the BOURC adjudged that this species does not yet occur in sufficient numbers in Britain to warrant any change in categorization or addition to category D4 of the British list (Vinicombe *et al* 1993). Nevertheless, it is a species to keep an eye on. A smattering of Cumbrian records includes at least three birds summering in the Eden Valley in 1995.

During *this Atlas*, a single bird accompanied nine Bar-headed Geese on Rockcliffe Marsh on 9th June 1998; two birds were seen at Haverigg on 18th June 1999 and a single frequented South Walney from 27th April to 6th June 1999. At South Walney, in 2000, a single bird paired with an Emperor × Bar-headed Goose hybrid; eggs were laid which failed to hatch. In 2001, 14 birds, including two pairs each with two young, arrived in July and were presumed to have bred nearby.

## Barnacle Goose *Branta leucopsis*

Rightly famed for the impressive numbers of wintering Barnacle Geese to be found on the Solway Firth, the county now also hosts an apparently well-established and increasing feral breeding population of these attractive wildfowl. The distribution of breeding records bears no relation to the wintering haunts, however, and must involve deliberate releases or escapes from captivity. In the *New Atlas,* birds were recorded in five of the county's 10km squares. By far the most now occur in the area of Park Farm, near Askam-in-Furness, where a feral colony has been resident since at least 1992 and, in 1997, there were 32

young in June and 170 birds were counted in September. However, due to hybridization with Cackling Canada Geese, it is thought that only about 10% of this population are now pure Barnacles. Elsewhere, during *this Atlas*, confirmed breeding occurred at Killington Reservoir, Barrow Park, Lodore and Derwent Water, while birds, often in double figures, were present during the summer months at Bassenthwaite Lake, Ullswater, and Esthwaite Water. The Naturalized Goose Survey in 2000 located a total of 96 adults and 18 young at inland sites in the county between 22nd June and 21st July. This included 57 birds at Derwent Water and the figures represent a significant increase on the total of 62 recorded during the 1991 summer survey of introduced geese.

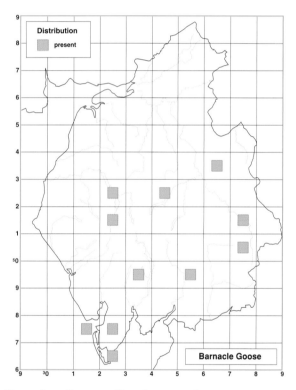

## Egyptian Goose *Alopochen aegyptiacus*

Egyptian Geese are now firmly established feral breeders in England, though largely confined to the southeast counties. However, there is evidence of a slow spread and two pairs bred in Greater Manchester in 1997 (Ogilvie *et al* 1999). Though Macpherson (1892) asserts that Egyptian Geese had occasionally been shot in Lakeland, he was not aware of it as a breeding species. Since then, relatively few of these peculiar-looking birds have reached Cumbria. The next documented record was not until 1977, when singles were recorded at Urswick Tarn on 11th May and Haverigg on 24th June. Between 1979 and 1984, a pair was regularly seen during the summer months on Windermere, though with no suggestion of breeding. Other records included a single at South

Ulverston for much of 1979; one on Coniston Water on 16th May 1981; four on the Kent Estuary from 2nd to 9th May 1988 and one at Hodbarrow on 27th April 1990. The *New Atlas* recorded possible breeding in SD38 but there were no records during *this Atlas*.

**Muscovy Duck** *Cairina moschata*

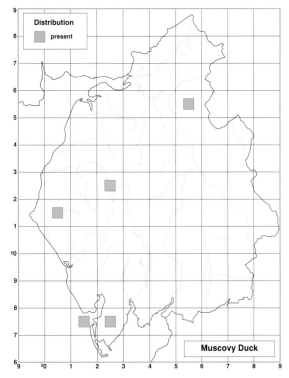

In the *New Atlas,* this rather ugly and ungainly duck was recorded breeding in four 10km squares in Britain and summering in one more. The BOURC considered that the species had not yet established a self-supporting population but felt that it should be monitored, placing it in Category D4 of the British list (Vinicombe *et al* 1993). In 1997, it was reported from seven counties in England and is apparently well established at sites in Suffolk and Norfolk (Ogilvie *et al* 1999). In Cumbria, it has largely been ignored, though occurring widely at sites such as Ormsgill Reservoir, Ulverston Canal, Bassenthwaite Lake, Derwent Water and Talkin Tarn.

During *this Atlas*, confirmed breeding occurred at Talkin Tarn in 1998 and birds were also seen regularly at Bassenthwaite Lake and Derwent Water, though, without doubt, this species will have gone unrecorded by most atlas workers.

**Wood Duck** *Aix sponsa*

The Wood Duck has never managed to colonize Britain as successfully as the only other member of its genus, the Mandarin. The *New Atlas* shows confirmed breeding in just six 10km squares in England, with birds present in a further 24. Appeals for information since then reveal just small numbers at large, with a

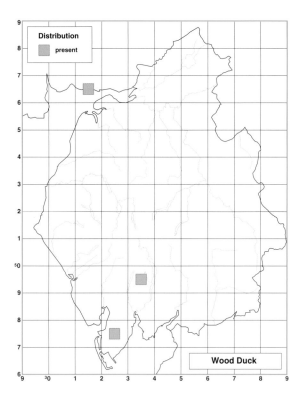

paucity of breeding records (Vinicombe *et al* 1993). Little seemed to have changed by 1999, when just two breeding season reports were received, involving 1–2 pairs (Ogilvie *et al* 2001). Records during the *Old Atlas* included a pair, which bred at Broughton-in-Furness, considered to be escapes from the nearby WAGBI reserve at The Haws, Millom. Between 1972 and 1974, a captive breeding and release scheme was attempted in Grizedale Forest but, for various reasons, it proved unsuccessful, though some unringed young and free-flying adults did survive for a time (J. Cubby pers comm). Singles on Windermere on a number of dates between August 1974 and the end of 1977 were thought to originate from this scheme. There have been relatively few reports in Cumbria in recent years, and the only ones during the breeding season involved a female at Silver Holme, Windermere on 18th May 1999, a drake which took up residence on the canal at Ulverston from December 1999 to December 2001, and another drake on the pools at North Plain Farm on the Solway from 20th to 22nd April 2000.

**Red-crested Pochard** *Netta rufina*

There is a well-established and apparently increasing population in the Cotswold Water Park, Gloucestershire/Wiltshire, though actual breeding records remain scarce. Confirmed breeding also occurred at five localities in three other counties in England in 1999 (Ogilvie *et al* 2001). Though the feral population was not thought large enough to merit promotion to Category C of the British List, the BOURC considered this another waterfowl species worthy of monitoring (Vinicombe *et al* 1993). In

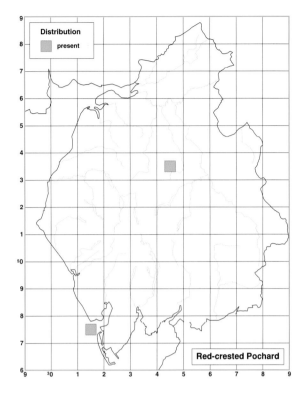

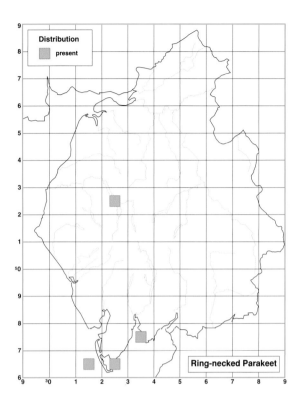

Cumbria, a drake summered on Windermere in 1967 (Hutcheson 1986), but in recent years – apart from a first-winter drake which arrived at Hodbarrow in January 2000 and remained into July, and a drake near Penrith in 1998 – Cumbrian records have involved birds, inevitably of unknown origin, outside the breeding season.

**Reeves' Pheasant** *Syrmaticus reevesii*

The *Old Atlas* mentions releases of Reeves' Pheasant in Cumberland in 1969. There was a short-lived and unsuccessful attempt to introduce the species into Grizedale in the mid-1970s. Between 1975 and 1977, some 22 young birds were hatched from around 60 eggs and, of the 17 that were released, at least ten reached maturity. Though two nests proved successful a year after release, the birds did not breed well in the wild. They proved particularly aggressive, attacking cars and even humans, and this behaviour, unsuitable in such a public location as Grizedale, ensured that the introduction attempt was not sustained (J. Cubby pers comm).

**Ring-necked Parakeet** *Psittacula krameri*

Rose-ringed Parakeet

Now firmly established as part of the British avifauna, Ring-necked Parakeets breed predominantly in the south of England. Former colonies in Merseyside and Greater Manchester appear to have dwindled away and the nearest breeding birds to Cumbria now seem to be no closer than Buckinghamshire. Nevertheless, numbers are still increasing and future colonization of the county cannot be ruled out. During *this Atlas*,

there were four birds in Keswick in May 1997, one flew over Humphrey Head towards Cartmel on 10th May 1998, and a single was on Walney Island during April and May 1998.

## Potential breeding species

This section deals with those species, considered to be of wild origin, that have been recorded in suitable habitat in the past or during *this Atlas*. Although they have not yet been proved to breed in the county they may do so in the future.

**Shag** *Phalacrocorax aristotelis*     European Shag

Somewhat surprisingly, this species has never been proved to breed in Cumbria, though a few birds, mainly immatures, regularly summered at St Bees Head in the 1970s and early 1980s, with display observed on occasions (Hutcheson 1986). Less regular sightings continued to occur here into the 1990s. The Shag remains largely a winter visitor to the county and there are few summer records during the period of *this Atlas*, the most significant being of a bird at St Bees Head on 18th May 2000. The cliffs here do support nesting Cormorants and must represent a potential breeding site for the future.

**Little Egret** *Egretta garzetta*

Having first bred in southern England in 1996, the Little Egret seems destined to establish itself and increase its range in Britain. But will it reach Cumbria? By the end of 2000, there had been a total of 34 Little Egrets in the county, mostly in spring or, more especially, autumn, with no indication, as yet, that nesting is even a possibility. However, 30–36 pairs nested at nine localities in England in 1999 (Ogilvie *et al* 2001) and a pair bred in northwest England in 2001, so who knows what the future will hold? During the period of *this Atlas*, singles were noted at Hodbarrow on 20th April 1998, Campfield Marsh on 9th May 1998, and North Plain Farm from 17th to 19th May 1999.

**Whooper Swan** *Cygnus cygnus*

It is thought that between two and five pairs of Whooper Swans breed in Britain in most years, though some are certainly from feral stock (Gibbons *et al* 1993). In 1997, escaped pairs bred, or may have bred, in Bedfordshire, Berkshire, Northumberland and Dunbartonshire and several more pairs or singles were present at localities in England (Ogilvie *et al* 1999). Though four to seven wild pairs bred in Scotland and Northern Ireland in 1999 (Ogilvie *et al* 2001), colonization of Cumbria by wild Whooper Swans seems a remote possibility and any potential for breeding in the county surely lies with feral or injured birds. A summering bird was recorded as far back as 1967, when an adult Whooper accompanied a pair of Mute Swans on the River Esk at Rockcliffe (Brown 1974). More recently, an injured bird summered at Little Salkeld in 1994.

During the period of *this Atlas*, an adult lingered at Rockcliffe Marsh until 27th May 1998; another adult summered on a small pond in Furness in the same year and a bird which spent most of the summer of 2000 on the Scottish side of the Solway was seen on the Eden near Old Sandsfield on 16th July.

**Garganey** *Anas querquedula*

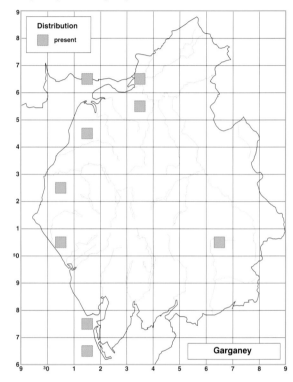

The first documented sighting of this species in Cumbria involves pairs on the River Eden near Carlisle and at Drumburgh during the spring of 1848. These were followed by a drake, again at Carlisle, in 1857 and two drakes shot at Tarn Wadling, before it was drained in 1858 – an early example of the habitat destruction which has had a detrimental effect on the species. Thereafter, the Garganey continued to occur as a sporadic passage migrant in the county, although the species' status became clouded for a time by activities at Netherby duck ponds. Captive breeding first occurred here in 1908 and small numbers of free-flying young were reared annually from pinioned stock up to 1929. This may have accounted for a number of sightings on the Solway Plain around this time (Macpherson 1892, Blezard *et al* 1943).

Despite being considered as a sparse, but regular, breeding species in adjacent counties, there is little to suggest that, at best, it is anything more than a very occasional breeder in Cumbria, where it has occurred almost annually since the 1970s, with the preponderance of records within ten kilometres of the coast, mainly along the Solway and Coastal Plains. To date the species has never been conclusively proven to breed, which is not surprising given its highly secretive nature. However, a female shot at Glasson on 15th August 1890 displayed heavily abraded plumage and a brood patch and was perhaps the first such attempt. More recently, long-staying pairs may have bred in the south of the county at Mere Tarn in 1989, South Walney in 1990, and Sandscale Haws in 1995; on at least one occasion eggs were considered to have been laid but no young were seen.

During *this Atlas*, the species was recorded in ten tetrads, within nine 10km squares, scattered mainly along the Coastal Plain and Solway Basin. Most referred to drakes, with no direct evidence of breeding, although pairs were briefly present at Sandscale Haws, Hodbarrow, Mockerkin Tarn, Carlisle, and Campfield Marsh. Latest estimates put the annual population in Britain within the range 14–120 pairs, with confirmed breeding in Lancashire in 1997 and 1999 (Ogilvie *et al* 1999, Ogilvie *et al* 2000, Ogilvie *et al* 2001). Surely the species will one day be proven to nest in Cumbria?

**Goldeneye**   *Bucephala clangula*   Common Goldeneye

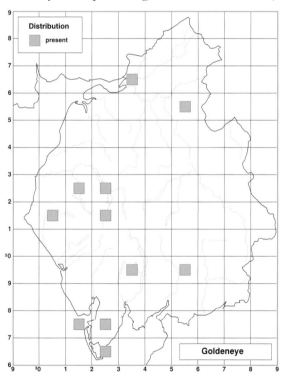

In Britain, breeding predominantly occurs in two nestbox schemes in the Highland Region of Scotland. In 1999, breeding occurred for the first time in Borders Region, perhaps indicating the start of a slow spread southwards. In addition, two pairs nested unsuccessfully in 1999 at a site in Lancashire, where birds, known to be of captive origin, have bred since at least 1988 (Ogilvie *et al* 2001).

Long mooted as an addition to the county's breeding list, with numerous examples of oversummering,

including an adult drake and a winged female at Killington Reservoir as long ago as June 1949 (Brown 1974), the Goldeneye has so far failed to fulfil expectations. Nestboxes erected in hope at Bassenthwaite Lake in the early 1990s remain unused. Still, birds do regularly linger well into May and reappear as early as the first few days of July.

During the period of *this Atlas*, birds were recorded in 11 10km squares, though the majority are likely to have been late spring migrants. However, single birds summered at Cavendish Dock in 1999; on the River Kent near Kendal in both 1999 and 2000 and at Bassenthwaite Lake and Ormsgill Reservoir in 2000, though the one on the River Kent, at least, was an injured individual. In addition, a pair was seen on the River Esk off Rockcliffe Marsh between 17th and 30th June 2000. The spread into the Borders Region of Scotland offers some prospect of future colonization but feral or released birds perhaps provide a more likely source for more imminent breeding in the county.

**Long-tailed Duck**   *Clangula hyemalis*
In Britain and Ireland, during the 19th and early 20th centuries, Long-tailed Ducks bred sporadically on Orkney and Shetland (Thom 1986). More recently, despite the presence, mainly of single birds, at various sites in Scotland, the only evidence of breeding concerns a pair that was strongly suspected to have bred on the Western Isles in 1969 (Mead 2000). In Cumbria there have been a number of instances of immature drakes oversummering, including birds at South Walney in 1986, Cavendish Dock in 1989 and Hodbarrow in 1990. More recently, what was considered to be the same returning individual consorted annually with Eiders at South Walney between 1993–1995.

During *this Atlas*, a drake again summered at South Walney in 2000, and what was presumably the same bird reappeared with a female in 2001. However, despite venturing onto the vegetated islands, amongst the gravel pools, on a number of occasions, there was no further evidence that a breeding attempt occurred.

**Avocet**   *Recurvirostra avosetta*   Pied Avocet
The Avocet first appeared in the county on 11th August 1934, when three were on the Kent Estuary (Blezard *et al* 1943). Since then, another 26 birds have been recorded and the species has become almost annual in recent years. In Britain, Avocets remain largely restricted to the southern and eastern counties of England but both the number of localities and the numbers of pairs are on the increase (Ogilvie *et al* 1999). A pair nested for the first time just outside the county at Leighton Moss, Lancashire in 2001 and

colonization of Cumbria is a possibility in the future. During *this Atlas*, a single bird appeared at Hodbarrow on 6th April 1998.

**Black Redstart** *Phoenicurus ochruros*
Although breeding has never been conclusively proven in the county, a young bird at South Walney on 14th July 1985 was only recently out of the nest and raised speculation that it had been reared locally (Dean 1990). Latest available data reveals that 15–50 breeding pairs were located in Britain during 1999 with a stronghold in southeast England (Ogilvie *et al* 2001). However a few pairs are now breeding in city centres as close as Greater Manchester and Lancashire, so perhaps Kendal, Carlisle or Barrow-in-Furness are likely candidates to hold future breeding pairs.

**Redwing** *Turdus iliacus*
In Britain, breeding Redwings are currently to be found only around and north of the Great Glen, but they have bred in a few English counties, particularly Kent, where at least five pairs bred between 1975 and 1991 (Gibbons *et al* 1993). Over the years, a few records have suggested the possibility of breeding in Cumbria. These include one in song in Lakeland on 28th June 1958 (Stokoe 1962); two at Burneside, near Kendal on 10th July 1971; a summering bird at High Harrington, near Workington in 1975; a singing male in the Upper Irthing on 1st June 1980; and a bird found dead near Grange-over-Sands on 19th July 1982 (Hutcheson 1986). More recently, one was near Dalston on 25th July 1987.

There was one interesting record, perhaps indicative of breeding, during *this Atlas*: at Spadeadam on 21st June 2000 a bird – presumably male – was singing on the edge of moorland bordered by mature plantations, where scattered trees advance across open country.

**Spanish Sparrow** *Passer hispaniolensis*
The male Spanish Sparrow, which resided in the village of Waterside, near Wigton from 13th July 1996 to 13th December 1998, was undoubtedly the most famous and well-watched individual bird ever recorded in the county. Despite singing his heart out and displaying enthusiastically, even to the extent of carrying nesting material on occasions, he apparently failed to convince any of the local female House Sparrows of his charms. This most unlikely episode in Cumbrian ornithology will surely never be repeated.

# Appendices

## Table A – Line Transect Survey results (pages 264–267)

This table show the results of the line transect work (253 visits to 141 1km² squares) described on pages 28–32. Note that the table includes only those species for which estimates were calculated from line transect data. Thus colonial-nesting species do not appear. For a proportion of species, other means of estimating population size were preferred to the line transect estimate. Column (9) of Table D summarises the method(s) used in each case. See also the discussion on page 35.

For each species, the tables provide the following data:

- 'Basis' – the data used to calculate the population (E = early count only, L = late count only, A = all data). For some species, particularly passerines, only counts of male birds were used. These are indicated by 'M'.
- 'Sample size' – this is the number of birds seen on the count used.
- 'Mean (range)' – the calculated mean is provided, with 95% confidence limits in brackets below. Allowing for rounding, the population estimate for Wren lies between 114,000 and 166,000 singing males. The mean population is estimated to be 138,000 males (implying about 130,000 pairs). Dipper, the estimate for which is based purely on the count of individual birds (sex unknown), gives a population of between 3,000 and 14,000 individuals (implying 1,500 to 7,000 pairs).
- At the top of each table is given the National Land Class number (ie. 5 to 25) of Land Classes occurring in Cumbria, with their area in the county given in square kilometres in brackets. (Note that none of the randomly selected line transect squares fell within Land Classes 6 (area 3km²) and 9 (area 31km²), so these do not appear in the table.)
- For each species where it could be calculated, there is a breakdown of the population estimate for each Land Class. These are summed to give the mean figure. Below the estimate is the percentage of the population occurring in that Land Class. Note that the breakdown could not be calculated for eleven species, for which the boxes remain blank.

We calculated population estimates for both the data stratified by National Land Class and the unstratified results. If these were statistically not significant (tested using a student's t-test), we used the stratified estimate in the table. This provides useful information about which areas are more important for the species. Where differences did occur, we used the unstratified estimate e.g. for Dipper.

It was also necessary to group together some of the smaller land classes for some species. These amalgamated land classes are 'boxed in' in the tables. It was felt that this would provide more useful information than simply using the unstratified Cumbrian data, eg. for Pied Wagtail.

## Table B – National Land Classification areas in Cumbria; areas sampled (page 368)

Areas of National Land Classes in Cumbria, with areas of each Land Class sampled in the Line Transect Survey.

## Map A: Cumbria – National Land Classification (pages 368–369)

Shows the Land Class for every 1km square in the county.

## Table C – Habitat codes (page 370)

Habitat codes used in Line Transect Survey (see page 29).

## Table D – Population size estimates (pages 372–376)

See page 371 for explanation.

## Gazetteer of place names (pages 377–378)

## Scientific names of other taxa (page 379)

| Species | Basis | Sample size | Mean (range) | 5 (15) | 7 (58) | 8 (232) | 10 (255) | 13 (839) | 15 (289) | 16 (733) | 17 (115) | 18 (543) | 19 (1809) | 22 (628) | 23 (659) | 25 (796) |
|---|---|---|---|---|---|---|---|---|---|---|---|---|---|---|---|---|
| Greylag Goose | E | 10 | 1,591 (379 6,686) | | | | | | | | | | | | | |
| Canada Goose | E | 4 | 1,172 (235 5,835) | | | | | | | | | | | | | |
| Shelduck | E | 6 | 2,998 (822 10,938) | | | | | 1,970 65.71% | 56 1.87% | 972 32.42% | | | | | | |
| Mallard | E | 73 | 32,918 (20,863 51,938) | | | 4,106 12.47% | 2,138 6.49% | 852 2.59% | 525 1.59% | 9,668 29.37% | | 3,627 11.02% | 6,131 18.63% | | | 5,871 17.84% |
| Tufted Duck | E | 12 | 6,116 (1,861 20,101) | | | | | | | 3,887 63.55% | | | 2,229 36.45% | | | |
| Goosander | E | 4 | 3,852 (759 19,543) | | | 2,737 71.05% | | | | | | | 1,115 28.95% | | | |
| Sparrowhawk | A | 6 | 946 (230 3,889) | | | | 91 9.62% | | | 51 5.39% | | 674 71.25% | 63 6.66% | | | 67 7.08% |
| Buzzard | E | 29 | 7,552 (2,897 19,690) | | 161 2.13% | | 159 2.11% | | | 103 1.36% | 575 7.61% | 535 7.08% | 1,535 20.33% | | 3,858 51.09% | 626 8.29% |
| Kestrel | E | 13 | 3,511 (1,517 8,126) | | | | | | | 1,445 41.16% | | 272 7.75% | 1,669 47.54% | | | 125 3.56% |
| Peregrine | A | 6 | 543 (106 2,984) | | | | | | | | | 214 39.41% | 63 11.60% | 266 48.99% | | |
| Red Grouse | L | 12 | 5,310 (1,924 14,657) | | | | | | | | | | 118 2.22% | 2,463 46.38% | 2,729 51.39% | |
| Grey Partridge | A | 21 | 5,303 (2,545 10,793) | | | | | 2,005 37.81% | | | | | 1,371 25.85% | | | 1,927 36.34% |
| Pheasant | E | 109 | 18,493 (12,175 28,092) | | | | | 8,238 44.55% | 504 2.73% | 861 4.66% | | 1,734 9.38% | 2,834 15.32% | 1,318 7.13% | | 3,004 16.24% |
| Moorhen | A | 17 | 9,837 (3,201 30,236) | | | | | | | 5,890 59.88% | | | 3,882 39.46% | | | 65 0.66% |
| Coot | A | 18 | 14,748 (3,423 63,543) | | | | | | | | | | | | | |
| Oystercatcher | E | 61 | 14,937 (8,584 26,762) | | | 2,320 15.53% | 2,133 14.28% | 904 6.05% | | 4,064 27.21% | | | 2,901 19.42% | | | 2,615 17.51% |
| Ringed Plover | E | 2 | 580 (4 79,472) | | | 580 100.00% | | | | | | | | | | |
| Golden Plover | L | 21 | 3,412 (1,403 8,302) | | | | | | | | | | | 858 25.15% | 2,554 74.85% | |
| Lapwing | E | 94 | 23,620 (17,463 40,837) | | | | 4,493 19.02% | 1,808 7.65% | | 618 2.62% | | 136 0.58% | 6,757 28.61% | 6,767 28.65% | | 3,041 12.87% |
| Dunlin | E | 1 | 157 (30 818) | | | | | | | | | | | | 157 100.00% | |
| Snipe | E | 13 | 8,231 (3,444 19,668) | | | | | | | | 1,355 16.46% | | 2,760 33.53% | 4,116 50.01% | | |
| Curlew | E | 149 | 21,794 (15,015 31,636) | | | | 478 2.19% | 2,531 11.61% | 840 3.85% | 2,226 10.21% | 287 1.32% | 1,821 8.36% | 8,737 40.09% | 906 4.16% | 618 2.84% | 3,350 15.37% |
| Redshank | E | 3 | 448 (153 1,309) | | | | | 181 40.40% | | | | | | 110 24.55% | 157 35.04% | |
| Common Sandpiper | A | 30 | 10,210 (5,002 20,838) | | | | | | | | | | | | | |
| Feral Pigeon | E | 15 | 9,281 (1,792 48,077) | | | 8,211 88.47% | | | | | | | 945 10.18% | | | 125 1.35% |
| Stock Dove | E | 51 | 12,872 (6,736 24,594) | | | | | | 56 0.44% | 206 1.60% | | | 4,180 32.47% | 2,934 22.79% | | 5,496 42.70% |

*Note: column group header — Land Class nos. (area in sq. km.); Calculated population per Land Class and percentage of population in this Land Class*

**Table A – Line Transect Survey results (1)**

| Species | Basis | Sample size | Mean (range) | 5 (15) | 7 (58) | 8 (232) | 10 (255) | 13 (839) | 15 (289) | 16 (733) | 17 (115) | 18 (543) | 19 (1,809) | 22 (628) | 23 (659) | 25 (796) |
|---|---|---|---|---|---|---|---|---|---|---|---|---|---|---|---|---|
| | | | | | | | Land Class nos. *(area in sq. km.)* | | | | | | Calculated population per Land Class and percentage of population in this Land Class | | | |
| Woodpigeon | E | 261 | 103,976 (81,915 131,980) | | | 3,812 3.67% | 7,663 7.37% | 24,566 23.63% | 1,064 1.02% | 12,210 11.74% | | 9,078 8.73% | 22,446 21.59% | 4,407 4.24% | 157 0.15% | 18,573 17.86% |
| Collared Dove | E | 55 | 17,556 (10,210 30,530) | | | 290 1.64% | 3,009 17.04% | 3,658 20.72% | 1,480 8.38% | 4,064 23.02% | | | | | 157 0.89% | 2,648 15.00% |
| Cuckoo | E | 20 | 2,162 (786 5,952) | | | 290 13.41% | | 181 8.37% | 56 2.59% | 859 39.73% | | | | 220 10.18% | | |
| Little Owl | E | 2 | 507 (29 8,779) | | | | | | | | | | 556 25.72% | | | |
| Tawny Owl | E | 3 | 3,058 (715 13,068) | | | | | | | | | | | | | 507 100.00% |
| Swift | L | 24 | 11,551 (4,403 30,304) | | | | | 1,266 10.96% | | 4,478 38.77% | | | 5,807 50.27% | | | |
| Kingfisher | L | 1 | 103 (14 329) | | | | | | | 103 100.00% | | | | | | |
| Green Woodpecker | E | 6 | 1,214 (319 4,625) | | | | | 181 14.91% | 56 4.61% | 859 70.76% | | | 118 9.72% | | | |
| Great Spotted Woodpecker | E | 30 | 6,976 (3,726 13,066) | | | | | 1,695 24.30% | 1,047 15.01% | 859 12.31% | | 550 7.88% | 1,439 20.63% | | 635 9.10% | 751 10.77% |
| Skylark | E M | 143 | 28,230 (19,225 41,456) | 263 0.93% | | 2,719 9.63% | | 3,126 11.07% | 680 2.41% | 3,294 11.67% | | 2,872 10.17% | 6,278 22.24% | 8,434 29.88% | 314 1.11% | 250 0.89% |
| Swallow | L | 465 | 171,560 (126,760 232,190) | 1,147 0.67% | | 16,423 9.57% | 1,504 0.88% | 13,020 7.59% | 10,012 5.84% | 38,915 22.68% | | 44,764 26.09% | 18,702 10.90% | 1,753 1.02% | | 25,320 14.76% |
| House Martin | L | 152 | 83,555 (52,349 133,370) | | | | | 5,774 6.91% | 1,020 1.22% | 31,822 38.09% | | 24,237 29.01% | 13,987 16.74% | | | 6,715 8.04% |
| Tree Pipit | A M | 97 | 14,784 (9,827 22,240) | | | 145 0.98% | 91 0.62% | 93 0.63% | 473 3.20% | 1,084 7.33% | | 851 5.76% | 6,561 44.38% | 3,371 22.80% | 1,583 10.71% | 532 3.60% |
| Meadow Pipit | L | 1,000 | 414,458 (366,430 468,790) | 861 0.21% | 483 0.12% | 16,279 3.93% | | 6,999 1.69% | 6,264 1.51% | 19,471 4.70% | 7,147 1.72% | 66,860 16.13% | 125,330 30.24% | 65,455 15.79% | 98,135 23.68% | 1,174 0.28% |
| Grey Wagtail | E | 17 | 10,331 (4,556 23,436) | | | | 159 1.54% | | 751 7.27% | 417 4.04% | 287 2.78% | 1,281 12.40% | 7,311 70.77% | | | 125 1.21% |
| Pied Wagtail | E | 176 | 96,573 (76,623 126,610) | | 10,176 10.54% | | 645 0.67% | 19,097 19.77% | 1,641 1.70% | 12,639 13.09% | 287 0.30% | 9,516 9.85% | 29,252 30.29% | 3,088 3.20% | 157 0.16% | 10,075 10.43% |
| Dipper | E | 12 | 6,893 (3,350 14,183) | | | | | | | | | | | | | |
| Wren | E M | 395 | 137,908 (114,400 166,260) | | 1,521 1.10% | 8,870 6.43% | 2,581 1.87% | 36,026 26.12% | 2,169 1.57% | 24,821 18.00% | | 6,692 4.85% | 25,790 18.70% | 4,500 3.26% | 3,551 2.57% | 21,387 15.51% |
| Dunnock | E | 138 | 83,335 (63,334 109,810) | | 7,820 9.38% | | | 36,339 43.61% | 1,575 1.89% | 10,618 12.74% | 5,276 6.33% | | 9,687 11.62% | | | 12,020 14.42% |
| Robin | E | 527 | 237,211 (204,960 271,520) | 177 0.07% | 161 0.07% | 8,536 3.60% | 1,315 0.55% | 57,411 24.20% | 15,881 6.69% | 30,186 12.73% | | 14,126 5.96% | 49,633 20.92% | 5,195 2.19% | 1,569 0.66% | 53,021 22.35% |
| Redstart | E M | 52 | 14,789 (9,366 23,524) | | | 319 2.16% | | 852 5.76% | 227 1.53% | 1,623 10.97% | | 543 3.67% | 10,833 73.25% | 110 0.74% | 157 1.06% | 125 0.85% |
| Whinchat | L M | 7 | 2,905 (909 9,373) | | | | | 181 6.23% | | | | 136 4.68% | 1,107 38.11% | | 1,481 50.98% | |
| Stonechat | L M | 13 | 2,598 (1,015 6,651) | | 161 6.20% | | | | | 445 17.13% | | 550 21.17% | 1,113 42.84% | 329 12.66% | | |
| Wheatear | L M | 55 | 30,726 (21,464 46,339) | | 161 0.52% | | | | | 485 1.58% | | 7,620 24.80% | 11,977 38.98% | | 7,555 24.59% | |
| Ring Ouzel | L M | 12 | 1,248 (289 5,834) | | | | | | | | | 299 23.96% | 118 9.46% | 517 41.43% | 314 25.16% | |
| Blackbird | E M | 386 | 171,807 (146,520 201,440) | 177 0.10% | | 16,702 9.72% | 5,622 3.27% | 53,992 31.43% | 11,293 6.57% | 23,394 13.62% | | 4,623 2.69% | 20,905 12.17% | 4,106 2.39% | | 30,993 18.04% |

**Table A – Line Transect Survey results (2)**

| Species | Basis | Sample size | Mean (range) | 5 (15) | 7 (58) | 8 (232) | 10 (255) | 13 (839) | 15 (289) | 16 (733) | 17 (115) | 18 (543) | 19 (1,809) | 22 (628) | 23 (659) | 25 (796) |
|---|---|---|---|---|---|---|---|---|---|---|---|---|---|---|---|---|
| | | | | Land Class nos. *(area in sq. km.)* | | | | Calculated population per Land Class and percentage of population in this Land Class | | | | | | | | |
| Song Thrush | E | 163 | 61,357 (45,844  82,118) | | | 6,001 9.78% | 8,215 13.39% | 12,938 21.09% | 1,388 2.26% | 12,191 19.87% | 287 0.47% | 2,787 4.54% | 10,980 17.90% | 110 0.18% | 157 0.26% | 6,303 10.27% |
| Mistle Thrush | E | 80 | 27,538 (16,851  45,006) | | 322 1.17% | 2,737 9.94% | 159 0.58% | 6,777 24.61% | 1,267 4.60% | 5,294 19.22% | | 2,321 8.43% | 5,424 19.70% | 475 1.72% | 157 0.57% | 2,605 9.46% |
| Grasshopper Warbler | L M | 1 | 181 (35  941) | | | | | 181 100.00% | | | | | | | | |
| Sedge Warbler | E M | 7 | 4,103 (1,353  13,431) | 37 0.90% | | | | 2,560 62.39% | | 1,381 33.66% | | | | | | 125 3.05% |
| Reed Warbler | L M | 2 | 1,584 (254  9,860) | | | | | | | | | | 1,584 100.00% | | | |
| Lesser Whitethroat | E M | 6 | 1,483 (199  11,045) | | | 1,143 77.07% | 159 10.72% | | 56 3.78% | | | | | | | 125 8.43% |
| Common Whitethroat | E M | 48 | 18,395 (11,269  30,027) | | 161 0.88% | 1,143 6.21% | | 10,823 58.84% | 112 0.61% | 2,853 15.51% | | | | | | 3,303 17.96% |
| Blackcap | E M | 65 | 24,069 (15,803  36,661) | | | 2,421 10.06% | 1,494 6.21% | 6,095 25.32% | 487 2.02% | 4,952 20.57% | | 640 2.66% | 2,903 12.06% | | | 5,077 21.09% |
| Garden Warbler | L M | 48 | 16,070 (10,081  25,616) | | | | 159 0.99% | 1,704 10.60% | 1,487 9.25% | 3,133 19.50% | | 1,821 11.33% | 3,612 22.48% | | | 4,154 25.85% |
| Wood Warbler | E M | 9 | 4,096 (1,555  10,796) | | | | | 852 20.80% | | | | | 510 12.45% | | | 2,734 66.75% |
| Chiffchaff | E M | 37 | 10,971 (5,252  22,916) | | | 2,737 24.95% | 159 1.45% | 2,846 25.94% | 728 6.64% | 805 7.34% | | | 1,664 15.17% | | | 2,032 18.52% |
| Willow Warbler | E M | 584 | 243,264 (208,420  283,930) | 162 0.07% | 483 0.20% | 28,151 11.57% | 11,685 4.80% | 33,285 13.68% | 4,731 1.94% | 24,294 9.99% | | 14,499 5.96% | 60,469 24.86% | 20,064 8.25% | 2,620 1.08% | 42,821 17.60% |
| Goldcrest | E | 74 | 32,293 (19,129  54,511) | | | 7,131 22.08% | 159 0.49% | | 3,575 11.07% | 2,070 6.41% | | 535 1.66% | 11,267 34.89% | 6,542 20.26% | | 1,014 3.14% |
| Spotted Flycatcher | L | 36 | 24,504 (15,692  38,265) | | | | | | | | | | | | | |
| Pied Flycatcher | E M | 13 | 4,667 (2,034  10,710) | | | | | | | 445 9.54% | | | 4,222 90.46% | | | |
| Long-tailed Tit | E | 24 | 11,543 (5,868  22,708) | | | | 2,772 24.01% | | 610 5.28% | 970 8.40% | | | 2,573 22.29% | | 1,310 11.35% | 3,308 28.66% |
| Marsh Tit | E | 3 | 541 (42  6,969) | | | | | | 56 10.35% | 485 89.65% | | | | | | |
| Coal Tit | E | 66 | 30,854 (21,384  44,519) | | | | | | | | | | | | | |
| Blue Tit | E | 451 | 248,472 (214,300  288,090) | | | 10,297 4.14% | 8,490 3.42% | 25,453 10.24% | 17,062 6.87% | 38,788 15.61% | | 18,950 7.63% | 60,302 24.27% | 2,700 1.09% | 8,429 3.39% | 58,001 23.34% |
| Great Tit | E | 214 | 106,632 (85,388  133,160) | | | 4,070 3.82% | 1,494 1.40% | 26,468 24.82% | 4,539 4.26% | 20,438 19.17% | | 2,546 2.39% | 13,573 12.73% | 110 0.10% | 4,193 3.93% | 29,201 27.38% |
| Nuthatch | E | 15 | 4,564 (1,997  10,430) | | | | | | 56 1.23% | 445 9.75% | | | 354 7.76% | | | 3,709 81.27% |
| Treecreeper | A | 28 | 8,572 (4,901  14,998) | | | | 2,403 28.03% | | 305 3.56% | 690 8.05% | | | 2,355 27.47% | | 132 1.54% | 2,687 31.35% |
| Jay | E | 8 | 914 (235  3,559) | | | | | | 56 6.13% | 103 11.27% | | 136 14.88% | 494 54.05% | | | 125 13.68% |
| Magpie | E | 66 | 19,010 (12,312  29,353) | | | | | | | | | | | | | |
| Jackdaw | E | 412 | 152,597 (112,520  206,960) | 37 0.02% | | | 1,504 0.99% | 12,949 8.49% | 5,461 3.58% | 14,093 9.24% | | 5,715 3.75% | 40,639 26.63% | 24,257 15.90% | | 47,942 31.42% |
| Carrion Crow | E | 318 | 66,140 (52,289  83,659) | 37 0.06% | | 2,421 3.66% | 5,621 8.50% | 13,121 19.84% | 1,442 2.18% | 8,219 12.43% | 1,164 1.76% | 7,688 11.62% | 18,166 27.47% | 1,473 2.23% | 157 0.24% | 6,631 10.03% |

**Table A – Line Transect Survey results (3)**

| Species | Basis | Sample size | Mean (range) | Land Class nos. (area in sq. km.) / Calculated population per Land Class and percentage of population in this Land Class | | | | | | | | | | | | |
|---|---|---|---|---|---|---|---|---|---|---|---|---|---|---|---|---|
| | | | | 5 (15) | 7 (58) | 8 (232) | 10 (255) | 13 (839) | 15 (289) | 16 (733) | 17 (115) | 18 (543) | 19 (1,809) | 22 (628) | 23 (659) | 25 (796) |
| Raven | E | 2 | 254 (72 – 891) | | | | | | | | | 136 53.54% | 118 46.46% | | | |
| Starling | E | 500 | 209,767 (160,700 – 273,820) | | | 33,847 16.14% | 159 0.08% | 68,425 32.62% | 4,583 2.18% | 32,271 15.38% | | 3,338 1.59% | 28,470 13.57% | 110 0.05% | | 38,564 18.38% |
| House Sparrow | E | 608 | 336,283 (263,080 – 429,860) | | 13,829 4.11% | | | 127,560 37.93% | 31,441 9.35% | 33,094 9.84% | 5,203 9.84% | | 20,926 6.22% | | | 104,230 30.99% |
| Tree Sparrow | E | 28 | 20,203 (7,626 – 53,519) | | | | 645 3.19% | 4,832 23.92% | | | | | 11,423 56.54% | | | 3,303 16.35% |
| Chaffinch | E M | 726 | 360,987 (316,350 – 411,910) | 352 0.10% | | 12,710 3.52% | 9,186 2.54% | 108,430 30.04% | 15,909 4.41% | 40,519 11.22% | 287 0.08% | 15,251 4.22% | 71,494 19.81% | 17,985 4.98% | 4,233 1.17% | 64,631 17.90% |
| Greenfinch | A | 259 | 68,757 (53,890 – 87,724) | | | 3,168 4.61% | 5,373 7.81% | 13,799 20.07% | 7,424 10.80% | 13,144 19.12% | 144 0.21% | 11,112 16.16% | 2,648 3.85% | 1,809 2.63% | 264 0.38% | 9,872 14.36% |
| Goldfinch | E | 140 | 87,955 (65,154 – 118,740) | | | | | | | | | | | | | |
| Siskin | A | 27 | 10,860 (2,857 – 19,345) | | | | | | | 1,839 16.93% | 2,725 25.09% | | 1,187 10.93% | 266 2.45% | | 4,843 44.59% |
| Linnet | E | 155 | 93,881 (55,865 – 123,620) | 503 0.54% | 322 0.34% | 35,460 37.77% | 1,504 1.60% | 28,466 30.32% | 3,258 3.47% | 5,294 5.64% | | | 15,246 16.24% | | | 3,828 4.08% |
| Lesser Redpoll | E | 19 | 7,004 (3,548 – 13,825) | | | | | | | | | | | 69 100.00% | | |
| Crossbill | A | 1 | 69 (15 – 312) | | | | | | | | | | | | | |
| Bullfinch | E | 7 | 6,258 (1,743 – 22,474) | | | | | 4,446 71.05% | | 103 1.65% | | | 1,584 25.31% | | | 125 2.00% |
| Hawfinch | A | 2 | 486 (68 – 3,642) | | | | | | | 486 100.00% | | | | | | |
| Yellowhammer | A | 179 | 44,296 (34,203 – 59,759) | 88 0.20% | | | 1,948 4.40% | 19,263 43.49% | 132 0.30% | 2,431 5.49% | | 7,326 16.54% | 6,710 15.15% | 69 0.16% | 1,236 2.79% | 5,093 11.50% |
| Reed Bunting | E M | 11 | 2,949 (1,188 – 7,321) | | | | | 181 6.14% | 1,377 46.69% | 103 3.49% | | 136 4.61% | 1,027 34.83% | | | 125 4.24% |

**Table A – Line Transect Survey results (4)**

## Table B: Areas of each National Land Class (NLC) in Cumbria and areas sampled

| NLC number | 5 | 6 | 7 | 8 | 9 | 10 | 13 | 15 | 16 | 17 | 18 | 19 | 22 | 23 |
|---|---|---|---|---|---|---|---|---|---|---|---|---|---|---|
| Total area (km²) | 15 | 3 | 58 | 232 | 31 | 255 | 839 | 289 | 733 | 115 | 534 | 1,809 | 628 | 659 |
| *% of total* | 0.21 | 0.04 | 0.83 | 3.31 | 0.44 | 3.64 | 11.98 | 4.13 | 10.46 | 1.64 | 7.75 | 25.82 | 8.97 | 9.41 |
| Squares sampled | 1 | 0 | 1 | 2 | 0 | 4 | 12 | 13 | 18 | 1 | 10 | 39 | 15 | 11 |
| *% of total* | 0.70 | 0.00 | 0.70 | 1.40 | 0.00 | 2.80 | 8.39 | 9.09 | 12.59 | 0.70 | 6.99 | 27.27 | 10.49 | 7.69 |
| Early samples | 1 | 0 | 1 | 2 | 0 | 3 | 12 | 13 | 18 | 1 | 10 | 35 | 9 | 2 |
| *% of total* | 0.81 | 0.00 | 0.81 | 1.63 | 0.00 | 2.44 | 9.76 | 10.57 | 14.63 | 0.81 | 8.13 | 28.46 | 7.32 | 1.63 |
| Late samples | 1 | 0 | 1 | 2 | 0 | 4 | 11 | 13 | 18 | 1 | 9 | 38 | 15 | 11 |
| *% of total* | 0.72 | 0.00 | 0.72 | 1.44 | 0.00 | 2.88 | 7.91 | 9.35 | 12.95 | 0.72 | 6.47 | 27.34 | 10.79 | 7.91 |

## Map A – National Land Classes in Cumbria (opposite)

The Land Classes represented in Cumbria. The dominant Land Class in each 1km square is plotted. (Map derived from data-file kindly provided by C.E.H.)

## Summary descriptions

(For full descriptions, see Benefield *et al* 1982)

**Land Class 5 (15km²):** Lowland somewhat enclosed land; varied agriculture and vegetation

**Land Class 6 (3km²):** Gently rolling country; mainly fertile pastures

**Land Class 7 (58km²):** Coastal, with varied morphology and vegetation

**Land Class 8 (232km²):** Coastal, often estuarine; mainly pasture, otherwise built-up

**Land Class 9 (31km²):** Fairly flat; often intensive agriculture, often built-up

**Land Class 10 (255km²):** Flat plains with intensive farming, often arable/grass mixture

**Land Class 13 (839km²):** Somewhat variable land forms; heterogeneous land use including urban

**Land Class 15 (289km²):** Valley bottoms with mixed agriculture, predominantly pastoral

**Land Class 16 (733km²):** Undulating lowlands, variable agriculture and native vegetation

**Land Class 17 (115km²):** Rounded intermediate slopes, mainly improvable permanent pasture

**Land Class 18 (543km²):** Rounded hills, some steeper slopes; varied moorlands

**Land Class 19 (1,809km²):** Smooth hills, mainly heather moors; often afforested

**Land Class 22 (628km²):** Margins of high mountains, moorlands; often afforested

**Land Class 23 (659km²):** High mountain summits, with well drained moorlands

**Land Class 25 (796km²):** Lowlands with variable land use, mainly arable

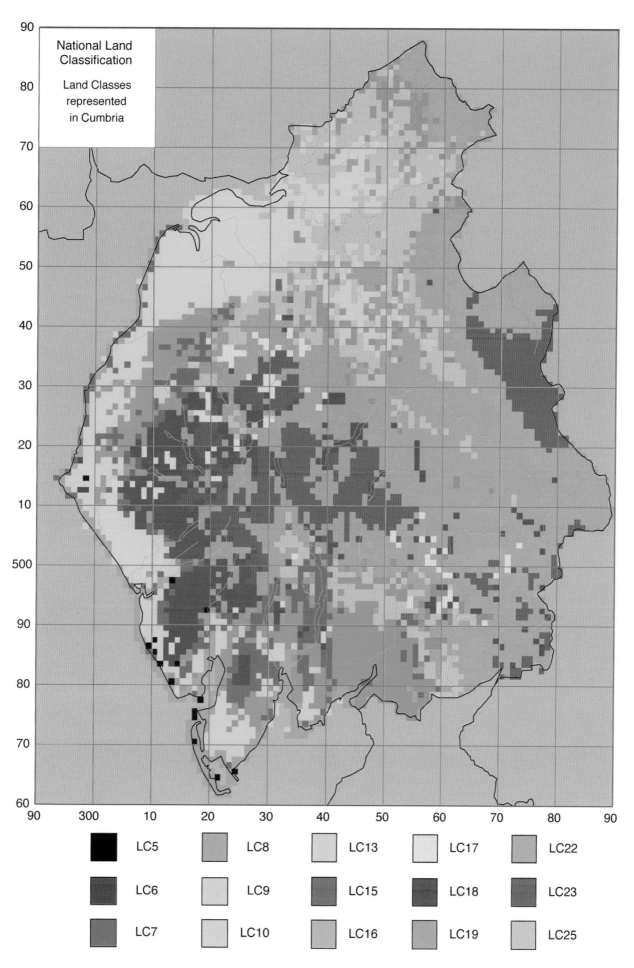

**Map A – National Land Classes in Cumbria**

# Habitat codes for Line Transect Survey

## A Woodland <5m tall

**Level 2**
1 Broadleaved
2 Coniferous
3 Mixed
4 Broadleaved (water-logged)
5 Coniferous (water-logged)
6 Mixed (water-logged)

**Level 3**
1 Mixed-aged or semi-natural
2 Coppice with standards
3 Coppice without standards
4 Plantations
5 Young plantations
6 Parkland
7 High/medium disturbance
8 Low disturbance
9 Near road (within 50m)

**Level 4**
1 Dense shrub layer
2 Moderate shrub layer
3 Sparse shrub layer
4 Dense field layer
5 Moderate field layer
6 Sparse field layer
7 Grazed (moderate to heavy)
8 Lightly grazed
9 Dead wood present
10 Dead wood absent

## B Scrubland or young woodland <5m tall

**Level 2**
1 Regenerating
2 Downland
3 Heath Scrub
4 Young Coppice
5 New plantation
6 Clear felled woodland
7 Other

**Level 3**
1 Broadleaved
2 Coniferous
3 Mixed
4 Broadleaved swamp scrub
5 Coniferous swamp scrub
6 Mixed swamp scrub
7 High/medium disturbance
8 Low disturbance
9 Near road (within 50m)

**Level 4**
1 Predominantly tall (3–5m)
2 Predominately low (1–3m)
3 Dense shrub layer
4 Moderate shrub layer
5 Sparse shrub layer
6 Extensive bracken
7 Dense field layer
8 Moderate field layer
9 Sparse field layer
10 Grazed (moderate to heavy)

## C Semi-natural grassland/marsh

**Level 2**
1 Chalk downland
2 Grass moor
3 Grass moor with heaths
4 Machair
5 Other dry grassland
6 Water meadow
7 Reed swamp
8 Other open marsh
9 Saltmarsh

**Level 3**
1 Hedgerow with trees
2 Hedgerow without trees
3 Tree-line without hedge
4 Other field boundary (wall, ditch etc)
5 Isolated group of 1-10 trees
6 No field boundary
7 Montane
8 High/medium disturbance
9 Low disturbance
10 Near road (within 50m)

**Level 4**
1 Ungrazed
2 Cattle
3 Sheep
4 Horses
5 Rabbits
6 Deer
7 Other grazers
8 Extensive bracken
9 Hay

## D Heathland and bogs

**Level 2**
1 Dry heath
2 Wet heath
3 Mixed heath
4 Bog
5 Breckland
6 Drained bog
7 Bare Peat

**Level 3**
1 Montane
2 Raised bog
3 Valley/basin Bog
4 Blanket Bog
5 Heath mixed with rough grass
6 Heath without grass
7 Heath with extensive bracken
8 Undetermined Bog
9 Isolated group of 1-10 Trees
10 High/medium disturbance
11 Low disturbance
12 Near road (within 50m)

**Level 4**
1 Ungrazed
2 Cattle
3 Sheep
4 Horses
5 Rabbits
6 Deer
7 Other grazers
8 Ploughed
9 Burned
10 Planted with seedlings less than 0.5m tall

## E Farmland

**Level 1** Farmland

**Level 2**
1 Improved Grassland
2 Unimproved Grassland
3 Mixed Grass/filled land
4 Tilled Land
5 Orchard
6 Other farming

**Level 3**
1 Hedgerow with trees
2 Hedgerow without trees
3 Tree-line without hedge (wall, ditch etc)
4 Other field boundary
5 Isolated group of trees
6 Farmyard (active)
7 Near road (within 50m)
8 No field boundary

**Level 4**
1 Ungrazed
2 Cattle
3 Sheep
4 Horses
5 Other stock
6 Bare earth/plough
7 Autumn cereal
8 Spring cereal
9 Root crops
10 Other crops
11 Oil-seed rape
12 Other brassicas
13 Stubble (clean)
14 Stubble (weedy)
15 Unsown/fallow
16 Recently cut grass

## F Human Sites

**Level 2**
1 Urban
2 Suburban
3 Rural

**Level 3**
1 Building
2 Gardens
3 Municipal parks, mown grass, golf courses, recreational areas
4 Sewage works urban
5 Near road (within 50m)
6 Near active railway line (50m)
7 Other
8 Rubbish tip

**Level 4**
1 Industrial
2 Residential
3 Well-wooded
4 Not well wooded
5 Area of large gardens
6 Area of medium gardens
7 Area of small gardens
8 Many shrubs
9 Few shrubs
10 Disused

## G Water bodies (freshwater)

**Level 2**
1 Ponds (>50m²)
2 Small water body (50-450m²)
3 Lake/unlined reservoir
4 Lined reservoir
5 Gravel pit, sand pit etc.
6 Stream (<3m wide)
7 River (>3m wide)
8 Ditch with water (<2m wide)
9 Small canal (2-5m wide)
10 Large canal (>5m wide)

**Level 3**
1 Undisturbed, disused
3 Water Sports (sailing etc)
4 Angling (coarse game)
4 Coarse angling
5 Game fishing
6 Industrial activity
5 Sewage processing (rural)
5 Other disturbance
9 Small island

**Level 4**
1 Eutrophic (green water)
2 Oligotrophic (clear water)
3 Dystrophic (black water)
4 Marl (clear water, large waterweeds)
5 Slow-medium running
6 Fast-running
7 Dredged
8 Undredged
9 banks cleared
10 Banks vegetated

## H Coastal

**Level 2**
1 Marine open shore
2 Marine shore - inlet, cove
3 Estuarine
4 Brackish lagoon
5 Open sea

**Level 3**
1 Mud or silt
2 Sand
3 Shingle
4 Rocky
5 Fully vegetated
6 Sparse/medium vegetation
7 Inter-tidal
5 Below low-water mark

**Level 4**
1 Cliff vertical, steep sloping
2 Dune
3 Flat, gently sloping
4 Small island
5 Spit
6 Dune slack
7 sloping ground
8 Undisturbed
9 Disturbed

## I Inland rock

**Level 2**
1 Cliff
2 Scree/boulder slope
3 Limestone pavement
4 Other rock outcrop
5 Quarry
6 Mine spoil, slag heap
7 Cave

**Level 3**
1 Active
2 Disused
3 Montane
4 Non-montane
5 High disturbance
6 Medium disturbance
7 Low disturbance

**Level 4**
1 Bare rock
2 Low vegetation present (mosses liverworts etc)
3 Grasses present
4 Scrub present

## J Miscellaneous

**Table C – Habitat codes**

## Table D – Population size estimates (pages 372–376)

This table summarises information on population sizes.

Column **8** summarises our estimated Cumbrian population sizes for all breeding species, repeated from the figures in the information box for each species. Figures refer to pairs except where stated in column 1.

Column **9** gives for each species the methods used to estimate the population size. 'Survey data' refers to count information obtained from timed visits to each tetrad. 'Supplementary data' refers to other counts, individual records, etc., submitted during the atlas. 'Colony counts' refer both to counts made during the atlas and other counts made by individuals, conservation bodies, etc. 'Line transect analysis' implies that the mean obtained by analysis of data from the line transect survey has been used. An asterisk (*) indicates that the analysis has been based upon a small sample, and is likely to be less statistically robust. In some cases where neither count data nor line transect analysis proved conclusive, a population figure has been suggested based upon an extrapolation from known or surmised density figures, using the known range as found from atlas fieldwork. 'CRSG data' are counts provided by Cumbria Raptor Study Group.

Column **2** gives the estimated British population, based on Mead (2000) (and converted into 'pairs' by halving, where necessary);

Column **3** gives the number of 10km squares occupied in Britain (from the *New Atlas*);

Column **4** gives the number of 10km squares occupied in Cumbria (from *this Atlas*);

Column **5** gives the Cumbrian range as a proportion of the British range (column 4 divided by column 3, given as a percentage);

Column **6** gives the anticipated Cumbrian population size, based on range (column 2 multiplied by column 5). This makes the assumption that the density in the Cumbrian portions of a species' range matches the density in the range as a whole;

Column **7** calculates 3% of the British figure given in column 2. The area of Cumbria is almost exactly 3% of the area of Britain (6,810km² versus 229,513km²). Thus if a species were to be evenly distributed over the land surface, it would be anticipated that 3% of its population would be in Cumbria.

The figures calculated in columns 6 and 7 are given as indicators against which to compare our Cumbrian population estimates. **Note that we quote such figures purely for interest: they have no statistical rigour,** and must not be read, or quoted, without due recognition of the provisos below.

Clearly for **no** species are the assumptions of uniform distribution and density, given above, closely approached; the nearest approximation will be for those species with the widest habitat occupancy and the widest range. The rarer, or the more localized, the species in Cumbrian and/or overall British terms, the less closely will the figures approach reality. The relevance of the figures will also reflect the accuracy of the population estimates for Britain, as quoted, on which they are based. The discerning reader will be able to assess the relevance of anticipated figures, in the particular circumstances of any individual species, and hence how they may or may not make a useful comparison with our estimated population figure. With these provisos kept firmly in mind, some of the figures – more especially for the commonest or most widespread species – make interesting comparisons.

Note that the anticipated figures have not been calculated for two groups of species, colonial species (where the distribution is too localized to make a useful comparison), and irregularly nesting species.

| 1. Species | 2. British population estimate (pairs except where indicated in column 1) | 3. Number of 10km squares occupied in Britain (from *New Atlas* data) | 4. Number of 10km squares occupied in Cumbria (from *this Atlas* data) | 5. Cumbrian range as % of British range based on 10km squares ocupied | 6. Anticipated Cumbrian population based on proportion of 10km squares (pairs) | 7. Anticipated Cumbrian population as 3% of British population (pairs) | 8. *This Atlas* population estimate for Cumbria (pairs except where indicated in col. 1) | 9. Methods used in estimating county population |
|---|---|---|---|---|---|---|---|---|
| Little Grebe | 7,500 | 1,275 | 41 | 3.2% | 241 | 225 | 100–120 | Survey data (etc) |
| Great Crested Grebe | 4,000 | 892 | 31 | 3.5% | 139 | 120 | 90–110 | Survey data (etc) |
| Black-necked Grebe | 55 | | | | | | 0–1 | Supplementary data |
| Fulmar | 539,000 | | | | | | 40–85 | Colony counts |
| Cormorant | 7,000 | | | | | | 120–150 | Colony counts |
| Grey Heron | 5,000 | | | | | | 270–300 | Colony counts |
| Mute Swan | 12,875 | 1,579 | 49 | 3.1% | 400 | 386 | 100–120 | Survey data (etc) |
| Greylag Goose | 7,150 | 718 | 51 | 7.1% | 508 | 214 | 500–600 | BTO & WWT data (etc) |
| Canada Goose | 23,350 | 1,196 | 42 | 3.5% | 820 | 700 | 100–150 | BTO & WWT data (etc) |
| Shelduck | 10,600 | 959 | 33 | 3.4% | 365 | 318 | 700 | Extrapolation of abundance data |
| Mandarin Duck | 3,500 | 218 | 3 | 1.4% | 48 | 105 | 5–10 | Survey data (etc) |
| Wigeon | 400 | 360 | 18 | 5.0% | 20 | 12 | 2–3 | Survey & supplementary data |
| Gadwall | 770 | 357 | 10 | 2.8% | 22 | 23 | 10–12 | Survey & supplementary data |
| Teal | 2,050 | 1,147 | 36 | 3.1% | 64 | 61 | 30–50 | Survey data (etc) |
| Mallard | 115,000 | 2,596 | 89 | 3.4% | 3,943 | 3,450 | 16,000 | Line transect analysis |
| Shoveler | 1,250 | 454 | 19 | 4.2% | 52 | 37 | 3–5 | Survey & supplementary data |
| Pochard | 380 | 511 | 10 | 2.0% | 7 | 11 | 3–5 | Survey & supplementary data |
| Tufted Duck | 7,500 | 1,484 | 56 | 3.8% | 283 | 225 | 400–550 | Extrapolation of abundance data |
| Eider – females | 31,000 | | | | | | 550–1,100 | Colony counts |
| Red-breasted Merganser | 2,200 | 674 | 33 | 4.9% | 108 | 66 | 120–150 | Survey & supplementary data (etc) |
| Goosander | 2,600 | 674 | 63 | 9.3% | 243 | 78 | 300–350 | Survey & supplementary data (etc) |
| Ruddy Duck | 570 | 292 | 10 | 3.4% | 20 | 17 | 3–5 | Survey & supplementary data |
| Honey Buzzard | 61 | 27 | 2 | 7.4% | 5 | 2 | 2–4 | Supplementary & CRSG data |
| Hen Harrier | 570 | 498 | 16 | 3.2% | 18 | 17 | 0–4 | CRSG data (etc) |
| Goshawk | 347 | 236 | 20 | 8.5% | 29 | 10 | 10–15 | Supplementary & CRSG data |
| Sparrowhawk | 32,000 | 2,178 | 79 | 3.6% | 1,161 | 960 | 1,000 | Survey data, supplementary & CRSG |
| Buzzard | 14,500 | 1,544 | 81 | 5.2% | 761 | 435 | 3,500 | Line transect analysis |
| Golden Eagle | 420 | 408 | 1 | 0.2% | 1 | 13 | 1 | CRSG data (etc) |
| Osprey | 136 | 168 | 8 | 4.8% | 6 | 4 | 3 | CRSG data (etc) |
| Kestrel | 50,000 | 2,481 | 84 | 3.4% | 1,693 | 1,500 | 1,500 | Line transect analysis |
| Merlin | 1,300 | 693 | 33 | 4.8% | 62 | 39 | 50 | Survey data & CRSG data |

**Table D – population size estimates (1)**

| 1. Species | 2. British population estimate (pairs except where indicated in column 1) | 3. Number of 10km squares occupied in Britain (from *New Atlas* data) | 4. Number of 10km squares occupied in Cumbria (from *this Atlas* data) | 5. Cumbrian range as % of British range based on 10km squares occupied | 6. Anticipated Cumbrian population based on proportion of 10km squares (pairs) | 7. Anticipated Cumbrian population as 3% of British population (pairs) | 8. *This Atlas* population estimate for Cumbria (pairs except where indicated in col. 1) | 9. Methods used in estimating county population |
|---|---|---|---|---|---|---|---|---|
| Peregrine Falcon | 1,200 | 1,048 | 56 | 5.3% | 64 | 36 | 90–100 | CRSG (etc) |
| Red Grouse | 250,000 | 945 | 47 | 5.0% | 12,434 | 7,500 | 2,500–3,000 | Extrapolation of density data |
| Black Grouse – males | 15,000 | 432 | 13 | 3.0% | 451 | 450 | 185 | North Pennines Black Grouse Project |
| Red-legged Partridge | 170,000 | 1,214 | 33 | 2.7% | 4,621 | 5,100 | 60–80 | Survey & supplementary data |
| Grey Partridge | 145,000 | 1,629 | 68 | 4.2% | 6,053 | 4,350 | 2,500 | Line transect analysis |
| Quail | 300 | 804 | 10 | 1.2% | 4 | 9 | 1–2 | Survey & supplementary data |
| Pheasant | 1,550,000 | 2,269 | 87 | 3.8% | 59,431 | 46,500 | 9,000 | Line transect analysis |
| Water Rail | 700 | 420 | 10 | 2.4% | 17 | 21 | 20–40 | Extrapolation of density data |
| Corncrake | 640 | 161 | 3 | 1.9% | 12 | 19 | 0–2 | Supplementary data |
| Moorhen | 240,000 | 2,032 | 73 | 3.6% | 8,622 | 7,200 | 4,500 | Line transect analysis (*) |
| Coot | 23,000 | 1,603 | 69 | 4.3% | 990 | 690 | 800–1,200 | Survey & supplementary data |
| Oystercatcher | 38,000 | 1,702 | 88 | 5.2% | 1,965 | 1,140 | 7,000 | Line transect analysis |
| Little Ringed Plover | 950 | 421 | 7 | 1.7% | 16 | 28 | 2–5 | Supplementary data |
| Ringed Plover | 8,500 | 1,025 | 27 | 2.6% | 224 | 255 | 200–250 | Survey & supplementary data |
| Dotterel | 900 | 99 | 9 | 9.1% | 82 | 27 | 1–2 | Supplementary data |
| Golden Plover | 22,600 | 784 | 30 | 3.8% | 865 | 678 | 1,500 | Line transect analysis (*) |
| Lapwing | 126,300 | 2,340 | 84 | 3.6% | 4,534 | 3,789 | 11,500 | Line transect analysis |
| Dunlin | 9,500 | 569 | 17 | 3.0% | 284 | 285 | 15–25 | Supplementary data |
| Snipe | 55,000 | 1,806 | 67 | 3.7% | 2,040 | 1,650 | 4,000 | Line transect analysis (*) |
| Woodcock | 15,000 | 1,204 | 42 | 3.5% | 523 | 450 | 600–1,000 | Extrapolation of density data |
| Curlew | 35,500 | 1,893 | 85 | 4.5% | 1,594 | 1,065 | 10,500 | Line transect analysis |
| Redshank | 32,100 | 1,473 | 63 | 4.3% | 1,373 | 963 | 250 | Survey data (etc) |
| Common Sandpiper | 15,800 | 1,424 | 67 | 4.7% | 743 | 474 | 5,000 | Line transect analysis (*) |
| Mediterranean Gull | 54 | | | | | | 1–2 | Supplementary data |
| Black-headed Gull | 167,000 | | | | | | 6,000 | Colony counts |
| Common Gull | 68,000 | | | | | | 0–1 | Supplementary data |
| Lesser Black-backed Gull | 83,000 | | | | | | 32,000–35,000 | Colony counts |
| Herring Gull | 160,000 | | | | | | 10,000–13,000 | Colony counts |
| Great Black-backed Gull | 19,000 | | | | | | 130–180 | Colony counts |
| Kittiwake | 490,000 | | | | | | 1,000–1,500 | Colony counts |
| Sandwich Tern | 14,000 | | | | | | 300–380 | Colony counts |

**Table D – population size estimates (2)**

| 1. Species | 2. British population estimate (pairs except where indicated in column 1) | 3. Number of 10km squares occupied in Britain (from *New Atlas* data) | 4. Number of 10km squares occupied in Cumbria (from *this Atlas* data) | 5. Cumbrian range as % of British range based on 10km squares occupied | 6. Anticipated Cumbrian population based on proportion of 10km squares (pairs) | 7. Anticipated Cumbrian population as 3% of British population (pairs) | 8. *This Atlas* population estimate for Cumbria (pairs except where indicated in col. 1) | 9. Methods used in estimating county population |
|---|---|---|---|---|---|---|---|---|
| Common Tern | 12,300 | | | | | | 60–100 | Colony counts |
| Arctic Tern | 44,000 | | | | | | 60 | Colony counts |
| Little Tern | 2,400 | | | | | | 70–80 | Colony counts |
| Guillemot – adults | 1,050,000 | | | | | | 6,540 | Colony counts |
| Razorbill – adults | 148,000 | | | | | | 242 | Colony counts |
| Black Guillemot – adults | 36,500 | | | | | | 8 | Colony counts |
| Puffin – adults | 898,000 | | | | | | 10 | Colony counts |
| Feral Pigeon | 200,000 | 2,086 | 60 | 2.9% | 5,753 | 6,000 | 4,500 | Line transect analysis (*) |
| Stock Dove | 240,000 | 1,821 | 73 | 4.0% | 9,621 | 7,200 | 6,000 | Line transect analysis |
| Woodpigeon | 2,350,000 | 2,510 | 89 | 3.5% | 83,327 | 70,500 | 50,000 | Line transect analysis |
| Collared Dove | 200,000 | 2,210 | 72 | 3.3% | 6,516 | 6,000 | 8,500 | Line transect analysis |
| Cuckoo | 19,500 | 2,418 | 77 | 3.2% | 621 | 585 | 1,000 | Line transect analysis (*) |
| Barn Owl | 4,400 | 1,110 | 53 | 4.8% | 210 | 132 | 150–200 | Survey data & CRSG data |
| Little Owl | 9,000 | 1,228 | 53 | 4.3% | 388 | 270 | 250–500 | Supplementary data (etc) |
| Tawny Owl | 20,000 | 2,054 | 72 | 3.5% | 701 | 600 | 5,000 | Extrapolation of density data |
| Long-eared Owl | 2,350 | 445 | 10 | 2.2% | 53 | 70 | 10–15 | Supplementary data (etc) |
| Short-eared Owl | 2,250 | 679 | 18 | 2.7% | 60 | 67 | 15–30 | Survey & supplementary data (etc) |
| Nightjar | 3,400 | 274 | 4 | 1.5% | 50 | 102 | 2–6 | Survey & supplementary data |
| Swift | 80,000 | 2,215 | 85 | 3.8% | 3,070 | 2,400 | 5,500 | Line transect analysis (*) |
| Kingfisher | 4,400 | 1,224 | 37 | 3.0% | 133 | 132 | 50–100 | Extrapolation of density data |
| Green Woodpecker | 15,000 | 1,555 | 51 | 3.3% | 492 | 450 | 250–300 | Survey & supplementary data (etc) |
| Great Spotted Woodpecker | 27,500 | 1,959 | 78 | 4.0% | 1,095 | 825 | 3,000 | Line transect analysis (*) |
| Lesser Spotted Woodpecker | 4,500 | 790 | 8 | 1.0% | 46 | 135 | 10–15 | Supplementary data |
| Skylark | 1,046,000 | 2,729 | 91 | 3.3% | 34,879 | 31,380 | 28,000 | Line transect analysis |
| Sand Martin | 160,000 | | | | | | 3,500–5,000 | Survey data |
| Swallow | 570,000 | 2,626 | 91 | 3.5% | 19,752 | 17,100 | 85,000 | Line transect analysis |
| House Martin | 375,000 | 2,393 | 84 | 3.5% | 13,163 | 11,250 | 41,500 | Line transect analysis |
| Tree Pipit | 120,000 | 1,524 | 64 | 4.2% | 5,039 | 3,600 | 14,000 | Line transect analysis |
| Meadow Pipit | 1,900,000 | 2,539 | 94 | 3.7% | 70,343 | 57,000 | 205,000 | Line transect analysis |
| Rock Pipit | 34,000 | 654 | 4 | 0.6% | 208 | 1,020 | 20–40 | Survey & supplementary data (etc) |
| Yellow Wagtail | 50,000 | 1,047 | 22 | 2.1% | 1,051 | 1,500 | 30–50 | Survey & supplementary data (etc) |

**Table D – population size estimates (3)**

| 1. Species | 2. British population estimate (pairs except where indicated in column 1) | 3. Number of 10km squares occupied in Britain (from *New Atlas* data) | 4. Number of 10km squares occupied in Cumbria (from *this Atlas* data) | 5. Cumbrian range as % of British range based on 10km squares occupied | 6. Anticipated Cumbrian population based on proportion of 10km squares (pairs) | 7. Anticipated Cumbrian population as 3% of British population (pairs) | 8. *This Atlas* population estimate for Cumbria (pairs except where indicated in col. 1) | 9. Methods used in estimating county population |
|---|---|---|---|---|---|---|---|---|
| Grey Wagtail | 34,000 | 1,979 | 80 | 4.0% | 1,374 | 1,020 | 5,000 | Line transect analysis (*) |
| Pied Wagtail | 300,000 | 2,669 | 90 | 3.4% | 10,116 | 9,000 | 48,000 | Line transect analysis |
| Dipper | 14,000 | 1,309 | 70 | 5.3% | 749 | 420 | 3,000 | Line transect analysis (*) |
| Wren | 7,100,000 | 2,747 | 93 | 3.4% | 240,371 | 213,000 | 130,000 | Line transect analysis |
| Dunnock | 2,000,000 | 2,511 | 88 | 3.5% | 70,092 | 60,000 | 41,500 | Line transect analysis |
| Robin | 4,200,000 | 2,629 | 91 | 3.5% | 145,378 | 126,000 | 115,000 | Line transect analysis |
| Redstart | 90,000 | 1,327 | 74 | 5.6% | 5,019 | 2,700 | 14,000 | Line transect analysis |
| Whinchat | 21,000 | 1,404 | 63 | 4.5% | 942 | 630 | 1,500 | Survey & supplementary data (etc) |
| Stonechat | 15,000 | 1,034 | 56 | 5.4% | 812 | 450 | 1,000 | Line transect analysis (*) (etc) |
| Wheatear | 55,000 | 1,738 | 84 | 4.8% | 2,658 | 1,650 | 30,000 | Line transect analysis |
| Ring Ouzel | 8,000 | 544 | 35 | 6.4% | 515 | 240 | 1,000 | Line transect analysis (*) |
| Blackbird | 4,400,000 | 2,664 | 91 | 3.4% | 150,300 | 132,000 | 170,000 | Line transect analysis |
| Fieldfare | 4 | | | | | | 0–1 | Supplementary data |
| Song Thrush | 990,000 | 2,620 | 90 | 3.4% | 34,008 | 29,700 | 30,500 | Line transect analysis |
| Mistle Thrush | 230,000 | 2,397 | 84 | 3.5% | 8,060 | 6,900 | 13,500 | Line transect analysis |
| Grasshopper Warbler | 10,500 | 1,189 | 49 | 4.1% | 433 | 315 | 300 | Supplementary data (etc) |
| Sedge Warbler | 250,000 | 1,887 | 74 | 3.9% | 9,804 | 7,500 | 4,000 | Line transect analysis (*) |
| Reed Warbler | 60,000 | 790 | 16 | 2.0% | 1,215 | 1,800 | 200 | Supplementary data (etc) |
| Lesser Whitethroat | 80,000 | 1,271 | 37 | 2.9% | 2,329 | 2,400 | 400 | Supplementary data (etc) |
| Whitethroat | 660,000 | 2,186 | 67 | 3.1% | 20,229 | 19,800 | 18,000 | Line transect analysis |
| Garden Warbler | 200,000 | 1,867 | 83 | 4.4% | 8,891 | 6,000 | 16,000 | Line transect analysis |
| Blackcap | 580,000 | 2,048 | 82 | 4.0% | 23,223 | 17,400 | 24,000 | Line transect analysis |
| Wood Warbler | 17,200 | 1,270 | 58 | 4.6% | 786 | 516 | 2,500 | Survey & supplementary data |
| Chiffchaff | 640,000 | 2,100 | 80 | 3.8% | 24,381 | 19,200 | 10,000 | Line transect analysis (*) |
| Willow Warbler | 2,300,000 | 2,602 | 91 | 3.5% | 80,438 | 69,000 | 240,000 | Line transect analysis |
| Goldcrest | 560,000 | 2,327 | 80 | 3.4% | 19,252 | 16,800 | 16,000 | Line transect analysis |
| Spotted Flycatcher | 120,000 | 2,378 | 81 | 3.4% | 4,087 | 3,600 | 12,000 | Line transect analysis (*) |
| Pied Flycatcher | 37,500 | 732 | 57 | 7.8% | 2,920 | 1,125 | 4,000 | Line transect analysis (*) |
| Long-tailed Tit | 210,000 | 2,106 | 78 | 3.7% | 7,778 | 6,300 | 5,500 | Line transect analysis (*) |
| Marsh Tit | 60,000 | 1,133 | 27 | 2.4% | 1,430 | 1,800 | 800 | Extrapolation of density data |
| Willow Tit | 25,000 | 1,100 | 21 | 1.9% | 477 | 750 | 100 | Survey & supplementary data (etc) |

**Table D – population size estimates (4)**

| 1. Species | 2. British population estimate (pairs except where indicated in column 1) | 3. Number of 10km squares occupied in Britain (from *New Atlas* data) | 4. Number of 10km squares occupied in Cumbria (from *this Atlas* data) | 5. Cumbrian range as % of British range based on 10km squares occupied | 6. Anticipated Cumbrian population based on proportion of 10km squares (pairs) | 7. Anticipated Cumbrian population as 3% of British population (pairs) | 8. *This Atlas* population estimate for Cumbria (pairs except where indicated in col. 1) | 9. Methods used in estimating county population |
|---|---|---|---|---|---|---|---|---|
| Coal Tit | 610,000 | 2,315 | 83 | 3.6% | 21,870 | 18,300 | 15,000 | Line transect analysis |
| Blue Tit | 3,300,000 | 2,480 | 88 | 3.5% | 117,097 | 99,000 | 120,000 | Line transect analysis |
| Great Tit | 1,600,000 | 2,443 | 88 | 3.6% | 57,634 | 48,000 | 53,000 | Line transect analysis |
| Nuthatch | 130,000 | 1,270 | 63 | 5.0% | 6,449 | 3,900 | 2,000 | Line transect analysis (*) |
| Treecreeper | 200,000 | 2,120 | 77 | 3.6% | 7,264 | 6,000 | 4,000 | Line transect analysis (*) |
| Jay | 160,000 | 1,713 | 63 | 3.7% | 5,884 | 4,800 | 1,500 | Survey & supplementary data (etc) |
| Magpie | 590,000 | 1,958 | 85 | 4.3% | 25,613 | 17,700 | 9,500 | Line transect analysis |
| Jackdaw | 390,000 | 2,344 | 88 | 3.8% | 14,642 | 11,700 | 75,000 | Line transect analysis |
| Rook | 855,000 | 2,237 | 82 | 3.7% | 31,341 | 25,650 | 45,000 | Colony counts; CBC 1996 survey |
| Carrion Crow | 970,000 | 2,342 | 92 | 3.9% | 38,104 | 29,100 | 33,000 | Line transect analysis |
| Raven | 7,000 | 1,131 | 55 | 4.9% | 340 | 210 | 80–110 | CRSG data |
| Starling | 1,100,000 | 2,620 | 88 | 3.4% | 36,947 | 33,000 | 100,000 | Line transect analysis |
| House Sparrow | 3,600,000 | 2,525 | 85 | 3.4% | 121,188 | 108,000 | 165,000 | Line transect analysis |
| Tree Sparrow | 110,000 | 1,346 | 45 | 3.3% | 3,678 | 3,300 | 5,000–10,000 | Line transect analysis (*) |
| Chaffinch | 5,400,000 | 2,602 | 90 | 3.5% | 186,779 | 162,000 | 360,000 | Line transect analysis |
| Greenfinch | 530,000 | 2,323 | 83 | 3.6% | 18,937 | 15,900 | 34,000 | Line transect analysis |
| Goldfinch | 220,000 | 2,209 | 86 | 3.9% | 8,565 | 6,600 | 43,500 | Line transect analysis |
| Siskin | 300,000 | 1,158 | 66 | 5.7% | 17,098 | 9,000 | 5,000 | Line transect analysis (*) |
| Linnet | 520,000 | 2,268 | 88 | 3.9% | 20,176 | 15,600 | 46,500 | Line transect analysis |
| Twite | 65,000 | 651 | 10 | 1.5% | 998 | 1,950 | 50 | Extrapolation of density data |
| Lesser Redpoll | 160,000 | 1,754 | 78 | 4.4% | 7,115 | 4,800 | 3,500 | Line transect analysis (*) |
| Crossbill | 10,000 | 763 | 28 | 3.7% | 367 | 300 | 100–150 | Extrapolation of density data |
| Common Rosefinch | 2 | | | | | | 0–1 | Supplementary data |
| Bullfinch | 190,000 | 2,173 | 73 | 3.4% | 6,383 | 5,700 | 1,500–2,000 | Survey data |
| Hawfinch | 4,750 | 315 | 13 | 4.1% | 196 | 142 | 30–40 | Extrapolation of density data |
| Yellowhammer | 1,200,000 | 2,224 | 76 | 3.4% | 41,007 | 36,000 | 22,000 | Line transect analysis |
| Reed Bunting | 220,000 | 2,188 | 78 | 3.6% | 7,843 | 6,600 | 1,500–2,000 | Extrapolation of density data |
| Corn Bunting | 19,800 | 921 | 5 | 0.5% | 107 | 594 | 4–6 | Supplementary data |

**Table D – population size estimates (5)**

# Place names used in text, with 10 km square location

| | | | | | |
|---|---|---|---|---|---|
| Abbeytown | NY15 | Cavendish Dock | SD26 | Geltside | NY55 |
| Abbots Moss | NY54 | Chapel Island | SD37 | Gilsland | NY66 |
| Aglionby | NY45 | Christianbury Crags | NY57 | Glasson Moss | NY26 |
| Allonby | NY04 | Claife Heights | SD39 | Glencoyne | NY31 |
| Alston | NY74 | Cliburn Moss | NY52 | Glenderaterra Valley | NY22 |
| Ambleside | NY30 | Cockermouth | NY13 | Glenridding | NY31 |
| Anthorn | NY15 | Colmire | NY25 | Gosforth | NY00 |
| Appleby | NY62 | Coniston | SD39 | Gowbarrow | NY42 |
| Appleby Castle | NY62 | Coniston Old Man | SD29 | Grange-over-Sands | SD47 |
| Armathwaite | NY54 | Coniston Water | SD29/39 | Grasmere | NY30 |
| Arnside | SD47 | Corby Castle | NY45 | Grasmoor | NY12 |
| Askam-in-Furness | SD27 | Crofton Lake | NY34 | Graythwaite | SD39 |
| Aspatria | NY14 | Crooklands | SD58 | Great Asby | NY61 |
| Ayside | SD38 | Cross Fell | NY63 | Great Gable | NY21 |
| BAE Systems | SD16 | Crummock Water | NY11 | Great Langdale | NY20 |
| Back o' Skiddaw | NY22 | Cumwhinton | NY45 | Greystoke | NY43 |
| Backbarrow | SD38 | Cumwhitton | NY55 | Greystoke Forest | NY33 |
| Barbon | SD68 | Cumwhitton Moss | NY55 | Grinsdale | NY35 |
| Barbon Fells | SD68 | Cunswick Scar | SD49 | Grizedale | SD39 |
| Baron Wood | NY54 | Dalemain | NY42 | Grizedale Forest | SD39 |
| Barrow-in-Furness | SD16/17/26/27 | Dallam Towers | SD48 | Grune Point | NY15 |
| Bassenthwaite Lake | NY22/23 | Dalston | NY35 | Gutterby | SD18 |
| Bassenthwaite Marsh | NY22 | Dalton-in-Furness | SD27 | Hallin Fell | NY42 |
| Beetham | SD47 | Dent Fell | NY01 | Harrington | NY92 |
| Bewcastle | NY57 | Dentdale | SD78 | Haverigg | SD17 |
| Biglands Bog | NY25 | Denton Fell | NY66 | Haweswater | NY41 |
| Black Dub | NY36 | Derwent Water | NY22 | Helton | NY52 |
| Blackwell | NY45 | Devoke Water | SD19 | Helton Tarn | SD48 |
| Blengdale | NY00 | Dodd Wood | NY22 | Heltondale Beck | NY52 |
| Bolton Fell | NY46 | Drigg | SD09 | Helvellyn | NY31 |
| Boot | NY10 | Drigg Dunes | SD09 | Hesket Newmarket | NY33 |
| Borrowdale | NY21 | Drumburgh | NY25 | Heversham | SD48 |
| Bowfell | NY20 | Drumburgh Moss | NY25 | High Cup Nick | NY72 |
| Bowness Bay | SD49 | Dubmill Point | NY04 | High Laverock | SD59 |
| Bowness Common | NY15/25 | Duddon Estuary | SD17 | High Street | NY41 |
| Bowness-on-Solway | NY26 | Duddon Moss | SD18 | Higham | NY13 |
| Brampton | NY56 | Durdar | NY45 | Hodbarrow | SD17 |
| Brigsteer | SD48 | Dykesfield | NY35 | Holker | SD37 |
| Broomhill Moss | NY46 | Eamont | NY53 | Howgill | SD69 |
| Brothers Water | NY41 | Easedale Tarn | NY30 | Humphrey Head | SD37 |
| Brough | NY71 | Edenhall | NY53 | Hutton Roof | SD57 |
| Broughton-in-Furness | SD28 | Elterwater | NY30 | Inglewood | NY43 |
| Broughton Mills | SD29 | Ennerdale | NY11 | Irt Estuary | SD09 |
| Burgh-by-Sands | NY35 | Eskdale | NY10/20 | Irthing Valley | NY56 |
| Burgh Marsh | NY26 | Eskmeals | SD09 | Irton | NY10 |
| Burnbanks | NY51 | Esthwaite Water | SD39 | Isel Bridge | NY13 |
| Burneside | SD59 | Fairfield | NY31 | Kendal | SD59 |
| Butterburn Flow | NY67 | Farleton Fell | SD58 | Kent Estuary | SD47/48 |
| Buttermere | NY11 | Faugh Moss | NY55 | Kentmere | NY40 |
| Caldbeck | NY34 | Faugh Quarry | NY55 | Kershope Forest | NY48/58 |
| Calder Bridge | NY00 | Fingland Rigg Wood | NY25 | Keskdale | NY21 |
| Caldew Valley | NY35 | Finsthwaite Tarn | SD38 | Keswick | NY22 |
| Camerton | NY03 | Fisher Tarn | SD59 | Killington Fells | SD69 |
| Campfield Marsh | NY16 | Fleswick Bay | NX91 | Killington Reservoir | SD59 |
| Cardurnock | NY15 | Floriston | NY36 | Kirkbampton | NY35 |
| Carlisle | NY35/45 | Foulney Island | SD26 | Kirkbride | NY25 |
| Carrock Fell | NY33 | Foulshaw Moss | SD48 | Kirkby Moor | SD28 |
| Cartmel | SD37 | Foxfield Moss | SD28 | Kirkby Stephen | NY70 |
| Castle Carrock Reservoir | NY55 | Frith Wood | NY51 | Kirklinton | NY46 |
| Castlerigg | NY22 | Garrigill | NY73 | Kirkoswald | NY54 |
| Causeway End | SD38 | Geltsdale | NY55 | Kirksanton | SD18 |

| | | | | | |
|---|---|---|---|---|---|
| Lambrigg Fell | SD59 | Oulton Moss | NY25 | Tarn Sike | NY70 |
| Lamplugh | NY02 | Over Water | NY23 | Tarns Dub | NY14 |
| Lanercost | NY56 | Parton | NX92 | Tebay | NY60 |
| Langstrath | NY21 | Penrith | NY52/53 | The Haws, Millom | SD18 |
| Langwathby | NY53 | Penrith Beacon | NY53 | The Riddings | NY32 |
| Lazonby | NY53 | Penton | NY47 | Thirlmere | NY31 |
| Leven Estuary | SD37 | Piel Island | SD26 | Thornthwaite | NY22 |
| Levens | SD48 | Pooley Bridge | NY42 | Thornthwaite Forest | NY13 |
| Levens Hall | SD48 | Portinscale | NY22 | Thurstonfield Lough | NY35 |
| Levens Park | SD48/58 | Rack Bridge | NY47 | Tindale Tarn | NY65 |
| Liddel Water | NY47 | RAF Carlisle | NY46 | Torver | SD29 |
| Lilymere | SD69 | Rampside | SD26 | Ullswater | NY31/42 |
| Little Salkeld | NY53 | Ravenglass | SD09 | Ulverston | SD27/37 |
| Lodore | NY21 | Ravenstonedale | NY70 | Unity Bog | NY55 |
| Long Newton Marsh | NY15/25 | Rigg Beck | NY22 | Upper Irthing | NY56 |
| Longsleddale | NY50 | Roanhead | SD27 | Urswick Tarn | SD27 |
| Longtown | NY36 | Rockcliffe | NY36 | Waberthwaite | SD19 |
| Longtown Ponds | NY36 | Rockcliffe Marsh | NY36 | Walney Island | SD16 |
| Loweswater | NY12 | Roudsea Moss | SD38 | Walton Moss | NY56 |
| Lowick | SD38 | Rusland Fells | SD38 | Warcop | NY71 |
| Lowther | NY51/52 | Rusland Moss | SD38 | Warcop Fells | NY72 |
| Loughrigg Fell | NY30 | Rusland Pool | SD38 | Warwick Bridge | NY45 |
| Lupton Moor | SD58 | Rusland Valley | SD38 | Wast Water | NY10 |
| Lyth Valley | SD48/49 | Rydal Water | NY30 | Watermillock | NY42 |
| Mallerstang | SD79 | Salta | NY04 | Waterside | NY24 |
| Mardale | NY41 | Salta Moss | NY04 | Wedholme Flow | NY25 |
| Martin Tarn | NY25 | Sandscale Haws | SD17 | Wetheral | NY45 |
| Martindale | NY41 | Sandwith | NX91 | Wet Sleddale | NY51 |
| Maryport | NY03 | Scafell | NY20 | Wet Sleddale Reservoir | NY51 |
| Maulds Meaburn | NY61 | Scales | NY11 | Whernside | SD78 |
| Mawbray | NY04 | Scotby | NY45 | Whinfell Tarn | SD59 |
| Meathop | SD48 | Scout Scar | SD49 | Whinlatter | NY12 |
| Meathop Moss | SD48 | Seascale | NY00 | Whins Pond | NY53 |
| Mere Tarn | SD27 | Seatoller | NY21 | Whinsfield Park | NY53 |
| Middleton | SD68 | Sebergham | NY34 | Whitbarrow | SD48 |
| Midgeholme | NY55 | Sedbergh | SD69 | Whitbarrow Scar | SD48 |
| Millom | SD18 | Sellafield | NY00 | Whitehaven | NX91 |
| Milnthorpe | SD48 | Shap | NY51 | Whiteside | NY31 |
| Milton | NY56 | Shap Fells | NY50/51 | Wigton | NY24 |
| Mockerin Tarn | NY02 | Siddick | NY03 | Windermere | SD39/NY30 |
| Moorhouse | NY73 | Siddick Pond | NY03 | Winderwath | NY52 |
| Moorthwaite | NY24 | Silecroft | SD18 | Winster Valley | SD48 |
| Moorthwaite Moss | NY55 | Silloth | NY15 | Witherslack | SD48 |
| Moricambe Bay | NY15 | Simpson Ground | SD48 | Witherslack Moss | SD48 |
| Muncaster | SD09 | Sizergh | SD48 | Wood Howe | NY41 |
| Naddle Forest | NY41 | Skelwith | NY30 | Woodside | NY45 |
| Natland | SD58 | Skiddaw | NY22 | Workington | NX92 |
| Naworth | NY56 | Skiddaw Forest | NY22 | Wreay | NY44 |
| Netherby | NY37 | Skinburness | NY15 | Wythop | NY22 |
| Nethertown | NX90 | Skinburness Marsh | NY15 | Wythop Hall | NY22 |
| Nether Wasdale | NY10 | Skirwith | NY63 | Wythop Woods | NY22 |
| Newby Bridge | SD38 | Solway Moss | NY36 | | |
| Newlands | NY22 | Southwaite | NY44 | | |
| Newton Arlosh | NY15 | South Walney | SD26 | | |
| Newton Common | NY35 | Spadeadam | NY67 | | |
| Newton Reigny Moss | NY43 | St Bees | NX91 | | |
| North Plain Farm | NY16 | St Bees Head | NX91 | | |
| North Scales | NY55 | Standing Tarn | SD27 | | |
| North Walney | SD17 | Sunbiggin Tarn | NY60 | | |
| Ormsgill Reservoir | SD17 | Talkin Tarn | NY55 | | |
| Orton | NY60 | Tarn House Tarn | NY70 | | |
| Orton Moss | NY35 | Tarn Moor | NY60 | | |
| Otter Bank | SD59 | Tarn Sike | NY60 | | |

## Scentific names of other taxa

**Vertebrates**

| | |
|---|---|
| Brown Rat | *Rattus norvegicus* |
| Capelin | *Mallotus villosus* |
| Common Shrew | *Sorex minutus* |
| Field Vole | *Microtus agrestis* |
| Grey Squirrel | *Sciurus carolinensis* |
| Hedgehog | *Erinaceus europaeus* |
| Herring | *Clupea harengus* |
| Knotgrass Beetle | *Gastrophysa polygoni* |
| Lemming | *Lemmus lemmus* |
| Mink | *Mustela vison* |
| Otter | *Lutra lutra* |
| Perch | *Perca fluviatilis* |
| Pike | *Esox lucius* |
| Rabbit | *Oryctolagus cuniculus* |
| Red Deer | *Cervus elaphus* |
| Red Fox | *Vulpes vulpes* |
| Red Squirrel | *Sciurus vulgaris* |
| Salmon | *Salmo* spp. |
| Sandeel | *Ammodytes/Gymnammodytes/ Hyperoplus* spp. |
| Sheep | *Ovis* spp. |
| Schelly | *Coregonus lavaretus* |
| Short-tailed Vole | *Microtus agrestis* |
| Short-toed Treecreeper | *Certhia brachydactyla* |
| Sprat | *Clupea sprattus* |
| Stoat | *Mustela erminea* |
| Trout | *Salmo* spp. |
| Weasel | *Mustela nivalis* |
| Wood Mouse | *Sylvaemus sylvaticus* |

**Invertebrates**

| | |
|---|---|
| Wood Ant | *Formica rufa* |
| Blue Mussel | *Mytilus edulis* |
| Chironomid midge | *Chironomus salinarius* |
| Cranefly | *Tipulid* spp. |
| Nematode Worm | *Trichostrongylus tenuis* |
| Spire-shell Snail | *Hydrobia ulvae* |
| Yellow Meadow Ant | *Lasius flavus* |
| Zebra Mussel | *Dreissnia polymorpha* |

**Plants**

| | |
|---|---|
| Alder | *Alnus glutinosa* |
| Ash | *Fraxinus excelsior* |
| Beech | *Fagus sylvatica* |
| Birch | *Betula* spp. |
| Blackthorn | *Prunus spinosa* |
| Bilberry | *Vaccinium myrtillus* |
| Bog Myrtle | *Myrica gale* |
| Bracken | *Pteridium aquilinum* |
| Bramble | *Rubus fruticosus* |
| Charlock | *Sinapis arvensis* |
| Cherry | *Prunus avium* |
| Chickweed | *Stellaria media* |
| Cottongrass | *Eriophorum* spp. |
| Damson | *Prunus domestica* ssp. *insititia* |
| Dock | *Rumex* spp. |
| Dog's Mercury | *Mercurialis perennis* |
| Elm | *Ulmus* spp. |
| Fat Hen | *Chenopodium album* |
| Gorse | *Ulex europaeus* |
| Groundsel | *Senecio vulgaris* |
| Hawthorn | *Crataegus monogyna* |
| Heather | *Calluna vulgaris* |
| Holly | *Ilex aquifolium* |
| Hornbeam | *Carpinus betulus* |
| Ivy | *Hedera helix* |
| Juniper | *Juniperus communis* |
| Larch | *Larix* spp. |
| Mistletoe | *Viscum album* |
| Nettle | *Urtica dioica* |
| Norway Spruce | *Picea abies* |
| Oak | *Quercus* spp |
| Oil-seed Rape | *Brassica napus* ssp. *oleifera* |
| Phragmites | *Phragmites australis* |
| Pine | *Pinus* spp. |
| Plum | *Prunus domestica* |
| Popular | *Populus* spp. |
| Rose | *Rosa* spp. |
| Rowan | *Sorbus aucuparia* |
| Sallow | *Salix* spp. |
| Scots Pine | *Pinus sylvestris* |
| Sea Buckthorn | *Hippophae rhamnoides* |
| Sitka Spruce | *Picea sitchensis* |
| Spruce | *Picea* spp. |
| Sycamore | *Acer pseudoplatanus* |
| Thistles | *Carduus/Cirsium* spp. |
| Willowherb | *Chamerion/Epilobium* spp. |
| Wych Elm | *Ulmus glabra* |
| Yellow Iris | *Iris pseudacorus* |
| Yew | *Taxus baccata* |

# References

ALEXANDER, W.B. and D. Lack. 1944. Changes in status among British breeding birds. British Birds **38**: 62–69.

ARMITAGE, M.1999. Goosander increase continues. BTO News **225**: 2–3.

ATKINS, R. and J.C. Callion. 1997. Woodpecker and Nuthatch Survey 1994–1995. Supplement to Cumbria Bird Club News **7**: 4.

ATKINSON, K.M. 1981. Changes in the Wildfowl Population of Windermere in recent years. Cumbria Trust for Nature Conservation Newsletter, August 1981.

AUSTIN, G. 2001. Estimating naturalised goose numbers precisely! BTO News **237**: 8–9.

AVERY, M. and R. Leslie. 1990. Birds and Forestry. Poyser, London.

BAILLIE, S.R. 1990. Integrated population monitoring of breeding birds in Britain and Ireland. *Ibis* **132**: 151–166.

BAILLIE, S.R. *et al.* 2001. Breeding Birds in the Wider Countryside: their conservation status 2000. BTO Research Report No 252. BTO, Thetford.

BAINES, D. 1988. The Effects of Improvement of Upland Marginal Grasslands on the Distribution and Density of Breeding Wading Birds in Northern England. Biol. Cons. **45**: 221–236.

BARRON, P. 1996. Breeding Survey of Common Sandpiper at Bassenthwaite Lake 1995. Birds & Wildlife in Cumbria 1995: 72–73.

BATTEN, L.A. 1976. Bird communities of some Killarney woodlands. Proc. Royal Irish Academy **76**: 285–313.

BATTEN, L.A. 2001. European Honey Buzzard survey 2000–2001: preliminary results and requests for further surveys. British Birds **94**: 143–144.

BATTEN, L. A., C. J. Bibby, P. Clement, G. D. Elliot and R. F. Porter (eds). 1990. Red Data Birds in Britain. Poyser, London.

BENEFIELD, C.E., and R.G.E. Bunce. 1982. Merlewood Research and Development Paper No. 91: A Preliminary Visual Presentation of Land Classes in Britain.

BERGERUD, A.T. 1970b. Population Dynamics of the Willow Ptarmigan *Lagopus lagopus alleni* in Newfoundland 1955–1965. Oikos **21**: 299–325.

BERRY, R. and C.J. Bibby. 1981. A Breeding Study of Nightjars. British Birds **74**: 161–169.

BISHOP, D.C. 1979. Changes of nest sites of Merlins in Cumbria. British Birds **72**: 120.

BLAKER, G.B. 1933. The Barn Owl in England. Bird Notes and News **15**: 169–172 and 207–211.

BLEZARD, E., M. Garnett, R. Graham and T.L. Johnston. 1943. The Birds of Lakeland. Transactions of the Carlisle Natural History Society. Vol. 6. Arbroath.

BLEZARD, E. 1946. The Birds of Lakeland. Transactions of the Carlisle Natural History Society. Vol. 7.

BLEZARD, E. 1954. The Birds of Lakeland: A Second Supplement. Transactions of the Carlisle Natural History Society. Vol. 8.

BLEZARD, E. 1958. The Birds of Lakeland: A Third Supplement. Transactions of the Carlisle Natural History Society. Vol. 9. Thurnam, Carlisle.

BOU. 1971. The Status of Birds in Britain and Ireland. Blackwell, Oxford, London and Edinburgh.

BOWES, A., P.C. Lack and M.R. Fletcher. 1984. Wintering Gulls in Britain, January 1983. Bird Study **31**: 161–171.

BRENCHLEY, A. 1986. The breeding distribution and abundance of the Rook *Corvus frugilegus* L. in Great Britain since the 1920's. Journal of Zoology, London. **10**: 261–278.

BRICKLE, N.W. 1998. The effect of agricultural intensification on the decline of the Corn Bunting *Miliaria calandra*. D. Phil. Thesis, University of Sussex.

BROOKE, M. De L. 1979. Differences in the quality of territories held by Wheatears *Oenanthe oenanthe*. Journal of Applied Animal Ecology 48: 21–32.

BROWN, A.F. and P.B. Grice. In Prep. Birds in England. Poyser.

BROWN, R.H. 1954. Lakeland Ornithology, The Warblers. Carlisle Natural History Society.

BROWN, R.H. 1974. Lakeland Birdlife 1920–1970. Charles Thurnam & Sons Ltd., Carlisle.

BUNCE, R.G.H., C.J. Barr, R.T. Clarke, D.C. Howard and A.M. J. Lane. 1996. ITE Merlewood Land Classification of Great Britain. Journal of Biogeography Vol 23: 25–634, Blackwell Science Ltd.

BUNN, D.S., A.B. Warburton and R.D.S. Wilson. 1982. The Barn Owl. Poyser, Calton.

BUXTON, E.J.M. 1961. The inland breeding of the Oystercatcher in Great Britain, 1958–59. Bird Study **8**: 194–209.

CALLION, J.C., N. White and D. Holloway. 1990. Grasshopper Warblers raising two and three broods in Cumbria. British Birds **83**: 506–508.

CAMERON, R.A.D. 1969. Predation by Song Thrushes *Turdus ericetorum* on the snails *Cepaea hortensis* and *Arianta arbustorum* near Rickmansworth. Journal of Applied Animal Ecology **38**: 547–553.

CAMPBELL, B. 1977. Birds of Coast and Sea. Oxford University Press, Oxford.

CARRIER, M. 1991. Birds in Cumbria 1990. Cumbria Naturalists Union.

CARRIER, M. 1992. Birds in Cumbria 1991. Cumbria Naturalists Union.

CARRIER, M. 1993. Birds in Cumbria 1992. Cumbria Naturalists Union.

CARRIER, M. 1994. Birds in Cumbria 1993. Cumbria Naturalists Union.

CARRIER, M. 1995. Birds in Cumbria 1994. Cumbria Naturalists Union.

CARRIER, M. 1996. Birds in Cumbria 1995. Cumbria Naturalists Union.

CARRIER, M. 1997. Birds and Wildlife in Cumbria 1996. Cumbria Naturalists Union.

CARRIER, M. 1998. Birds and Wildlife in Cumbria 1997. Cumbria Naturalists Union.

CARRIER, M. & D. Clarke. 1990. Birds in Cumbria 1989. Cumbria Naturalists Union.

CAWTHORNE, R.A. and J.H. Marchant. 1980. The effect of the 1978/79 winter on British bird populations. Bird Study **27**: 163–172.

CHAMBERLAIN, D.E., B.J. Hatchwell and C.M. Perrins. 1999. Importance of feeding ecology to the reproductive success of Blackbirds *Turdus merula* nesting in rural habitats. Ibis **141**: 415–427.

CHAPMAN, A. 1999. The Hobby. Arlequin Press, Chelmsford.

# References

CLEASBY, I. 1994. The 'Not-so Common' Sandpiper. Cumbrian Wildlife No 39.

CLEASBY, I. 1999. Birds and Boys at Sedbergh. Ingram Cleasby.

CLEMENT, P. 1995. The Chiffchaff. Hamlyn, London.

CONDER, P. 1989. The Wheatear. Christopher Helm, London.

COOMBES, R.A.H. 1933. Barn-owls nesting in crags high up in Westmorland. British Birds **26**: 309.

COOMBS, F. 1978. The Crows. Batsford, London.

COWARD, T.A. and J.A.G. Barnes. 1969. Birds of the British Isles and their eggs. Warne, London.

COWIE, R.G. and S.A. Hinsley. 1987. Breeding success of Blue Tits and Great Tits in suburban gardens. Ardea **75**: 81–90.

CRAMP, S., K.E.L. Simmons and C.M. Perrins. 1974–94. Handbook of the Birds of Europe, the Middle East and North Africa. The Birds of the Western Palearctic. Vols 1–9. Oxford University Press, Oxford.

CRICK, H.Q.P. and T.H. Sparks. 1999. Climate change related to egg-laying trends. Nature **399**: 423–4.

CRICK, H., M. Raven, P. Beaven and David Glue. 2001. Yellow Wagtail and Red-throated Diver – new Nest Record Scheme Alerts. BTO News **234**: 8–9.

CUTHBERTSON, E.J. *et al.* 1952. A census of Common Sandpipers in the Sedbergh area 1951. British Birds **45**:171–175.

DARE, P.J. 1966. The breeding and wintering populations of the Oystercatcher in the British Isles. Fishery Invest. 2 XXV (5)

DARE, P.J. 1986. Raven *Corus corax* populations in two upland regions of North Wales. Bird Study **33**: 179–189.

DAVIES, N.B. 1992. Dunnock Behaviour and Social Evolution. Oxford University Press, Oxford.

DAY, J.C., M. Hodgson and N. Rossiter. 1995. The Atlas of Breeding Birds in Northumbria. Northumberland and Tyneside Bird Club, Newcastle.

DEAN, T. 1987. The Nuthatch in Cumbria, its status and distribution. Birds in Cumbria, A County Natural History Report 1986: 55–59.

DEAN, T. 1990. The Natural History of Walney Island. Faust Publications, Burnley.

DELIUS, J.D. 1965. A Population Study of Skylarks. Ibis **107**: 466–492.

DONALD, P.F. and A.D. Evans. 1995. Habitat selection and population size of Corn Bunting *Miliaria calandra* breeding in Britain in 1993. Bird Study **42**: 190–204.

DUNLOP, E.B. 1923. Lakeland Ornithology. Trans. Carlisle Natural History Society. Vol iii. Carlisle.

ETHERIDGE, B., R.W. Summers and R.E. Green. 1997. The effects of illegal killing and destruction of nests by humans on the population dynamics of the hen harrier *Circus cyaneus* in Scotland. Journal of Applied Ecology **34**: 1081–1105.

FEARE, C.J. 1984. The Starling. Oxford University Press, Oxford.

FISHER, J. and R.M. Lockley. 1989. Seabirds. Collins, London.

FLEGG, J. 1987. The Blue Tit. Shire Natural History No: 17. Princes Risborough.

FOX, A.D. 1988. Breeding status of the Gadwall in Britain and Ireland. British Birds **81**: 51–66.

FOX, A.D. 1991. Pochards Breeding in Britain. British Birds **84**: 83–98.

FOX, A.D., H. Jarrett, H. Gitay and D. Paynter. 1989. Late summer habitat selection by breeding waterfowl in Northern Scotland. Wildfowl **40**: 106–114.

FOX, A.D. and E.R. Meek. 1993. History of the Northern Pintail breeding in Britain and Ireland. British Birds **86**: 151–163.

FURNESS, R.W. and T.R. Birkhead. 1984. Seabird colony distributions suggest competition for food supplies during the breeding season. Nature 311, no. 5987: 655–656.

GARNER, D.J. and B.S. Milne.1998. A Study of the Long-eared Owl *Asio otus* using wicker nesting baskets. Bird Study **45**: 62–67.

GIBBONS, D.W., M.I. Avery and A.F. Brown. 1996. Population trends of breeding birds in the United Kingdom since 1800. British Birds **89**: 291–305.

GIBBONS, D.W. *et al.* 1996. Bird Species of Conservation Concern in the United Kingdom, Channel Islands and Isle of Man: revising the Red Data List. RSPB Conservation Review **10**: 7–18.

GIBBONS, D.W., J.B. Reid and A.R. Chapman. 1993. The New Atlas of Breeding Birds in Britain and Ireland: 1988–1991. Poyser. London.

GLEN, N.W. and C.M. Perrins. 1988. Co-operative breeding by Long-tailed Tits. British Birds **81**: 630–641.

GOOCH, S., S. Baillie and T.R. Birkhead. 1991. The impact of Magpies *Pica pica* on songbird populations. Retrospective investigation of trends in population density and breeding success. Journal of Applied Ecology **28**: 1068–1086.

GORDON, S. 1912. The Charm of the Hills.

GOODHART, C.B. 1958. Thrush predation on the snail *Cepaea hortensis*. Journal of Applied Animal Ecology **27**: 47–57.

GRAHAM, R. 1937. The North Western Naturalist. Vol. X11

GRAHAM, R. 1993. A Border Naturalist – The Birds and Wildlife of the Bewcastle Fells and the Gilsland Moors, 1930–1966. Bookcase, Carlisle.

GRANT, M. 1997. Breeding Curlews in the UK: RSPB Research and Implications for Conservation. RSPB Conservation Review **11**: 67–73.

GRAY, D.B. 1974. Breeding behaviour of Whinchats. Bird Study **21**: 280–282.

GREEN, R.E. 1984. Double nesting of the Red-legged Partridge *Alectoris rufa*. Ibis **126**: 332–346.

GREEN, R.E. 1996. The status of the Golden Eagle in Britain in 1992. Bird Study **43**: 20–27.

GREENHALGH, M.E. 1969. The breeding of the Oystercatcher in Northern England. The Naturalist **921**: 49–51.

GREENHALGH, M.E. 1972. The breeding of the Oystercatcher in North-western England. The Naturalist **909**: 43–47.

GREGORY, R.D., S.P. Carter and S.R. Baillie. 1997. Abundance, Distribution and Habitat Use of Breeding Goosanders *Mergus merganser* and Red-breasted Mergansers *Mergus serrrator* on British Rivers. Bird Study **44**: 1–12.

GREGORY, R.D. and S.R. Baillie. 1998. Large-scale habitat use of some declining British Birds. Journal of Applied Animal Ecology **35**: 785–799.

GREGORY, R.D., D.G. Noble, L.H. Campbell and D.W. Gibbons. 2000. The State of the UK's Birds 1999. RSPB and BTO. Sandy.

GRIMMETT, R. 1987. A Review of the Problems Affecting Palearctic Migratory Birds in Africa. ICPB Migratory Birds Programme, Cambridge.

GROOM, D.W. 1993. Magpie *Pica pica* predation on Blackbird *Turdus merula* nests in urban areas. Bird Study **40**: 55–62.

HAGEMEIJER, E.J.M., M.J. Blair (eds). 1997. The EBCC Atlas of European Breeding Birds: Their Distribution and Abundance. Poyser. London

HARDY, E. 1979. Birdwatching in Lancashire. Dalesman Books, Clapham, Yorkshire.

HARRISON, J. 1973. A Wealth of Wildfowl. Corgi.

HARRISON, K. (ed) 1995. An Atlas of Breeding Birds of Lancaster and District. Lancaster and District Birdwatching Society.

HARTING, J.E. 1864. The Birds of Walney Island. The Zoologist **22**: 9156–9165.

HARTLEY, I.R., M. Shepherd and D.B.A. Thompson. 1994. Habitat selection and polygymy in breeding Corn Buntings *Miliaria calandra*. Ibis **137**: 508–514.

HATCHWELL, B.J., D.E. Chamberlain and C.M. Perrins. 1996. The reproductive success of Blackbirds *Turdus merula* in relation to habitat structure and choice of nest site. Ibis **138**: 256–262.

HEWITSON, J. 1998. Fulmars at Parton. Cumbria Bird Club News **9**: 55.

HEWITT, S. 2001. Birds and Wildlife in Cumbria 2000. Cumbria Naturalists Union.

HEYSHAM, J. 1794. List of Cumberland Birds, in J. Hutchinson's History of Cumberland. Carlisle.

HOLLOWAY, S. 1996. The Historical Atlas of Breeding Birds in Britain & Ireland: 1875–1900. Poyser. London.

HUDSON, R. 1965. The Spread of the Collared Dove in Britain and Ireland. British Birds **58**: 105–139.

HUGHES, B. 1992. The ecology and behaviour of the North American Ruddy Duck *Oxyura jamaicensis* in Great Britain. Ph.D. Thesis, University of Bristol.

HUGHES, B., M. Underhill and S. Delany. 1998. Ruddy Ducks breeding in the United Kingdom in 1994. British Birds **91**: 336–353.

HUGHES, S.W.M., P. Bacon and J.J.M. Flegg. 1979. The 1975 census of the Great Crested Grebe in Britain. Bird Study **26**: 213–226.

HULME, M. and G.J. Jenkins. 1998. Climate change scenarios for the UK : scientific reports. UKCIP Tech. Rep.1. Climatic Research Unit, Norwich.

HUME, R. 1993. The Common Tern. Hamlyn. London.

HUTCHESON, M. 1978. Birds in Cumbria 1977. The Association of Natural History Societies in Cumbria.

HUTCHESON, M. 1979. Birds in Cumbria 1978. The Association of Natural History Societies in Cumbria.

HUTCHESON, M. 1980. Birds in Cumbria 1979. The Association of Natural History Societies in Cumbria.

HUTCHESON, M. 1981. Birds in Cumbria 1980. The Association of Natural History Societies in Cumbria.

HUTCHESON, M. 1982. Birds in Cumbria 1981. The Association of Natural History Societies in Cumbria.

HUTCHESON, M. 1983. Birds in Cumbria 1982. The Association of Natural History Societies in Cumbria.

HUTCHESON, M. 1984. Birds in Cumbria 1983. The Association of Natural History Societies in Cumbria.

HUTCHESON, M. 1985. Birds in Cumbria 1984. The Association of Natural History Societies in Cumbria.

HUTCHESON, M. 1986a. Birds in Cumbria 1985. The Association of Natural History Societies in Cumbria.

HUTCHESON, M. 1986b. Cumbrian Birds. A review of status and distribution 1964–1984. Frank Peters Ltd. Kendal.

HUTCHESON, M. 1987. Birds in Cumbria 1986. The Association of Natural History Societies in Cumbria.

HUTCHESON, M. 1988. Birds in Cumbria 1987. The Association of Natural History Societies in Cumbria.

HUTCHESON, M. 1989. Birds in Cumbria 1988. The Association of Natural History Societies in Cumbria.

HUXLEY, C.R. and N.A. Wood. 1976. Aspects of the Breeding Moorhen in Britain. Bird Study **23**: 1–10.

JENKINS, D. 1957. The breeding of the Red-legged Partridge. Bird Study **4**: 97–100.

JENKINS, D., A. Watson and G.R. Miller. 1963. Population studies on red grouse *Lagopus lagopus scoticus* (Lath.) in northeast Scotland. Journal of Applied Animal Ecology **32**: 317–376.

JOHNSGARD, P.A. 1988. The Quails, Partridges and Francolins of the World. Oxford University Press, Oxford.

JOHNSTON, T.L. 1936. Nesting Habits of the Willow-Tit in Cumberland. British Birds **29**: 378–380.

JONES, N.G.B. 1956. Census of Breeding Canada Geese 1953. Bird Study **3**: 153–170.

KALCHREUTER, H. 1982. The Woodcock. Hoffman, Germany.

KEARSLEY, L. 1999. The International Mediterranean Gull Project website.

KELLY, P.G. and K.A. Perry. 1990. Wildlife Habitat in Cumbria. Research and Survey in Nature Conservation **30**: NCC Peterborough.

KENMIR, B. 2001. Buzzard account in Cumbria Bird Club Raptor Study Group Report for 2000.

KINLEY, I. 1991. The 1990 Mute Swan Survey in Cumbria. Birds in Cumbria, A County Natural History Report for 1990: 80–81.

KOCH, L. 1956. The Encyclopaedia of British Birds. Waverley Book Co. London.

KNOX, A.G. 1992. Checklist of Birds of Britain and Ireland. Helm, Hartnolls Ltd.

LACK, D. 1965. The Life of the Robin. Collins, London.

LACK, D. 1966. Population Studies of Birds. Clarendon Press, Oxford.

LEE, J.A., J.H. Tallis and S.J. Woodin. 1988. Acidic deposition on British upland vegetation. In Usher and Thompson (eds) Ecological Change in the Uplands. Blackwell Scientific Publications, Oxford.

LEVER, C. 1977. The Naturalized Animals of the British Isles. Hutchinson, London.

LITTLEWOOD, N. 1996. Foulney Island Nature Reserve, Warden's Report, 22nd April to 5th August 1996. Unpublished report to Cumbria Wildlife Trust.

LLOYD, C., M.L. Tasker and K. Partridge. 1991. The Status of Seabirds in Britain and Ireland. Poyser, London.

LOCKIE, J.D. 1955. The breeding habitats and food of Short-eared Owls after a vole plague. Bird Study **3**: 53–69.

LONG, J.L. 1981. Introduced Birds of the World. David & Charles, Newton Abbot, London.

# References

LOVAT, Lord., A.S. Leslie and A.E. Shipley. 1911. The Grouse in Health and in Disease. Smith, Elder & Co. 15 Waterloo Place, London.

LOWE, P.R. 1933. The Differential Characters in the Tarso-metataris of Gallus and Phasianus as they bear on the Problem of the Introduction of the Pheasant into Europe and the British Isles. Ibis **3**: 332–343.

MACPHERSON, H.A. 1892. A Vertebrate Fauna of Lakeland. David Douglas, Edinburgh. Reprint by P.P.B. Minet, Chicheley, Bucks. 1972.

MACPHERSON, H.A., and W. Duckworth. 1886. Birds of Cumberland. Thurnham and Sons, Carlisle.

MARCHANT, J.H., R. Hudson, S.P. Carter and P. Whittington. 1990. Population Trends in British Breeding Birds. BTO/NCC. Tring.

MARCHANT, J.H., D.G. Noble, M.J. Raven, G.M. Siriwardena, R. Thewlis and C.V. Wernham. 2001. Breeding Birds in the Wider Countryside: their conservation status 2000. BTO Research Report No. 252. BTO, Thetford.

MARQUISS, M., D.N. Carss, J.D. Armstrong and R. Gardner. 1998. Fish-eating Birds and Salmonids in Scotland. The Scottish Office.

MASON, C.F. 1976. A breeding Biology of the *Sylvia* Warblers. Bird Study **23**: 213–232.

MASON, C.F. and S.M. Macdonald. 1976. Aspects of the Breeding Biology of the Snipe. Bird Study **23**: 33–38.

MASON, C.F. 1995. The Blackcap. Hamlyn London.

MASON, C.F. and F. Lyczynski. 1980. Breeding Biology of the Pied and Yellow Wagtails. Bird Study **27**: 1–10.

MAWBY, F.J. and R. Armstrong. 1996. Breeding waders in lowland wet grasslands in Cumbria in 1995. Cumbria Bird Club News **7**: 34–37.

MAXWELL, J. 1999. "Pure dead brilliant box, Jimmy". BTO News **221**: 12–13.

McALONE, D. 1994. Status of the Lesser Whitethroat in Cumbria. Birds in Cumbria, A County Natural History Report for 1993: 79–81.

McALONE, D., M. Carrier, B. Makin and K. Milligan. 1997. Cumbria Bird Club Rookery Survey April 1996. Birds in Cumbria, A County Natural History Report for 1996: 71–76.

MEAD, C.J., P.M. North and B.R. Warmough. 1979. The mortality of British Grey Herons. Bird Study **26**: 13–23.

MEAD, C. 2000. The State of the Nations' Birds. Whittet, Stowmarket.

MIKKOLA, H. 1983. Owls of Europe. T&AD Poyser, Calton.

MILLS, D.H. 1962. The Goosander and Red-breasted Merganser in Scotland. The Wildfowl Trust 13th Report.

MITCHELL, F.S. 1885. The Birds of Lancashire. Van Voorst. London.

MITCHELL, F.S. 1892. The Birds of Lancashire. Gurney & Jackson, London. 2nd edition, revised and annotated by Howard Saunders.

MITCHELL, W.R. and R.W. Robson. 1974. Lakeland Birds. Dalesman.

MONAGHAN, P. and J.C. Coulson. 1977. Status of large gulls nesting on buildings. Bird Study **44**: 13–34.

MORRIS, A., D. Burges, R.J. Fuller, A.D. Evans and K.W. Smith. 1994. The Status and Distribution of Nightjars *Caprimulgus europaeus* in Britain in 1992. A report to the British Trust for Ornithology. Bird Study **41**: 181–191.

MOULE, G.W.H. 1973. Natural History in Cumbria 1970–1972. The Association of Cumbria Natural History Societies.

MOULE, G.W.H. 1974. Natural History in Cumbria 1973. The Association of Cumbria Natural History Societies.

MOUNTFORT, G. 1957. The Hawfinch. Collins, London.

MURTON, R.K. 1965. The Woodpigeon. Collins, London.

NCC Survey. 1984. Nature Conservation in Great Britain. NCC, Peterborough.

NATURE CONSERVANCY COUNCIL. 1987. Changes in the Cumbrian Countryside. Research and Survey. Nature Conservation No 6. NCC, Peterborough.

NETHERSOLE-THOMPSON, D. 1973. The Dotterel. Collins, London.

NETHERSOLE-THOMPSON, D. and M. 1986. Waders, their breeding, haunts and watchers. Poyser, Calton.

NEWTON, I. 1972. Finches. Collins, London.

NEWTON, I. 1979. Population Ecology of Raptors. Poyser, London.

NEWTON, I. 1986. The Sparrowhawk. Poyser, London.

NEWTON, I. and M.B. Haas. 1984. The return of the Sparrowhawk. British Birds **77**: 47–70.

NEWTON, I. and M.B. Haas. 1988. Pollutants in Merlin eggs and their effects on breeding. British Birds 81: 258–269.

NEWTON, I., L. Dale and P. Rothery. 1997. Apparent lack of impact of Sparrowhawks on the breeding densities of some woodland songbirds. Bird Study **44**: 129–135.

NOBLE, D.G., R.I. Bashford, J.H. Marchant, S.R. Baillie and R.D. Gregory. 1999. The Breeding Bird Survey 1998. BTO, JNCC and RSPB.

NOBLE, D.G., M.J. Raven and S.R. Baillie. 2001. The Breeding Bird Survey 2000. BTO Research Report No: 265.

NORMAN, S.C. 1992. Dispersal and site fidelity in Lesser Whitethroat *Sylvia curruca*. Ringing and Migration **13**: 167–174.

NORMAN, D. 1994. The Fieldfare. Hamlyn, London.

OAKES, C. 1953. The Birds of Lancashire. Oliver and Boyd, Edinburgh and London.

O'CONNOR, R.J. and M. Shrubb. 1986. Farming and Birds. Cambridge University Press, Cambridge.

O'CONNOR, R.J. and D.N. Pearman. 1987. Long term trends in breeding success of some British Birds. BTO Research Report 4.

OGILVIE, M.A. 1986. The Mute Swan *Cygnus olor* in Britain, 1983. Bird Study **33**: 121–137.

OGILVIE, M.A. and the Rare Breeding Birds Panel 1999. Rare Breeding Birds in the United Kingdom in 1997. British Birds **92**: 389–428.

OGILVIE, M.A. and the Rare Breeding Birds Panel 1999. Non-native Birds breeding in the United Kingdom in 1997. British Birds **92**: 472–476.

OGILVIE, M.A. and the Rare Breeding Birds Panel. 2000. Rare Breeding Birds in the United Kingdom in 1998. British Birds **93**: 358–393.

OGILVIE, M.A. and the Rare Breeding Birds Panel 2000. Non-native Birds breeding in the United Kingdom in 1998. British Birds **93**: 428–433.

OGILVIE, M.A. and the Rare Breeding Birds Panel 2001. Rare Breeding Birds in the United Kingdom in 1999. British Birds **94**: 344–381.

OGILVIE, M.A. and the Rare Breeding Birds Panel 2001. Non-native Birds breeding in the United Kingdom in 1999. British Birds **94**: 518–522.

ORMEROD, S. and S. Tyler. 1987. Dippers *Cinclus cinclus* and Grey Wagtails *Motacilla cinerea* as an indicator of stream acidity in Upland Wales. International Council for Bird Preservation Tech. Publ. 6: 191–208.

ORMEROD, S.J. and S.J. Tyler. 1987. Aspects of the breeding ecology of Welsh Grey Wagtails Motacilla cinerea. Bird Study **34**: 43–51.

PALMER, P. 2000. Firsts for Britain and Ireland. Arlequin Press. Chelmsford.

PARKIN, D.T. and J.M. McMeeking. 1985. The Increase in Canada Geese in Nottinghamshire from 1980. Bird Study **32**: 132–140.

PARRINDER, E.D. 1989. Little Ringed Plovers *Charadrius dubius* in Britain in 1984. Bird Study **36**: 147–153.

PARSLOW, J. 1973. Breeding Birds of Britain and Ireland : A Historical Survey. Poyser, Berkhamsted.

PEACH, W.J., H.Q.P. Crick and J.H. Marchant. 1995. The demography of the decline in the British Willow Warbler population. Journal of Applied Statistics 22: Nos. 5 & 6.

PENNANT, T. 1778. A Tour in Wales. Privately published. London.

PERRINS, C. 1979. British Tits. Collins, London.

PETER, S. 1999. Little Terns at Hodbarrow. Birds and Wildlife in Cumbria, A County Natural History Report for 1998: 64–66.

PETTY, S. 1996. History of the Northern Goshawk *Accipter gentilis* in Britain. The introduction and naturalisation of birds 95–102. The Stationery Office. London.

PHILLIPSON, M. 1952. North-eastern bird studies. Lakeland Ornithology.

PODOR, M. 1984. The male Red-legged Partridge *Alectoris rufa* helping with incubation. Alauda **52**: 70.

POLLARD, E., M. D. Hooper and N. W. Moore. 1974. Hedges. The New Naturalist, Collins. London.

PRESTT, I. 1965. An enquiry into the Recent Breeding Status of some of the smaller Birds of Prey and Crows in Britain. Bird Study **12**: 196–221.

PRIESTLEY, M.M. 1992. Wintering Goosanders in Cumbria 1990/91. Birds in Cumbria, A County Natural History Report for 1991: 79–84.

PRYTHERCH, R. 1997. My Buzzard buzz. BBC Wildlife vol.15. no.3. March 1997: 22–29.

RADFORD, D.J. 1995. Breeding waders of the Duddon Estuary in 1994. Birds and Wildlife in Cumbria, A County Natural History Report for 1994: 79–84.

RANKIN, G.D. 1979. Aspects of the breeding biology of wading birds on a saltmarsh. Unpublished Ph.D. thesis. University of Durham.

RANKIN, M.N. and E.A.G. Duffey. 1948. A study of the bird life of the North Atlantic. British Birds. 41 Supplement, July 1948: 1–42.

RATCLIFFE, D.A. 1976. Observations on the breeding of the Golden Plover in Great Britain. Bird Study **23**: 63–116.

RATCLIFFE, D.A. 1993. The Peregrine Falcon. Poyser, London.

RATCLIFFE, D.A. 1997. The Raven. Poyser, London.

RAVEN, C. and L.H. Sanderson. 1997. Walney Island Breeding Bird Survey. Walney Bird Observatory Report for 1997.

RAVEN, S.J. and J.C. Coulson. 1997. The distribution and abundance of *Larus* gulls nesting on buildings in Britain and Ireland. Bird Study **44**: 13–34.

REBECCA, G.W. and I.P. Bainbridge. 1998. The breeding status of the Merlin in Britain in 1993–1994. Bird Study **45**: 172–179.

REED, S. 1995. Factors Limiting the Distribution and Population Size of Twite *Carduelis flavirostris* in the Pennines. The Naturalist 120.

RICCI, J.C. 1983. Two cases of male Red-legged Partridge *Alectoris rufa* helping with incubation. Alauda **51**: 64–65.

ROBERTS, F.J. 2000. Common Rosefinch breeding in Cumbria. Cumbria Bird Club News **9**: 63–69.

ROBERTS, S.J., J.M.S. Lewis and I.T. Williams. 1999. Breeding European Honey Buzzard in Britain. British Birds **92**: 326–345.

ROBERTSON, P.A. and S.A. Dowell. 1990. The effects of handrearing on wild gamebird populations. Pp 58–171 in Lumeij, J.T. & Y.R. Hoogeveen (eds), The Future of Wild Galliformes in the Netherlands. Organisatiecommissie Nederlandse Wilde Hoenders, Amersfoot, Netherlands.

ROBINSON, J.R. 1888. Transcript of the Cumberland Association. Vol. 13.

ROBSON, R.W. 1956. The breeding of the Dipper in Westmorland. Bird Study **3**:170–180.

ROSSITER, B.N. 1995. Account of Common Gull. The Atlas of Breeding Birds in Northumbria. Northumberland and Tyneside Bird Club.

ROUND, P.D. and M. Moss. 1964. The waterbird populations of three Welsh rivers. Bird Study **31**: 61–68.

SAGE, B. and P.A. Whittington. 1985. The 1980 Sample Survey of Rookeries. Bird Study **32**: 77–81.

SANDERSON, F., J. Marchant and D. Glue. 2000. Changes in breeding bird populations 1998–1999. BTO News **228**: 10–13.

SCOTT, G.W., D.C. Jardine, G. Hills and B. Sweeney. 1998. Changes in Nightjar *Caprimulgus europaeus* populations in upland forests in Yorkshire. Bird Study **45**: 219–225.

SERLE, W. 1965. A Third Contribution to the Ornithology of the British Cameroons. Ibis **107**: 60–94.

SHACKLETON, D. 1996. Merlins in Cumbria – status and trends. Birds and Wildlife in Cumbria, A County Natural History Report 1995: 74–77.

SHARROCK, J.T.R. (comp.). 1976. The Atlas of Breeding Birds in Britain and Ireland. BTO. Tring.

SHAWYER, C. 1987. The Barn Owl in the British Isles – its Past, Present and Future. The Hawk and Owl Trust, London.

SHAWYER, C. 1998. The Barn Owl. Arlequin Press, Chelmsford.

SHIELD, E. 1999. Birds and Wildlife in Cumbria 1998. Cumbria Naturalists Union.

SHIELD, E. 2000. Birds and Wildlife in Cumbria 1999. Cumbria Naturalists Union.

SIM, I.M.W., D.W. Gibbons, I.P. Bainbridge and W.A. Mattingley. 2001. Status of Hen Harrier *Circus cyaneus* in the UK and the Isle of Man in 1998. Bird Study **48**: 341–353.

SIMMS, E. 1978. British Thrushes. Collins, London.

SIMMS, E. 1992. British Larks, Pipits and Wagtails. Harper Collins, London.

SIRIWARDENA, G. 2001. Why are 'brown tits' declining? BTO News **235**: 23–24.

SMITH, S. 1950. The Yellow Wagtail. Collins, London.

SOUTHERN, H.N. 1962. Proc. Zoological Society. London. Ibis **96**: 384–410.

SPENCER, K.G. 1973. The Status and Distribution of Birds in Lancashire. Turner and Earnshaw, Burnley.

SPENCER, R. and the Rare Breeding Birds Panel 1986. Rare Breeding Birds in the United Kingdom in 1984. British Birds **79**: 470–495.

STAFFORD, J.1962. Nightjar Enquiry 1957–58. Bird Study **9**: 104–115.

STOKOE, R. 1962. The Birds of the Lake Counties. Transactions of the Carlisle Natural History Society. Vol.10. Thurnam, Carlisle.

STONE, B.H., *et al.* 1997. Population estimates of birds in Britain and the United Kingdom. British Birds **90**: 1–21.

STOTT, M.1998. Hen Harrier breeding success on English grouse moors. British Birds **91**: 107–108.

STOTT, M. In prep. Success of Hen Harriers nesting in England – a comparison between grouse moor and similar habitat with protection schemes.

SUMMERS-SMITH, J.D. 1989. A history of the status of the Tree Sparrow *Passer montanus* in the British Isles. Bird Study **36**: 23–31.

TEMPERLEY, G.K. and E. Blezard. 1951. Status of the Green Woodpecker in Northern England. British Birds **44**: 24–26.

THOM, V.M. 1986. Birds in Scotland. Poyser, Calton.

THOMPSON, K.R., G. Pickerell and M. Heubeck. 1999. Seabird numbers and Breeding Success in Britain and Ireland, 1998. JNCC, Peterborough.

THOMSON, D.L., S.R. Baillie and W.J. Peach. 1997. The demography and age-specific annual survival of song thrushes during periods of population stability and decline. Journal of Applied Animal Ecology **66**: 414–424.

THORPE, A.W. (Ed.) 2001. The North Sea Bird Club Seventeenth Annual Report, For the Year 1999. North Sea Bird Club, Newburgh, Aberdeenshire.

TUCKER, G.M. and M.F. Heath. 1994. Birds in Europe, Their Conservation Status. Birdlife International, Cambridge.

UNDERHILL-DAY, J.C., M. Carrier and D. White. 1993. Cumbria Sand Martin Survey 1991. Birds in Cumbria, A County Natural History Report 1992: 75–78.

VEEN, J. 1977. Functional and casual aspects of nest distribution in colonies of Sandwich Tern (*Sterna s. sandvicensis* Lath.). Behaviour, suppl. xx: 1–193.

VICKERMAN, G.P. and M. O'Bryan. 1979. Partridges and insects. Ann. Rev. Game Conservancy 1978: 35–43.

VINICOMBE, K., J. Marchant and A. Knox, on behalf of the BOURC 1993. Review of status and categorisation of feral birds on the British List. British Birds **86**: 605–614.

VOOUS, K.H. 1960. Atlas of European Birds. Nelson and Son, London.

VOOUS, K.H. 1977. List of recent Holarctic bird species, Passerines. Ibis **119**: 2–250.

WALNEY BIRD OBSERVATORY. Annual Reports 1980–2001.

WARBURTON, A.D. 1979. Owls in Cumbria. Birds in Cumbria, A County Natural History Report 1978: 39–43.

WATSON, J. 1997. The Golden Eagle. Poyser, London.

WEBB, A., N.M. Harrison, G.M. Leaper, R.D. Steele, M.L. Tasker and M.W. Pienkowski. 1990. Seabird Distribution west of Britain. NCC, Peterborough.

WILLIAMSON, K. 1971. A bird census study of a Dorset dairy farm. Bird Study **18**: 80–96.

WILLIAMSON, K. 1974. Breeding Birds in the Deciduous Woodland of Mid-Argyll, Scotland. Bird Study 21: 29–44.

WILSON, G. 1975. Natural History in Cumbria 1974. The Association of Natural History Societies in Cumbria.

WILSON, G. 1976. Natural History in Cumbria 1975. The Association of Natural History Societies in Cumbria.

WILSON, G. 1977. Natural History in Cumbria 1976. The Association of Natural History Societies in Cumbria.

WILSON, J.O. 1933. Birds of Westmorland and the North Pennines. Hutchinson & Co. Ltd.

WITHERBY, H.F. Rev F.C.R. Jourdain, N.F. Ticehurst and B.W. Tucker. 1938–1941. The Handbook of British Birds. H.F. & G. Witherby Ltd. London.

YALDEN, D.W. 1986. The habitat and activity of Common Sandpipers *Actitis hypoleucos* breeding by upland rivers. Bird Study **33**: 214–222.

YALDEN, D.W. and P.E. Yalden. 1990. Recreational disturbance of breeding Golden Plovers. Biol. Cons. **51**: 243–262.

YARKER, B. and G.L. Atkinson-Willes. 1972. The numerical distribution of some British breeding ducks. Wildfowl 22: 63–70.

# Index

**Cumbria**
The old counties

C U M B E R L A N D

W E S T M O R L A N D

F U R N E S S
(Lancashire North
of the Sands)

Y O R K S H I R E
(West Riding)

L A N C A S H I R E